VECTOR IDENTITIES

If $\mathbf{u} = u_1\mathbf{i} + u_2\mathbf{j} + u_3\mathbf{k}$ then   (dot product) $\mathbf{u} \bullet \mathbf{v} = u_1 v_1 + u_2 v_2 + u_3 v_3$

$\mathbf{v} = v_1\mathbf{i} + v_2\mathbf{j} + v_3\mathbf{k}$

$\mathbf{u} = w_1\mathbf{i} + w_2\mathbf{j} + w_3\mathbf{k}$ (cross product) $\mathbf{u} \times \mathbf{v} = \begin{vmatrix} \mathbf{i} & \mathbf{j} & \mathbf{k} \\ u_1 & u_2 & u_3 \\ v_1 & v_2 & v_3 \end{vmatrix} = (u_2 v_3 - u_3 v_2)\mathbf{i} + (u_3 v_1 - u_1 v_3)\mathbf{j} + (u_1 v_2 - u_2 v_1)\mathbf{k}$

length of $\mathbf{u} = |\mathbf{u}| = \sqrt{\mathbf{u} \bullet \mathbf{u}} = \sqrt{u_1^2 + u_2^2 + u_3^2}$ angle between $\mathbf{u}$ and $\mathbf{v} = \cos^{-1}\left(\dfrac{\mathbf{u} \bullet \mathbf{v}}{|\mathbf{u}||\mathbf{v}|}\right)$

triple product identities $\mathbf{u} \bullet (\mathbf{v} \times \mathbf{w}) = \mathbf{v} \bullet (\mathbf{w} \times \mathbf{u}) = \mathbf{w} \bullet (\mathbf{u} \times \mathbf{v})$ $\mathbf{u} \times (\mathbf{v} \times \mathbf{w}) = (\mathbf{u} \bullet \mathbf{w})\mathbf{v} - (\mathbf{u} \bullet \mathbf{v})\mathbf{w}$

IDENTITIES INVOLVING GRADIENT, DIVERGENCE, CURL, AND LAPLACIAN

(del operator) $\nabla = \mathbf{i}\dfrac{\partial}{\partial x} + \mathbf{j}\dfrac{\partial}{\partial y} + \mathbf{k}\dfrac{\partial}{\partial z}$

$\mathbf{grad}\ \phi(x,y,z) = \nabla\phi(x,y,z) = \dfrac{\partial\phi}{\partial x}\mathbf{i} + \dfrac{\partial\phi}{\partial y}\mathbf{j} + \dfrac{\partial\phi}{\partial z}\mathbf{k}$

$\mathbf{div}\ \mathbf{F}(x,y,z) = \nabla \bullet \mathbf{F}(x,y,z) = \dfrac{\partial F_1}{\partial x} + \dfrac{\partial F_2}{\partial y} + \dfrac{\partial F_3}{\partial z},$

$\nabla^2\phi(x,y,z) = \nabla \bullet \nabla\phi(x,y,z) = \mathbf{div\ grad}\ \phi = \dfrac{\partial^2\phi}{\partial x^2} + \dfrac{\partial^2\phi}{\partial y^2} + \dfrac{\partial^2\phi}{\partial z^2}$

$\mathbf{curl}\ \mathbf{F}(x,y,z) = \nabla \times \mathbf{F}(x,y,z) = \begin{vmatrix} \mathbf{i} & \mathbf{j} & \mathbf{k} \\ \dfrac{\partial}{\partial x} & \dfrac{\partial}{\partial y} & \dfrac{\partial}{\partial z} \\ F_1 & F_2 & F_3 \end{vmatrix}$

$= \left(\dfrac{\partial F_3}{\partial y} - \dfrac{\partial F_2}{\partial z}\right)\mathbf{i} + \left(\dfrac{\partial F_1}{\partial z} - \dfrac{\partial F_3}{\partial x}\right)\mathbf{j} + \left(\dfrac{\partial F_2}{\partial x} - \dfrac{\partial F_1}{\partial y}\right)\mathbf{k}$

$\nabla(\phi\psi) = \phi\nabla\psi + \psi\nabla\phi$

$\nabla \times (\phi\mathbf{F}) = (\nabla\phi) \times \mathbf{F} + \phi(\nabla \times \mathbf{F})$

$\nabla \times (\mathbf{F} \times \mathbf{G}) = (\nabla \bullet \mathbf{G})\mathbf{F} + (\mathbf{G} \bullet \nabla)\mathbf{F} - (\nabla \bullet \mathbf{F})\mathbf{G} - (\mathbf{F} \bullet \nabla)\mathbf{G}$

$\nabla \bullet (\nabla \times \mathbf{F}) = 0$ (**div curl** $= 0$)

$\nabla \times (\nabla \times \mathbf{F}) = \nabla(\nabla \bullet \mathbf{F}) - \nabla^2\mathbf{F}$ (**curl curl** $=$ **grad div** $-$ Laplacian)

$\nabla \bullet (\phi\mathbf{F}) = (\nabla\phi) \bullet \mathbf{F} + \phi(\nabla \bullet \mathbf{F})$

$\nabla \bullet (\mathbf{F} \times \mathbf{G}) = (\nabla \times \mathbf{F}) \bullet \mathbf{G} - \mathbf{F} \bullet (\nabla \times \mathbf{G})$

$\nabla(\mathbf{F} \bullet \mathbf{G}) = \mathbf{F} \times (\nabla \times \mathbf{G}) + \mathbf{G} \times (\nabla \times \mathbf{F}) + (\mathbf{F} \bullet \nabla)\mathbf{G} + (\mathbf{G} \bullet \nabla)\mathbf{F}$

$\nabla \times (\nabla\phi) = \mathbf{0}$ (**curl grad** $= \mathbf{0}$)

VERSIONS OF THE FUNDAMENTAL THEOREM OF CALCULUS

$\displaystyle\int_a^b f'(t)\,dt = f(b) - f(a)$ (the one-dimensional **Fundamental Theorem**)

$\displaystyle\int_C \mathbf{grad}\ \phi \bullet d\mathbf{r} = \phi\big(\mathbf{r}(b)\big) - \phi\big(\mathbf{r}(a)\big)$ if C is the curve $\mathbf{r} = \mathbf{r}(t)$, $(a \le t \le b)$.

$\displaystyle\oint_C \mathbf{F} \bullet d\mathbf{r} = \oint_C F_1(x,y)\,dx + F_2(x,y)\,dy = \iint_R \left(\dfrac{\partial F_2}{\partial x} - \dfrac{\partial F_1}{\partial y}\right)dA$ where C is the positively oriented boundary of R (**Green's Theorem**)

$\displaystyle\oint_C \mathbf{F} \bullet d\mathbf{r} = \oint_C F_1(x,y,z)\,dx + F_2(x,y,z)\,dy + F_3(x,y,z)\,dz = \iint_S \mathbf{curl}\ \mathbf{F} \bullet \hat{\mathbf{N}}\,dS$ where C is the oriented boundary of S.   (**Stokes's Theorem**)

Three-dimensional versions: S is the closed boundary of D, with outward normal $\hat{\mathbf{N}}$

$\displaystyle\iiint_D \mathbf{div}\ \mathbf{F}\,dV = \oiint_S \mathbf{F} \bullet \hat{\mathbf{N}}\,dS$ **Divergence Theorem** $\displaystyle\iiint_D \mathbf{curl}\ \mathbf{F}\,dV = -\oiint_S \mathbf{F} \times \hat{\mathbf{N}}\,dS$

$\displaystyle\iiint_D \mathbf{grad}\ \phi\,dV = \oiint_S \phi\hat{\mathbf{N}}\,dS$

FORMULAS RELATING TO CURVES IN 3-SPACE

Curve: $\mathbf{r} = \mathbf{r}(t) = x(t)\mathbf{i} + y(t)\mathbf{j} + z(t)\mathbf{k}$ Velocity: $\mathbf{v} = \dfrac{d\mathbf{r}}{dt} = v\hat{\mathbf{T}}$ Speed: $v = |\mathbf{v}| = \dfrac{ds}{dt}$

Arc length: $s = \displaystyle\int_{t_0}^t v\,dt$ Acceleration: $\mathbf{a} = \dfrac{d\mathbf{v}}{dt} = \dfrac{d^2\mathbf{r}}{dt^2}$ Tangential and normal components: $\mathbf{a} = \dfrac{dv}{dt}\hat{\mathbf{T}} + v^2\kappa\hat{\mathbf{N}}$

Unit tangent: $\hat{\mathbf{T}} = \dfrac{\mathbf{v}}{v}$ Binormal: $\hat{\mathbf{B}} = \dfrac{\mathbf{v} \times \mathbf{a}}{|\mathbf{v} \times \mathbf{a}|}$ Normal: $\hat{\mathbf{N}} = \hat{\mathbf{B}} \times \hat{\mathbf{T}}$

Curvature: $\kappa = \dfrac{|\mathbf{v} \times \mathbf{a}|}{v^3}$ Radius of curvature: $\rho = \dfrac{1}{\kappa}$ Torsion: $\tau = \dfrac{(\mathbf{v} \times \mathbf{a}) \bullet (d\mathbf{a}/dt)}{|\mathbf{v} \times \mathbf{a}|^2}$

The Frenet-Serret formulas: $\dfrac{d\hat{\mathbf{T}}}{ds} = \kappa\hat{\mathbf{N}},$ $\dfrac{d\hat{\mathbf{N}}}{ds} = -\kappa\hat{\mathbf{T}} + \tau\hat{\mathbf{B}},$ $\dfrac{d\hat{\mathbf{B}}}{ds} = -\tau\hat{\mathbf{N}}$

ORTHOGONAL CURVILINEAR COORDINATES

transformation: $x = x(u, v, w), \quad y = y(u, v, w), \quad z = z(u, v, w)$

position vector: $\mathbf{r} = x(u, v, w)\mathbf{i} + y(u, v, w)\mathbf{j} + z(u, v, w)\mathbf{k}$

scale factors: $h_u = \left|\dfrac{\partial \mathbf{r}}{\partial u}\right|, \quad h_v = \left|\dfrac{\partial \mathbf{r}}{\partial v}\right|, \quad h_w = \left|\dfrac{\partial \mathbf{r}}{\partial w}\right|$

local basis: $\hat{\mathbf{u}} = \dfrac{1}{h_u}\dfrac{\partial \mathbf{r}}{\partial u}, \quad \hat{\mathbf{v}} = \dfrac{1}{h_v}\dfrac{\partial \mathbf{r}}{\partial v}, \quad \hat{\mathbf{w}} = \dfrac{1}{h_w}\dfrac{\partial \mathbf{r}}{\partial w}$

volume element: $dV = h_u h_v h_w \, du\, dv\, dw$

scalar field: $f(u, v, w)$

vector field: $\mathbf{F}(u, v, w) = F_u(u, v, w)\hat{\mathbf{u}} + F_v(u, v, w)\hat{\mathbf{v}} + F_w(u, v, w)\hat{\mathbf{w}}$

gradient: $\nabla f = \dfrac{1}{h_u}\dfrac{\partial f}{\partial u}\hat{\mathbf{u}} + \dfrac{1}{h_v}\dfrac{\partial f}{\partial v}\hat{\mathbf{v}} + \dfrac{1}{h_w}\dfrac{\partial f}{\partial w}\hat{\mathbf{w}}$

curl: $\nabla \times \mathbf{F} = \dfrac{1}{h_u h_v h_w}\begin{vmatrix} h_u\hat{\mathbf{u}} & h_v\hat{\mathbf{v}} & h_w\hat{\mathbf{w}} \\ \dfrac{\partial}{\partial u} & \dfrac{\partial}{\partial v} & \dfrac{\partial}{\partial w} \\ F_u h_u & F_v h_v & F_w h_w \end{vmatrix}$

divergnece: $\nabla \bullet \mathbf{F} = \dfrac{1}{h_u h_v h_w}\left[\dfrac{\partial}{\partial u}\left(h_v h_w F_u\right) + \dfrac{\partial}{\partial v}\left(h_u h_w F_v\right) + \dfrac{\partial}{\partial w}\left(h_u h_v F_w\right)\right]$

PLANE POLAR COORDINATES

transformation: $x = r\cos\theta, \quad y = r\sin\theta$

position vector: $\mathbf{r} = r\cos\theta\,\mathbf{i} + r\sin\theta\,\mathbf{j}$

scale factors: $h_r = \left|\dfrac{\partial \mathbf{r}}{\partial r}\right| = 1, \quad h_\theta = \left|\dfrac{\partial \mathbf{r}}{\partial \theta}\right| = r$

local basis: $\hat{\mathbf{r}} = \cos\theta\mathbf{i} + \sin\theta\mathbf{j}, \quad \hat{\boldsymbol{\theta}} = -\sin\theta\mathbf{i} + \cos\theta\mathbf{j}$

area element: $dV = r\, dr\, d\theta$

scalar field: $f(r, \theta)$

vector field: $\mathbf{F}(r, \theta) = F_r(r, \theta)\hat{\mathbf{r}} + F_\theta(r, \theta)\hat{\boldsymbol{\theta}}$

gradient: $\nabla f = \dfrac{\partial f}{\partial r}\hat{\mathbf{r}} + \dfrac{1}{r}\dfrac{\partial f}{\partial \theta}\hat{\boldsymbol{\theta}}$

curl: $\nabla \times \mathbf{F} = \left[\dfrac{\partial F_\theta}{\partial r} + \dfrac{F_\theta}{r} - \dfrac{1}{r}\dfrac{\partial F_r}{\partial \theta}\right]\mathbf{k}$

divergnece: $\nabla \bullet \mathbf{F} = \dfrac{\partial F_r}{\partial r} + \dfrac{1}{r}F_r + \dfrac{1}{r}\dfrac{\partial F_\theta}{\partial \theta}$

CYLINDRICAL COORDINATES

transformation: $x = r\cos\theta, \quad y = r\sin\theta, \quad z = z$

position vector: $\mathbf{r} = r\cos\theta\,\mathbf{i} + r\sin\theta\,\mathbf{j} + z\mathbf{k}$

scale factors: $h_r = \left|\dfrac{\partial \mathbf{r}}{\partial r}\right| = 1, \quad h_\theta = \left|\dfrac{\partial \mathbf{r}}{\partial \theta}\right| = r, \quad h_z = \left|\dfrac{\partial \mathbf{r}}{\partial z}\right| = 1$

local basis: $\hat{\mathbf{r}} = \cos\theta\mathbf{i} + \sin\theta\mathbf{j}, \quad \hat{\boldsymbol{\theta}} = -\sin\theta\mathbf{i} + \cos\theta\mathbf{j}, \quad \hat{\mathbf{z}} = \mathbf{k}$

volume element: $dV = r\, dr\, d\theta\, dz$

scalar field: $f(r, \theta, z)$

vector field: $\mathbf{F}(r, \theta, z) = F_r(r, \theta, z)\hat{\mathbf{r}} + F_\theta(r, \theta, z)\hat{\boldsymbol{\theta}} + F_z(r, \theta, z)\mathbf{k}$

gradient: $\nabla f = \dfrac{\partial f}{\partial r}\hat{\mathbf{r}} + \dfrac{1}{r}\dfrac{\partial f}{\partial \theta}\hat{\boldsymbol{\theta}} + \dfrac{\partial f}{\partial z}\mathbf{k}$

curl: $\nabla \times \mathbf{F} = \dfrac{1}{r}\begin{vmatrix} \hat{\mathbf{r}} & r\hat{\boldsymbol{\theta}} & \mathbf{k} \\ \dfrac{\partial}{\partial r} & \dfrac{\partial}{\partial \theta} & \dfrac{\partial}{\partial z} \\ F_r & rF_\theta & F_z \end{vmatrix}$

divergnece: $\nabla \bullet \mathbf{F} = \dfrac{\partial F_r}{\partial r} + \dfrac{1}{r}F_r + \dfrac{1}{r}\dfrac{\partial F_\theta}{\partial \theta} + \dfrac{\partial F_z}{\partial z}$

SPHERICAL COORDINATES

transformation: $x = R\sin\phi\cos\theta, \quad y = R\sin\phi\sin\theta, \quad z = R\cos\phi$

position vector: $\mathbf{r} = R\sin\phi\cos\theta\,\mathbf{i} + R\sin\phi\sin\theta\,\mathbf{j} + R\cos\phi\mathbf{k}$

scale factors: $h_R = \left|\dfrac{\partial \mathbf{r}}{\partial R}\right| = 1, \quad h_\phi = \left|\dfrac{\partial \mathbf{r}}{\partial \phi}\right| = R, \quad h_\theta = \left|\dfrac{\partial \mathbf{r}}{\partial \theta}\right| = R\sin\phi$

local basis: $\hat{\mathbf{R}} = \sin\phi\cos\theta\,\mathbf{i} + \sin\phi\sin\theta\,\mathbf{j} + \cos\phi\,\mathbf{k}, \quad \hat{\boldsymbol{\phi}} = \cos\phi\cos\theta\,\mathbf{i} + \cos\phi\sin\theta\,\mathbf{j}, \quad \hat{\boldsymbol{\theta}} = -\sin\theta\,\mathbf{i} + \cos\theta\,\mathbf{j}$

volume element: $dV = R^2\sin\phi\, dR\, d\phi\, d\theta$

scalar field: $f(R, \phi, \theta)$

vector field: $\mathbf{F}(R, \phi, \theta) = F_R(R, \phi, \theta)\hat{\mathbf{R}} + F_\phi(R, \phi, \theta)\hat{\boldsymbol{\phi}} + F_\theta(R, \phi, \theta)\hat{\boldsymbol{\theta}}$

gradient: $\nabla f = \dfrac{\partial f}{\partial R}\hat{\mathbf{R}} + \dfrac{1}{R}\dfrac{\partial f}{\partial \phi}\hat{\boldsymbol{\phi}} + \dfrac{1}{R\sin\phi}\dfrac{\partial f}{\partial \theta}\hat{\boldsymbol{\theta}}$

curl: $\nabla \times \mathbf{F} = \dfrac{1}{R^2\sin\phi}\begin{vmatrix} \hat{\mathbf{R}} & R\hat{\boldsymbol{\phi}} & R\sin\phi\hat{\boldsymbol{\theta}} \\ \dfrac{\partial}{\partial R} & \dfrac{\partial}{\partial \phi} & \dfrac{\partial}{\partial \theta} \\ F_R & RF_\phi & R\sin\phi F_\theta \end{vmatrix}$

divergnece: $\nabla \bullet \mathbf{F} = \dfrac{\partial F_R}{\partial R} + \dfrac{2}{R}F_R + \dfrac{1}{R}\dfrac{\partial F_\phi}{\partial \phi} + \dfrac{\cot\phi}{R}F_\phi + \dfrac{1}{R\sin\phi}\dfrac{\partial F_\theta}{\partial \theta}$

CALCULUS
OF SEVERAL VARIABLES
SECOND EDITION

ADDISON-WESLEY
PUBLISHERS LIMITED

Don Mills, Ontario
Reading, Massachusetts
Menlo Park, California
New York • Wokingham,
England • Amsterdam
Bonn • Sydney
Singapore • Tokyo
Madrid • San Juan

ROBERT A. ADAMS
Department of Mathematics
University of British Columbia

to my family

SPONSORING EDITOR: Jim Grant
DESIGN: Pronk&Associates
TYPE OUTPUT: Tony Gordon Limited

Canadian Cataloguing in Publication Data

Adams, Robert A. (Robert Alexander), 1940–
Calculus of several variables

2nd ed.
Includes index.
ISBN 0-201-57958-8

1. Functions of several real variables.   2. Vector
analysis.   I. Title.

QA303.A32   1991   515'.84   C91-093481-9

ISBN 0-201-57958-8

A B C D E F –ALG– 95 94 93 92 91

CONTENTS

PREFACE

Like the first edition that preceded it, this second edition of *Calculus of Several Variables* is intended for students in science and engineering who have already completed a study of the techniques and applications of differential and integral calculus of real-valued functions of a single real variable. Thus it is designed for the third and fourth semesters of a two-year calculus program. Typically, the third semester deals with partial differentiation and multiple integration, and the fourth with vector-valued functions.

Although this book was written as a sequel to the author's *Single-Variable Calculus, 2nd Edition* (Addison-Wesley, 1990), it does not require previous use of that book, nor makes specific reference to it. Most of this book corresponds to the last seven chapters of the author's *Calculus: A Complete Course* (Addison-Wesley, 1990). Chapters 1 to 7 of this book are essentially identical to Chapters 12 to 18 of the *Complete Course*; all sections and exercises are the same except that this book has one extra section in Chapter 7 devoted to orthogonal curvilinear coordinates. Also, the four appendices in this book present, respectively, material on two-dimensional vectors, conic sections, first-order differential equations, and second-order differential equations, all of which have been drawn from various chapters and appendices of *Calculus: A Complete Course*.

Although this book treats the same topics as the first edition, and largely in the same order, many local revisions have been made to clarify explanations, to improve exercise sets (by additions, deletions, and reorderings), and to provide some extra material. Some sections, such as those dealing with parametric surfaces and surface integrals, have been completely rewritten. A new section (7.6) develops formulas for the vector operators **grad**, **div**, and **curl** in terms of general orthogonal curvilinear coordinates. This was added at the request of some students who needed that material in electrical engineering courses.

Some Features of the Text

- There is an emphasis on geometry and the use of geometric reasoning in solving problems.
- Wherever appropriate the relationship between several-variable calculus and linear algebra is noted. For example, the Chain Rule is interpreted in terms of matrix multiplication. A brief, optional section on matrix algebra is included in the first chapter for this purpose.

- Partial differential equations, in particular Laplace's equation, the heat (diffusion) equation, and the wave equation, are used to illustrate elementary calculations involving partial derivatives.
- Numerous applications of multivariable calculus are included in the book. Some, such as the method of least squares, perturbation methods, envelopes of families of curves and surfaces, and Newton's method for systems of equations, are not always to be found in calculus books.
- Classical mechanics is emphasized, especially in the applications of multiple integrals, line and surface integrals. Such applications are facilitated by constantly regarding integrals as "sums" of elements.
- Vector methods can greatly simplify the solution of problems in classical mechanics. As an example, Kepler's laws of planetary motion are derived via elementary vector calculations rather than by the usual method of making auspicious (but obscure) changes of variables in the appropriate differential equation.
- Chapter 5 deals with the differential geometry of general curves in 3-space, developing the Frenet-Serret formulas and showing that the shape of a curve is determined by its curvature and torsion functions. Rotating frames of reference (the Coriolis effect) is also discussed.
- The fundamental theorems of calculus in 3-space (Stokes's Theorem and Gauss's Divergence Theorem) are applied to problems in fluid mechanics, electrostatics and magnetostatics.
- The properties of conic sections are developed in Appendix 2, partly by analytic methods and partly by elementary geometric arguments. Polar equations of conics are treated in Section 5.4 on Kepler's Laws.

Core and Optional Material

Any division of material into "core" and "optional" is necessarily somewhat arbitrary. Most instructors would agree that the material of Sections 1.1–1.4, 2.1–2.6, 4.1–4.5, 5.1–5.2, 6.1—6.6, and 7.1–7.4 constitute a core course in multivariable and vector calculus. However, most of us would also be loath to teach a course devoid of applications so we would certainly want to include part of Chapter 3, say Sections 3.1–3.3, and at least parts of Sections 4.6 and 7.5. Some of the most interesting applications are in Sections 5.3 and 5.4, and they should be included in any course where time permits or need for the topics requires. Each of Sections 3.4–3.6 is self-contained and optional. Section 3.6 contains the only strictly numerical topic, Newton's method. Even for functions of only two variables, multivariable numerical methods can be sufficiently complicated that the student should have a sophisticated programmable calculator or, preferably, a computer to use them.

Acknowledgments

The first edition of *Calculus of Several Variables* has been used, since its publication, for classes of engineering and science students at the University of British Columbia. I am grateful to colleagues and students at UBC, and at other institutions where the book has been used, for their encouragement and useful comments and criticisms.

Especially helpful comments were made by Jim Carrell and John Walsh at UBC. Many of the changes in this edition are a result of that feedback. I am also very grateful to Ken MacKenzie (McGill University) who undertook a thorough checking of the Answers section.

I typeset this volume using TEX and PostScript on an AT microcomputer. I also generated most of the figures in PostScript using the *MG System*, a PC-based mathematical graphics software package developed by my colleague Professor Robert Israel and myself. Some of the three dimensional air-brush art was prepared by Iris Ward.

I wish to thank several people at Addison-Wesley for their assistance and encouragement. These include Sponsoring Editor Jim Grant, who guided the three-volume project of which this is the final installment, Vice-President Andy Yull, with whom I enjoyed stimulating discussions on matters of design and on problems involving the TEX–PostScript interface, and especially Executive Editor Ron Doleman who has supervised the publication of several of my books, and who first introduced me to TEX and PostScript.

While I have tried, with much excellent help, to make this second edition as free from errors and obscurities as possible, I am not so naïve as to believe that there are none left. Any comments, corrections, and suggestions for future revisions from readers will be much appreciated.

R.A.A.
Vancouver, Canada
January, 1991

CHAPTER 1

Coordinate Geometry and Vectors in 3-Space

A complete real-variable calculus program involves the study of

    i) real-valued functions of a single real variable,

   ii) real-valued functions of a real vector variable,

  iii) vector-valued functions of a single real variable,

  iv) vector-valued functions of a real vector variable.

Item (i) is the subject of a single-variable calculus course; we assume that the reader is already familiar with that subject. This book is about items (ii), (iii), and (iv). Specifically, Chapters 2–4 are concerned with the differentiation and integration of real-valued functions of several real variables, that is, of a real vector variable. Chapter 5 and part of Chapter 6 deal with vector-valued functions of a single real variable. Most of Chapters 6 and 7 present aspects of the calculus of functions whose domains and ranges both have dimension greater than one, that is, vector-valued functions of a vector variable. Mostly we will limit our attention to vector functions in two- and three-dimensional space.

In this chapter we will lay the foundation for multi-variable calculus by discussing analytic geometry and vectors in three and more dimensions. We assume that the student, having already undertaken a study of single-variable calculus, is familiar with the coordinate geometry of the Cartesian plane. We also introduce matrices in spaces of any dimension, as these are useful (but not essential) for formulating some of the concepts of calculus. This chapter is not intended to be a course in linear algebra. We develop only those aspects which we will use in later chapters, and omit most proofs.

1.1   ANALYTIC GEOMETRY IN THREE AND MORE DIMENSIONS

We say that the physical world in which we live is three dimensional because through any point there can pass three, and no more, straight lines which are **mutually perpendicular**, that is to say, each of them is perpendicular to the other two. This is equivalent to the fact that we require three numbers to locate a point in space with respect to some reference point (the *origin*). One way to use three numbers to locate a point is by having them represent (signed) distances from the origin, measured in the directions of three mutually perpendicular lines passing through the origin. We call such a set of lines a Cartesian coordinate system, and each of the lines is called a coordinate axis. We shall usually call these axes the x-axis, the y-axis and the z-axis, regarding the x- and y-axes as lying in a horizontal plane and the z-axis as vertical. Moreover, the coordinate system should have a **right-handed orientation**. This means that the thumb, forefinger and middle finger of the right hand can be extended so as to point respectively in the directions of the positive x-axis, the positive y-axis and the positive z-axis. For the more mechanically minded, a right-handed screw will advance in the positive z direction if twisted in the direction of rotation from the positive x-axis towards the positive y-axis. (See Fig. 1.1.1.)

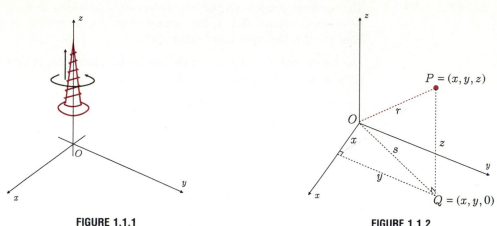

FIGURE 1.1.1   **FIGURE 1.1.2**

With respect to such a Cartesian coordinate system, the *coordinates* of a point P in 3-space constitute an ordered triple of real numbers, (x, y, z). The numbers x, y and z are, respectively, the signed distances of P from the origin, measured in the directions of the x-axis, the y-axis and the z-axis. (See Fig. 1.1.2.)

Let Q be the point with coordinates $(x, y, 0)$. Then Q lies in the xy-plane directly under (or over) P. (Q is the vertical projection of P onto the xy-plane.) If r is the distance from the origin O to P and s is the distance from O to Q, then, using two right-angled triangles, we have

$$s^2 = x^2 + y^2 \qquad \text{and} \qquad r^2 = s^2 + z^2 = x^2 + y^2 + z^2.$$

Thus the distance from P to the origin is given by

$$r = \sqrt{x^2 + y^2 + z^2}.$$

Similarly, the distance between points $P_1 = (x_1, y_1, z_1)$ and $P_2 = (x_2, y_2, z_2)$ is

$$\sqrt{(x_2 - x_1)^2 + (y_2 - y_1)^2 + (z_2 - z_1)^2}.$$

Just as the x- and y-axes divide the xy-plane into four quadrants so also the three **coordinate planes** in 3-space (the xy-plane, the xz-plane and the yz-plane) divide 3-space into eight **octants**. We call the octant in which $x \geq 0$, $y \geq 0$ and $z \geq 0$ the **first octant**. When we draw graphs in 3-space it is sometimes easier to draw only the part lying in the first octant.

Equations and inequalities involving the three variables x, y and z generally define subsets of points in 3-space. Usually a single equation represents a surface (a two-dimensional object), and a single inequality represents a three-dimensional region (having volume). Two equations represent the intersection of the two surfaces represented by each of them, and so usually represent a curve or line (a one-dimensional object).

EXAMPLE 1.1.1   i)   The equation $y = 0$ is satisfied by those points, and only those points, which lie in the xz-plane, that is, the vertical plane containing the x- and z-axes. Thus $y = 0$ is the equation of that plane.

        ii)   The equation $z = 1$ represents the horizontal plane consisting of all points lying at distance one unit above the xy-plane.

       iii)   The inequality $z \geq 1$ represents the *half-space* consisting of all points lying on or above the plane in (ii).

       iv)   The equation $y = x$ represents the vertical plane (the plane parallel to the z-axis) passing through the line with equation $y = x$ in the xy-plane. (See Fig. 1.1.3.)

plane $x = y$

FIGURE 1.1.3

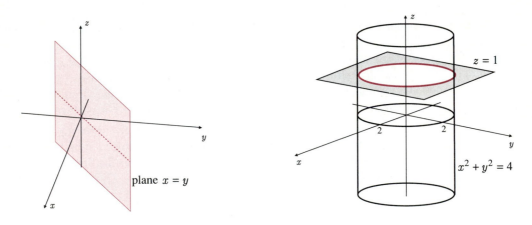

FIGURE 1.1.4

       v)   The equation $x^2 + y^2 + z^2 = 4$ represents the *sphere* consisting of all points at distance 2 from the origin.

      vi)   The inequality $x^2 + y^2 + z^2 \leq 4$ represents the *ball* consisting of all points inside or on the sphere in (v).

     vii)   In the xy-plane the equation $x^2 + y^2 = 4$ represents a circle of radius 2 centred at the origin. In 3-space it represents the circular cylinder with axis along the z-axis which intersects the xy-plane in that circle. (See Fig. 1.1.4.) Since the equation does not depend on z, all points on the vertical line through any point on the surface will also lie on the surface.

    viii)   The pair of equations $x^2 + y^2 = 4$, $z = 1$ represents the circle in which the horizontal plane $z = 1$ intersects the vertical cylinder $x^2 + y^2 = 4$. The circle has radius 2 and centre at the point $(0, 0, 1)$. (See Fig. 1.1.4.)

       In Section 1.4 we will see many more examples of geometric objects in 3-space represented by simple equations.

Euclidean n-Space

Mathematicians and users of mathematics frequently need to consider n-**dimensional space** where n is greater than three, and may even be infinite. Students sometimes have difficulty in visualizing a space of dimension four or higher. The secret to dealing with these spaces is to regard the points in n-space as *being* ordered n-tuples of real numbers; that is, $(x_1, x_2, \ldots, x_n)$ is a point in n-space instead of just being the coordinates of such a point. We stop thinking of points as existing in physical space and start thinking of them as algebraic objects. We usually denote n-space by the symbol $\mathbb{R}^n$ to show that its points are n-tuples of *real* numbers. Thus $\mathbb{R}^2$ and $\mathbb{R}^3$ denote the plane and 3-space respectively. Note that in passing from $\mathbb{R}^3$ to $\mathbb{R}^n$ we have altered the notation a bit — in $\mathbb{R}^3$ we called the coordinates x, y and z while in $\mathbb{R}^n$ we called them x_1, x_2, ... and x_n so as not to run out of letters. We could, of course, talk about coordinates (x_1, x_2, x_3) in $\mathbb{R}^3$, and (x_1, x_2) in the plane $\mathbb{R}^2$, but (x, y, z) and (x, y) are traditionally used there.

While we think of points in $\mathbb{R}^n$ as n-tuples rather than geometric objects, we do not want to lose all sight of the underlying geometry. By analogy with the two- and three-dimensional cases, we still consider the quantity

$$\sqrt{(y_1 - x_1)^2 + (y_2 - x_2)^2 + \cdots + (y_n - x_n)^2}$$

as representing the *distance* between the points with coordinates $(x_1, x_2, \ldots, x_n)$ and $(y_1, y_2, \ldots, y_n)$. Also, we call the $(n-1)$-dimensional set of points in $\mathbb{R}^n$ which satisfy the equation $x_n = 0$ a "hyperplane" by analogy with the plane $z = 0$ in $\mathbb{R}^3$.

EXERCISES

Find the distance between the pairs of points in Exercises 1–4.

1. $(0, 0, 0)$ and $(2, -1, -2)$ **2.** $(-1, -1, -1)$ and $(1, 1, 1)$

3. $(1, 1, 0)$ and $(0, 2, -2)$ **4.** $(3, 8, -1)$ and $(-2, 3, -6)$

5. What is the shortest distance from the point (x, y, z) to
a) the xy-plane? b) the x-axis?

6. Show that the triangle with vertices $(1, 2, 3)$, $(4, 0, 5)$ and $(3, 6, 4)$ has a right angle.

7. Find the area of the triangle with vertices $(1, 1, 0)$, $(1, 0, 1)$ and $(0, 1, 1)$.

8. What is the distance from the origin to the point $(1, 1, \ldots, 1)$ in $\mathbb{R}^n$?

9. What is the distance from the point $(1, 1, \ldots, 1)$ in n-space to the closest point on the x_1-axis?

In Exercises 10–21 describe (and sketch if possible) the set of points in $\mathbb{R}^3$ which satisfy the given equation or inequality.

10. $z = 2$

11. $y \geq -1$

12. $z = x$

13. $x + y = 1$

14. $x^2 + y^2 + z^2 = 4$

15. $(x - 1)^2 + (y + 2)^2 + (z - 3)^2 = 4$

16. $x^2 + y^2 + z^2 = 2z$ **17.** $x^2 + y^2 \leq 4$

18. $x^2 + z^2 = 4$ **19.** $z = y^2$

20. $z \geq \sqrt{x^2 + y^2}$ **21.** $x + y + z = 1$

In Exercises 22–31 describe (and sketch if possible) the set of points in $\mathbb{R}^3$ which satisfy the given pair of equations or inequalities.

22. $\begin{cases} x = 1 \\ y = 2 \end{cases}$ **23.** $\begin{cases} x = 1 \\ y = z \end{cases}$

24. $\begin{cases} x^2 + y^2 + z^2 = 4 \\ z = 1 \end{cases}$ **25.** $\begin{cases} x^2 + y^2 + z^2 = 4 \\ x^2 + y^2 + z^2 = 4x \end{cases}$ **28.** $\begin{cases} y \geq x \\ z \leq y \end{cases}$ **29.** $\begin{cases} x^2 + y^2 \leq 1 \\ z \geq y \end{cases}$

26. $\begin{cases} x^2 + y^2 + z^2 = 4 \\ x^2 + z^2 = 1 \end{cases}$ **27.** $\begin{cases} x^2 + y^2 = 1 \\ z = x \end{cases}$ **30.** $\begin{cases} x^2 + y^2 + z^2 \leq 1 \\ \sqrt{x^2 + y^2} \leq z \end{cases}$ **31.** $\begin{cases} z \geq x^2 \\ x^2 + y^2 + z^2 \leq 1 \end{cases}$

1.2   VECTORS IN 3-SPACE

A vector is a quantity possessing both magnitude and direction. In this section we are assuming that you have encountered vectors in your previous mathematical studies. A brief introduction to two-dimensional vectors is given in Appendix 1, where they are used to describe the motion of an object in the plane $\mathbb{R}^2$. It is a good idea to read the first four pages of that appendix before proceeding further with this section. The algebra and geometry of plane vectors described there extends to spaces of any number of dimensions; we can still think of vectors as represented by arrows, and sums and scalar multiples are formed just as for plane vectors.

In this section we state properties of vectors, as developed in Appendix 1, for vectors in 3-space. It will be evident how extensions can be made to higher dimensions.

Given a Cartesian coordinate system in 3-space, we define three **standard basis vectors**, **i**, **j**, and **k**, represented by arrows from the origin to the points $(1, 0, 0)$, $(0, 1, 0)$, and $(0, 0, 1)$ respectively. See Fig. 1.2.1. Any vector in 3-space can be written as a *linear combination* of these basis vectors; for instance, the vector **r** from the origin to the point (x, y, z) is given by

$$\mathbf{r} = x\mathbf{i} + y\mathbf{j} + z\mathbf{k}.$$

We say that **r** has **components** x, y, and z. The length of **r** is

$$|\mathbf{r}| = \sqrt{x^2 + y^2 + z^2}.$$

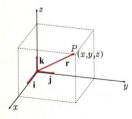

FIGURE 1.2.1

Such a vector from the origin to a point is called the **position vector** of that point. Generally, however, vectors do not have any specific location; two vectors are regarded as being equal if they have the same length and the same direction, that is, if they have the same components.

If $P_1 = (x_1, y_1, z_1)$ and $P_2 = (x_2, y_2, z_2)$ are two points in 3-space, then the vector $\mathbf{v} = \overrightarrow{P_1 P_2}$ from P_1 to P_2 has components $x_2 - x_1$, $y_2 - y_1$, and $z_2 - z_1$, and is therefore represented in terms of the standard basis vectors by

$$\mathbf{v} = \overrightarrow{P_1 P_2} = (x_2 - x_1)\mathbf{i} + (y_2 - y_1)\mathbf{j} + (z_2 - z_1)\mathbf{k}.$$

Sums and scalar multiples of vectors are easily expressed in terms of components. If $\mathbf{u} = u_1\mathbf{i} + u_2\mathbf{j} + u_3\mathbf{k}$ and $\mathbf{v} = v_1\mathbf{i} + v_2\mathbf{j} + v_3\mathbf{k}$, and if t is a scalar (i.e. a real number) then

$$\mathbf{u} + \mathbf{v} = (u_1 + v_1)\mathbf{i} + (u_2 + v_2)\mathbf{j} + (u_3 + v_3)\mathbf{k},$$
$$t\mathbf{u} = (tu_1)\mathbf{i} + (tu_2)\mathbf{j} + (tu_3)\mathbf{k}.$$

The zero vector is $\mathbf{0} = 0\mathbf{i} + 0\mathbf{j} + 0\mathbf{k}$. It has length zero, and so we may regard its direction as arbitrary. For any vector $\mathbf{u}$ we have $0\mathbf{u} = \mathbf{0}$. A **unit vector** is a vector of length 1. The standard basis vectors $\mathbf{i}$, $\mathbf{j}$ and $\mathbf{k}$ are unit vectors. Given any nonzero vector $\mathbf{v}$, we can form a unit vector $\hat{\mathbf{v}}$ in the same direction as $\mathbf{v}$ by dividing $\mathbf{v}$ by its length:

$$\hat{\mathbf{v}} = \left(\frac{1}{|\mathbf{v}|}\right)\mathbf{v}.$$

EXAMPLE 1.2.1   If $\mathbf{u} = 2\mathbf{i} + \mathbf{j} - 2\mathbf{k}$ and $\mathbf{v} = 3\mathbf{i} - 2\mathbf{j} - \mathbf{k}$, find $\mathbf{u} + \mathbf{v}$, $\mathbf{u} - \mathbf{v}$, $3\mathbf{u} - 2\mathbf{v}$, $|\mathbf{u}|$, $|\mathbf{v}|$, and a unit vector $\hat{\mathbf{u}}$ in the direction of $\mathbf{u}$.

SOLUTION   We have

$$\mathbf{u} + \mathbf{v} = 5\mathbf{i} - \mathbf{j} - 3\mathbf{k}$$
$$\mathbf{u} - \mathbf{v} = -\mathbf{i} + 3\mathbf{j} - \mathbf{k}$$
$$3\mathbf{u} - 2\mathbf{v} = 7\mathbf{j} - 4\mathbf{k}$$
$$|\mathbf{u}| = \sqrt{4 + 1 + 4} = 3, \qquad |\mathbf{v}| = \sqrt{9 + 4 + 1} = \sqrt{14}$$
$$\hat{\mathbf{u}} = \left(\frac{1}{|\mathbf{u}|}\right)\mathbf{u} = \frac{2}{3}\mathbf{i} + \frac{1}{3}\mathbf{j} - \frac{2}{3}\mathbf{k}.$$

The following example illustrates the use of vectors to solve problems involving relative velocities. If A moves with velocity $\mathbf{v}_{A\,\mathrm{rel}\,B}$ relative to B, and B moves with velocity $\mathbf{v}_{B\,\mathrm{rel}\,C}$ relative to C, then A moves with velocity $\mathbf{v}_{A\,\mathrm{rel}\,C}$ relative to C, where

$$\mathbf{v}_{A\,\mathrm{rel}\,C} = \mathbf{v}_{A\,\mathrm{rel}\,B} + \mathbf{v}_{B\,\mathrm{rel}\,C}.$$

EXAMPLE 1.2.2   An aircraft cruises with a speed of 300 km/h in still air. In what direction should it head in order to fly in a straight line from city P to city Q, 400 km north northeast of P, if the wind is blowing from the east at 100 km/h? How long will the trip take?

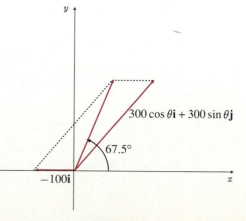

FIGURE 1.2.2

SOLUTION   The problem is two dimensional, so we use plane vectors. Let us choose our coordinate system so that the x- and y-axes point east and north respectively. (See Fig. 1.2.2.) The velocity of the air relative to the ground is

$$\mathbf{v}_{\text{air rel ground}} = -100\,\mathbf{i}.$$

If the aircraft heads in a direction making angle θ with the positive direction of the x-axis then the velocity of the aircraft relative to the air is

$$\mathbf{v}_{\text{aircraft rel air}} = 300\cos\theta\,\mathbf{i} + 300\sin\theta\,\mathbf{j}.$$

Thus the velocity of the aircraft relative to the ground is

$$\mathbf{v}_{\text{aircraft rel ground}} = \mathbf{v}_{\text{aircraft rel air}} + \mathbf{v}_{\text{air rel ground}}$$
$$= (300\cos\theta - 100)\,\mathbf{i} + 300\sin\theta\,\mathbf{j}.$$

We want this latter velocity to be in a north northeasterly direction, that is in the direction making angle $3\pi/8 = 67.5°$ with the positive direction of the x-axis. Thus we will have

$$\mathbf{v}_{\text{aircraft rel ground}} = v\left[(\cos 67.5°)\,\mathbf{i} + (\sin 67.5°)\,\mathbf{j}\right],$$

where v is the actual groundspeed of the aircraft. Comparing the two expressions for $\mathbf{v}_{\text{aircraft rel ground}}$ we obtain

$$300\cos\theta - 100 = v\,\cos 67.5°$$
$$300\sin\theta = v\,\sin 67.5°.$$

Eliminating v between these two equations we get

$$300\cos\theta\,\sin 67.5° - 300\sin\theta\,\cos 67.5° = 100\sin 67.5°,$$

or,

$$3\,\sin(67.5° - \theta) = \sin 67.5°.$$

Therefore the aircraft should head in direction θ given by

$$\theta = 67.5° - \text{Arcsin}\left(\frac{1}{3}\sin 67.5°\right) \approx 49.56°,$$

that is, $49.56°$ north of east. The groundspeed is now seen to be

$$v = 300\sin\theta / \sin 67.5° \approx 247.15 \text{ km/h},$$

so the 400 km trip will take about 1 hour and 37 minutes.

The Dot Product and Projections

The dot product of two plane vectors, $\mathbf{u} = u_1\mathbf{i} + u_2\mathbf{j}$ and $\mathbf{v} = v_1\mathbf{i} + v_2\mathbf{j}$, is defined (see Appendix 1) to be the *number*

$$\mathbf{u} \bullet \mathbf{v} = u_1v_1 + u_2v_2.$$

A similar formula with one more term serves to define the dot product of two vectors in 3-space:

1.2.3
The Dot Product

> If $\mathbf{u} = u_1\mathbf{i} + u_2\mathbf{j} + u_3\mathbf{k}$ and $\mathbf{v} = v_1\mathbf{i} + v_2\mathbf{j} + v_3\mathbf{k}$, then the **dot product $\mathbf{u} \bullet \mathbf{v}$** is the number
>
> $$\mathbf{u} \bullet \mathbf{v} = u_1v_1 + u_2v_2 + u_3v_3.$$

So defined, the dot product has the same algebraic and geometric properties as noted for vectors in 2-space in Appendix 1, namely

$$\mathbf{u} \bullet \mathbf{v} = \mathbf{v} \bullet \mathbf{u}, \qquad \text{(commutative law)}$$
$$\mathbf{u} \bullet (\mathbf{v} + \mathbf{w}) = \mathbf{u} \bullet \mathbf{v} + \mathbf{u} \bullet \mathbf{w}, \qquad \text{(distributive law)}$$
$$(t\mathbf{u}) \bullet \mathbf{v} = \mathbf{u} \bullet (t\mathbf{v}) = t(\mathbf{u} \bullet \mathbf{v}), \qquad \text{for real } t,$$
$$\mathbf{u} \bullet \mathbf{u} = |\mathbf{u}|^2,$$
$$\mathbf{u} \bullet \mathbf{v} = |\mathbf{u}||\mathbf{v}| \cos \theta,$$

where θ is the angle between $\mathbf{u}$ and $\mathbf{v}$. Note that two vectors are perpendicular if and only if their dot product is zero. The angle between the vectors is acute if the dot product is positive, and obtuse if the dot product is negative.

EXAMPLE 1.2.4 The angle θ between the vectors $\mathbf{u} = 2\mathbf{i} + \mathbf{j} - 2\mathbf{k}$ and $\mathbf{v} = 3\mathbf{i} - 2\mathbf{j} - \mathbf{k}$ is

$$\theta = \cos^{-1} \frac{\mathbf{u} \bullet \mathbf{v}}{|\mathbf{u}||\mathbf{v}|} = \cos^{-1} \left(\frac{(2)(3) + (1)(-2) + (-2)(-1)}{3\sqrt{14}} \right)$$
$$= \cos^{-1} \frac{2}{\sqrt{14}} \approx 57.69°.$$

It is sometimes useful to project one vector along another. We define both scalar and vector projections of $\mathbf{u}$ in the direction of $\mathbf{v}$:

1.2.5
Scalar Projection

> The **scalar projection** s of any vector $\mathbf{u}$ in the direction of a nonzero vector $\mathbf{v}$ is the dot product of $\mathbf{u}$ with a unit vector in the direction of $\mathbf{v}$. Thus it is the *number*
>
> $$s = \frac{\mathbf{u} \bullet \mathbf{v}}{|\mathbf{v}|} = |\mathbf{u}| \cos \theta$$
>
> where θ is the angle between $\mathbf{u}$ and $\mathbf{v}$.

Note that $|s|$ is the length of the line segment along the line of $\mathbf{v}$ obtained by dropping perpendiculars to that line from the tail and head of $\mathbf{u}$. (See Fig. 1.2.3.) Also, s is negative if $\theta > 90°$.

1.2.6
Vector
Projection

> The **vector projection**, $\mathbf{u_V}$, of $\mathbf{u}$ in the direction of $\mathbf{v}$ (see Fig. 1.2.3) is the scalar multiple of a unit vector in the direction of $\mathbf{v}$, by the scalar projection of $\mathbf{u}$ in the direction of $\mathbf{v}$, that is,
>
> $$\text{vector projection of } \mathbf{u} \text{ along } \mathbf{v} = \mathbf{u_V} = \frac{\mathbf{u} \bullet \mathbf{v}}{|\mathbf{v}|^2}\mathbf{v}.$$

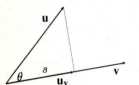

FIGURE 1.2.3

All of the above ideas make sense for vectors in spaces of any dimension. Vectors in $\mathbb{R}^n$ are expressed in terms of the standard basis consisting of the n unit vectors

$\mathbf{e_1}$	from the origin to the point	$(1, 0, 0, \ldots, 0)$
$\mathbf{e_2}$	from the origin to the point	$(0, 1, 0, \ldots, 0)$
$\vdots$		
$\mathbf{e_n}$	from the origin to the point	$(0, 0, 0, \ldots, 1)$.

The n-vector $\mathbf{x}$ with components $x_1, x_2, \ldots, x_n$ is expressed as

$$\mathbf{x} = x_1\mathbf{e_1} + x_2\mathbf{e_2} + \cdots + x_n\mathbf{e_n}.$$

The length of the n-vector $\mathbf{x}$ is

$$|\mathbf{x}| = \sqrt{x_1{}^2 + x_2{}^2 + \cdots + x_n{}^2}.$$

The angle between two vectors $\mathbf{x}$ and $\mathbf{y}$ is defined to be

$$\theta = \cos^{-1}\frac{\mathbf{x} \bullet \mathbf{y}}{|\mathbf{x}||\mathbf{y}|},$$

where,

$$\mathbf{x} \bullet \mathbf{y} = x_1y_1 + x_2y_2 + \cdots + x_ny_n.$$

We shall not make much use of n-vectors for $n > 3$ but you should be aware that everything said up until now for 2-vectors or 3-vectors extends to n-vectors.

EXERCISES

In Exercises 1–3 calculate the following for the given vectors **u** and **v**.

a) $\mathbf{u} + \mathbf{v}$, $\mathbf{u} - \mathbf{v}$, $2\mathbf{u} - 3\mathbf{v}$,

b) The lengths $|\mathbf{u}|$ and $|\mathbf{v}|$,

c) Unit vectors $\hat{\mathbf{u}}$ and $\hat{\mathbf{v}}$ in the directions of **u** and **v** respectively,

d) The dot product $\mathbf{u} \bullet \mathbf{v}$,

e) The angle between **u** and **v**,

f) The scalar projection of **u** in the direction of **v**,

g) The vector projection of **v** along **u**.

1. $\mathbf{u} = 3\mathbf{i} + 4\mathbf{j} - 5\mathbf{k}$ and $\mathbf{v} = 3\mathbf{i} - 4\mathbf{j} - 5\mathbf{k}$

2. $\mathbf{u} = \mathbf{i} - \mathbf{j}$ and $\mathbf{v} = \mathbf{j} + 2\mathbf{k}$

3. $\mathbf{u} = \mathbf{i} - 2\mathbf{j}$ and $\mathbf{v} = 2\mathbf{i} + 2\mathbf{j} - 3\mathbf{k}$

4. A straight river 500 metres wide flows due east at a constant speed of 3 km/h. If you can row your boat at a speed of 5 km/h in still water, in what direction should you head if you wish to row from point A on the south shore to point B on the north shore directly north of A? How long will the trip take?

5.*In what direction should you head to cross the river in the previous exercise if you can only row at 2 km/h, and you wish to row from A to point C on the north shore, k km downstream from B. For what values of k is the trip not possible?

6. A certain aircraft flies with an airspeed of 750 km/h. In what direction should it head in order to make progress in a true easterly direction if the wind is from the northeast at 100 km/h? How long will it take to complete a trip to a city 1500 km from its starting point?

7. A weather vane mounted on the top of a car moving due north at 50 km/h indicates that the wind is coming from the west. When the car doubles its speed, the weather vane indicates that the wind is coming from the northwest. From what direction is the wind coming, and what is its speed?

8. Find the angle between a diagonal of a cube and one of the edges of the cube.

9. Find the angle between a diagonal of a cube and a diagonal of one of the faces of the cube. Give all possible answers.

10. If a vector **u** in $\mathbb{R}^3$ makes angles α, β and γ with the coordinate axes, show that

$$\hat{\mathbf{u}} = \cos\alpha\,\mathbf{i} + \cos\beta\,\mathbf{j} + \cos\gamma\,\mathbf{k}$$

is a unit vector in the direction of **u**. Hence show that

$$\cos^2\alpha + \cos^2\beta + \cos^2\gamma = 1.$$

11. Find a unit vector which makes equal angles with the three coordinate axes.

12. Find the three angles of the triangle with vertices $(1, 0, 0)$, $(0, 2, 0)$ and $(0, 0, 3)$.

13. If $\mathbf{r}_1$ and $\mathbf{r}_2$ are the position vectors of two points, P_1 and P_2, and λ is a real number, show that

$$\mathbf{r} = \lambda\mathbf{r}_1 + (1 - \lambda)\mathbf{r}_2$$

is the position vector of a point P on the straight line joining P_1 and P_2. Where is P if $\lambda = 1/2$? if $\lambda = 2/3$? if $\lambda = -1$? if $\lambda = 2$?

14. If **a** is a nonzero vector and **w** is any vector, find vectors **u** and **v** such that $\mathbf{w} = \mathbf{u} + \mathbf{v}$, **u** is parallel to **a**, and **v** is perpendicular to **a**.

15. Find a unit vector which bisects the angle between the two nonzero vectors **u** and **v**.

16.*Given constants a, b and c, with $a \neq 0$ and $b \neq 0$, and given a vector **a** satisfying $|\mathbf{a}|^2 > 4abc$, solve the system of equations

$$\begin{cases} a\mathbf{x} + b\mathbf{y} = \mathbf{a} \\ \mathbf{x} \bullet \mathbf{y} = c \end{cases}$$

for the unknown vectors **x** and **y**.

◤ 1.3   THE CROSS PRODUCT IN 3-SPACE

There is defined, *in 3-space only*, another kind of product of vectors called a **cross product** or **vector product**, and denoted $\mathbf{u} \times \mathbf{v}$. For any vectors **u** and **v** in $\mathbb{R}^3$,

$\mathbf{u} \times \mathbf{v}$ is itself a vector in $\mathbb{R}^3$ with length

$$|\mathbf{u} \times \mathbf{v}| = |\mathbf{u}||\mathbf{v}| \sin\theta,$$

where θ is the angle between $\mathbf{u}$ and $\mathbf{v}$. If $\mathbf{u} = \mathbf{0}$ or $\mathbf{v} = \mathbf{0}$, or if $\mathbf{u}$ and $\mathbf{v}$ are parallel (so that $\theta = 0$ or $\theta = \pi$) then $|\mathbf{u} \times \mathbf{v}| = 0$ and hence $\mathbf{u} \times \mathbf{v} = \mathbf{0}$, the zero vector. Otherwise, through any point in $\mathbb{R}^3$ there is only one straight line which is perpendicular to both $\mathbf{u}$ and $\mathbf{v}$. $\mathbf{u} \times \mathbf{v}$ is parallel to this line and points in such a direction that $\mathbf{u}$, $\mathbf{v}$ and $\mathbf{u} \times \mathbf{v}$ form a right-handed triad; a right-handed screw advances in the direction of $\mathbf{u} \times \mathbf{v}$ if rotated in the direction from $\mathbf{u}$ towards $\mathbf{v}$. (This is equivalent to saying that the thumb, forefinger and middle finger of the right hand can be made to point in the directions of $\mathbf{u}$, $\mathbf{v}$ and $\mathbf{u} \times \mathbf{v}$ respectively.)

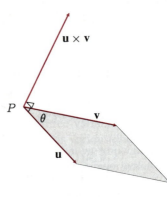

FIGURE 1.3.1

If $\mathbf{u}$ and $\mathbf{v}$ have their tails at the point P then $\mathbf{u} \times \mathbf{v}$ is normal (i.e. perpendicular) to the plane through P in which $\mathbf{u}$ and $\mathbf{v}$ lie, and $\mathbf{u} \times \mathbf{v}$ has length equal to the area of the parallelogram spanned by $\mathbf{u}$ and $\mathbf{v}$. (See Fig. 1.3.1.) These properties make the cross product very useful for the description of tangent planes and normal lines to surfaces in $\mathbb{R}^3$.

The definition of cross product given above does not involve any coordinate system and therefore does not directly show the components of the cross product with respect to the standard basis. These components are provided by the following theorem:

THEOREM 1.3.1   If $\mathbf{u} = u_1\mathbf{i} + u_2\mathbf{j} + u_3\mathbf{k}$ and $\mathbf{v} = v_1\mathbf{i} + v_2\mathbf{j} + v_3\mathbf{k}$ then

$$\mathbf{u} \times \mathbf{v} = (u_2 v_3 - u_3 v_2)\mathbf{i} + (u_3 v_1 - u_1 v_3)\mathbf{j} + (u_1 v_2 - u_2 v_1)\mathbf{k}.$$

PROOF   First we observe that the vector

$$\mathbf{w} = (u_2v_3 - u_3v_2)\mathbf{i} + (u_3v_1 - u_1v_3)\mathbf{j} + (u_1v_2 - u_2v_1)\mathbf{k}$$

is perpendicular to both **u** and **v** since

$$\mathbf{u} \bullet \mathbf{w} = u_1(u_2v_3 - u_3v_2) + u_2(u_3v_1 - u_1v_3) + u_3(u_1v_2 - u_2v_1) = 0,$$

and similarly $\mathbf{v} \bullet \mathbf{w} = 0$. Thus $\mathbf{u} \times \mathbf{v}$ is parallel to **w**. Next we show that **w** and $\mathbf{u} \times \mathbf{v}$ have the same length. In fact

$$\begin{aligned}
|\mathbf{w}|^2 &= (u_2v_3 - u_3v_2)^2 + (u_3v_1 - u_1v_3)^2 + (u_1v_2 - u_2v_1)^2 \\
&= u_2^2v_3^2 + u_3^2v_2^2 - 2u_2v_3u_3v_2 + u_3^2v_1^2 + u_1^2v_3^2 \\
&\quad - 2u_3v_1u_1v_3 + u_1^2v_2^2 + u_2^2v_1^2 - 2u_1v_2u_2v_1,
\end{aligned}$$

while

$$\begin{aligned}
|\mathbf{u} \times \mathbf{v}|^2 &= |\mathbf{u}|^2|\mathbf{v}|^2 \sin^2 \theta \\
&= |\mathbf{u}|^2|\mathbf{v}|^2 (1 - \cos^2 \theta) \\
&= |\mathbf{u}|^2|\mathbf{v}|^2 - (\mathbf{u} \bullet \mathbf{v})^2 \\
&= (u_1^2 + u_2^2 + u_3^2)(v_1^2 + v_2^2 + v_3^2) - (u_1v_1 + u_2v_2 + u_3v_3)^2 \\
&= u_1^2v_1^2 + u_1^2v_2^2 + u_1^2v_3^2 + u_2^2v_1^2 + u_2^2v_2^2 + u_2^2v_3^2 + u_3^2v_1^2 + u_3^2v_2^2 + u_3^2v_3^2 \\
&\quad - u_1^2v_1^2 - u_2^2v_2^2 - u_3^2v_3^2 - 2u_1v_1u_2v_2 - 2u_1v_1u_3v_3 - 2u_2v_2u_3v_3 \\
&= |\mathbf{w}|^2.
\end{aligned}$$

Since **w** is parallel to, and has the same length as $\mathbf{u} \times \mathbf{v}$, we must have either $\mathbf{u} \times \mathbf{v} = \mathbf{w}$ or $\mathbf{u} \times \mathbf{v} = -\mathbf{w}$. It remains to be shown that the first of these is the correct choice. To see this, suppose that the triad of vectors **u**, **v** and **w** are rigidly rotated in 3-space so that **u** points in the direction of the positive x-axis and **v** lies in the upper half of the xy-plane. Then $\mathbf{u} = u_1\mathbf{i}$, and $\mathbf{v} = v_1\mathbf{i} + v_2\mathbf{j}$, where $u_1 > 0$ and $v_2 > 0$. By the "right-hand rule" $\mathbf{u} \times \mathbf{v}$ must point in the direction of the positive z-axis. But $\mathbf{w} = u_1v_2\mathbf{k}$ which does point in that direction, so $\mathbf{u} \times \mathbf{v} = \mathbf{w}$ as asserted. $\square$

The formula for the cross product in terms of components may seem awkward and asymmetric. As we shall see shortly, however, it can be written more easily in terms of determinants which we introduce below.

EXAMPLE 1.3.2   a) $\mathbf{i} \times \mathbf{i} = \mathbf{0}, \qquad \mathbf{i} \times \mathbf{j} = \mathbf{k}, \qquad \mathbf{j} \times \mathbf{i} = -\mathbf{k},$
$\qquad\qquad\qquad\quad \mathbf{j} \times \mathbf{j} = \mathbf{0}, \qquad \mathbf{j} \times \mathbf{k} = \mathbf{i}, \qquad \mathbf{k} \times \mathbf{j} = -\mathbf{i},$
$\qquad\qquad\qquad\quad \mathbf{k} \times \mathbf{k} = \mathbf{0}, \qquad \mathbf{k} \times \mathbf{i} = \mathbf{j}, \qquad \mathbf{i} \times \mathbf{k} = -\mathbf{j}.$

b) $(2\mathbf{i} + \mathbf{j} - 3\mathbf{k}) \times (-2\mathbf{j} + 5\mathbf{k})$
$\qquad = \big((1)(5) - (-2)(-3)\big)\mathbf{i} + \big((-3)(0) - (2)(5)\big)\mathbf{j} + \big((2)(-2) - (1)(0)\big)\mathbf{k}$
$\qquad = -\mathbf{i} - 10\mathbf{j} - 4\mathbf{k}.$

The cross product has some, but not all of the properties we usually ascribe to products. We summarize its algebraic properties as follows: if $\mathbf{u}$, $\mathbf{v}$ and $\mathbf{w}$ are any vectors in $\mathbb{R}^3$, and t is a real number (a scalar), then

i) $\mathbf{u} \times \mathbf{v} = -\mathbf{v} \times \mathbf{u}$ (the cross product is **anticommutative**,)

ii) $(\mathbf{u} + \mathbf{v}) \times \mathbf{w} = \mathbf{u} \times \mathbf{w} + \mathbf{v} \times \mathbf{w}$,

iii) $\mathbf{u} \times (\mathbf{v} + \mathbf{w}) = \mathbf{u} \times \mathbf{v} + \mathbf{u} \times \mathbf{w}$,

iv) $(t\mathbf{u}) \times \mathbf{v} = \mathbf{u} \times (t\mathbf{v}) = t(\mathbf{u} \times \mathbf{v})$,

v) $\mathbf{u} \times \mathbf{u} = \mathbf{0}$,

vi) $\mathbf{u} \bullet (\mathbf{u} \times \mathbf{v}) = \mathbf{v} \bullet (\mathbf{u} \times \mathbf{v}) = \mathbf{0}$.

These identities are all easily verified by using the components or geometric definition of the cross product. They are left as exercises for the reader. Note the absence of an associative law. The cross product is not associative. (See Exercise 15 at the end of this section.)

Determinants

In order to simplify certain formulas such as the component representation of the cross product we introduce 2×2 and 3×3 **determinants**. General $n \times n$ determinants are normally studied in courses on linear algebra; we will encounter them in Section 1.5. In this section we will outline enough of the properties of determinants to enable us to use them as a shorthand in some otherwise complicated formulas.

The 2×2 determinant $\left| \begin{smallmatrix} a & b \\ c & d \end{smallmatrix} \right|$ is a symbol representing the algebraic expression $ad - bc$:

$$\begin{vmatrix} a & b \\ c & d \end{vmatrix} = ad - bc.$$

This is the product of elements in the "downward diagonal" of the array, minus the product of elements in the "upward diagonal." For example,

$$\begin{vmatrix} 1 & 2 \\ 3 & 4 \end{vmatrix} = (1)(4) - (2)(3) = -2.$$

Similarly, a 3×3 determinant is a shorthand symbol representing a certain algebraic expression involving the elements in its rows and columns:

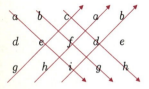

$$\begin{vmatrix} a & b & c \\ d & e & f \\ g & h & i \end{vmatrix} = aei + bfg + cdh - gec - hfa - idb.$$

Observe that each of the six products in the expansion of the determinant involves exactly one element from each row and exactly one from each column. As such, each term is the product of elements in a "diagonal" of an array obtained by repeating the first two columns of the determinant to the right of the third column as shown at the left. The determinant is the sum of products corresponding to the three complete "downward" diagonals minus the sum corresponding to the three "upward" diagonals. With practice you will be able to form these diagonal products without having to write the extended array.

If we group the terms in the expansion of the determinant to factor out the elements of the first row we obtain

$$\begin{vmatrix} a & b & c \\ d & e & f \\ g & h & i \end{vmatrix} = a(ei - fh) - b(di - fg) + c(dh - eg)$$

$$= a\begin{vmatrix} e & f \\ h & i \end{vmatrix} - b\begin{vmatrix} d & f \\ g & i \end{vmatrix} + c\begin{vmatrix} d & e \\ g & h \end{vmatrix}.$$

The 2×2 determinants appearing here (called *minors* of the given 3×3 determinant) are those obtained by deleting the row and column containing the corresponding element from the original 3×3 determinant. This process is called *expanding* the 3×3 determinant *in minors* about the first row.

Such expansions in minors can be carried out about any row or column. Note that a minus sign "$-$" appears in any term whose minor is obtained by deleting the ith row and jth column, where $i + j$ is an *odd* number. For example, we can expand the above determinant in minors about the second column as follows:

$$\begin{vmatrix} a & b & c \\ d & e & f \\ g & h & i \end{vmatrix} = -b\begin{vmatrix} d & f \\ g & i \end{vmatrix} + e\begin{vmatrix} a & c \\ g & i \end{vmatrix} - h\begin{vmatrix} a & c \\ d & f \end{vmatrix}$$

$$= -bdi + bfg + eai - ecg - haf + hcd.$$

(Of course this is the same value obtained previously.)

EXAMPLE 1.3.3

$$\begin{vmatrix} 1 & 4 & -2 \\ -3 & 1 & 0 \\ 2 & 2 & -3 \end{vmatrix} = 3\begin{vmatrix} 4 & -2 \\ 2 & -3 \end{vmatrix} + 1\begin{vmatrix} 1 & -2 \\ 2 & -3 \end{vmatrix}$$

$$= 3(-8) + 1 = -23.$$

We expanded about the second row; the third column would also have been a good choice. (Why?)

Any row (or column) of a determinant may be regarded as the components of a vector. Then the determinant is a *linear function* of that vector. For example

$$\begin{vmatrix} a & b & c \\ d & e & f \\ sx + tl & sy + tm & sz + tn \end{vmatrix} = s\begin{vmatrix} a & b & c \\ d & e & f \\ x & y & z \end{vmatrix} + t\begin{vmatrix} a & b & c \\ d & e & f \\ l & m & n \end{vmatrix}$$

because the determinant is a linear function of its third row. This and other properties of determinants follow directly from the definition. Some other properties are summarized below. These are stated for rows and for 3×3 determinants but similar statements can be made for columns and for determinants of any order.

  i) If two rows of a determinant are interchanged, the determinant changes sign:

$$\begin{vmatrix} d & e & f \\ a & b & c \\ g & h & i \end{vmatrix} = -\begin{vmatrix} a & b & c \\ d & e & f \\ g & h & i \end{vmatrix}.$$

ii) If two rows of a determinant are equal the determinant has value 0:

$$\begin{vmatrix} a & b & c \\ a & b & c \\ g & h & i \end{vmatrix} = 0.$$

iii) If a multiple of one row is added to another row the determinant is unchanged:

$$\begin{vmatrix} a & b & c \\ d+ta & e+tb & f+tc \\ g & h & i \end{vmatrix} = \begin{vmatrix} a & b & c \\ d & e & f \\ g & h & i \end{vmatrix}.$$

The formula for the cross product of vectors

$$\mathbf{u} = u_1\mathbf{i} + u_2\mathbf{j} + u_3\mathbf{k}, \quad \text{and} \quad \mathbf{v} = v_1\mathbf{i} + v_2\mathbf{j} + v_3\mathbf{k}$$

presented in Theorem 1.3.1 can be expressed symbolically as a determinant with the standard basis vectors as the elements of the first row:

1.3.4
The Cross
Product

$$\mathbf{u} \times \mathbf{v} = \begin{vmatrix} \mathbf{i} & \mathbf{j} & \mathbf{k} \\ u_1 & u_2 & u_3 \\ v_1 & v_2 & v_3 \end{vmatrix}.$$

The formula for the cross product given in that theorem amounts to the expansion of this determinant in minors about the first row.

EXAMPLE 1.3.5   Find the area of the triangle with vertices at the points $A = (1,1,0)$, $B = (3,0,2)$ and $C = (0,-1,1)$.

SOLUTION   Two sides of the triangle (see Fig. 1.3.2) are given by the vectors:

$$\overrightarrow{AB} = 2\mathbf{i} - \mathbf{j} + 2\mathbf{k}$$
$$\overrightarrow{AC} = -\mathbf{i} - 2\mathbf{j} + \mathbf{k}.$$

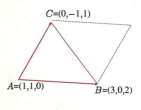

FIGURE 1.3.2

The area of the triangle is half the area of the parallelogram spanned by $\overrightarrow{AB}$ and $\overrightarrow{AC}$. By the geometric definition of cross product, the area of the triangle must therefore be

$$\frac{1}{2}|\overrightarrow{AB} \times \overrightarrow{AC}| = \frac{1}{2}\left|\begin{vmatrix} \mathbf{i} & \mathbf{j} & \mathbf{k} \\ 2 & -1 & 2 \\ -1 & -2 & 1 \end{vmatrix}\right|$$

$$= \frac{1}{2}|3\mathbf{i} - 4\mathbf{j} - 5\mathbf{k}|$$

$$= \frac{1}{2}\sqrt{9+16+25} = \frac{5}{2}\sqrt{2} \text{ sq. units.}$$

A **parallelepiped** is the three dimensional analogue of a parallelogram. It is a solid with three pairs of parallel planar faces, each face being in the shape of a parallelogram. A rectangular brick is a special case of a parallelepiped in which nonparallel faces intersect at right angles. We say that a parallelepiped is **spanned** by three vectors coinciding with three of its edges which meet at one vertex. (See Fig. 1.3.3.)

EXAMPLE 1.3.6   Find the volume of the parallelepiped spanned by **u**, **v** and **w**.

SOLUTION   The volume of the parallelepiped is equal to the area of one of its faces, say the face spanned by **v** and **w**, multiplied by the height of the parallelepiped measured in a direction perpendicular to that face. The area of the face is $|\mathbf{v} \times \mathbf{w}|$. Since $\mathbf{v} \times \mathbf{w}$ is perpendicular to the face, the height of the parallelepiped will be the absolute value of the scalar projection of **u** along $\mathbf{v} \times \mathbf{w}$. If θ is the angle between **u** and $\mathbf{v} \times \mathbf{w}$, then the volume of the parallelepiped is given by

$$\text{Volume} = |\mathbf{u}||\mathbf{v} \times \mathbf{w}||\cos\theta| = |\mathbf{u} \bullet (\mathbf{v} \times \mathbf{w})|.$$

FIGURE 1.3.3

The quantity $\mathbf{u} \bullet (\mathbf{v} \times \mathbf{w})$ is called the **scalar triple product** of the vectors **u**, **v** and **w**. It is easily expressed in terms of a determinant. If $\mathbf{u} = u_1\mathbf{i} + u_2\mathbf{j} + u_3\mathbf{k}$, and similar representations hold for **v** and **w** then

$$\mathbf{u} \bullet (\mathbf{v} \times \mathbf{w}) = u_1 \begin{vmatrix} v_2 & v_3 \\ w_2 & w_3 \end{vmatrix} - u_2 \begin{vmatrix} v_1 & v_3 \\ w_1 & w_3 \end{vmatrix} + u_3 \begin{vmatrix} v_1 & v_2 \\ w_1 & w_2 \end{vmatrix}$$

$$= \begin{vmatrix} u_1 & u_2 & u_3 \\ v_1 & v_2 & v_3 \\ w_1 & w_2 & w_3 \end{vmatrix}.$$

The volume of the parallelepiped is thus the absolute value of this determinant.

EXERCISES

1. Calculate $\mathbf{u} \times \mathbf{v}$ if $\mathbf{u} = \mathbf{i} - 2\mathbf{j} + 3\mathbf{k}$ and $\mathbf{v} = 3\mathbf{i} + \mathbf{j} - 4\mathbf{k}$.

2. Calculate $\mathbf{u} \times \mathbf{v}$ if $\mathbf{u} = \mathbf{j} + 2\mathbf{k}$ and $\mathbf{v} = -\mathbf{i} - \mathbf{j} + \mathbf{k}$.

3. Find the area of the triangle with vertices $(1, 2, 0)$, $(1, 0, 2)$ and $(0, 3, 1)$.

4. Find a unit vector perpendicular to the plane containing the points $(a, 0, 0)$, $(0, b, 0)$ and $(0, 0, c)$. What is the area of the triangle with these vertices?

5. Find a unit vector perpendicular to the vectors $\mathbf{i} + \mathbf{j}$ and $\mathbf{j} + 2\mathbf{k}$.

6. Verify the six identities in the paragraph following Example 1.3.2, either by using the definition of cross product or by using properties of determinants.

7. If $\mathbf{u} + \mathbf{v} + \mathbf{w} = \mathbf{0}$ show that $\mathbf{u} \times \mathbf{v} = \mathbf{v} \times \mathbf{w} = \mathbf{w} \times \mathbf{u}$.

8. A **tetrahedron** is a pyramid with a triangular base and three other triangular faces. It has four vertices and six edges. Like any pyramid or cone, its volume is equal to $\frac{1}{3}Ah$, where A is the area of the base and h is the height measured perpendicular to the base. If **u**, **v** and **w** are vectors coinciding with three concurrent edges of a tetrahedron, (edges meeting in a point), show that the tetrahedron has volume given by

$$\text{Volume} = \frac{1}{6}|\mathbf{u} \bullet (\mathbf{v} \times \mathbf{w})| = \frac{1}{6}\left|\begin{vmatrix} u_1 & u_2 & u_3 \\ v_1 & v_2 & v_3 \\ w_1 & w_2 & w_3 \end{vmatrix}\right|.$$

Thus the volume of a tetrahedron spanned by three vectors is one sixth the volume of the parallelepiped spanned by the same vectors.

9. Find the volume of the tetrahedron with vertices $(1,0,0)$, $(1,2,0)$, $(2,2,2)$ and $(0,3,2)$.

10. Find the volume of the parallelepiped spanned by the diagonals of the three faces of a cube of side a which meet at one of the vertices of the cube.

11. What can you conclude geometrically about the vectors $\mathbf{u}$, $\mathbf{v}$ and $\mathbf{w}$ if you are given that $\mathbf{u} \bullet (\mathbf{v} \times \mathbf{w}) = 0$?

12. For what value of k do the four points $(1,1,-1)$, $(0,3,-2)$, $(-2,1,0)$ and $(k,0,2)$ all lie on a plane?

13. Verify the identities

$$\mathbf{u} \bullet (\mathbf{v} \times \mathbf{w}) = \mathbf{v} \bullet (\mathbf{w} \times \mathbf{u}) = \mathbf{w} \bullet (\mathbf{u} \times \mathbf{v}).$$

14. If $\mathbf{u} \bullet (\mathbf{v} \times \mathbf{w}) \neq 0$ and $\mathbf{x}$ is an arbitrary 3-vector, find the numbers λ, μ and ν such that

$$\mathbf{x} = \lambda\mathbf{u} + \mu\mathbf{v} + \nu\mathbf{w}.$$

15. Calculate $\mathbf{u} \times (\mathbf{v} \times \mathbf{w})$ and $(\mathbf{u} \times \mathbf{v}) \times \mathbf{w}$ given $\mathbf{u} = \mathbf{i} + 2\mathbf{j} + 3\mathbf{k}$, $\mathbf{v} = 2\mathbf{i} - 3\mathbf{j}$, and $\mathbf{w} = \mathbf{j} - \mathbf{k}$. Why would you not expect these to be equal?

16. Does the notation $\mathbf{u} \bullet \mathbf{v} \times \mathbf{w}$ make sense? Why? How about the notation $\mathbf{u} \times \mathbf{v} \times \mathbf{w}$?

17. The product $\mathbf{u} \times (\mathbf{v} \times \mathbf{w})$ is called a **vector triple product**. Since it is perpendicular to $\mathbf{v} \times \mathbf{w}$ it must lie in the plane of $\mathbf{v}$ and $\mathbf{w}$. Show that

$$\mathbf{u} \times (\mathbf{v} \times \mathbf{w}) = (\mathbf{u} \bullet \mathbf{w})\mathbf{v} - (\mathbf{u} \bullet \mathbf{v})\mathbf{w}.$$

(Hint: This can be done by direct calculation of the components of both sides of the equation, but the job is much simpler if you choose coordinate axes so that $\mathbf{v}$ lies along the x-axis and $\mathbf{w}$ lies in the xy- plane.)

1.4   LINES, PLANES AND QUADRIC SURFACES

A single equation in the three variables, x, y and z, constitutes a single constraint on the freedom of the point $P = (x, y, z)$ to lie anywhere in $\mathbb{R}^3$. Such a constraint usually results in a loss of exactly one "degree of freedom" and so forces P to lie on a two-dimensional surface in $\mathbb{R}^3$. For example, the equation

$$x^2 + y^2 + z^2 = 4$$

states that the point (x, y, z) is at distance 2 from the origin. All such points satisfying this condition lie on a **sphere** (that is, on the surface of a ball), of radius 2 centred at the origin. The equation above therefore represents that sphere, and the sphere is the graph of the equation. In this section we shall investigate the graphs of linear and some quadratic equations in three variables.

Planes in 3-Space

Let $P_0 = (x_0, y_0, z_0)$ be a point in $\mathbb{R}^3$ with position vector

$$\mathbf{r}_0 = x_0\mathbf{i} + y_0\mathbf{j} + z_0\mathbf{k}.$$

If $\mathbf{n} = A\mathbf{i} + B\mathbf{j} + C\mathbf{k}$ is any given *nonzero* vector then there exists exactly one **plane** (flat surface) passing through P_0 and perpendicular to $\mathbf{n}$. We say that $\mathbf{n}$ is a **normal vector** to the plane. The plane is the set of all points P for which $\overrightarrow{P_0P}$ is perpendicular to $\mathbf{n}$. (See Fig. 1.4.1.)

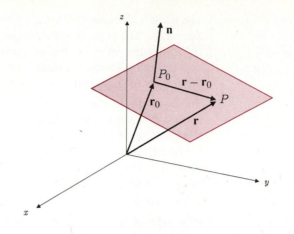

FIGURE 1.4.1

If $P = (x, y, z)$ has position vector $\mathbf{r}$ and P lies in the plane, then the vector $\overrightarrow{P_0P} = \mathbf{r} - \mathbf{r}_0$ is perpendicular to $\mathbf{n}$, so $\mathbf{n} \bullet (\mathbf{r} - \mathbf{r}_0) = 0$. Thus we obtain an equation of the plane:

1.4.1
Equation of a Plane

> The plane having nonzero normal vector $\mathbf{n} = A\mathbf{i} + B\mathbf{j} + C\mathbf{k}$, and passing through the point $P_0 = (x_0, y_0, z_0)$ has equation
>
> $$A(x - x_0) + B(y - y_0) + C(z - z_0) = 0,$$
>
> or, more simply,
>
> $$Ax + By + Cz = D,$$
>
> where $D = Ax_0 + By_0 + Cz_0$.

Such a *linear equation* in x, y and z always represents a plane in $\mathbb{R}^3$. A vector normal to the plane can always be determined from the coefficients of x, y and z. From the first form of the equation one can also read the coordinates of a particular point, P_0, on the plane, but from the second form no particular point is immediately obvious unless $D = 0$, in which case the plane must pass through the origin.

EXAMPLE 1.4.2

a) The equation $2x - 3y - 4z = 0$ represents a plane passing through the origin and having normal vector $\mathbf{n} = 2\mathbf{i} - 3\mathbf{j} - 4\mathbf{k}$.

b) The plane passing through the point $(2, 0, 1)$ which is perpendicular to the straight line passing through the points $(1, 1, 0)$ and $(4, -1, -2)$ has normal vector $\mathbf{n} = (4 - 1)\mathbf{i} + (-1 - 1)\mathbf{j} + (-2 - 0)\mathbf{k} = 3\mathbf{i} - 2\mathbf{j} - 2\mathbf{k}$. Therefore its equation is $3(x - 2) - 2(y - 0) - 2(z - 1) = 0$, or, more simply, $3x - 2y - 2z = 4$.

c) The plane with equation $2x - y = 1$ has normal $2\mathbf{i} - \mathbf{j}$ which is perpendicular to the z-axis. The plane is therefore parallel to the z-axis. Note that the equation is independent of z. In the xy-plane the equation represents a straight line; in 3-space it represents a plane containing that line and parallel to the z-axis. What does the equation $y = z$ represent in $\mathbb{R}^3$? The equation $y = -2$?

d) The equation $2x + y + 3z = 6$ represents a plane with normal $\mathbf{n} = 2\mathbf{i} + \mathbf{j} + 3\mathbf{k}$. In this case we cannot directly read from the equation the coordinates of a particular point on the plane, but it is not difficult to discover some points. For instance, if we put $y = z = 0$ in the equation we get $x = 3$, and so $(3, 0, 0)$ is a point on the plane. We say that the x-**intercept** of the plane is 3 since $(3, 0, 0)$ is the point where the plane intersects the x-axis. Similarly, the y-intercept is 6 and the z-intercept is 2.

e) In general, if a, b and c are all nonzero, the plane with equation

$$\frac{x}{a} + \frac{y}{b} + \frac{z}{c} = 1$$

has intercepts a, b and c on the coordinate axes. (See Fig. 1.4.2.)

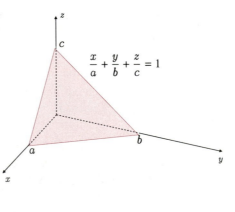

FIGURE 1.4.2

EXAMPLE 1.4.3   Find an equation of the plane which passes through the three points $A = (1, 1, 0)$, $B = (0, 2, 1)$ and $C = (3, 2, -1)$.

SOLUTION   We need to find a vector, $\mathbf{n}$, normal to the plane. Such a vector will be perpendicular to the vectors $\overrightarrow{AB} = -\mathbf{i} + \mathbf{j} + \mathbf{k}$ and $\overrightarrow{AC} = 2\mathbf{i} + \mathbf{j} - \mathbf{k}$. Therefore we can use

$$\mathbf{n} = \overrightarrow{AB} \times \overrightarrow{AC} = \begin{vmatrix} \mathbf{i} & \mathbf{j} & \mathbf{k} \\ -1 & 1 & 1 \\ 2 & 1 & -1 \end{vmatrix} = -2\mathbf{i} + \mathbf{j} - 3\mathbf{k}.$$

An equation is therefore $-2(x - 1) + 1(y - 1) - 3(z - 0) = 0$, or $2x - y + 3z = 1$. (If the cross product had yielded the zero vector for $\mathbf{n}$ what would have been true of the positions of the three points A, B and C? Would they have determined a unique plane?)

EXAMPLE 1.4.4   Show that the two planes

$$x - y = 3 \qquad \text{and} \qquad x + y + z = 0$$

intersect and find a vector, $\mathbf{v}$, parallel to their line of intersection.

SOLUTION   The two planes have respective normal vectors

$$\mathbf{n_1} = \mathbf{i} - \mathbf{j} \qquad \text{and} \qquad \mathbf{n_2} = \mathbf{i} + \mathbf{j} + \mathbf{k}.$$

Since these vectors are not parallel, the planes are not parallel, and so they intersect in a straight line perpendicular to both $\mathbf{n_1}$ and $\mathbf{n_2}$. This line is parallel to

$$\mathbf{v} = \mathbf{n_1} \times \mathbf{n_2} = \begin{vmatrix} \mathbf{i} & \mathbf{j} & \mathbf{k} \\ 1 & -1 & 0 \\ 1 & 1 & 1 \end{vmatrix} = -\mathbf{i} - \mathbf{j} + 2\mathbf{k}.$$

A family of planes intersecting in a straight line is called a **pencil of planes**. Such a pencil of planes is determined by any two nonparallel planes in it, since these have a unique line of intersection. If the two nonparallel planes have equations

$$A_1 x + B_1 y + C_1 z = D_1 \qquad \text{and} \qquad A_2 x + B_2 y + C_2 z = D_2$$

then, for any value of the real number λ, the equation

$$A_1 x + B_1 y + C_1 z - D_1 + \lambda(A_2 x + B_2 y + C_2 z - D_2) = 0$$

represents a plane in the pencil. To see this, observe that the equation is linear, and so represents a plane, and that any point (x, y, z) satisfying the equations of both given planes also satisfies this equation for any value of λ. Any plane in the pencil except the second defining plane, $A_2 x + B_2 y + C_2 z = D_2$, can be obtained by suitably choosing λ.

EXAMPLE 1.4.5   Find an equation of the plane passing through the line of intersection of the two planes

$$x + y - 2z = 6 \qquad \text{and} \qquad 2x - y + z = 2$$

and also passing through the point $(-2, 0, 1)$.

SOLUTION   For any constant λ the equation

$$x + y - 2z - 6 + \lambda(2x - y + z - 2) = 0$$

represents a plane, and is satisfied by the coordinates of all points on the line of intersection of the given planes. This plane passes through the point $(-2, 0, 1)$ if $-2 - 2 - 6 + \lambda(-4 + 1 - 2) = 0$, that is, if $\lambda = -2$. The required plane therefore has equation $3x - 3y + 4z + 2 = 0$. (Note: the method would not have worked if the given point had been on the second plane, $2x - y + z = 2$. Why?)

Straight Lines in 3-Space

As we have observed above, any two nonparallel planes in $I\!\!R^3$ determine a unique line of intersection, and a vector parallel to this line can be obtained by taking the cross product of normal vectors to the two planes.

Suppose that $\mathbf{r}_0 = x_0\mathbf{i} + y_0\mathbf{j} + z_0\mathbf{k}$ is the position vector of point P_0 and $\mathbf{a} = a\mathbf{i} + b\mathbf{j} + c\mathbf{k}$ is a nonzero vector. Evidently there is a unique straight line passing through P_0 parallel to $\mathbf{a}$. If $\mathbf{r} = x\mathbf{i} + y\mathbf{j} + z\mathbf{k}$ is the position vector of any other point, P, on the line then $\mathbf{r} - \mathbf{r}_0$ lies along the line and so is parallel to $\mathbf{a}$. (See Fig. 1.4.3.) Thus $\mathbf{r} - \mathbf{r}_0 = t\mathbf{a}$ for some real number t. This equation, usually rewritten in the form

$$\mathbf{r} = \mathbf{r}_0 + t\mathbf{a},$$

is called the **vector parametric** equation of the straight line. All points on the line can be obtained as t ranges from $-\infty$ to ∞.

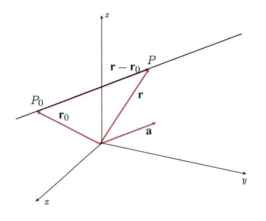

FIGURE 1.4.3

Breaking the vector parametric equation down into its components yields the **scalar parametric** equations of the line:

1.4.6
Parametric Equations of a Straight Line

The straight line parallel to nonzero vector $\mathbf{a} = a\mathbf{i} + b\mathbf{j} + c\mathbf{k}$ and passing through the point $P_0 = (x_0, y_0, z_0)$ has parametric equations

$$\begin{cases} x = x_0 + at \\ y = y_0 + bt \\ z = z_0 + ct. \end{cases}$$

This appears to be *three* linear equations, but the parameter t can be eliminated to give two linear equations in x, y and z. If $a \neq 0$, $b \neq 0$ and $c \neq 0$, then we can solve each of the scalar equations for t, and so obtain

$$\frac{x - x_0}{a} = \frac{y - y_0}{b} = \frac{z - z_0}{c},$$

which is sometimes called the **standard form** for the equations of the straight line through (x_0, y_0, z_0) parallel to **a**. The standard form must be modified if any component of **a** vanishes. For example, if $c = 0$ the equations are

$$\frac{x - x_0}{a} = \frac{y - y_0}{b}, \qquad z = z_0.$$

Note that none of above equations for straight lines is unique; each depends on the particular choice of the point (x_0, y_0, z_0) on the line.

EXAMPLE 1.4.7   a) The equations

$$\begin{cases} x = 2 + t \\ y = 3 \\ z = -4t \end{cases}$$

represent a straight line through $(2, 3, 0)$ parallel to the vector $\mathbf{i} - 4\mathbf{k}$.

b) The straight line through $(1, -2, 3)$ normal to the plane $x + 4z = 5$ has vector parametric equation

$$\mathbf{r} = \mathbf{i} - 2\mathbf{j} + 3\mathbf{k} + t(\mathbf{i} + 4\mathbf{k}).$$

EXAMPLE 1.4.8   Find a set of equations in standard form for the straight line of intersection of the two planes

$$x + y - z = 0 \qquad \text{and} \qquad y + 2z = 6.$$

SOLUTION   We could find a vector **a** parallel to the line by taking the cross product of the normals to the two planes. However, since we have to find one point on the line in any event, we might as well find two and use the difference of their position vectors for **a**. Taking $z = 0$ in the two equations we are led to $y = 6$ and $x = -6$, so $(-6, 6, 0)$ is one point on the line. Taking $x = 0$ in the two equations we get $y = z$ and $y + 2z = 6$ which leads to another point, $(0, 2, 2)$. Hence we could use $6\mathbf{i} - 4\mathbf{j} + 2\mathbf{k}$ for **a**. Instead let us divide by 2 and use $\mathbf{a} = 3\mathbf{i} - 2\mathbf{j} + \mathbf{k}$. The line has equations

$$\frac{x + 6}{3} = \frac{y - 6}{-2} = z.$$

(This answer is not unique as there are infinitely many choices for the specific point (x_0, y_0, z_0). For example,

$$\frac{x}{3} = \frac{y - 2}{-2} = z - 2$$

is also a possible answer.)

Distances

The **distance** between two geometric objects always means the minimum distance between two points, one in each object. In the case of "flat" objects like lines or planes defined by linear equations, such minimum distances can usually be determined by geometric arguments without having to use calculus.

EXAMPLE 1.4.9   Let $\mathcal{P}$ be the plane $Ax + By + Cz = D$ with normal $\mathbf{n} = A\mathbf{i} + B\mathbf{j} + C\mathbf{k}$ and let $\mathbf{r}_0$ be the position vector of a point P_0 in $\mathbb{R}^3$. The distance from P_0 to $\mathcal{P}$ is $s = |\overrightarrow{P_1P_0}|$, where P_1 is the point on $\mathcal{P}$ which is closest to P_0. If P, having position vector $\mathbf{r}$, is any point on $\mathcal{P}$ then s is the length of the projection of $\overrightarrow{PP_0} = \mathbf{r}_0 - \mathbf{r}$ in the direction of $\mathbf{n}$. (See Fig. 1.4.4.) Thus

$$s = \left| \frac{\overrightarrow{PP_0} \bullet \mathbf{n}}{|\mathbf{n}|} \right| = \frac{|(\mathbf{r}_0 - \mathbf{r}) \bullet \mathbf{n}|}{|\mathbf{n}|} = \frac{|\mathbf{r}_0 \bullet \mathbf{n} - \mathbf{r} \bullet \mathbf{n}|}{|\mathbf{n}|}.$$

Since P lies on $\mathcal{P}$ we have $\mathbf{r} \bullet \mathbf{n} = D$. In terms of the coordinates (x_0, y_0, z_0) of P_0, we can therefore represent the distance from P_0 to $\mathcal{P}$ as

1.4.10
Distance from
a Point to
a Plane

$$s = \frac{|Ax_0 + By_0 + Cz_0 - D|}{\sqrt{A^2 + B^2 + C^2}}.$$

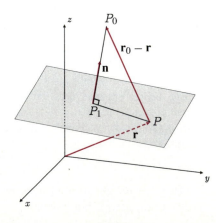

FIGURE 1.4.4

EXAMPLE 1.4.11 Let $\mathcal{L}$ be the line through the point P_1 (with position vector $\mathbf{r}_1$) and parallel to the nonzero vector $\mathbf{a}$. The distance from point P_0 (with position vector $\mathbf{r}_0$) to $\mathcal{L}$ is $s = |\mathbf{r}_2 - \mathbf{r}_0|$, where $\mathbf{r}_2$ is the position vector of the point P_2 on $\mathcal{L}$ closest to P_0. (See Fig. 1.4.5.) Since $\overrightarrow{P_0P_2}$ is perpendicular to $\mathcal{L}$, we have $s = |\mathbf{r}_1 - \mathbf{r}_0| \sin \theta$ where θ is the angle between $\overrightarrow{P_1P_0}$ and $\mathbf{a}$. Thus

$$|(\mathbf{r}_1 - \mathbf{r}_0) \times \mathbf{a}| = |\mathbf{r}_1 - \mathbf{r}_0||\mathbf{a}| \sin \theta = s|\mathbf{a}|,$$

and

1.4.12
**Distance from
a Point to a
Straight Line**

$$s = \frac{|(\mathbf{r}_1 - \mathbf{r}_0) \times \mathbf{a}|}{|\mathbf{a}|}.$$

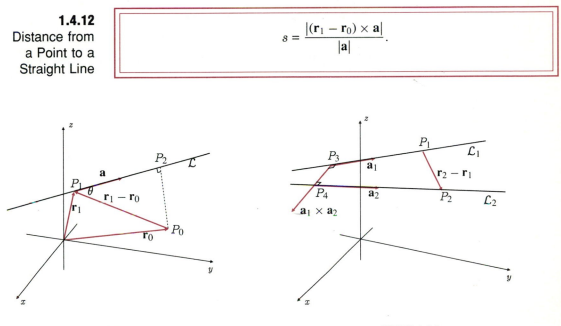

FIGURE 1.4.5   FIGURE 1.4.6

EXAMPLE 1.4.13 Find the distance between the two lines $\mathcal{L}_1$ and $\mathcal{L}_2$ where, for $i = 1, 2$, line $\mathcal{L}_i$ passes through point P_i (with position vector $\mathbf{r}_i$) and is parallel to the nonzero vector $\mathbf{a}_i$.

SOLUTION If P_3 and P_4 (with position vectors $\mathbf{r}_3$ and $\mathbf{r}_4$) are the points on $\mathcal{L}_1$ and $\mathcal{L}_2$ respectively such that the distance between P_3 and P_4 is minimum, then $\overrightarrow{P_3P_4}$ is perpendicular to both lines, and is therefore parallel to $\mathbf{a}_1 \times \mathbf{a}_2$. (See Fig. 1.4.6.) $\overrightarrow{P_3P_4}$ is the vector projection of $\overrightarrow{P_1P_2}$ along $\mathbf{a}_1 \times \mathbf{a}_2$. Therefore

1.4.14
**Distance Between
Striaght Lines**

$$s = |\mathbf{r}_4 - \mathbf{r}_3| = \frac{|(\mathbf{r}_2 - \mathbf{r}_1) \bullet (\mathbf{a}_1 \times \mathbf{a}_2)|}{|\mathbf{a}_1 \times \mathbf{a}_2|}.$$

Some Quadric Surfaces

The most general second-degree equation in three variables is

$$ax^2 + by^2 + cz^2 + dxy + exz + fyz + gx + hy + iz = j.$$

We will not attempt the (rather difficult) task of classifying all the surfaces which can be represented by such an equation, but will examine some interesting special cases. Let us observe at the outset that if the above equation can be factored in the form

$$(A_1x + B_1y + C_1z - D_1)(A_2x + B_2y + C_2z - D_2) = 0$$

then the graph is, in fact, a pair of planes,

$$A_1x + B_1y + C_1z = D_1, \qquad \text{and} \qquad A_2x + B_2y + C_2z = D_2,$$

or one plane if the two linear equations represent the same plane. This is considered a degenerate case. Where such factorization is not possible the surface, called a **quadric surface**, will not be flat.

Spheres. The equation $x^2 + y^2 + z^2 = a^2$ represents a sphere of radius a centred at the origin. More generally,

$$(x - x_0)^2 + (y - y_0)^2 + (z - z_0)^2 = a^2$$

represents a sphere of radius a centred at the point (x_0, y_0, z_0). If a quadratic equation in x, y and z has equal coefficients for the x^2, y^2 and z^2 terms and has no other second-degree terms then it will represent, if any surface at all, a sphere. The centre can be found by completing the squares as for circles in the plane.

Cylinders. The equation $x^2 + y^2 = a^2$, being independent of z, represents a circular cylinder of radius a and axis along the z-axis. (See Fig. 1.4.7.) The intersection of the cylinder with the horizontal plane $z = k$ is the circle with equations

$$\begin{cases} x^2 + y^2 = a^2 \\ z = k. \end{cases}$$

Quadric cylinders also come in other shapes — elliptic, parabolic and hyperbolic. For instance, $z = x^2$ represents a parabolic cylinder with vertex line along the y-axis. (See Fig. 1.4.8.) In general, an equation in two variables only will represent a cylinder in 3-space.

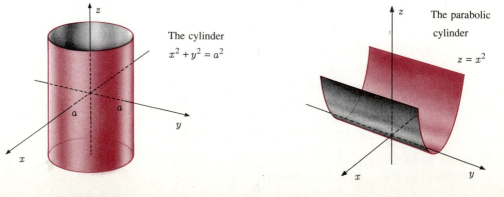

The cylinder $x^2 + y^2 = a^2$

The parabolic cylinder $z = x^2$

FIGURE 1.4.7   **FIGURE 1.4.8**

Cones. The equation $z^2 = x^2 + y^2$ represents a right circular cone with axis along the z-axis. The surface is generated by rotating about the z-axis the line $z = y$ in the yz-plane. This *generator* makes an angle of 45° with the axis of the cone. Cross-sections of the cone in planes parallel to the xy-plane are circles. The equation $x^2 + y^2 = a^2 z^2$ also represents a right circular cone with vertex at the origin and axis along the z-axis, but having semi-vertical angle $\alpha = \tan^{-1} a$ as shown in Fig. 1.4.9. Cones may also have more general cross-sections than circular.

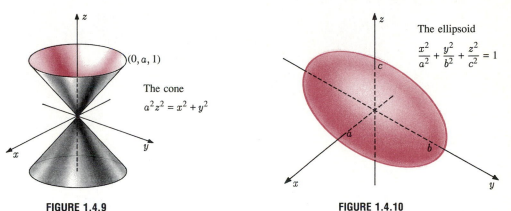

The cone
$a^2 z^2 = x^2 + y^2$

The ellipsoid
$$\frac{x^2}{a^2} + \frac{y^2}{b^2} + \frac{z^2}{c^2} = 1$$

FIGURE 1.4.9   **FIGURE 1.4.10**

Ellipsoids. The equation

$$\frac{x^2}{a^2} + \frac{y^2}{b^2} + \frac{z^2}{c^2} = 1$$

represents an ellipsoid with *semi-axes* a, b and c. (See Fig. 1.4.10.) The surface is oval, and it is enclosed inside the rectangular parallelepiped $-a \le x \le a$, $-b \le y \le b$, $-c \le z \le c$. If $a = b = c$ the ellipsoid is a sphere. In general, all plane cross-sections of ellipsoids are ellipses. This is easy to see for cross-sections parallel to coordinate planes, but somewhat harder to see for other planes.

Paraboloids. The equations

$$z = \frac{x^2}{a^2} + \frac{y^2}{b^2}, \qquad \text{and} \qquad z = \frac{x^2}{a^2} - \frac{y^2}{b^2}$$

represent, respectively, an elliptic paraboloid and a hyperbolic paraboloid. (See Figs. 1.4.11 and 1.4.12.) Cross-sections in planes $z = k$ (k a positive constant) are ellipses (circles if $a = b$) and hyperbolas, respectively. Parabolic reflective mirrors have the shape of circular paraboloids. The hyperbolic paraboloid is a *ruled surface.* (A ruled surface is one through every point of which there passes a straight line lying wholly on the surface. Cones and cylinders are also examples of ruled surfaces.) There are two one-parameter families of straight lines which lie on the hyperbolic paraboloid, namely

$$\begin{cases} \lambda z = \dfrac{x}{a} - \dfrac{y}{b} \\ \dfrac{1}{\lambda} = \dfrac{x}{a} + \dfrac{y}{b} \end{cases} \qquad \text{and} \qquad \begin{cases} \mu z = \dfrac{x}{a} + \dfrac{y}{b} \\ \dfrac{1}{\mu} = \dfrac{x}{a} - \dfrac{y}{b} \end{cases}$$

where λ and μ are real parameters. Every point on the hyperbolic paraboloid lies on one line of each family.

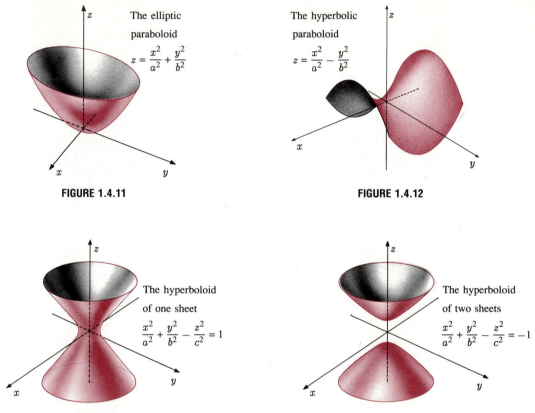

The elliptic paraboloid

$$z = \frac{x^2}{a^2} + \frac{y^2}{b^2}$$

FIGURE 1.4.11

The hyperbolic paraboloid

$$z = \frac{x^2}{a^2} - \frac{y^2}{b^2}$$

FIGURE 1.4.12

The hyperboloid of one sheet

$$\frac{x^2}{a^2} + \frac{y^2}{b^2} - \frac{z^2}{c^2} = 1$$

FIGURE 1.4.13

The hyperboloid of two sheets

$$\frac{x^2}{a^2} + \frac{y^2}{b^2} - \frac{z^2}{c^2} = -1$$

FIGURE 1.4.14

Hyperboloids. The equation

$$\frac{x^2}{a^2} + \frac{y^2}{b^2} - \frac{z^2}{c^2} = 1$$

represents a surface called a *hyperboloid of one sheet*. (See Fig. 1.4.13.) The equation

$$\frac{x^2}{a^2} + \frac{y^2}{b^2} - \frac{z^2}{c^2} = -1$$

represents a *hyperboloid of two sheets*. (See Fig. 1.4.14.) Both surfaces have elliptical cross-sections in horizontal planes and hyperbolic cross-sections in vertical planes. Both are *asymptotic* to the elliptic cone with equation

$$\frac{x^2}{a^2} + \frac{y^2}{b^2} = \frac{z^2}{c^2};$$

they approach arbitrarily close to the cone as they recede arbitrarily far away from the origin. Like the hyperbolic paraboloid, the hyperboloid of one sheet is a ruled surface.

EXERCISES

1. A single equation involving the coordinates (x, y, z) need not always represent a two-dimensional "surface" in $\mathbb{R}^3$. For example, $x^2 + y^2 + z^2 = 0$ represents the single point $(0, 0, 0)$, which has dimension zero. Give examples of single equations in x, y and z which represent

   a) a (one-dimensional) straight line,

   b) the whole of $\mathbb{R}^3$,

   c) no points at all (that is, the empty set).

In Exercises 2–9 find equations of the planes satisfying the given conditions.

2. Passing through $(0, 2, -3)$ and normal to the vector $4\mathbf{i} - \mathbf{j} - 2\mathbf{k}$.

3. Passing through the origin and having normal $\mathbf{i} - \mathbf{j} + 2\mathbf{k}$.

4. Passing through $(1, 2, 3)$ and parallel to the plane $3x + y - 2z = 15$.

5. Passing through the three points $(1, 1, 0)$, $(2, 0, 2)$ and $(0, 3, 3)$.

6. Passing through the three points $(-2, 0, 0)$, $(0, 3, 0)$ and $(0, 0, 4)$.

7. Passing through $(1, 1, 1)$ and $(2, 0, 3)$ and perpendicular to the plane $x + 2y - 3z = 0$.

8. Passing through the line of intersection of the planes $2x + 3y - z = 0$ and $x - 4y + 2z = -5$, and passing through the point $(-2, 0, -1)$.

9. Passing through the line $x + y = 2$, $y - z = 3$, and perpendicular to the plane $2x + 3y + 4z = 5$.

10. Under what geometric condition will three distinct points in $\mathbb{R}^3$ not determine a unique plane passing through them? How can this condition be expressed algebraically in terms of the position vectors, $\mathbf{r}_1$, $\mathbf{r}_2$ and $\mathbf{r}_3$, of the three points?

11. Give a condition on the position vectors of four points which guarantees that the four points are *coplanar*, that is, all lie on one plane.

Describe geometrically the one parameter families of planes in Exercises 12–14. (λ is a real parameter.)

12. $x + y + z = \lambda$.

13.*$x + \lambda y + \lambda z = \lambda$.

14.*$\lambda x + \sqrt{1 - \lambda^2}\, y = 1$.

In Exercises 15–19 find equations of the line specified in vector and scalar parametric forms and in standard form.

15. through the point $(1, 2, 3)$ and parallel to $2\mathbf{i} - 3\mathbf{j} - 4\mathbf{k}$.

16. Through $(-1, 0, 1)$ and perpendicular to the plane $2x - y + 7z = 12$.

17. Through the origin and parallel to the line

$$x + 2y - z = 2, \qquad 2x - y + 4z = 5.$$

18. Through $(2, -1, -1)$ and parallel to each of the two planes $x + y = 0$ and $x - y + 2z = 0$.

19. Through $(1, 2, -1)$ and making equal angles with the positive directions of the coordinate axes.

In Exercises 20–22 find the equations of the given line in standard form.

20. $\mathbf{r} = (1 - 2t)\mathbf{i} + (4 + 3t)\mathbf{j} + (9 - 4t)\mathbf{k}$.

21. $\begin{cases} x = 4 - 5t \\ y = 3t \\ z = 7 \end{cases}$.

22. $\begin{cases} x - 2y + 3z = 0 \\ 2x + 3y - 4z = 4 \end{cases}$.

23. Under what conditions on the position vectors of four distinct points P_1, P_2, P_3 and P_4 will the straight line through P_1 and P_2 intersect the straight line through P_3 and P_4 in a unique point.?

Find the required distances in Exercises 24–27.

24. From the origin to the plane $x + 2y + 3z = 4$.

25. From $(1, 2, 0)$ to the plane $3x - 4y - 5z = 2$.

26. From the origin to the line $x + y + z = 0$, $2x - y - 5z = 1$.

27. Between the lines

$$\begin{cases} x + 2y = 3 \\ y + 2z = 3 \end{cases} \quad \text{and} \quad \begin{cases} x + y + z = 6 \\ x - 2z = -5. \end{cases}$$

28. Show that the line

$$x - 2 = \frac{y + 3}{2} = \frac{z - 1}{4}$$

is parallel to the plane $2y - z = 1$. What is the distance between the line and the plane?

In Exercises 29–30 describe the one-parameter families of straight lines represented by the given equations. (λ is a real parameter.)

29.*$(1 - \lambda)(x - x_0) = \lambda(y - y_0)$, $z = z_0$.

30.*$\dfrac{x - x_0}{\sqrt{1 - \lambda^2}} = \dfrac{y - y_0}{\lambda} = z - z_0$.

31. Why does the factored second-degree equation

$$(A_1 x + B_1 y + C_1 z - D_1)(A_2 x + B_2 y + C_2 z - D_2) = 0$$

represent a pair of planes rather than a single straight line?

Identify the surfaces represented by the equations in Exercises 32–46 and sketch their graphs.

32. $2x^2 + 2y^2 + 2z^2 - 4x + 8y - 12z + 27 = 0.$

33. $x^2 + 4y^2 + 9z^2 = 36.$

34. $x^2 + 4y^2 + 9z^2 + 4x - 8y = 8.$

35. $z = x^2 + 2y^2.$

36. $z = x^2 - 2y^2.$

37. $x^2 - y^2 - z^2 = 4.$

38. $-x^2 + y^2 + z^2 = 4.$

39. $z = xy.$

40. $x^2 + 4z^2 = 4.$

41. $x^2 - 4z^2 = 4.$

42. $y = z^2.$

43. $x = z^2 + z.$

44. $x^2 = y^2 + 2z^2.$

45. $(z - 1)^2 = (x - 2)^2 + (y - 3)^2.$

46. $(z - 1)^2 = (x - 2)^2 + (y - 3)^2 + 4.$

Describe and sketch the geometric objects represented by the systems of equations in Exercises 47–50.

47. $\begin{cases} x^2 + y^2 + z^2 = 4 \\ x + y + z = 1. \end{cases}$

48. $\begin{cases} x^2 + y^2 = 1 \\ z = x + y. \end{cases}$

49. $\begin{cases} z^2 = x^2 + y^2 \\ z = 1 + x. \end{cases}$

50. $\begin{cases} x^2 + 2y^2 + 3z^2 = 6 \\ y = 1. \end{cases}$

51. Find two one-parameter families of straight lines which lie on the hyperboloid of one sheet

$$\frac{x^2}{a^2} + \frac{y^2}{b^2} - \frac{z^2}{c^2} = 1.$$

52. Find two one-parameter families of straight lines which lie on the hyperbolic paraboloid $z = xy$.

▨ 1.5   A LITTLE MATRIX ALGEBRA

Differential calculus is essentially the study of linear approximations to functions. The tangent line to the graph $y = f(x)$ at $x = x_0$ provides the "best linear approximation" to $f(x)$ near x_0. Differentiation of functions of several variables can also be viewed as a process of finding *best linear approximations*. Therefore the language of linear algebra can be very useful for expressing certain concepts in the calculus of several variables.

Linear algebra is a vast subject, usually studied independently of calculus. This is unfortunate, because understanding the relationship between the two subjects can greatly enhance a student's understanding and appreciation of each of them. Knowledge of linear algebra, and therefore familiarity with the material covered in this section, is *not essential* for fruitful study of the rest of this book. However, we shall from time to time comment on the significance of the subject at hand from the point of view of linear algebra. To this end we need only a little of the terminology and content of linear algebra, especially that part pertaining to matrix manipulation and systems of linear equations. In the rest of this section we present an outline of this material. Some students will already be familiar with it; others will encounter it later. We make no attempt at completeness here, and refer interested students to standard linear algebra texts for proofs of some assertions. Students proceeding beyond this book to further study of advanced calculus and differential equations will certainly need a much more extensive background in linear algebra.

Matrices

By an $m \times n$ **matrix** $\mathcal{A}$ we mean a rectangular array of mn numbers arranged in m rows and n columns. If a_{ij} is the element in the ith row and the jth column, then

$$\mathcal{A} = \begin{pmatrix} a_{11} & a_{12} & \cdots & a_{1n} \\ a_{21} & a_{22} & \cdots & a_{2n} \\ \vdots & \vdots & & \vdots \\ a_{m1} & a_{m2} & \cdots & a_{mn} \end{pmatrix}.$$

Sometimes, as a shorthand notation, we write $\mathcal{A} = (a_{ij})$. In this case i is assumed to range from 1 to m and j from 1 to n. If $m = n$ we say that $\mathcal{A}$ is a square matrix. The elements a_{ij} of the matrices we use in this book will always be real numbers.

The **transpose** of an $m \times n$ matrix $\mathcal{A}$ is the $n \times m$ matrix $\mathcal{A}^T$ whose rows are the columns of $\mathcal{A}$:

$$\mathcal{A}^T = \begin{pmatrix} a_{11} & a_{21} & \cdots & a_{m1} \\ a_{12} & a_{22} & \cdots & a_{m2} \\ \vdots & \vdots & & \vdots \\ a_{1n} & a_{2n} & \cdots & a_{mn} \end{pmatrix}.$$

Matrix $\mathcal{A}$ is called **symmetric** if $\mathcal{A}^T = \mathcal{A}$. Symmetric matrices are necessarily square. Observe that $(\mathcal{A}^T)^T = \mathcal{A}$ for *every* matrix $\mathcal{A}$. Frequently we want to consider an n-vector $\mathbf{x}$ as an $n \times 1$ matrix having n rows and one column:

$$\mathbf{x} = \begin{pmatrix} x_1 \\ x_2 \\ \vdots \\ x_n \end{pmatrix}.$$

As such, $\mathbf{x}$ is called a **column vector**. $\mathbf{x}^T$ has one row and n columns, and so is called a **row vector**:

$$\mathbf{x}^T = (x_1 \ x_2 \ \cdots \ x_n).$$

Most of the usefulness of matrices depends on the following definition of matrix multiplication, which enables two arrays to be combined into a single one in a manner that preserves linear relationships.

**1.5.1
Multiplying
Matrices**

If $\mathcal{A} = (a_{ij})$ is an $m \times n$ matrix and $\mathcal{B} = (b_{ij})$ is an $n \times p$ matrix then the product $\mathcal{A}\mathcal{B}$ is the $m \times p$ matrix $\mathcal{C} = (c_{ij})$ with elements given by

$$c_{ij} = \sum_{k=1}^{n} a_{ik} b_{kj}, \qquad i = 1\ldots, m \quad j = 1, \ldots, p.$$

That is, c_{ij} is the *dot product* of the ith row of $\mathcal{A}$ and the jth column of $\mathcal{B}$ (both of which are n-vectors).

EXAMPLE 1.5.2

$$\begin{pmatrix} 1 & 0 & 3 \\ 2 & 1 & -1 \end{pmatrix} \begin{pmatrix} 2 & 1 & 1 & 0 \\ 0 & -1 & 3 & 1 \\ 1 & 0 & 4 & 5 \end{pmatrix} = \begin{pmatrix} 5 & 1 & 13 & 15 \\ 3 & 1 & 1 & -4 \end{pmatrix}$$

The left factor has 2 rows and 3 columns, and the right factor has 3 rows and 4 columns. Therefore the product has 2 rows and 4 columns. The element in the first row and third column of the product, 13, is the dot product of the first row, (1,0,3), of the left factor and the third column, (1,3,4), of the second factor:

$$1 \times 1 + 0 \times 3 + 3 \times 4 = 13.$$

With a little practice you can easily calculate the elements of a matrix product by simultaneously running your left index finger across rows of the left factor and your right index finger down columns of the right factor while taking the dot products.

EXAMPLE 1.5.3

$$\begin{pmatrix} 1 & 2 & 3 \\ 0 & 1 & -1 \\ -2 & 3 & 0 \end{pmatrix} \begin{pmatrix} x \\ y \\ z \end{pmatrix} = \begin{pmatrix} x + 2y + 3z \\ y - z \\ -2x + 3y \end{pmatrix}$$

The product of a 3×3 matrix with a column 3-vector is a column 3-vector.

Matrix multiplication is *associative:*

$$A(BC) = (AB)C$$

(provided A, B and C have dimensions compatible with the formation of the various products) and therefore it makes sense to write ABC. However, matrix multiplication is *not commutative*. Indeed, if A is an $m \times n$ matrix and B is an $n \times p$ matrix then the product AB is defined, but the product BA is not defined unless $m = p$. Even if A and B are square matrices of the same size it is not necessarily true that $AB = BA$.

EXAMPLE 1.5.4

$$\begin{pmatrix} 1 & 2 \\ 3 & 0 \end{pmatrix} \begin{pmatrix} 1 & -1 \\ 1 & 1 \end{pmatrix} = \begin{pmatrix} 3 & 1 \\ 3 & -3 \end{pmatrix} \quad \text{but} \quad \begin{pmatrix} 1 & -1 \\ 1 & 1 \end{pmatrix} \begin{pmatrix} 1 & 2 \\ 3 & 0 \end{pmatrix} = \begin{pmatrix} -2 & 2 \\ 4 & 2 \end{pmatrix}$$

The reader should verify for himself that if the product AB is defined then the transpose of the product is the product of the transposes *in the reverse order*:

$$(AB)^T = B^T A^T.$$

Determinants and Matrix Inverses

In Section 1.3 we introduced 2×2 and 3×3 determinants as certain algebraic expressions associated with 2×2 and 3×3 square arrays of numbers. In general, it is possible to define the determinant $\det(A)$ for any square matrix. For an $n \times n$ matrix A we continue to denote

$$\det(A) = \begin{vmatrix} a_{11} & a_{12} & \cdots & a_{1n} \\ a_{21} & a_{22} & \cdots & a_{2n} \\ \vdots & \vdots & \ddots & \vdots \\ a_{n1} & a_{n2} & \cdots & a_{nn} \end{vmatrix}.$$

We will not attempt to give a formal definition of the determinant here, but will note that the properties of determinants stated for the 3×3 case in Section 1.3 continue to be true. In particular, an $n \times n$ determinant can be expanded in minors about any row or column and so expressed as a sum of multiples of $(n-1) \times (n-1)$ determinants. Continuing this process we can eventually reduce the evaluation of any $n \times n$ determinant to the evaluation of (perhaps many) 2×2 or 3×3 determinants. It is important to realize that the "diagonal" method for evaluating 2×2 or 3×3 determinants does not extend to 4×4 or higher order determinants.

EXAMPLE 1.5.5

$$\begin{vmatrix} 2 & 1 & 0 & 1 \\ 1 & 0 & 1 & 1 \\ 3 & 0 & 0 & 2 \\ -1 & 1 & 1 & 0 \end{vmatrix} = - \begin{vmatrix} 2 & 1 & 1 \\ 3 & 0 & 2 \\ -1 & 1 & 0 \end{vmatrix} - \begin{vmatrix} 2 & 1 & 1 \\ 1 & 0 & 1 \\ 3 & 0 & 2 \end{vmatrix}$$

$$= - \left(-3 \begin{vmatrix} 1 & 1 \\ 1 & 0 \end{vmatrix} - 2 \begin{vmatrix} 2 & 1 \\ -1 & 1 \end{vmatrix} \right) - \left(-1 \begin{vmatrix} 1 & 1 \\ 3 & 2 \end{vmatrix} \right)$$

$$= 3(0-1) + 2(2+1) + 1(2-3) = 2.$$

We expanded the 4×4 determinant in minors about the third column to obtain the two 3×3 determinants. The first of these was expanded about the second row, the other about the second column.

In addition to the properties stated in Section 1.3, determinants have two other very important properties stated in the following theorem.

THEOREM 1.5.6   If A and B are $n \times n$ matrices then

a) $\det(A^T) = \det(A)$.

b) $\det(AB) = \det(A)\det(B)$. $\square$

We will not attempt any proof of this or other theorems in this section. The reader is referred to texts on linear algebra. Part (a) is not very difficult to prove, even in the case of general n. Part (b) cannot really be proved in general without a formal definition of determinant. However, the reader should verify (b) in the 2×2 case by direct calculation.

We say that the square matrix A is **singular** if $\det(A) = 0$. If $\det(A) \neq 0$ we say that A is **nonsingular**.

REMARK: If $\mathcal{A}$ is a 3×3 matrix then $\det(\mathcal{A})$ is the scalar triple product of the rows of $\mathcal{A}$, and, as we showed in Example 1.3.6, its absolute value is the volume of the parallelepiped spanned by those rows. Therefore $\mathcal{A}$ is nonsingular if and only if its rows span a parallelepiped of positive volume; the row vectors cannot all lie in the same plane. The same may be said of the columns of $\mathcal{A}$.

In general, an $n \times n$ matrix is singular if its rows (or columns), considered as vectors, satisfy one or more linear equations of the form

$$c_1\mathbf{x}_1 + c_2\mathbf{x}_2 + \cdots + c_n\mathbf{x}_n = \mathbf{0},$$

with at least one nonzero coefficient c_i. A set of vectors satisfying such a linear equations is called **linearly dependent** because one of the vectors can always be expressed as a linear combination of the others; if $c_1 \neq 0$ then

$$\mathbf{x}_1 = -\frac{c_2}{c_1}\mathbf{x}_2 - \frac{c_3}{c_1}\mathbf{x}_3 - \cdots - \frac{c_n}{c_1}\mathbf{x}_n.$$

All linear combinations of the vectors in a linearly dependent set of n vectors in $\mathbb{R}^n$ must lie in a "subspace" of dimension lower than n.

The $n \times n$ **identity matrix** is the matrix

$$\mathcal{I} = \begin{pmatrix} 1 & 0 & \cdots & 0 \\ 0 & 1 & \cdots & 0 \\ \vdots & \vdots & \ddots & \vdots \\ 0 & 0 & \cdots & 1 \end{pmatrix}$$

with "1" in every position on the "main diagonal" and "0" in every other position. Evidently $\mathcal{I}$ commutes with every $n \times n$ matrix: $\mathcal{I}\mathcal{A} = \mathcal{A}\mathcal{I} = \mathcal{A}$. Also $\det(\mathcal{I}) = 1$. The identity matrix plays the same role in matrix algebra that the number 1 plays in arithmetic.

Any nonzero number x has a reciprocal x^{-1} such that $xx^{-1} = x^{-1}x = 1$. A similar situation holds for square matrices. The **inverse** of a *nonsingular* square matrix $\mathcal{A}$ is a nonsingular square matrix $\mathcal{A}^{-1}$ satisfying

$$\mathcal{A}\mathcal{A}^{-1} = \mathcal{A}^{-1}\mathcal{A} = \mathcal{I}.$$

THEOREM 1.5.7   Every nonsingular square matrix $\mathcal{A}$ has a *unique* inverse $\mathcal{A}^{-1}$. Moreover, the inverse satisfies

a) $\det(\mathcal{A}^{-1}) = \frac{1}{\det(\mathcal{A})}$,

b) $(\mathcal{A}^{-1})^T = (\mathcal{A}^T)^{-1}$.   □

We will not have much cause to calculate inverses, but we note that it can be done by solving systems of linear equations, as the following simple example illustrates.

EXAMPLE 1.5.8   Show that the matrix $A = \begin{pmatrix} 1 & -1 \\ 1 & 1 \end{pmatrix}$ is nonsingular and find its inverse.

SOLUTION $\det(A) = \begin{vmatrix} 1 & -1 \\ 1 & 1 \end{vmatrix} = 1 + 1 = 2$. Therefore A is nonsingular and invertible. Let

$A^{-1} = \begin{pmatrix} a & b \\ c & d \end{pmatrix}$. Then

$$\begin{pmatrix} 1 & 0 \\ 0 & 1 \end{pmatrix} = \begin{pmatrix} 1 & -1 \\ 1 & 1 \end{pmatrix} \begin{pmatrix} a & b \\ c & d \end{pmatrix} = \begin{pmatrix} a-c & b-d \\ a+c & b+d \end{pmatrix},$$

so a, b, c and d must satisfy the systems of equations

$$\begin{cases} a - c = 1 \\ a + c = 0 \end{cases} \qquad \begin{cases} b - d = 0 \\ b + d = 1. \end{cases}$$

Evidently $a = b = d = 1/2$, $c = -1/2$ and

$$A^{-1} = \begin{pmatrix} \frac{1}{2} & \frac{1}{2} \\ -\frac{1}{2} & \frac{1}{2} \end{pmatrix}.$$

Generally, matrix inversion is not carried out by the method of the above example, but rather by an orderly process of performing operations on the rows of the matrix to transform it into the identity. When the same operations are performed on the rows of the identity matrix, the inverse of the original matrix results. See a text on linear algebra for a description of the method.

Linear Transformations

A function F whose domain is the m-dimensional space $\mathbb{R}^m$ and whose range is contained in the n-dimensional space $\mathbb{R}^n$ is called a **linear transformation from $\mathbb{R}^m$ to $\mathbb{R}^n$** if it satisfies

$$F(\lambda \mathbf{x} + \mu \mathbf{y}) = \lambda F(\mathbf{x}) + \mu F(\mathbf{y})$$

for all points $\mathbf{x}$ and $\mathbf{y}$ in $\mathbb{R}^m$ and all real numbers λ and μ. To such a linear transformation F there corresponds an $n \times m$ matrix $\mathcal{F}$ such that for all $\mathbf{x}$ in $\mathbb{R}^m$,

$$F(\mathbf{x}) = \mathcal{F}\mathbf{x},$$

or expressing it in terms of the components of $\mathbf{x}$,

$$F(x_1, x_2, \cdots, x_m) = \mathcal{F} \begin{pmatrix} x_1 \\ x_2 \\ \vdots \\ x_m \end{pmatrix}.$$

We say that $\mathcal{F}$ is a **matrix representation** of the linear transformation F. If $m = n$ so that F maps $\mathbb{R}^m$ into itself then $\mathcal{F}$ is a square matrix. In this case $\mathcal{F}$ is nonsingular if and only if F is one-to-one and has the whole of $\mathbb{R}^m$ as range.

A composition of linear transformations is still a linear transformation and so will have a matrix representation. The real motivation lying behind the definition of matrix multiplication is that the matrix representation of a *composition* of linear transformations is the *product* of the individual matrix representations of the transformations being composed.

THEOREM 1.5.9   If F is a linear transformation from $I\!\!R^m$ to $I\!\!R^n$ represented by the $n \times m$ matrix $\mathcal{F}$, and if G is a linear transformation from $I\!\!R^n$ to $I\!\!R^p$ represented by the $p \times n$ matrix $\mathcal{G}$ then the composition $G \circ F$ defined by

$$G \circ F(x_1, x_2, \ldots, x_m) = G\Big(F(x_1, x_2, \ldots, x_m)\Big)$$

is itself a linear transformation from $I\!\!R^m$ to $I\!\!R^p$ represented by the $p \times m$ matrix $\mathcal{G}\mathcal{F}$. That is,

$$G\Big(F(\mathbf{x})\Big) = \mathcal{G}\mathcal{F}\mathbf{x}. \quad \square$$

Linear Equations

A system of n linear equations in n unknowns:

$$a_{11}x_1 + a_{12}x_2 + \cdots + a_{1n}x_n = b_1$$
$$a_{21}x_1 + a_{22}x_2 + \cdots + a_{2n}x_n = b_2$$
$$\vdots$$
$$a_{n1}x_1 + a_{n2}x_2 + \cdots + a_{nn}x_n = b_n$$

can be written compactly as a single matrix equation

$$\mathcal{A}\mathbf{x} = \mathbf{b}$$

where

$$\mathcal{A} = \begin{pmatrix} a_{11} & a_{12} & \cdots & a_{1n} \\ a_{21} & a_{22} & \cdots & a_{2n} \\ \vdots & \vdots & \ddots & \vdots \\ a_{n1} & a_{n2} & \cdots & a_{nn} \end{pmatrix}, \qquad \mathbf{x} = \begin{pmatrix} x_1 \\ x_2 \\ \vdots \\ x_n \end{pmatrix} \quad \text{and} \quad \mathbf{b} = \begin{pmatrix} b_1 \\ b_2 \\ \vdots \\ b_n \end{pmatrix}.$$

Compare the equation $\mathcal{A}\mathbf{x} = \mathbf{b}$ with the equation $ax = b$ for a single unknown x. $ax = b$ has the unique solution $x = a^{-1}b$ provided $a \neq 0$. By analogy, the linear system $\mathcal{A}\mathbf{x} = \mathbf{b}$ has a unique solution given by

$$\mathbf{x} = \mathcal{A}^{-1}\mathbf{b},$$

provided $\mathcal{A}$ is nonsingular. To see this, just multiply both sides of the equation $\mathcal{A}\mathbf{x} = \mathbf{b}$ on the left by $\mathcal{A}^{-1}$.

If $\mathcal{A}$ is singular, then the system $\mathcal{A}\mathbf{x} = \mathbf{b}$ may or may not have a solution, and if a solution exists it will not be unique. Consider the case $\mathbf{b} = \mathbf{0}$ (the zero vector). Then any vector $\mathbf{x}$ perpendicular to all the rows of $\mathcal{A}$ will satisfy the system. Since the rows of $\mathcal{A}$ lie in a space of dimension less than n (because $\det(\mathcal{A}) = 0$) there will be at least a line of such vectors $\mathbf{x}$. Thus solutions of $\mathcal{A}\mathbf{x} = \mathbf{0}$ are not unique if $\mathcal{A}$ is singular. The same must be true of the system $\mathcal{A}^T\mathbf{y} = \mathbf{0}$; there will be nonzero vectors $\mathbf{y}$ satisfying it if $\mathcal{A}$ is singular. But then, if the system $\mathcal{A}\mathbf{x} = \mathbf{b}$ has any solution $\mathbf{x}$ we must have

$$(\mathbf{y} \bullet \mathbf{b}) = \mathbf{y}^T\mathbf{b} = \mathbf{y}^T\mathcal{A}\mathbf{x} = (\mathbf{x}^T\mathcal{A}^T\mathbf{y})^T = (\mathbf{x}^T\mathbf{0})^T = (0).$$

Hence $\mathcal{A}\mathbf{x} = \mathbf{b}$ can only have solutions for those vectors $\mathbf{b}$ which are perpendicular to *every* solution $\mathbf{y}$ of $\mathcal{A}^T\mathbf{y} = \mathbf{0}$.

We conclude this section by stating a result of some theoretical importance expressing the solution of the system $\mathcal{A}\mathbf{x} = \mathbf{b}$ for nonsingular $\mathcal{A}$ in terms of determinants.

THEOREM 1.5.10   *Cramer's Rule* Let A be a nonsingular $n \times n$ matrix. Then the solution $\mathbf{x}$ of the system

$$A\mathbf{x} = \mathbf{b}$$

has components given by

$$x_1 = \frac{\det(A_1)}{\det(A)}, \quad x_2 = \frac{\det(A_2)}{\det(A)}, \quad \cdots, \quad x_n = \frac{\det(A_n)}{\det(A)},$$

where A_j is the matrix A with its jth column replaced by the column vector $\mathbf{b}$. That is

$$\det(A_j) = \begin{vmatrix} a_{11} & \cdots & a_{1(j-1)} & b_1 & a_{1(j+1)} & \cdots & a_{1n} \\ a_{21} & \cdots & a_{2(j-1)} & b_2 & a_{2(j+1)} & \cdots & a_{2n} \\ \vdots & & \vdots & \vdots & \vdots & & \vdots \\ a_{n1} & \cdots & a_{n(j-1)} & b_n & a_{n(j+1)} & \cdots & a_{nn} \end{vmatrix}. \quad \square$$

The following example provides a concrete illustration of use of Cramer's rule to solve a specific linear system. However, Cramer's rule is primarily used in a more general (theoretical) context; we would not usually use cannons to shoot sparrows like this.

EXAMPLE 1.5.11   Find the point of intersection of the three planes

$$x + y + 2z = 1$$
$$3x + 6y - z = 0$$
$$x - y - 4z = 3.$$

SOLUTION   The solution of the linear system above provides the coordinates of the intersection point. The determinant of the coefficient matrix of this system is

$$\det(A) = \begin{vmatrix} 1 & 1 & 2 \\ 3 & 6 & -1 \\ 1 & -1 & -4 \end{vmatrix} = -32,$$

so the system does have a unique solution. We have

$$x = \frac{1}{-32} \begin{vmatrix} 1 & 1 & 2 \\ 0 & 6 & -1 \\ 3 & -1 & -4 \end{vmatrix} = \frac{-64}{-32} = 2,$$

$$y = \frac{1}{-32} \begin{vmatrix} 1 & 1 & 2 \\ 3 & 0 & -1 \\ 1 & 3 & -4 \end{vmatrix} = \frac{32}{-32} = -1,$$

$$z = \frac{1}{-32} \begin{vmatrix} 1 & 1 & 1 \\ 3 & 6 & 0 \\ 1 & -1 & 3 \end{vmatrix} = \frac{0}{-32} = 0.$$

The intersection point is $(2, -1, 0)$.

EXERCISES

Evaluate the matrix products in Exercises 1–4.

1. $\begin{pmatrix} 3 & 0 & -2 \\ 1 & 1 & 2 \\ -1 & 1 & -1 \end{pmatrix} \begin{pmatrix} 2 & 1 \\ 3 & 0 \\ 0 & -2 \end{pmatrix}$

2. $\begin{pmatrix} 1 & 1 & 1 \\ 0 & 1 & 1 \\ 0 & 0 & 1 \end{pmatrix} \begin{pmatrix} 1 & 1 & 1 \\ 0 & 1 & 1 \\ 0 & 0 & 1 \end{pmatrix}$

3. $\begin{pmatrix} a & b \\ c & d \end{pmatrix} \begin{pmatrix} w & x \\ y & z \end{pmatrix}$ 4. $\begin{pmatrix} w & x \\ y & z \end{pmatrix} \begin{pmatrix} a & b \\ c & d \end{pmatrix}$

5. Evaluate $\mathcal{A}\mathcal{A}^T$ and $\mathcal{A}^2 = \mathcal{A}\mathcal{A}$ where

$$\mathcal{A} = \begin{pmatrix} 1 & 1 & 1 & 1 \\ 0 & 1 & 1 & 1 \\ 0 & 0 & 1 & 1 \\ 0 & 0 & 0 & 1 \end{pmatrix}$$

6. Evaluate $\mathbf{x}\mathbf{x}^T$, $\mathbf{x}^T\mathbf{x}$ and $\mathbf{x}^T\mathcal{A}\mathbf{x}$ where

$$\mathbf{x} = \begin{pmatrix} x \\ y \\ z \end{pmatrix} \quad \text{and} \quad \mathcal{A} = \begin{pmatrix} a & p & q \\ p & b & r \\ q & r & c \end{pmatrix}.$$

Evaluate the determinants in Exercises 7–8.

7. $\begin{vmatrix} 2 & 3 & -1 & 0 \\ 4 & 0 & 2 & 1 \\ 1 & 0 & -1 & 1 \\ -2 & 0 & 0 & 1 \end{vmatrix}$

8. $\begin{vmatrix} 1 & 1 & 1 & 1 \\ 1 & 2 & 3 & 4 \\ -2 & 0 & 2 & 4 \\ 3 & -3 & 2 & -2 \end{vmatrix}$

9. Show that if $\mathcal{A} = (a_{ij})$ is an $n \times n$ matrix for which $a_{ij} = 0$ whenever $i > j$ then $\det(\mathcal{A}) = \prod_{k=1}^{n} a_{kk}$, the product of the elements on the main diagonal of $\mathcal{A}$.

10. Show that $\begin{vmatrix} 1 & 1 \\ x & y \end{vmatrix} = y - x$, and

$$\begin{vmatrix} 1 & 1 & 1 \\ x & y & z \\ x^2 & y^2 & z^2 \end{vmatrix} = (y - x)(z - x)(z - y).$$

Try to generalize this result to the $n \times n$ case.

11. Verify the associative law $(\mathcal{A}\mathcal{B})\mathcal{C} = \mathcal{A}(\mathcal{B}\mathcal{C})$ by direct calculation for three arbitrary 2×2 matrices.

12. Show that $\det(\mathcal{A}^T) = \det(\mathcal{A})$ for $n \times n$ matrices by induction on n. Start with the 2×2 case.

13. Verify by direct calculation that $\det(\mathcal{A}\mathcal{B}) = \det(\mathcal{A})\det(\mathcal{B})$ holds for two arbitrary 2×2 matrices.

14. Let $\mathcal{A}_\theta = \begin{pmatrix} \cos\theta & \sin\theta \\ -\sin\theta & \cos\theta \end{pmatrix}$. Show that $(\mathcal{A}_\theta)^T = (\mathcal{A}_\theta)^{-1} = \mathcal{A}_{-\theta}$.

Find the inverses of the matrices in Exercises 15–16.

15. $\begin{pmatrix} 1 & 1 & 1 \\ 0 & 1 & 1 \\ 0 & 0 & 1 \end{pmatrix}$ 16. $\begin{pmatrix} 1 & 0 & -1 \\ -1 & 1 & 0 \\ 2 & 1 & 3 \end{pmatrix}$

17. Use your result from the previous exercise to solve the linear system
$$\begin{cases} x - z = -2 \\ -x + y = 1 \\ 2x + y + 3z = 13. \end{cases}$$

18. Solve the system of the previous exercise by using Cramer's rule.

19. Solve the system $\begin{cases} x_1 + x_2 + x_3 + x_4 = 0 \\ x_1 + x_2 + x_3 - x_4 = 4 \\ x_1 + x_2 - x_3 - x_4 = 6 \\ x_1 - x_2 - x_3 - x_4 = 2 \end{cases}$

20. Verify Theorem 1.5.9 for the special case where F and G are linear transformations from $\mathbb{R}^2$ to $\mathbb{R}^2$.

CHAPTER 2

Partial Differentiation

This chapter is concerned with extending the idea of the derivative to real functions of a vector variable, that is, to functions depending on several real variables.

⌁ 2.1 FUNCTIONS OF SEVERAL VARIABLES

The notation $y = f(x)$ is used to denote that the variable y depends on the single real variable x, that is, that y is a function of x. The domain of such a function f is a set of real numbers. Many quantities can be regarded as depending on more than one real variable, and thus to be functions of more than one variable. For example, the volume of a circular cylinder of radius r and height h is given by $V = \pi r^2 h$; we say that V is a function of the two variables r and h. If we choose to denote this function by f, then we would write $V = f(r, h)$ where

$$f(r, h) = \pi r^2 h, \qquad (r > 0, \quad h > 0).$$

Thus f is a function of two variables having as *domain* the set of points in the rh-plane with coordinates (r, h) satisfying $r > 0$ and $h > 0$. Similarly, the relationship $w = f(x, y, z) = x + 2y - 3z$ defines w as a function of the three variables x, y and z, with domain the whole of $\mathbb{R}^3$, or, if we state explicitly, some particular subset of $\mathbb{R}^3$.

By analogy with the corresponding definition for functions of one variable, we define a function of n variables as follows:

2.1.1
Functions

A **function** f of n real variables is a rule which assigns a *unique* real number $f(x_1, x_2, \ldots, x_n)$ to each point $(x_1, x_2, \ldots, x_n)$ in some subset $\mathcal{D}(f)$ of $\mathbb{R}^n$. $\mathcal{D}(f)$ is called the **domain** of f. The set of real numbers $f(x_1, x_2, \ldots, x_n)$ obtained from points in the domain is called the **range** of f.

As for functions of one variable, it is conventional to take the domain of such a function of n variables to be the largest set of points $(x_1, x_2, \ldots, x_n)$ for which $f(x_1, x_2, \ldots, x_n)$ makes sense as a real number, unless the domain is explicitly stated to be a smaller set.

Most of the examples we consider hereafter will be functions of two or three independent variables. When a function f depends on two variables we shall usually call these variables x and y, and use z to denote the value of the function; that is, $z = f(x, y)$. We will normally use x, y and z as the independent variables of a function depending on three variables, and w as the value of the function; $w = f(x, y, z)$. Some theorems will be stated (and proved) only for the two-variable case, but extensions to three and more variables will usually be obvious.

Graphical Representations

The graph of a function f of one variable, that is, the graph of the equation $y = f(x)$, is the set of points in the xy-plane which have coordinates $(x, f(x))$, where x is in the domain of f. Similarly, the graph of a function f of 2 variables, (the graph of the equation $z = f(x,y)$), is the set of points in 3-space having coordinates $(x, y, f(x,y))$, where (x,y) belongs to the domain of f. This graph is, therefore, a surface in $\mathbb{R}^3$ lying above (if $f(x,y) > 0$) or below (if $f(x,y) < 0$) the domain of f in the xy-plane. (See Fig. 2.1.1.) The graph of a function of three variables is a three-dimensional "hypersurface" in a 4-space, $\mathbb{R}^4$. In general, the graph of a function of n variables is an n-dimensional "surface" in $\mathbb{R}^{n+1}$. We will not attempt to *draw* graphs of functions of more than two variables!

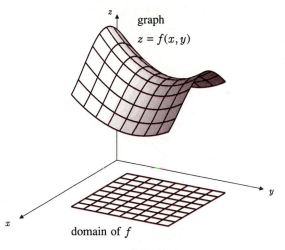

graph
$z = f(x,y)$

domain of f

FIGURE 2.1.1

EXAMPLE 2.1.2   Consider the function

$$f(x,y) = 3\left(1 - \frac{x}{2} - \frac{y}{4}\right), \qquad (0 \le x \le 2, \quad 0 \le y \le 4 - 2x).$$

The graph of f is the plane triangular surface with vertices at $(2,0,0)$, $(0,4,0)$, and $(0,0,3)$. (See Fig. 2.1.2.) If the domain of f had not been explicitly stated to be a particular set in the xy-plane, the graph would have been the whole plane through these three points.

EXAMPLE 2.1.3   Consider $f(x,y) = \sqrt{9 - x^2 - y^2}$. Here the domain is the disc $x^2 + y^2 \le 9$ in the xy-plane. If we square the equation $z = \sqrt{9 - x^2 - y^2}$ we can rewrite the result in the form $x^2 + y^2 + z^2 = 9$. This is a sphere of radius 3 centred at the origin. However, the graph of f is only the upper hemisphere where $z \ge 0$. (See Fig. 2.1.3.)

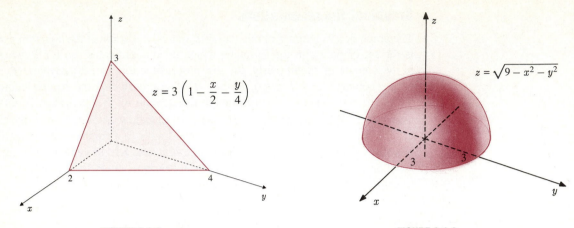

FIGURE 2.1.2   **FIGURE 2.1.3**

Since it is necessary to project the surface $z = f(x, y)$ onto a two-dimensional page, most such graphs are difficult to sketch without considerable artistic talent and training. Nevertheless, you should always try to visualize such a graph, and sketch it as best you can. Sometimes it is convenient to sketch only part of a graph, for instance, the part lying in the first octant. It is also helpful to determine (and sketch) the intersections of the graph with various planes, especially planes parallel to the coordinate planes. Students with a programming background may find it challenging to try to write a program to sketch graphs of functions of two variables by ruling them with families of curves, say the intersections of the surface with planes perpendicular to the x- and y-axes. Figure 2.1.1 is an example of such a computer-drawn graph.

Another way of representing the function $f(x, y)$ graphically is to produce a two-dimensional "topographic map" of the surface $z = f(x, y)$. Thus we sketch, in the xy-plane, the curves $f(x, y) = C$ for various choices of the constant C. These curves are called **level curves** of f because they are the vertical projections onto the xy-plane of the curves in which the graph $z = f(x, y)$ intersects horizontal planes $z = C$. The graph and some level curves of the function $f(x, y) = x^2 + y^2$ are shown in Fig. 2.1.4. The graph is a circular paraboloid; the level curves are circles centred at the origin.

The contour curves in the topographic map in Fig. 2.1.5 show the elevations, in 200 ft increments above sea level, on part of Nelson Island on the British Columbia coast. Since these contours are drawn for equally spaced values of C, the spacing of the contours themselves conveys information about the relative steepness at various places on the mountains; the land is steepest where the contour lines are closest together. Observe also that the streams shown cross the contours at right angles. They take the route of steepest descent. Isotherms (curves of constant temperature) and isobars (curves of constant pressure) on weather maps are also examples of level curves.

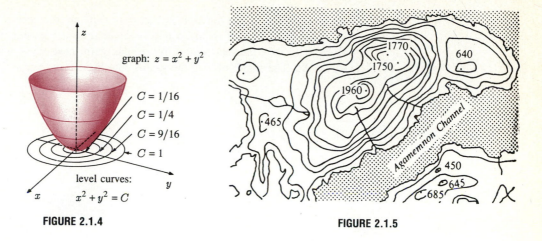

FIGURE 2.1.4

FIGURE 2.1.5

EXAMPLE 2.1.4   The level curves of the function $f(x,y) = 3\left(1 - \dfrac{x}{2} - \dfrac{y}{4}\right)$ of Example 2.1.2 are the segments of the straight lines

$$3\left(1 - \frac{x}{2} - \frac{y}{4}\right) = C, \qquad \text{or} \qquad \frac{x}{2} + \frac{y}{4} = 1 - \frac{C}{3}, \qquad (0 \le C \le 3)$$

which lie in the first quadrant. (See Fig. 2.1.6.)

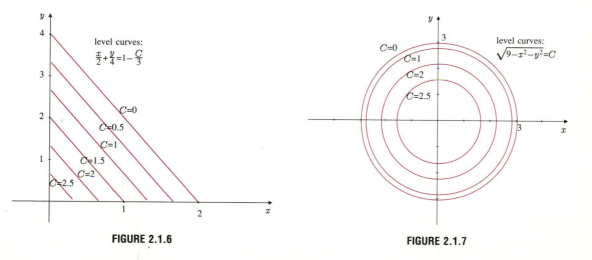

FIGURE 2.1.6

FIGURE 2.1.7

EXAMPLE 2.1.5   The level curves of the function $f(x,y) = \sqrt{9 - x^2 - y^2}$ of Example 2.1.3 are the concentric circles (see Fig. 2.1.7)

$$\sqrt{9 - x^2 - y^2} = C, \qquad \text{or} \qquad x^2 + y^2 = 9 - C^2, \qquad (0 \le C \le 3).$$

EXAMPLE 2.1.6 The level curves of the function $f(x,y) = x^2 - y^2$ are the curves $x^2 - y^2 = C$. For $C = 0$ the level "curve" is the pair of straight lines $x = y$ and $x = -y$. For other values of C they are rectangular hyperbolas with these lines as asymptotes. (See Fig. 2.1.8.) The graph of f is the saddle-like hyperbolic paraboloid of Fig. 2.1.9.

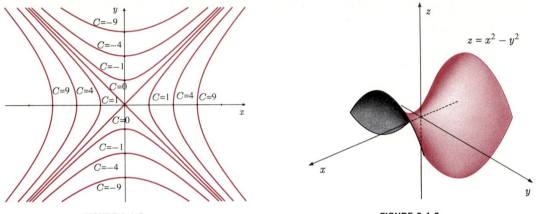

FIGURE 2.1.8   FIGURE 2.1.9

A function $f(x,y,z)$ of three variables has **level surfaces**, the surfaces in $\mathbb{R}^3$ with equations $f(x,y,z) = C$ for various choices of the constant C. For instance, the level surfaces of the function $f(x,y,z) = x^2 + y^2 + z^2$ are concentric spheres centred at the origin.

Limits and Continuity

The concept of limit of a function of several variables is similar to that for functions of one variable. For clarity we present the definition for functions of two variables only; the general case is similar.

We say that $f(x,y)$ approaches the limit L as the point (x,y) approaches the point (a,b), and we write

$$\lim_{(x,y)\to(a,b)} f(x,y) = L,$$

if all points of a disc of positive radius centred at (a,b), except possibly the point (a,b) itself, belong to the domain of f, and if $f(x,y)$ approaches arbitrarily close to L as (x,y) approaches (a,b). We make this more formal in the following definition.

2.1.7
Definition of Limit

We say that $\lim_{(x,y)\to(a,b)} f(x,y) = L$ if and only if for every positive number ϵ there exists a positive number $\delta = \delta(\epsilon)$, depending on ϵ, such that

$$|f(x,y) - L| < \epsilon \quad \text{whenever} \quad 0 < \sqrt{(x-a)^2 + (y-b)^2} < \delta.$$

If a limit exists it is unique. For a single-variable function f, the existence of $\lim_{x \to a} f(x)$ implies, that $f(x)$ approaches the same finite number as x approaches a from either the right or the left. Similarly, for a function of two variables, $\lim_{(x,y) \to (a,b)} f(x,y)$ exists only if $f(x,y)$ approaches the same number no matter how (x,y) approaches (a,b). The examples below will illustrate this.

All the usual laws of limits extend to functions of several variables in the obvious way. For example, if $\lim_{(x,y) \to (a,b)} f(x,y) = L$ and $\lim_{(x,y) \to (a,b)} g(x,y) = M$ then

$$\lim_{(x,y) \to (a,b)} \big(f(x,y) \pm g(x,y)\big) = L \pm M,$$

$$\lim_{(x,y) \to (a,b)} f(x,y)\,g(x,y) = LM,$$

$$\lim_{(x,y) \to (a,b)} \frac{f(x,y)}{g(x,y)} = \frac{L}{M} \qquad \text{provided } M \neq 0.$$

EXAMPLE 2.1.8

a) $\lim_{(x,y) \to (2,3)} 2x - y^2 = 4 - 9 = -5.$

b) $\lim_{(x,y) \to (a,b)} x^2 y = a^2 b.$

c) $\lim_{(x,y) \to (\pi/3,2)} y \sin(x/y) = 2\sin(\pi/6) = 1.$

EXAMPLE 2.1.9 Let

$$f(x,y) = \frac{2xy}{x^2 + y^2}.$$

Note that $f(x,y)$ is defined at all points of the xy-plane except the origin $(0,0)$. We can still ask whether $\lim_{(x,y) \to (0,0)} f(x,y)$ exists or not. If we let (x,y) approach $(0,0)$ along the x-axis, we get $f(x,y) = f(x,0) = 0$ identically, so the limit must be 0 if it exists at all. Similarly, at all points of the y-axis we have $f(x,y) = f(0,y) = 0$. However, at points of the line $x = y$, f has a different constant value; $f(x,x) = 1$. Since the limit of $f(x,y)$ is 1 as (x,y) approaches $(0,0)$ along this line, it follows that $f(x,y)$ cannot have a unique limit at the origin. That is,

$$\lim_{(x,y) \to (0,0)} \frac{2xy}{x^2 + y^2} \qquad \text{does not exist.}$$

Observe that $f(x,y)$ has a constant value on any ray from the origin (on the ray $y = kx$ the value is $2k/(1 + k^2)$), but these values differ on different rays. The level curves of f are the rays from the origin (with the origin itself removed). It is difficult to sketch the graph of f near the origin. The first-octant part of the graph is the "hood-shaped" surface in Fig. 2.1.10.

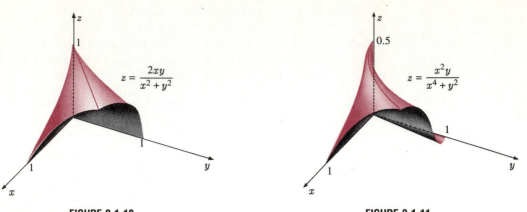

FIGURE 2.1.10　　　　　　　　　　　　　　　**FIGURE 2.1.11**

EXAMPLE 2.1.10　Consider the function

$$f(x, y) = \frac{x^2 y}{x^4 + y^2}.$$

As in the previous example, $f(x, y)$ vanishes identically on the coordinate axes so $\lim_{(x,y)\to(0,0)} f(x, y)$ must be 0 if it exists at all. If we examine $f(x, y)$ at points of the ray $y = kx$, we obtain

$$f(x, kx) = \frac{kx^3}{x^4 + k^2 x^2} = \frac{kx}{x^2 + k^2} \to 0 \quad \text{as} \quad x \to 0 \quad (k \neq 0).$$

Thus $f(x, y) \to 0$ as $(x, y) \to (0, 0)$ along *any* straight line through the origin. We might be led to infer, therefore, that $\lim_{(x,y)\to(0,0)} f(x, y) = 0$, but this would be incorrect. Observe the behavior of $f(x, y)$ along the curve $y = x^2$:

$$f(x, x^2) = \frac{x^4}{x^4 + x^4} = \frac{1}{2}.$$

Thus $f(x, y)$ does not approach 0 as (x, y) approaches the origin along this curve, and so $\lim_{(x,y)\to(0,0)} f(x, y)$ does not exist. The level curves of f are pairs of parabolas of the form $y = kx^2$, $y = x^2/k$ with the origin removed. See Fig. 2.1.11 for the first octant part of the graph of f.

EXAMPLE 2.1.11　The function

$$f(x, y) = \frac{x^2 y}{x^2 + y^2}$$

actually does have a limit at the origin; in fact

$$\lim_{(x,y)\to(0,0)} \frac{x^2 y}{x^2 + y^2} = 0.$$

To see this, observe that since $x^2 \leq x^2 + y^2$, we have

$$|f(x, y) - 0| = \left| \frac{x^2 y}{x^2 + y^2} \right| \leq |y|$$

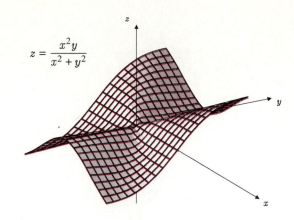

$$z = \frac{x^2 y}{x^2 + y^2}$$

FIGURE 2.1.12

what does this tell us?

which approaches zero as $(x, y) \to (0, 0)$. (See Fig. 2.1.12.) Formally, if $\epsilon > 0$ is given and we take $\delta = \epsilon$, then $|f(x, y) - 0| < \epsilon$ whenever $0 < \sqrt{x^2 + y^2} < \delta$.

2.1.12
Continuity

> The function $f(x, y)$ is continuous at the point (a, b) if
>
> $$\lim_{(x,y)\to(a,b)} f(x, y) = f(a, b).$$

As for functions of one variable, sums, differences, products, quotients and compositions of continuous functions are continuous. The functions of Examples 2.1.9–11 above are continuous wherever they are defined, that is, at all points except the origin. There is no way to define $f(0, 0)$ so that the functions in Examples 2.1.9 and 2.1.10 become continuous at the origin. However, the function of Example 2.1.11 will be continuous at the origin if we define $f(0, 0) = \lim_{(x,y)\to(0,0)} f(x, y) = 0$.

not defined?!!

so if the lim. exists at (0,0) does this mean its continuos at (0,0)?

Definition 2.1.7 requires that $f(x, y)$ be defined at all points of a disc centred at (a, b) (except the point (a, b) itself) in order that $\lim_{(x,y)\to(a,b)} f(x, y)$ can exist. This means that continuity is defined by Definition 2.1.12 only for *interior* points of the domain of f. We can modify the definition of limit to allow for limits at points of the *boundary* of the domain of f in a manner analogous to that used for *one-sided limits* of functions of one variable. Definition 2.1.13 below is thus an extension of (and supersedes) Definition 2.1.7 so that Definition 2.1.12 can be used to determine continuity up to the boundary of the domain.

2.1.13
Revised definition
of limit

We say that

$$\lim_{(x,y)\to(a,b)} f(x,y) = L$$

provided that

i) every disc of positive radius centred at (a, b) contains points of the domain of f different from (a, b), and

ii) for every positive number ϵ there exists a positive number $\delta = \delta(\epsilon)$ such that

$$|f(x,y) - L| < \epsilon$$

holds whenever (x, y) is in the domain of f and satisfies

$$0 < \sqrt{(x-a)^2 + (y-b)^2} < \delta.$$

Condition i) is included in Definition 2.1.13 because, without it, limits at *isolated points* of the domain of f would not be unique.

EXAMPLE 2.1.14   The function $f(x, y) = \sqrt{1 - x^2 - y^2}$ is continuous at all points of its domain, the *closed* disc $x^2 + y^2 \leq 1$. Of course (x, y) can approach points of the bounding circle $x^2 + y^2 = 1$ only from within the disc.

EXERCISES

Specify the domains of the functions in Exercises 1–10.

1. $f(x,y) = \dfrac{x+y}{x-y}$ **2.** $f(x,y) = \sqrt{xy}$

3. $f(x,y) = \dfrac{x}{x^2 + y^2}$ **4.** $f(x,y) = \dfrac{xy}{x^2 - y^2}$

5. $f(x,y) = \sqrt{4x^2 + 9y^2 - 36}$

6. $f(x,y) = \dfrac{1}{\sqrt{x^2 - y^2}}$ **7.** $f(x,y) = \ln(1 + xy)$

8. $f(x,y) = \sin^{-1}(x + y)$

9. $f(x,y,z) = \dfrac{xyz}{x^2 + y^2 + z^2}$

10. $f(x,y,z) = \dfrac{e^{xyz}}{\sqrt{xyz}}$

Sketch the graphs of the functions in Exercises 11–18.

11. $f(x,y) = x,$ $(0 \leq x \leq 2, \quad 0 \leq y \leq 3)$

12. $f(x,y) = \sin x,$ $(0 \leq x \leq 2\pi, \quad 0 \leq y \leq 1)$

13. $f(x,y) = y^2,$ $(-1 \leq x \leq 1, \quad -1 \leq y \leq 1)$

14. $f(x,y) = 4 - x^2 - y^2,$ $(x^2 + y^2 \leq 4, \ x \geq 0, \ y \geq 0)$

15. $f(x,y) = \sqrt{x^2 + y^2}$ **16.** $f(x,y) = 4 - x^2$

17. $f(x,y) = |x| + |y|$ **18.** $f(x,y) = 6 - x - 2y$

Sketch some of the level curves of the functions in Exercises 19–25.

19. $f(x,y) = x - y$ **20.** $f(x,y) = x^2 + 2y^2$

21. $f(x,y) = xy$ **22.** $f(x,y) = \dfrac{x^2}{y}$

23. $f(x,y) = \dfrac{x-y}{x+y}$ **24.** $f(x,y) = \dfrac{y}{x^2+y^2}$

25. $f(x,y) = xe^{-y}$

26. If we assume $z \geq 0$, the equation $4z^2 = (x-z)^2 + (y-z)^2$ defines z as a function of x and y. Sketch some level curves of this function. Describe its graph.

27. Find $f(x,y)$ if each level curve $f(x,y) = C$ is a circle centred at the origin and having radius
    a) C,   b) C^2,   c) $\sqrt{C}$,   d) $\ln C$.

28. Find $f(x,y,z)$ if for each constant C the level surface $f(x,y,z) = C$ is a plane having intercepts C^3, $2C^3$ and $3C^3$ on the x-axis, the y-axis and the z-axis respectively.

Describe the level surfaces of the functions specified in Exercises 29–33.

29. $f(x,y,z) = x^2 + y^2 + z^2$

30. $f(x,y,z) = x + 2y + 3z$

31. $f(x,y,z) = x^2 + y^2$ **32.** $f(x,y,z) = \dfrac{x^2+y^2}{z^2}$

33. $f(x,y,z) = |x| + |y| + |z|$

34. Describe the "level hypersurfaces" of the function

$$f(x,y,z,t) = x^2 + y^2 + z^2 + t^2.$$

In Exercises 35–42 evaluate the indicated limit or explain why it does not exist.

35. $\displaystyle\lim_{(x,y)\to(2,-1)} xy + x^2$ **36.** $\displaystyle\lim_{(x,y)\to(0,0)} \dfrac{x}{x^2+y^2}$

37. $\displaystyle\lim_{(x,y)\to(0,0)} \dfrac{y^3}{x^2+y^2}$ **38.** $\displaystyle\lim_{(x,y)\to(0,0)} \dfrac{\sin(x-y)}{\cos(x+y)}$

39. $\displaystyle\lim_{(x,y)\to(0,0)} \dfrac{\sin(xy)}{x^2+y^2}$ **40.** $\displaystyle\lim_{(x,y)\to(0,0)} \dfrac{2x^2-xy}{4x^2-y^2}$

41. $\displaystyle\lim_{(x,y)\to(0,0)} \dfrac{x^2y^2}{x^2+y^4}$ **42.** $\displaystyle\lim_{(x,y)\to(0,0)} \dfrac{x^2y^2}{2x^4+y^4}$

43. How can the function

$$f(x,y) = \frac{x^2+y^2-x^3y^3}{x^2+y^2}, \qquad (x,y)\neq(0,0),$$

be defined at the origin so that it becomes continuous at all points of the xy-plane?

44. How can the function

$$f(x,y) = \frac{x^3-y^3}{x-y}, \qquad (x\neq y),$$

be defined along the line $x = y$ so that the resulting function is continuous on the whole xy-plane?

45.*What is the domain of

$$f(x,y) = \frac{x-y}{x^2-y^2}?$$

Does $f(x,y)$ have a limit by Definition 2.1.7 as $(x,y) \to (1,1)$? By Definition 2.1.13? Can the domain of f be extended so that the resulting function is continuous at $(1,1)$? Can the domain be extended so that the resulting function is continuous everywhere in the xy-plane?

46.*Given a function $f(x,y)$ and a point (a,b) in its domain, let single-variable functions g and h be defined as follows:

$$g(x) = f(x,b), \qquad h(y) = f(a,y).$$

If g is continuous at $x = a$ and h is continuous at $y = b$ does it follow that f is continuous at (a,b)? Conversely, does the continuity of f at (a,b) guarantee the continuity of g at a and the continuity of h at b? Justify your answers.

2.2   PARTIAL DERIVATIVES

In this section we begin the process of extending the concepts and techniques of single-variable calculus to functions of more than one variable. It is convenient to begin by considering the dependence of such functions on one variable at a time. Thus a function of n variables has n *first partial derivatives*, one with respect to each of its independent variables. For a function of two variables we make this precise in the following definition.

2.2.1
Definition of First
Partial Derivatives

> The **first partial derivatives** of the function $f(x, y)$ **with respect to the variables** x and y are the functions $f_1(x, y)$ and $f_2(x, y)$ given by
>
> $$f_1(x, y) = \lim_{h \to 0} \frac{f(x+h, y) - f(x, y)}{h}$$
> $$f_2(x, y) = \lim_{k \to 0} \frac{f(x, y+k) - f(x, y)}{k}$$
>
> provided the limits exist.

EXAMPLE 2.2.2   If $f(x, y) = x^2 \sin y$, then $f_1(x, y) = 2x \sin y$ and $f_2(x, y) = x^2 \cos y$. Observe that $f_1(x, y)$ is just the ordinary first derivative of $f(x, y)$ considered as a function of x only, regarding y as a constant parameter. Similarly, $f_2(x, y)$ is the first derivative of $f(x, y)$ considered as a function of y alone, with x held fixed.

The subscripts "1" and "2" in the notations for the partial derivatives refer to the "first" and "second" variables of f. For functions of one variable we use the notation "f'" for the derivative — the "prime" denotes differentiation with respect to the only variable on which f depends. For functions f of two variables we use "f_1" or "f_2" to show with respect to which variable the differentiation is taken. Do not confuse these subscripts with subscripts for, say, components of vectors.

The partial derivative $f_1(a, b)$ measures the rate of change of $f(x, y)$ with respect to x at $x = a$ while y is held fixed at b. In graphical terms, the surface $z = f(x, y)$ intersects the vertical plane $y = b$ in a curve. If we take horizontal and vertical lines through the point $(0, b, 0)$ as coordinate axes in that plane, then the curve has equation $z = f(x, b)$, and its slope at $x = a$ is $f_1(a, b)$. (See Fig. 2.2.1.) Similarly, $f_2(a, b)$ represents the rate of change of f with respect to y with x is held fixed at a. The surface $z = f(x, y)$ intersects the vertical plane $x = a$ in a curve $z = f(a, y)$ whose slope at $y = b$ is $f_2(a, b)$. (See Fig. 2.2.2.)

Various notations can be used to denote the partial derivatives of $z = f(x, y)$ considered as functions of x and y:

2.2.3
Notations for First
Partial Derivatives

> $$\frac{\partial z}{\partial x} = \frac{\partial}{\partial x} f(x, y) = f_1(x, y) = D_1 f(x, y)$$
> $$\frac{\partial z}{\partial y} = \frac{\partial}{\partial y} f(x, y) = f_2(x, y) = D_2 f(x, y)$$

The symbol "∂" should be read as "partial" so "$\partial z / \partial x$" is "partial z with respect to x." The reason for distinguishing "∂" from the "d" of ordinary derivatives of single-variable functions will become obvious later.

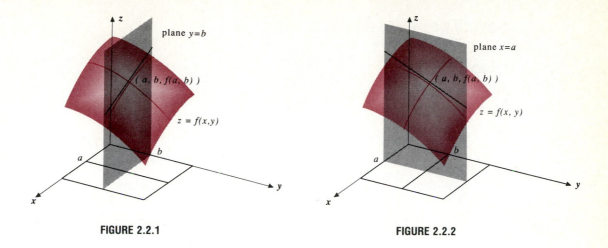

FIGURE 2.2.1   FIGURE 2.2.2

Values of partial derivatives at a particular point (a, b) are denoted similarly:

2.2.4
Values of
Parital Derivatives

$$\left.\frac{\partial z}{\partial x}\right|_{(a,b)} = \left.\left(\frac{\partial}{\partial x}f(x,y)\right)\right|_{(a,b)} = f_1(a,b) = D_1 f(a,b)$$

$$\left.\frac{\partial z}{\partial y}\right|_{(a,b)} = \left.\left(\frac{\partial}{\partial y}f(x,y)\right)\right|_{(a,b)} = f_2(a,b) = D_2 f(a,b)$$

Some authors prefer to use f_x or $\partial f/\partial x$ and f_y or $\partial f/\partial y$ instead of f_1 and f_2. However, this can lead to problems of ambiguity when compositions of functions arise. For instance, suppose $f(x,y) = x^2 y$. By $f_1(x^2, xy)$ we clearly mean

$$\left.\left(\frac{\partial}{\partial x}f(x,y)\right)\right|_{(x^2,xy)} = \left.2xy\right|_{(x^2,xy)} = (2)(x^2)(xy) = 2x^3 y.$$

But does $f_x(x^2, xy)$ mean the same thing? One could argue that $f_x(x^2, xy)$ should mean

$$\frac{\partial}{\partial x}\left(f(x^2, xy)\right) = \frac{\partial}{\partial x}\left((x^2)^2(xy)\right) = \frac{\partial}{\partial x}(x^5 y) = 5x^4 y.$$

In order to avoid such ambiguities we usually prefer to use f_1 and f_2 instead of f_x and f_y. (However, in some situations where no confusion is likely to occur we may still use the notations f_x and f_y, and also $\partial f/\partial x$ and $\partial f/\partial y$.)

EXAMPLE 2.2.5   Find $\partial z/\partial x$ and $\partial z/\partial y$ if $z = x^3 y^2 + x^4 y + y^4$.

SOLUTION $\partial z/\partial x = 3x^2 y^2 + 4x^3 y$, $\quad \partial z/\partial y = 2x^3 y + x^4 + 4y^3$.

EXAMPLE 2.2.6   Find $f_1(0, \pi)$ if $f(x, y) = e^{xy} \cos(x + y)$.

SOLUTION

$$f_1(x, y) = y \, e^{xy} \cos(x + y) - e^{xy} \sin(x + y),$$
$$f_1(0, \pi) = \pi \, e^0 \cos(\pi) - e^0 \sin(\pi) = -\pi.$$

EXAMPLE 2.2.7   If f is an everywhere differentiable function of one variable show that $z = f(x/y)$ satisfies the *partial differential equation*

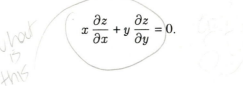

$$x \frac{\partial z}{\partial x} + y \frac{\partial z}{\partial y} = 0.$$

SOLUTION   By the (single-variable) Chain Rule

$$\frac{\partial z}{\partial x} = f'\left(\frac{x}{y}\right)\left(\frac{1}{y}\right), \qquad \text{and} \qquad \frac{\partial z}{\partial y} = f'\left(\frac{x}{y}\right)\left(\frac{-x}{y^2}\right).$$

Hence

$$x \frac{\partial z}{\partial x} + y \frac{\partial z}{\partial y} = f'\left(\frac{x}{y}\right)\left(\frac{x}{y} - \frac{x}{y}\right) = 0.$$

Definition 2.2.1 can be extended in the obvious way to cover functions of more than two variables. If f is a function of n variables $x_1, x_2, \ldots, x_n$ then f has n first partial derivatives, $f_1(x_1, x_2, \ldots, x_n)$, $f_2(x_1, x_2, \ldots, x_n)$, $\ldots$, $f_n(x_1, x_2, \ldots, x_n)$, one with respect to each variable.

EXAMPLE 2.2.8

$$\frac{\partial}{\partial z}\left(\frac{2xy}{1 + xz + yz}\right) = -\frac{2xy}{(1 + xz + yz)^2}(x + y).$$

Note that all the standard differenatiation rules are applied to calculate partial derivatives.

Tangent Planes and Normals

If the graph $z = f(x, y)$ is a "smooth" surface near the point P with coordinates $(a, b, f(a, b))$, then that graph will have a **tangent plane** and a **normal line** at P. The normal line is the line through P which is perpendicular to the surface; for instance, a line joining a point on a sphere to the centre of the sphere is normal to the sphere. The tangent plane to the surface $z = f(x, y)$ at P is the plane through P which has the normal line as its normal.

Let us assume that the surface $z = f(x, y)$ has a *nonvertical* tangent plane (and therefore a *nonhorizontal* normal line) at point P. (Later in this chapter we will state precise conditions which will guarantee that the graph of a function has a nonvertical tangent plane at a point.) Evidently, the tangent plane intersects the vertical plane $y = b$ in a straight line which is tangent at P to the curve of intersection of the surface $z = f(x, y)$ and the plane $y = b$. (See Figures 2.2.1 and 2.2.3.) This line has slope $f_1(a, b)$, and so is parallel to the vector $\mathbf{T}_1 = \mathbf{i} + f_1(a, b)\mathbf{k}$. Similarly, the tangent plane intersects the vertical plane $x = a$ in a straight line having slope $f_2(a, b)$, which is therefore parallel to the vector $\mathbf{T}_2 = \mathbf{j} + f_2(a, b)\mathbf{k}$. It follows that the tangent plane, and therefore the surface $z = f(x, y)$ itself, has normal vector

$$\mathbf{n} = \mathbf{T}_2 \times \mathbf{T}_1 = \begin{vmatrix} \mathbf{i} & \mathbf{j} & \mathbf{k} \\ 0 & 1 & f_2(a, b) \\ 1 & 0 & f_1(a, b) \end{vmatrix} = f_1(a, b)\mathbf{i} + f_2(a, b)\mathbf{j} - \mathbf{k}.$$

2.2.9

Normal vector to
$z = f(x, y)$ **at** (a, b)

$$\mathbf{n} = f_1(a, b)\mathbf{i} + f_2(a, b)\mathbf{j} - \mathbf{k}$$

Since the tangent plane passes through $P = (a, b, f(a, b))$, it has equation

$$f_1(a, b)(x - a) + f_2(a, b)(y - b) - (z - f(a, b)) = 0,$$

or, equivalently,

2.2.10

Equation of the Tangent Plane

$$z = f(a, b) + f_1(a, b)(x - a) + f_2(a, b)(y - b).$$

We shall obtain this result by a different method in Section 2.6.

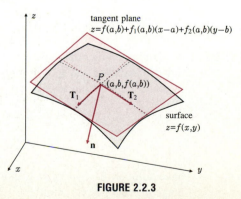

FIGURE 2.2.3

Since it is parallel to the vector $\mathbf{n} = f_1(a,b)\mathbf{i} + f_2(a,b)\mathbf{j} - \mathbf{k}$, the normal line to $z = f(x,y)$ at $(a, b, f(a,b))$ must have equations

2.2.11
Equation of the
Normal Line

$$\frac{x-a}{f_1(a,b)} = \frac{y-b}{f_2(a,b)} = \frac{z - f(a,b)}{-1}.$$

EXAMPLE 2.2.12 Find a normal vector and equations of the tangent plane and normal line to the graph $z = \sin(xy)$ at the point where $x = \pi/3$ and $y = -1$.

SOLUTION The point on the graph has coordinates $(\pi/3, -1, -\sqrt{3}/2)$ Now

$$\frac{\partial z}{\partial x} = y\,\cos(xy), \qquad \text{and} \qquad \frac{\partial z}{\partial y} = x\,\cos(xy).$$

At $(\pi/3, -1)$ we have $\partial z/\partial x = -1/2$ and $\partial z/\partial y = \pi/6$. Therefore the surface has normal vector $\mathbf{n} = -(1/2)\mathbf{i} + (\pi/6)\mathbf{j} - \mathbf{k}$, and tangent plane

$$z = \frac{-\sqrt{3}}{2} - \frac{1}{2}\left(x - \frac{\pi}{3}\right) + \frac{\pi}{6}(y+1),$$

or, more simply,

$$3x - \pi y + 6z = 2\pi - 3\sqrt{3}.$$

The normal line has equation

$$\frac{x - \dfrac{\pi}{3}}{-1} = \frac{y+1}{\dfrac{\pi}{6}} = \frac{z + \dfrac{\sqrt{3}}{2}}{-1},$$

or

$$\frac{6x - 2\pi}{-3} = \frac{6y + 6}{\pi} = \frac{6z + 3\sqrt{3}}{-6}.$$

EXAMPLE 2.2.13 What horizontal plane is tangent to the surface

$$z = x^2 - 4xy - 2y^2 + 12x - 12y - 1$$

and what is the point of tangency?

SOLUTION A plane is horizontal only if its equation is of the form $z = k$, that is, it is independent of x and y. Therefore we must have $\partial z/\partial x = \partial z/\partial y = 0$ at the point of tangency. The equations

$$\frac{\partial z}{\partial x} = 2x - 4y + 12 = 0$$

$$\frac{\partial z}{\partial y} = -4x - 4y - 12 = 0$$

have solution $x = -4$, $y = 1$. For these values we have $z = -31$ so the required tangent plane has equation $z = -31$ and the point of tangency is $(-4, 1, -31)$.

EXAMPLE 2.2.14   Find the distance from the point $(3, 0, 0)$ to the hyperbolic paraboloid with equation $z = x^2 - y^2$.

SOLUTION   This is an optimization problem of a sort we will deal with in a more systematic way in the next chapter. However, such problems involving minimizing distances from points to surfaces can frequently be solved by using geometric methods. If $Q = (X, Y, Z)$ is the point on the surface $z = x^2 - y^2$ which is closest to $P = (3, 0, 0)$ then the vector $\overrightarrow{PQ} = (X - 3)\mathbf{i} + Y\mathbf{j} + Z\mathbf{k}$ must be normal to the surface at Q. (See Fig. 2.2.4.) Using the partial derivatives of $z = x^2 - y^2$ we know that the vector $\mathbf{n} = 2X\mathbf{i} - 2Y\mathbf{j} - \mathbf{k}$ is normal to the surface at Q. Thus $\overrightarrow{PQ}$ must be parallel to $\mathbf{n}$, and so $\overrightarrow{PQ} = t\mathbf{n}$ for some scalar t. Separated into components, this vector equation states that

$$X - 3 = 2Xt, \qquad Y = -2Yt, \qquad Z = -t.$$

The middle equation implies that either $Y = 0$ or $t = -\frac{1}{2}$. We must consider both of these possibilities.

If $Y = 0$ then

$$X = \frac{3}{1 - 2t}, \qquad \text{and} \qquad Z = -t.$$

But $Z = X^2 - Y^2$ so we must have

$$-t = \frac{9}{(1 - 2t)^2}.$$

Evidently $t = -1$ is a solution of this equation. The graphs of both sides of the equation are shown in Fig. 2.2.5, and convince us that $t = -1$ is the only solution. Therefore $(1, 0, 1)$ is a candidate for Q. The distance from this point to P is $\sqrt{5}$. (If we had not observed that $t = -1$ was a solution of the equation above, we would have had to resort to numerical means for solving it, for instance, Newton's Method.)

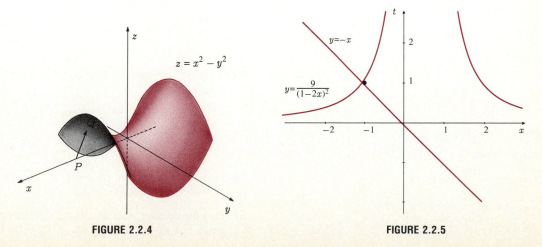

FIGURE 2.2.4   FIGURE 2.2.5

If $t = -1/2$, then $X = 3/2$, $Z = 1/2$ and $Y = \pm\sqrt{X^2 - Z} = \pm\sqrt{7}/2$, and the distance from these points to P is $\sqrt{17}/2$. Since $\frac{17}{4} < 5$, the points $(3/2, \pm\sqrt{7}/2, 1/2)$ are the points on $z = x^2 - y^2$ closest to $(3, 0, 0)$, and the distance from $(3,0,0)$ to the surface is $\sqrt{17}/2$ units.

EXERCISES

In Exercises 1–9 find all the first partial derivatives of the functions specified and evaluate them at the given point.

1. $f(x, y) = x - y + 2$; $(3, 2)$

2. $f(x, y) = xy + x^2$; $(2, 0)$

3. $f(x, y, z) = x^3 y^4 z^5$; $(0, -1, -1)$

4. $g(x, y, z) = \dfrac{yz}{y + z}$; $(1, 1, 1)$

5. $z = \tan^{-1}\left(\dfrac{y}{x}\right)$; $(-1, 1)$

6. $w = \ln(1 + e^{xyz})$; $(2, 0, -1)$

7. $f(x, y) = \sin(x\sqrt{y})$; $\left(\dfrac{\pi}{3}, 4\right)$

8. $f(x, y) = \dfrac{1}{\sqrt{x^2 + y^2}}$; $(-3, 4)$

9. $w = x^{(y \ln z)}$; $(e, 2, e)$

10. Find $f_1(0, 0)$ and $f_2(0, 0)$ if
$$f(x, y) = \begin{cases} \dfrac{x^2 - 2y^2}{x - y} & \text{if } x \neq y \\ 0 & \text{if } x = y. \end{cases}$$

In Exercises 11–20 find equations of the tangent plane and normal line to the graph of the given function at the point with specified values of x and y.

11. $f(x, y) = x^2 - y^2$ at $(-2, 1)$

12. $f(x, y) = \dfrac{x - y}{x + y}$ at $(1, 1)$

13. $f(x, y) = \cos(x/y)$ at $(\pi, 4)$

14. $f(x, y) = e^{xy}$ at $(2, 0)$

15. $f(x, y) = \dfrac{x}{x^2 + y^2}$ at $(1, 2)$

16. $f(x, y) = y\, e^{-x^2}$ at $(0, 1)$

17. $f(x, y) = \ln(x^2 + y^2)$ at $(1, -2)$

18. $f(x, y) = \dfrac{2xy}{x^2 + y^2}$ at $(0, 2)$

19. $f(x, y) = \tan^{-1}(y/x)$ at $(1, -1)$

20. $f(x, y) = \sqrt{1 + x^3 y^2}$ at $(2, 1)$

21. Find the coordinates of all points on the surface with equation $z = x^4 - 4xy^3 + 6y^2 - 2$ where the surface has a horizontal tangent plane.

22. Find all horizontal planes which are tangent to the surface with equation $z = xye^{-(x^2+y^2)/2}$. At what points are they tangent?

In Exercises 23–29 show that the given function satisfies the given partial differential equation. (The symbol † is used to mark exercises involving differential equations.)

23.† $z = x e^y$, $x\dfrac{\partial z}{\partial x} = \dfrac{\partial z}{\partial y}$

24.† $z = \dfrac{x + y}{x - y}$, $x\dfrac{\partial z}{\partial x} + y\dfrac{\partial z}{\partial y} = 0$

25.† $z = \sqrt{x^2 + y^2}$, $x\dfrac{\partial z}{\partial x} + y\dfrac{\partial z}{\partial y} = z$

26.† $w = x^2 + yz$, $x\dfrac{\partial w}{\partial x} + y\dfrac{\partial w}{\partial y} + z\dfrac{\partial w}{\partial z} = 2w$

27.† $w = \dfrac{1}{x^2 + y^2 + z^2}$, $x\dfrac{\partial w}{\partial x} + y\dfrac{\partial w}{\partial y} + z\dfrac{\partial w}{\partial z} = -2w$

28.† $z = f(x^2 + y^2)$, where f is any differentiable function of one variable,
$$y\dfrac{\partial z}{\partial x} - x\dfrac{\partial z}{\partial y} = 0.$$

29.† $z = f(x^2 - y^2)$, where f is any differentiable function of one variable,
$$y\dfrac{\partial z}{\partial x} + x\dfrac{\partial z}{\partial y} = 0.$$

30.* Find the distance from the point $(1, 1, 0)$ to the circular paraboloid with equation $z = x^2 + y^2$.

31.* Find the distance from the point $(0, 0, 1)$ to the elliptic paraboloid having equation $z = x^2 + 2y^2$.

32.*Let $f(x,y) = \begin{cases} \dfrac{2xy}{x^2+y^2}, & \text{if } (x,y) \neq (0,0) \\ 0, & \text{if } (x,y) = (0,0). \end{cases}$

As noted in Section 2.1, f is not continuous at (0,0). (See Example 2.1.9.) Therefore its graph is not smooth there. Show, however, that $f_1(0,0)$ and $f_2(0,0)$ both exist. Hence the existence of partial derivatives does not imply that a function of several variables is continuous. This is in contrast to the single-variable case.

2.3   HIGHER ORDER DERIVATIVES

Second and higher order partial derivatives are calculated by taking partial derivatives of already calculated partial derivatives. The order in which the differentiations are performed is indicated in the notations used. If $z = f(x,y)$, we can calculate *four* partial derivatives of second order, namely

two **pure** second partial derivatives with respect to x or y,

2.3.1
Pure Second
Partial Derivatives

$$\frac{\partial^2 z}{\partial x^2} = \frac{\partial}{\partial x}\frac{\partial z}{\partial x} = f_{11}(x,y) = f_{xx}(x,y),$$
$$\frac{\partial^2 z}{\partial y^2} = \frac{\partial}{\partial y}\frac{\partial z}{\partial y} = f_{22}(x,y) = f_{yy}(x,y),$$

and two **mixed** second partial derivatives with respect to x and y,

2.3.2
Mixed Second
Partial Derivatives

$$\frac{\partial^2 z}{\partial x \partial y} = \frac{\partial}{\partial x}\frac{\partial z}{\partial y} = f_{21}(x,y) = f_{yx}(x,y),$$
$$\frac{\partial^2 z}{\partial y \partial x} = \frac{\partial}{\partial y}\frac{\partial z}{\partial x} = f_{12}(x,y) = f_{xy}(x,y).$$

Again we remark that the notations f_{11}, f_{12}, f_{21} and f_{22} are preferable to f_{xx}, f_{xy}, f_{yx} and f_{yy}. Note that f_{12} indicates differentiation of f *first* with respect to the first variable and *then* with respect to the second variable; f_{21} indicates the opposite order of differentiation.

Similarly, if $w = f(x,y,z)$ then

$$\frac{\partial^5 w}{\partial y \partial x \partial y^2 \partial z} = \frac{\partial}{\partial y}\frac{\partial}{\partial x}\frac{\partial}{\partial y}\frac{\partial}{\partial y}\frac{\partial w}{\partial z} = f_{32212}(x,y,z) = f_{zyyxy}(x,y,z).$$

EXAMPLE 2.3.3   Find the four second partial derivatives of $f(x, y) = x^3 y^4$.

SOLUTION

$$f_1(x, y) = 3x^2 y^4, \qquad\qquad f_2(x, y) = 4x^3 y^3,$$

$$f_{11}(x, y) = \frac{\partial}{\partial x}(3x^2 y^4) = 6xy^4, \qquad f_{21}(x, y) = \frac{\partial}{\partial x}(4x^3 y^3) = 12x^2 y^3,$$

$$f_{12}(x, y) = \frac{\partial}{\partial y}(3x^2 y^4) = 12x^2 y^3, \qquad f_{22}(x, y) = \frac{\partial}{\partial y}(4x^3 y^3) = 12x^3 y^2.$$

EXAMPLE 2.3.4   Calculate $f_{223}(x, y, z)$, $f_{232}(x, y, z)$ and $f_{322}(x, y, z)$ for the function $f(x, y, z) = e^{x-2y+3z}$.

SOLUTION

$$\begin{aligned} f_{223}(x, y, z) &= \frac{\partial}{\partial z} \frac{\partial}{\partial y} \frac{\partial}{\partial y} e^{x-2y+3z} \\ &= \frac{\partial}{\partial z} \frac{\partial}{\partial y} \left(-2e^{x-2y+3z}\right) \\ &= \frac{\partial}{\partial z} \left(4e^{x-2y+3z}\right) = 12\, e^{x-2y+3z}. \end{aligned}$$

$$\begin{aligned} f_{232}(x, y, z) &= \frac{\partial}{\partial y} \frac{\partial}{\partial z} \frac{\partial}{\partial y} e^{x-2y+3z} \\ &= \frac{\partial}{\partial y} \frac{\partial}{\partial z} \left(-2e^{x-2y+3z}\right) \\ &= \frac{\partial}{\partial y} \left(-6e^{x-2y+3z}\right) = 12\, e^{x-2y+3z}. \end{aligned}$$

$$\begin{aligned} f_{322}(x, y, z) &= \frac{\partial}{\partial y} \frac{\partial}{\partial y} \frac{\partial}{\partial z} e^{x-2y+3z} \\ &= \frac{\partial}{\partial y} \frac{\partial}{\partial y} \left(3e^{x-2y+3z}\right) \\ &= \frac{\partial}{\partial y} \left(-6e^{x-2y+3z}\right) = 12\, e^{x-2y+3z}. \end{aligned}$$

In both of the examples above observe that the mixed partial derivatives taken with respect to the same variables but in different orders turned out to be equal. This is not a coincidence. It will always occur for sufficiently smooth functions. In particular the mixed partial derivatives involved are required to be *continuous*. The following theorem presents a more precise statement of this important phenomenon.

THEOREM 2.3.5   *(Equality of mixed partials)* Suppose that two mixed partial derivatives of a function f involve the same differentiations but in different orders. If those partials are continuous at a point P, and if f and all lower order partials of f are continuous at all points sufficiently near P, then the two mixed partials are equal at P.

PROOF

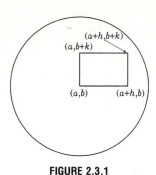

FIGURE 2.3.1

We shall prove only a representative special case, showing the equality of $f_{12}(a, b)$ and $f_{21}(a, b)$ for a function f of two variables provided f_{12} and f_{21} are defined and f_1, f_2 and f are continuous throughout a disc of positive radius centred at (a, b), and f_{12} and f_{21} are continuous at (a, b). Let h and k have sufficiently small absolute values that the point $(a + h, b + k)$ lies in this disc. Then so do all points of the rectangle with sides parallel to the coordinate axes and diagonally opposite corners at (a, b) and $(a + h, b + k)$. (See Fig. 2.3.1.)

Let $Q = f(a+h, b+k) - f(a+h, b) - f(a, b+k) + f(a, b)$ and define single-variable functions $u(x)$ and $v(y)$ by

$$u(x) = f(x, b + k) - f(x, b), \qquad \text{and} \qquad v(y) = f(a + h, y) - f(a, y).$$

Evidently $Q = u(a+h) - u(a)$ and also $Q = v(b+k) - v(b)$. By the (single-variable) Mean-Value Theorem, there is a point $a + \theta_1 h$ between a and $a + h$ (that is, the number θ_1 satisfies $0 < \theta_1 < 1$) such that

$$Q = u(a + h) - u(a) = h\, u'(a + \theta_1 h) = h\left[f_1(a + \theta_1 h, b + k) - f_1(a + \theta_1 h, b) \right].$$

Now we apply the Mean-Value Theorem again, this time to f_1 considered as a function of its second variable, and obtain another number θ_2 satisfying $0 < \theta_2 < 1$ such that

$$f_1(a + \theta_1 h, b + k) - f_1(a + \theta_1 h, b) = k\, f_{12}(a + \theta_1 h, b + \theta_2 k).$$

Thus $Q = hk\, f_{12}(a + \theta_1 h, b + \theta_2 k)$. Two similar applications of the Mean-Value Theorem to $Q = v(b + k) - v(b)$ lead to $Q = hk\, f_{21}(a + \theta_3 h, b + \theta_4 k)$, where θ_3 and θ_4 are two numbers each between 0 and 1. Equating these two expressions for Q and cancelling the common factor hk, we obtain

$$f_{12}(a + \theta_1 h, b + \theta_2 k) = f_{21}(a + \theta_3 h, b + \theta_4 k).$$

Since f_{12} and f_{21} are continuous at (a, b), we can let h and k approach zero to obtain $f_{12}(a, b) = f_{21}(a, b)$, as required. $\square$

Exercise 18 at the end of this section develops an example of a function for which f_{12} and f_{21} are not continuous at $(0, 0)$ and for which $f_{12}(0, 0) \neq f_{21}(0, 0)$.

The Laplace and Wave Equations

Many important and interesting phenomena are modelled by functions of several variables which satisfy certain *partial differential equations*. In the following examples we encounter two particular partial differential equations which arise frequently in mathematics and the physical sciences. Exercises 16 and 17 at the end of this section introduce another such equation with important applications.

EXAMPLE 2.3.6

Show that for any real number k the functions

$$z = e^{kx}\cos(ky), \qquad \text{and} \qquad z = e^{kx}\sin(ky)$$

satisfy the partial differential equation

$$\frac{\partial^2 z}{\partial x^2} + \frac{\partial^2 z}{\partial y^2} = 0$$

at every point in the xy-plane.

SOLUTION   For $z = e^{kx} \cos(ky)$ we have

$$\frac{\partial z}{\partial x} = k\, e^{kx} \cos(ky), \qquad \frac{\partial z}{\partial y} = -k\, e^{kx} \sin(ky),$$

$$\frac{\partial^2 z}{\partial x^2} = k^2\, e^{kx} \cos(ky), \qquad \frac{\partial^2 z}{\partial y^2} = -k^2\, e^{kx} \cos(ky).$$

Thus

$$\frac{\partial^2 z}{\partial x^2} + \frac{\partial^2 z}{\partial y^2} = k^2\, e^{kx} \cos(ky) - k^2\, e^{kx} \cos(ky) = 0.$$

The calculation for $z = e^{kx} \sin(ky)$ is similar.

REMARK: The partial differential equation in the above example is called the (two-dimensional) **Laplace equation**. A function of two variables having continuous second partial derivatives in a region of the plane is said to be **harmonic** there if it satisfies Laplace's equation. Such functions play a critical role in the theory of differentiable functions of a *complex variable,* and are used to model various physical quantities such as steady-state temperature distributions, fluid flows, and electric and magnetic potential fields. Harmonic functions have many interesting properties. They have derivatives of all orders, and are *analytic,* that is, they are the sums of their (multi-variable) Taylor series. Moreover a harmonic function can achieve maximum and minimum values only on the boundary of its domain. Laplace's equation, and therefore harmonic functions, can be considered in any number of dimensions. (See Exercises 13 and 14 below.)

EXAMPLE 2.3.7   If f and g are any twice differentiable functions of one variable, show that

$$w = f(x - ct) + g(x + ct)$$

satisfies the partial differential equation

$$\frac{\partial^2 w}{\partial t^2} = c^2\, \frac{\partial^2 w}{\partial x^2}.$$

SOLUTION   Using the Chain Rule for functions of one variable we obtain

$$\frac{\partial w}{\partial t} = -c\, f'(x - ct) + c\, g'(x + ct), \qquad \frac{\partial w}{\partial x} = f'(x - ct) + g'(x + ct),$$

$$\frac{\partial^2 w}{\partial t^2} = c^2\, f''(x - ct) + c^2\, g''(x + ct), \qquad \frac{\partial^2 w}{\partial x^2} = f''(x - ct) + g''(x + ct).$$

Thus w satisfies the given differential equation.

REMARK: The partial differential equation in the above example is called the (one-dimensional) **wave equation**. If t measures time, then $f(x - ct)$ represents a waveform travelling to the right along the x-axis with speed c. (See Fig. 2.3.2.) Similarly, $g(x+ct)$ represents a waveform travelling to the left with speed c. Unlike the solutions of Laplace's equation which must be infinitely differentiable, solutions of the wave equation need only have enough derivatives to satisfy the differential equation. The functions f and g are arbitrary.

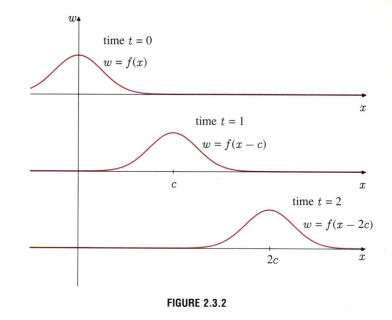

FIGURE 2.3.2

EXERCISES

In Exercises 1–6 find all the second partial derivatives of the given function.

1. $z = x^2(1 + y^2)$

2. $f(x, y) = x^2 + y^2$

3. $w = x^3 y^3 z^3$

4. $z = \sqrt{3x^2 + y^2}$

5. $z = x e^y - y e^x$

6. $f(x, y) = \ln\left(1 + \sin(xy)\right)$

7.*How many mixed partial derivatives of order 3 can a function of three variables have? If they are all continuous, how many different values can they have at one point? Find the mixed partials of order 3 for $f(x, y, z) = x e^{xy} \cos(xz)$ which involve two differentiations with respect to z and one with respect to x.

Show that the functions in Exercises 8–12 are harmonic in the plane regions indicated.

8. $f(x, y) = A(x^2 - y^2) + Bxy$ in the whole plane. (A, B are constants.)

9. $f(x, y) = 3x^2 y - y^3$ in the whole plane. (Can you think of another polynomial of degree 3 in x and y which is also harmonic?)

10. $f(x, y) = \dfrac{x}{x^2 + y^2}$ everywhere except at the origin.

11. $f(x, y) = \ln(x^2 + y^2)$ everywhere except at the origin.

12. $\tan^{-1}(y/x)$ except at points on the y-axis.

13. Show that $w = e^{3x+4y} \sin(5z)$ is harmonic in all of $\mathbb{R}^3$, that is, it satisfies everywhere the 3-dimensional Laplace equation

$$\frac{\partial^2 w}{\partial x^2} + \frac{\partial^2 w}{\partial y^2} + \frac{\partial^2 w}{\partial z^2} = 0.$$

14. Assume that $f(x,y)$ is harmonic in the xy-plane. Show that each of the functions $z\,f(x,y)$, $x\,f(y,z)$, and $y\,f(z,x)$ is harmonic in the whole of $\mathbb{R}^3$. What condition should the constants a, b and c satisfy to ensure that $f(ax+by, cz)$ is harmonic in $\mathbb{R}^3$?

15. Suppose the functions $u(x,y)$ and $v(x,y)$ have continuous second partial derivatives and satisfy the **Cauchy-Riemann equations**

$$\frac{\partial u}{\partial x} = \frac{\partial v}{\partial y}, \qquad \frac{\partial v}{\partial x} = -\frac{\partial u}{\partial y}.$$

Show that u and v are both harmonic.

16.†Show that the function

$$u(x,t) = t^{-1/2}\, e^{-x^2/4t}$$

satisfies the partial differential equation

$$\frac{\partial u}{\partial t} = \frac{\partial^2 u}{\partial x^2}.$$

This equation is called the (one-dimensional) **heat equation** as it models heat diffusion in an insulated rod (with $u(x,t)$ representing the temperature at position x at time t) and other similar phenomena.

17.*Show that the function

$$u(x,y,t) = t^{-1}\, e^{-(x^2+y^2)/4t}$$

satisfies the two-dimensional heat equation

$$\frac{\partial u}{\partial t} = \frac{\partial^2 u}{\partial x^2} + \frac{\partial^2 u}{\partial y^2}.$$

Comparing this result with that of the previous exercise, guess a solution to the three-dimensional heat equation

$$\frac{\partial u}{\partial t} = \frac{\partial^2 u}{\partial x^2} + \frac{\partial^2 u}{\partial y^2} + \frac{\partial^2 u}{\partial z^2}.$$

Verify your guess.

18.*Let $F(x,y) = (x^2 - y^2)f(x,y)$ where $f(x,y)$ is the function defined in Exercise 32 of Section 2.2. Calculate $F_1(x,y)$, $F_2(x,y)$, $F_{12}(x,y)$ and $F_{21}(x,y)$ at points $(x,y) \neq (0,0)$. Also calculate these derivatives at $(0,0)$. Observe that $F_{21}(0,0) = 2$ and $F_{12}(0,0) = -2$. Does this result contradict Theorem 2.3.5? Explain why.

2.4   THE CHAIN RULE

The Chain Rule for functions of one variable is a formula giving the derivative of a composition $f\big(g(x)\big)$ of two functions f and g:

$$\frac{d}{dx}\, f\big(g(x)\big) = f'\big(g(x)\big)g'(x).$$

The situation for several variables is more complicated. If f depends on more than one variable, and any of those variables can be functions of one or more other variables, we cannot expect a simple formula for partial derivatives of the composition to cover all possible cases. We must come to think of the Chain Rule as a *procedure for differentiating compositions* rather than as a formula for the derivatives. In order to motivate a formulation of the Chain Rule for functions of two variables we begin with a concrete example.

EXAMPLE 2.4.1   Suppose you are hiking in a certain mountainous region for which you have a map. Let (x, y) be the coordinates of your position on the map (that is, the horizontal coordinates of your actual position in the region). Let $z = f(x, y)$ denote the height of land (above sea level, say), at position (x, y). Suppose you are walking along a trail so that your position at time t is given by $x = u(t)$, $y = v(t)$. (These are parametric equations of the trail on the map.) At time t your altitude above sea level is given by the composite function

$$z = f\big(u(t), v(t)\big) = g(t),$$

a function of only one variable. How fast is your altitude changing with respect to time at time t?

SOLUTION   Evidently the answer is the derivative of $g(t)$:

$$g'(t) = \lim_{h \to 0} \frac{g(t + h) - g(t)}{h}$$

$$= \lim_{h \to 0} \frac{f\big(u(t + h), v(t + h)\big) - f\big(u(t), v(t)\big)}{h}$$

$$= \lim_{h \to 0} \frac{f\big(u(t + h), v(t + h)\big) - f\big(u(t), v(t + h)\big)}{h}$$

$$+ \lim_{h \to 0} \frac{f\big(u(t), v(t + h)\big) - f\big(u(t), v(t)\big)}{h}.$$

We added 0 to the numerator of the Newton quotient in a creative way so as to separate that quotient into the sum of two quotients, in the first of which the difference of values of f involves only the first variable of f, and in the second of which the difference involves only the second variable of f. The single-variable Chain Rule suggests that the sum of the two limits above is

$$g'(t) = f_1\big(u(t), v(t)\big) u'(t) + f_2\big(u(t), v(t)\big) v'(t).$$

The above formula is the Chain Rule for $\dfrac{d}{dt} f\big(u(t), v(t)\big)$. In terms of Leibniz notation we have

2.4.2
A Version of
the Chain Rule

> If z is a function of x and y with continuous first partial derivatives, and if x and y are differentiable functions of t, then
>
> $$\frac{dz}{dt} = \frac{\partial z}{\partial x} \frac{dx}{dt} + \frac{\partial z}{\partial y} \frac{dy}{dt}.$$

Note that there are two terms in the expression for dz/dt (or $g'(t)$), one arising from each variable of f that depends on t.

Now consider a function f of two variables, x and y, each of which is in turn a function of two other variables, s and t:

$$z = f(x, y), \qquad \text{where} \qquad x = u(s,t), \quad y = v(s,t).$$

We may again form the composite function

$$z = f\big(u(s,t), v(s,t)\big) = g(s,t).$$

For instance, if $f(x,y) = x^2 + 3y$, $u(s,t) = st^2$ and $v(s,t) = s - t$ then $g(s,t) = s^2 t^4 + 3(s - t)$.

Let us assume that f, u and v have first partial derivatives with respect to their respective variables, and that those of f are continuous. Then g has first partial derivatives given by

$$g_1(s,t) = f_1\big(u(s,t), v(s,t)\big)u_1(s,t) + f_2\big(u(s,t), v(s,t)\big)v_1(s,t),$$
$$g_2(s,t) = f_1\big(u(s,t), v(s,t)\big)u_2(s,t) + f_2\big(u(s,t), v(s,t)\big)v_2(s,t),$$

or, expressed more simply using Leibniz notation,

2.4.3
Another Version
of the Chain Rule

$$\frac{\partial z}{\partial s} = \frac{\partial z}{\partial x}\frac{\partial x}{\partial s} + \frac{\partial z}{\partial y}\frac{\partial y}{\partial s},$$
$$\frac{\partial z}{\partial t} = \frac{\partial z}{\partial x}\frac{\partial x}{\partial t} + \frac{\partial z}{\partial y}\frac{\partial y}{\partial t}.$$

This can be deduced from the version obtained in Example 2.4.1; by allowing u and v there to depend on two variables, but holding one of them fixed while we differentiate with respect to the other. A more formal proof of this simple, but representative case of the Chain Rule will be given in the next section.

The two equations in Box 2.4.3 can be combined into a single matrix equation

$$\begin{pmatrix} \dfrac{\partial z}{\partial s} & \dfrac{\partial z}{\partial t} \end{pmatrix} = \begin{pmatrix} \dfrac{\partial z}{\partial x} & \dfrac{\partial z}{\partial y} \end{pmatrix} \begin{pmatrix} \dfrac{\partial x}{\partial s} & \dfrac{\partial x}{\partial t} \\ \dfrac{\partial y}{\partial s} & \dfrac{\partial y}{\partial t} \end{pmatrix}.$$

We will comment on the significance of this matrix form at the end of the next section.

In general, if z is a function of several "primary" variables, and each of these depends on some "secondary" variables then the partial derivative of z with respect to one of the secondary variables will have several terms, one for the contribution to the derivative arising from each of primary variables on which z depends.

REMARK: Note the significance of the various subscripts denoting partial derivatives in the functional form of the Chain Rule given above Box 2.4.3. The "1" in $g_1(s,t)$ refers to differentiation with respect to s, the first variable on which g depends. By contrast, the "1" in $f_1(u(s,t), v(s,t))$ refers to differentiation with respect to x, the first variable on which f depends. (This derivative is then evaluated at $x = u(s,t)$, $y = v(s,t)$.)

EXAMPLE 2.4.4   If $z = \sin(x^2 y)$ where $x = st^2$ and $y = s^2 + \dfrac{1}{t}$, find $\partial z/\partial s$ and $\partial z/\partial t$

    a) by direct substitution and the single-variable form of the Chain Rule, and

    b) by using the (two-variable) Chain Rule.

SOLUTION   a) By direct substitution

$$z = \sin\left((st^2)^2\left(s^2 + \frac{1}{t}\right)\right) = \sin(s^4 t^4 + s^2 t^3),$$

$$\frac{\partial z}{\partial s} = (4s^3 t^4 + 2st^3)\cos(s^4 t^4 + s^2 t^3),$$

$$\frac{\partial z}{\partial t} = (4s^4 t^3 + 3s^2 t^2)\cos(s^4 t^4 + s^2 t^3).$$

b) Using the Chain Rule

$$\frac{\partial z}{\partial s} = \frac{\partial z}{\partial x}\frac{\partial x}{\partial s} + \frac{\partial z}{\partial y}\frac{\partial y}{\partial s}$$
$$= \left(2xy\cos(x^2 y)\right)t^2 + \left(x^2\cos(x^2 y)\right)2s$$
$$= \left(2st^2\left(s^2 + \frac{1}{t}\right)t^2 + 2s^3 t^4\right)\cos(s^4 t^4 + s^2 t^3)$$
$$= (4s^3 t^4 + 2st^3)\cos(s^4 t^4 + s^2 t^3),$$

$$\frac{\partial z}{\partial t} = \frac{\partial z}{\partial x}\frac{\partial x}{\partial t} + \frac{\partial z}{\partial y}\frac{\partial y}{\partial t}$$
$$= \left(2xy\cos(x^2 y)\right)2st + \left(x^2\cos(x^2 y)\right)\left(\frac{-1}{t^2}\right)$$
$$= \left(2st^2(s^2 + \frac{1}{t})2st + s^2 t^4\left(\frac{-1}{t^2}\right)\right)\cos(s^4 t^4 + s^2 t^3)$$
$$= (4s^4 t^3 + 3s^2 t^2)\cos(s^4 t^4 + s^2 t^3).$$

Note that we still had to use direct substitution on the derivatives obtained in (b) in order to show that the values were the same as those obtained in (a).

EXAMPLE 2.4.5   Find $\dfrac{\partial}{\partial x} f(x^2 y, x + 2y)$ and $\dfrac{\partial}{\partial y} f(x^2 y, x + 2y)$ in terms of the partial derivatives of f, assuming that these partial derivatives are continuous.

SOLUTION $\dfrac{\partial}{\partial x} f(x^2 y, x + 2y) = f_1(x^2 y, x + 2y)\dfrac{\partial}{\partial x}(x^2 y) + f_2(x^2 y, x + 2y)\dfrac{\partial}{\partial x}(x + 2y)$

$$= 2xy f_1(x^2y, x + 2y) + f_2(x^2y, x + 2y),$$

$$\frac{\partial}{\partial y} f(x^2y, x + 2y) = f_1(x^2y, x + 2y)\frac{\partial}{\partial y}(x^2y) + f_2(x^2y, x + 2y)\frac{\partial}{\partial y}(x + 2y)$$

$$= x^2 f_1(x^2y, x + 2y) + 2f_2(x^2y, x + 2y).$$

Here is a very simple version of the Chain Rule. If $z = f(x)$ where $x = g(s, t)$ then we can regard z as being a function of the two variables s and t:

$$z = f\big(g(s, t)\big) = h(s, t).$$

The partial derivatives of h can be calculated using the single-variable version of the Chain Rule:

$$h_1(s, t) = \frac{\partial z}{\partial s} = \frac{dz}{dx}\frac{\partial x}{\partial s} = f'\big(g(s, t)\big)g_1(s, t),$$

$$h_2(s, t) = \frac{\partial z}{\partial t} = \frac{dz}{dx}\frac{\partial x}{\partial t} = f'\big(g(s, t)\big)g_2(s, t).$$

The following example involves a hybrid application of the chain rule to a function depending both directly and indirectly on the variable of differentiation.

EXAMPLE 2.4.6   Find dz/dt where $z = f(x, y, t)$ and $x = g(t)$, $\quad y = h(t)$. (Assume that f, g and h all have continuous derivatives.)

SOLUTION   Since z depends on t through each of the three variables of f, there will be three terms in the appropriate Chain Rule:

$$\frac{dz}{dt} = \frac{\partial z}{\partial x}\frac{dx}{dt} + \frac{\partial z}{\partial y}\frac{dy}{dt} + \frac{\partial z}{\partial t}$$

$$= f_1(x, y, t)g'(t) + f_2(x, y, t)h'(t) + f_3(x, y, t).$$

REMARK: In the above example we can easily distinguish between the meanings of the symbols dz/dt and $\partial z/\partial t$. If, however, we had been dealing with the situation

$$z = f(x, y, s, t), \qquad \text{where} \quad x = g(s, t) \quad \text{and} \quad y = h(s, t),$$

then the meaning of the symbol $\partial z/\partial t$ would be unclear; it could refer to either the simple partial derivative of f with respect to its fourth primary variable (i.e. $f_4(x, y, s, t)$), or it could refer to the derivative of the composite function $f(g(s, t), h(s, t), s, t)$. Three of the four primary variables of f depend on t, and therefore contribute to the rate of change of z with respect to t. The partial derivative $f_4(x, y, s, t)$ denotes the contribution of only one of these three variables. It is conventional to use $\partial z/\partial t$ to denote the derivative of the composite function with respect to the secondary variable t:

$$\frac{\partial z}{\partial t} = \frac{\partial}{\partial t} f(g(s, t), h(s, t), s, t)$$

$$= f_1(x, y, s, t)g_2(s, t) + f_2(x, y, s, t)h_2(s, t) + f_4(x, y, s, t).$$

When necessary, we can denote the contribution coming from the primary variable t by

$$\left.\frac{\partial z}{\partial t}\right|_{x,y,s} = \frac{\partial}{\partial t}f(x,y,s,t) = f_4(x,y,s,t).$$

Here the subscripts denote those primary variables of f whose contributions to the rate of change of z with respect to t are being *ignored*. Of course, in the situation described above, $\left.\dfrac{\partial z}{\partial t}\right|_s$ means the same as $\dfrac{\partial z}{\partial t}$.

In applications, the variables contributing to a particular partial derivative will usually be clear from the context. The following example contains such an application. This is an example of a procedure called *differentiation following the motion*.

EXAMPLE 2.4.7 Atmospheric temperature depends on position and time. If we denote position by three spatial coordinates (x, y, z) and time by t then the temperature T is a function of four variables, $T(x, y, z, t)$. If a thermometer is attached to a weather balloon and moves through the atmosphere on a path with parametric equations $x = f(t)$, $y = g(t)$ and $z = h(t)$, what is the rate of change of the temperature recorded by the thermometer at time t? Find the rate of change of that recorded temperature at time $t = 1$ if

$$T(x, y, z, t) = \frac{e^{-z}\sin t}{5 + x^2 + y^2},$$

and if the balloon moves along the curve

$$x = f(t) = t, \qquad y = g(t) = 2t, \qquad z = h(t) = t - t^4.$$

SOLUTION Here the rate of change of the thermometer reading must take into account the change in position of the thermometer as well as increasing time, so none of the four variables of T can be ignored in the differentiation. The rate is given by

$$\frac{dT}{dt} = \frac{\partial T}{\partial x}\frac{dx}{dt} + \frac{\partial T}{\partial y}\frac{dy}{dt} + \frac{\partial T}{\partial z}\frac{dz}{dt} + \frac{\partial T}{\partial t}.$$

Here the term $\partial T/\partial t$ refers only to the rate of change of the temperature with respect to time at a fixed position in the atmosphere, and the other three terms arise from the motion of the balloon.

For the special case we have, at $t = 1$, $x = 1$, $y = 2$, $z = 0$, $dx/dt = 1$, $dy/dt = 2$, $dz/dt = -3$ and

$$\frac{\partial T}{\partial x} = -2x\frac{e^{-z}\sin t}{(5 + x^2 + y^2)^2} = -2\frac{\sin(1)}{100} = -\frac{\sin(1)}{50},$$

$$\frac{\partial T}{\partial y} = -2y\frac{e^{-z}\sin t}{(5 + x^2 + y^2)^2} = -4\frac{\sin(1)}{100} = -\frac{\sin(1)}{25},$$

$$\frac{\partial T}{\partial z} = -\frac{e^{-z}\sin t}{5 + x^2 + y^2} = -\frac{\sin(1)}{10},$$

$$\frac{\partial T}{\partial t} = \frac{e^{-z}\cos t}{5 + x^2 + y^2} = \frac{\cos(1)}{10}.$$

Thus

$$\frac{dT}{dt}\bigg|_{t=1} = -\sin(1)\left(\frac{1}{50} + \frac{2}{25} - \frac{3}{10}\right) + \frac{\cos(1)}{10}$$

$$\approx 0.2223.$$

The discussion and examples above show that the Chain Rule for functions of several variables can take different forms depending on the numbers of variables of the various functions being composed. As an aid in determining the correct form of the chain rule in a given situation you can construct a simple chart showing which variables depend on which. Fig. 2.4.1 shows such a chart for the temperature function of the previous example.

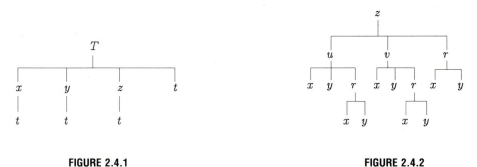

FIGURE 2.4.1   FIGURE 2.4.2

The Chain Rule for dT/dt involves a term for every route from T to t in the chart. The route from T through x to t produces the term $\dfrac{\partial T}{\partial x}\dfrac{dx}{dt}$ and so on.

EXAMPLE 2.4.8   Write the appropriate Chain Rule for $\partial z/\partial x$, where $z = f(u,v,r)$, $u = g(x,y,r)$, $v = h(x,y,r)$ and $r = k(x,y)$.

SOLUTION   The appropriate chart is shown in Fig. 2.4.2. There are five routes from z to x:

$$\frac{\partial z}{\partial x} = \frac{\partial z}{\partial u}\frac{\partial u}{\partial x} + \frac{\partial z}{\partial u}\frac{\partial u}{\partial r}\frac{\partial r}{\partial x} + \frac{\partial z}{\partial v}\frac{\partial v}{\partial x} + \frac{\partial z}{\partial v}\frac{\partial v}{\partial r}\frac{\partial r}{\partial x} + \frac{\partial z}{\partial r}\frac{\partial r}{\partial x}.$$

Homogeneous Functions

A function $f(x_1, \ldots, x_n)$ is said to be **positively homogeneous of degree** k if, for every point $(x_1, x_2, \ldots, x_n)$ in its domain and every real number $t > 0$, we have

$$f(tx_1, tx_2, \ldots, tx_n) = t^k f(x_1, \ldots, x_n).$$

For example

$$f(x, y) = x^2 + xy - y^2 \quad \text{is positively homogeneous of degree 2,}$$

$$f(x, y) = \sqrt{x^2 + y^2} \quad \text{is positively homogeneous of degree 1,}$$

$$f(x, y) = \frac{2xy}{x^2 + y^2} \quad \text{is positively homogeneous of degree 0,}$$

$$f(x, y, z) = \frac{x - y + 5z}{yz - z^2} \quad \text{is positively homogeneous of degree } -1,$$

$$f(x, y) = x^2 + y \quad \text{is not positively homogeneous.}$$

Observe that a homogeneous function of degree 0 remains constant along rays from the origin. More generally, along such rays a positively homogeneous function of degree k grows or decays proportionally to the kth power of distance from the origin.

THEOREM 2.4.9   *(Euler's Theorem)* If $f(x_1, \ldots, x_n)$ has continuous first partial derivatives and is positively homogeneous of degree k then

$$x_1 f_1(x_1, \ldots, x_n) + x_2 f_2(x_1, \ldots, x_n) + \ldots + x_n f_n(x_1, \ldots, x_n) = k f(x_1, \ldots, x_n).$$

PROOF   Differentiate the equation $f(tx_1, tx_2, \ldots, tx_n) = t^k f(x_1, \ldots, x_n)$ with respect to t to get

$$x_1 f_1(tx_1, \ldots, tx_n) + x_2 f_2(tx_1, \ldots, tx_n) + \ldots + x_n f_n(tx_1, \ldots, tx_n)$$
$$= k t^{k-1} f(x_1, \ldots, x_n).$$

Now substitute $t = 1$ to get the desired result. $\square$

Note that Exercises 24–27 in Section 2.2 illustrate this theorem.

Higher Order Derivatives

Applications of the Chain Rule to higher order derivatives can become quite complicated. It is important to keep in mind at each stage which variables are independent of one another.

EXAMPLE 2.4.10   Calculate $\dfrac{\partial^2}{\partial x \partial y} f(x^2 - y^2, xy)$ in terms of partial derivatives of the function f.

SOLUTION   In this problem symbols for the primary variables on which f depends are not stated explicitly. We could let them be u and v and so calculate $\dfrac{\partial^2}{\partial x \partial y} f(u, v)$ where $u = x^2 - y^2$ and $v = xy$. However, it is more convenient to get along without referring to them explicitly except via subscripts denoting various partial derivatives of f. Differentiating first with respect to y we obtain

$$\frac{\partial}{\partial y} f(x^2 - y^2, xy) = -2y f_1(x^2 - y^2, xy) + x f_2(x^2 - y^2, xy).$$

Now we differentiate this result with respect to x. Note that the second term on the right is a product to two functions of x so the product rule must be used:

$$\frac{\partial^2}{\partial x \partial y} f(x^2 - y^2, xy) = -2y\left(2xf_{11}(x^2 - y^2, xy) + yf_{12}(x^2 - y^2, xy)\right)$$
$$+ f_2(x^2 - y^2, xy)$$
$$+ x\left(2xf_{21}(x^2 - y^2, xy) + yf_{22}(x^2 - y^2, xy)\right)$$
$$= -4xyf_{11}(x^2 - y^2, xy) + 2(x^2 - y^2)f_{12}(x^2 - y^2, xy)$$
$$+ xyf_{22}(x^2 - y^2, xy) + f_2(x^2 - y^2, xy).$$

In the last step we have assumed that the mixed partials of f are continuous so we could equate f_{12} and f_{21}.

Review the above calculation very carefully and make sure you understand what is being done at each step. Note that it is necessary to write the full argument $(x^2 - y^2, xy)$ every time f or its derivatives appear because x and y are not themselves the primary variables on which f depends.

In the following example we show that the two-dimensional Laplace differential equation (see Example 2.3.6) takes the form

$$\frac{\partial^2 z}{\partial r^2} + \frac{1}{r}\frac{\partial z}{\partial r} + \frac{1}{r^2}\frac{\partial^2 z}{\partial \theta^2} = 0$$

when stated for a function z expressed in terms of polar coordinates r and θ.

EXAMPLE 2.4.11   If $z = f(x, y)$ has continuous partial derivatives of second order, and if $x = r\cos\theta$, and $y = r\sin\theta$, show that

$$\frac{\partial^2 z}{\partial r^2} + \frac{1}{r}\frac{\partial z}{\partial r} + \frac{1}{r^2}\frac{\partial^2 z}{\partial \theta^2} = \frac{\partial^2 z}{\partial x^2} + \frac{\partial^2 z}{\partial y^2}.$$

SOLUTION   First note that,

$$\frac{\partial x}{\partial r} = \cos\theta, \qquad \frac{\partial x}{\partial \theta} = -r\sin\theta, \qquad \frac{\partial y}{\partial r} = \sin\theta, \qquad \frac{\partial y}{\partial \theta} = r\cos\theta.$$

Thus

$$\frac{\partial z}{\partial r} = \frac{\partial z}{\partial x}\frac{\partial x}{\partial r} + \frac{\partial z}{\partial y}\frac{\partial y}{\partial r} = \cos\theta\frac{\partial z}{\partial x} + \sin\theta\frac{\partial z}{\partial y}.$$

Now differentiate with respect to r again. Remember that r and θ are independent variables, so that the factors $\cos\theta$ and $\sin\theta$ can be regarded as constants. However, $\partial z/\partial x$ and $\partial z/\partial y$ depend on x and y, and therefore on r and θ.

$$\frac{\partial^2 z}{\partial r^2} = \cos\theta\frac{\partial}{\partial r}\frac{\partial z}{\partial x} + \sin\theta\frac{\partial}{\partial r}\frac{\partial z}{\partial y}$$
$$= \cos\theta\left(\cos\theta\frac{\partial^2 z}{\partial x^2} + \sin\theta\frac{\partial^2 z}{\partial y\partial x}\right) + \sin\theta\left(\cos\theta\frac{\partial^2 z}{\partial x\partial y} + \sin\theta\frac{\partial^2 z}{\partial y^2}\right)$$
$$= \cos^2\theta\frac{\partial^2 z}{\partial x^2} + 2\cos\theta\sin\theta\frac{\partial^2 z}{\partial x\partial y} + \sin^2\theta\frac{\partial^2 z}{\partial y^2}.$$

!!DANGER!!

This is a difficult, but important example. Examine each step carefully to make sure you understand what is being done.

We have used the equality of mixed partials in the last line. Similarly,

$$\frac{\partial z}{\partial \theta} = -r \sin \theta \, \frac{\partial z}{\partial x} + r \cos \theta \, \frac{\partial z}{\partial y}.$$

When we differentiate a second time with respect to θ we can regard r as constant, but each term above is still a product of two functions depending on θ. Thus

$$\frac{\partial^2 z}{\partial \theta^2} = -r \left(\cos \theta \, \frac{\partial z}{\partial x} + \sin \theta \, \frac{\partial}{\partial \theta} \, \frac{\partial z}{\partial x} \right) + r \left(-\sin \theta \, \frac{\partial z}{\partial y} + \cos \theta \, \frac{\partial}{\partial \theta} \, \frac{\partial z}{\partial y} \right)$$

$$= -r \frac{\partial z}{\partial r} - r \sin \theta \left(-r \sin \theta \, \frac{\partial^2 z}{\partial x^2} + r \cos \theta \, \frac{\partial^2 z}{\partial y \partial x} \right)$$

$$+ r \cos \theta \left(-r \sin \theta \, \frac{\partial^2 z}{\partial x \partial y} + r \cos \theta \, \frac{\partial^2 z}{\partial y^2} \right)$$

$$= -r \frac{\partial z}{\partial r} + r^2 \left(\sin^2 \theta \, \frac{\partial^2 z}{\partial x^2} - 2 \sin \theta \cos \theta \, \frac{\partial^2 z}{\partial x \partial y} + \cos^2 \theta \, \frac{\partial^2 z}{\partial y^2} \right).$$

Combining these results we obtain the desired formula

$$\frac{\partial^2 z}{\partial r^2} + \frac{1}{r} \frac{\partial z}{\partial r} + \frac{1}{r^2} \frac{\partial^2 z}{\partial \theta^2} = \frac{\partial^2 z}{\partial x^2} + \frac{\partial^2 z}{\partial y^2}.$$

EXERCISES

In Exercises 1–6 write appropriate versions of the Chain Rule for the indicated derivatives.

1. for $\partial w / \partial t$ if $w = f(x, y, z)$ where $x = g(s, t)$, $y = h(s, t)$ and $z = k(s, t)$.

2. for $\partial w / \partial t$ if $w = f(x, y, z)$ where $x = g(s)$, $y = h(s, t)$ and $z = k(t)$.

3. for $\partial z / \partial u$ if $z = g(x, y)$ where $y = f(x)$ and $x = h(u, v)$.

4. for dw / dx if $w = f(x, y, z)$ where $y = g(x, z)$ and $z = h(x)$.

5. for $\partial w / \partial x \big|_z$ if $w = f(x, y, z)$ and $y = g(x, z)$.

6. for dw / dt if $w = f(x, y)$, $x = g(r, s)$, $y = h(r, t)$, $r = k(s, t)$ and $s = m(t)$.

7. If $w = f(x, y, z)$ where $x = g(y, z)$, and $y = h(z)$, state appropriate versions of the Chain Rule for $\dfrac{dw}{dz}$, $\dfrac{\partial w}{\partial z} \Big|_x$, and $\dfrac{\partial w}{\partial z} \Big|_{x,y}$.

8. Use two different methods to calculate $\partial u / \partial t$ if $u = \sqrt{x^2 + y^2}$, $x = e^{st}$, and $y = 1 + s^2 \cos t$.

9. Use two different methods to calculate $\partial z / \partial x$ if $z = \tan^{-1}(u/v)$, $u = 2x + y$ and $v = 3x - y$.

10. Use two methods to calculate dz / dt given that $z = txy^2$, $x = t + \ln(y + t^2)$ and $y = e^t$.

In Exercises 11–16 find the indicated derivatives, assuming that the function $f(x, y)$ has continuous first partial derivatives.

11. $\dfrac{\partial}{\partial x} f(2x, 3y)$ **12.** $\dfrac{\partial}{\partial x} f(2y, 3x)$

13. $\dfrac{\partial}{\partial x} f(y^2, x^2)$ **14.** $\dfrac{\partial}{\partial t} f(st^2, s^2 + t)$

15. $\dfrac{\partial}{\partial x} f\left(f(x, y), f(x, y) \right)$ **16.** $\dfrac{\partial}{\partial y} f\left(yf(x, t), f(y, t) \right)$

17. Suppose that the temperature T in a certain liquid varies with depth z and time t according to the formula $T = e^{-t}z$. Find the rate of change of temperature with respect to time at a point which is moving through the liquid so that at time t its depth is $f(t)$. What is this rate if $f(t) = e^t$? What is happening in this case?

18. Suppose the strength E of an electric field in space varies with position (x, y, z) and time t according to the formula $E = f(x, y, z, t)$. Find the rate of change with respect to time of the electric field strength measured by an instrument moving through space along the spiral path $x = \sin t$, $y = \cos t$, $z = t$.

In Exercises 19–26 assume that f has continuous partial derivatives of all orders.

19. If $z = f(x, y)$ where $x = 2s + 3t$ and $y = 3s - 2t$ find

a) $\dfrac{\partial^2 z}{\partial s^2}$, b) $\dfrac{\partial^2 z}{\partial s \partial t}$, c) $\dfrac{\partial^2 z}{\partial t^2}$.

20. If $f(x, y)$ is harmonic show that $f(ax + by, bx - ay)$ is also harmonic. (See the Remark following Example 2.3.6.)

21. If $f(x, y)$ is harmonic show that $f(x^2 - y^2, 2xy)$ is also harmonic.

22. If $f(x, y)$ is harmonic show that $f\left(\dfrac{x}{x^2 + y^2}, \dfrac{-y}{x^2 + y^2}\right)$ is also harmonic.

23. If $x = t \sin s$ and $y = t \cos s$ find $\dfrac{\partial^2}{\partial s \partial t} f(x, y)$

24. Find $\dfrac{\partial^3}{\partial x \partial y^2} f(2x + 3y, xy)$ in terms of partial derivatives of f.

25. Find $\dfrac{\partial^2}{\partial y \partial x} f(y^2, xy, -x^2)$ in terms of partial derivatives of f.

26. Find $\dfrac{\partial^3}{\partial t^2 \partial s} f(s^2 - t, s + t^2)$ in terms of partial derivatives of f.

27. If $x = e^s \cos t$, $y = e^s \sin t$ and $z = u(x, y) = v(s, t)$ show that

$$\frac{\partial^2 z}{\partial s^2} + \frac{\partial^2 z}{\partial t^2} = (x^2 + y^2)\left(\frac{\partial^2 z}{\partial x^2} + \frac{\partial^2 z}{\partial y^2}\right).$$

28. If $f(x, y)$ is positively homogeneous of degree k and has continuous partial derivatives of second order show that
$$x^2 f_{11}(x, y) + 2xy f_{12}(x, y) + y^2 f_{22}(x, y) = k(k-1)f(x, y).$$

29.*Generalize the result of the previous exercise to functions of n variables.

30.*Generalize the results of the two previous exercises to expressions involving mth order partial derivatives of the function f.

31.†Use the change of variables $\xi = x + ct$, $\eta = x$ to transform the partial differential equation

$$\frac{\partial u}{\partial t} = c\frac{\partial u}{\partial x}, \qquad (c = \text{constant}),$$

into the simpler equation $\partial v / \partial \eta = 0$, where $v(\xi, \eta) = v(x + ct, x) = u(x, t)$. This equation says that $v(\xi, \eta)$ does not depend on η, so $v = f(\xi)$ for some arbitrary differentiable function f. What is the corresponding "general solution" $u(x, t)$ of the original partial differential equation?

32.†Having considered the previous exercise, guess a "general solution" $w(r, s)$ of the second order partial differential equation

$$\frac{\partial^2}{\partial r \partial s} w(r, s) = 0.$$

Your answer should involve two arbitrary functions.

33.†Use the change of variables $r = x + ct$, $s = x - ct$, $w(r, s) = u(x, t)$ to transform the one-dimensional wave equation

$$\frac{\partial^2 u}{\partial t^2} = c^2 \frac{\partial^2 u}{\partial x^2}$$

to a simpler form. Now use the result of the previous exercise to find the "general solution" of this wave equation in the form given in Example 2.3.7.

34.†Show that the "initial value problem" for the one-dimensional wave equation:

$$\begin{cases} u_t(x, t) = c^2 u_{xx}(x, t), \\ u(x, 0) = p(x), \\ u_t(x, 0) = q(x). \end{cases}$$

has solution

$$u(x, t) = \frac{1}{2}\left[p(x - ct) + p(x + ct)\right] + \frac{1}{2c}\int_{x-ct}^{x+ct} q(s)\,ds.$$

(Note that we have used subscripts "x" and "t" instead of "1" and "2" to denote the partial derivatives here. This is common usage in dealing with partial differential equations.)

Remark. The initial value problem in the exercise above gives the small lateral displacement $u(x,t)$ at position x at time t of a vibrating string held under tension along the x-axis. The function $p(x)$ gives the *initial* displacement at position x, that is, the displacement at time $t = 0$. Similarly $q(x)$ gives the initial velocity at position x. Observe that the position at time t depends only on values of these initial data at points no further than ct units away. This is consistent with the previous observation that the solutions of the wave equation represent waves travelling with speed c. (See the remark following Example 2.3.7.)

2.5 APPROXIMATIONS, DIFFERENTIABILITY AND DIFFERENTIALS

The tangent line to the graph $y = f(x)$ at $x = a$ provides a convenient way of approximating the value of $f(x)$ for x near a:

$$f(a + h) \approx f(a) + f'(a)h.$$

The mere existence of $f'(a)$ is sufficient to guarantee that the error in this approximation is small compared to the distance h between a and $a + h$, that is to say,

$$\lim_{h \to 0} \frac{f(a + h) - f(a) - f'(a)h}{h} = f'(a) - f'(a) = 0.$$

Similarly, we can use the height to the tangent plane

$$z = f(a, b) + f_1(a, b)(x - a) + f_2(a, b)(y - b)$$

to the graph $z = f(x, y)$ at (a, b) to approximate the value of $f(x, y)$ for (x, y) near (a, b): putting $x = a + h$ and $y = b + k$ we have

2.5.1
Tangent Plane
Approximation

$$f(a + h, b + k) \approx f(a, b) + f_1(a, b)h + f_2(a, b)k.$$

EXAMPLE 2.5.2   Find an approximate value for $f(x, y) = \sqrt{2x^2 + e^{2y}}$ at $(2.2, -0.2)$.

SOLUTION   It is convenient to use the tangent plane at $(2, 0)$:

$$f_1(x, y) = \frac{2x}{\sqrt{2x^2 + e^{2y}}}, \qquad f(2, 0) = 3,$$
$$f_1(2, 0) = \frac{4}{3},$$
$$f_2(x, y) = \frac{e^{2y}}{\sqrt{2x^2 + e^{2y}}}, \qquad f_2(2, 0) = \frac{1}{3}.$$

Taking $h = 0.2$ and $k = -0.2$ we obtain

$$f(2.2, -0.2) = f(2 + h, 0 + k) \approx f(2, 0) + f_1(2, 0)h + f_2(2, 0)k$$
$$= 3 + \frac{0.8}{3} - \frac{0.2}{3} = 3.2.$$

Unlike the single-variable case, the mere existence of the partial derivatives $f_1(a,b)$ and $f_2(a,b)$ does not even imply that f is continuous at (a,b), let alone that the error in the approximation 2.5.1 is small compared to the distance $\sqrt{h^2+k^2}$ between (a,b) and $(a+h,b+k)$. We adopt this latter condition as our definition of what it means for a function to be *differentiable* at a point.

2.5.3
Definition of
Differentiability

We say that the function $f(x,y)$ is **differentiable** at the point (a,b) if

$$\lim_{h,k\to 0}\frac{f(a+h,b+k)-f(a,b)-h\,f_1(a,b)-kf_2(a,b)}{\sqrt{h^2+k^2}}=0.$$

This definition and the following theorems can be generalized to functions of any number of variables in the obvious way. For the sake of simplicity, we state them for the two-variable case only.

The function $f(x,y)$ is differentiable if and only if the surface $z=f(x,y)$ has a *nonvertical tangent plane* at (a,b). (Compare this with the single-variable situation.) In particular, the function is *continuous* wherever it is differentiable. We shall establish a two-variable version of the Mean-Value Theorem and use it to show that functions with *continuous* first partial derivatives are differentiable.

THEOREM 2.5.4   *(A mean-value theorem)* If $f_1(x,y)$ and $f_2(x,y)$ are continuous in a disc of positive radius centred at (a,b), and if the absolute values of h and k are sufficiently small, then there exist numbers θ_1 and θ_2, each between 0 and 1, such that

$$f(a+h,b+k)-f(a,b)=hf_1(a+\theta_1 h,b+k)+kf_2(a,b+\theta_2 k). \quad \square$$

The proof of this theorem is very similar to that of Theorem 2.3.5, so we give only a sketch here. The reader should fill in the details. Write

$$f(a+h,b+k)-f(a,b)=\big(f(a+h,b+k)-f(a,b+k)\big)+\big(f(a,b+k)-f(a,b)\big),$$

and then apply the single-variable Mean-Value theorem separately to $f(x,b+k)$ on the interval between a and $a+h$, and to $f(a,y)$ on the interval between b and $b+k$ to get the desired result.

THEOREM 2.5.5   If f_1 and f_2 are continuous in a disc of positive radius centred at the point (a,b) then f is differentiable at (a,b).

PROOF   Using Theorem 2.5.4 and the fact that

$$\left|\frac{h}{\sqrt{h^2+k^2}}\right|\le 1 \quad \text{and} \quad \left|\frac{k}{\sqrt{h^2+k^2}}\right|\le 1,$$

we estimate

$$\left| \frac{f(a+h,b+k) - f(a,b) - hf_1(a,b) - kf_2(a,b)}{\sqrt{h^2+k^2}} \right|$$

$$= \left| \frac{h}{\sqrt{h^2+k^2}} \Big(f_1(a+\theta_1 h, b+k) - f_1(a,b) \Big) \right.$$

$$\left. + \frac{k}{\sqrt{h^2+k^2}} \Big(f_2(a, b+\theta_2 k) - f_2(a,b) \Big) \right|$$

$$\le \big| f_1(a+\theta_1 h, b+k) - f_1(a,b) \big| + \big| f_2(a, b+\theta_2 k) - f_2(a,b) \big|.$$

Since f_1 and f_2 are continuous at (a,b) each of these latter terms approaches 0 as h and k approach 0. This is what we wanted to prove. □

Let us illustrate differentiability with an example where we can calculate directly the error in the tangent plane approximation.

EXAMPLE 2.5.6   Calculate $f(x+h, y+k) - f(x,y) - f_1(x,y)h - f_2(x,y)k$ if $f(x,y) = x^3 + xy^2$.

SOLUTION   Since $f_1(x,y) = 3x^2 + y^2$ and $f_2(x,y) = 2xy$, we have

$$f(x+h, y+k) - f(x,y) - f_1(x,y)h - f_2(x,y)k$$

$$= (x+h)^3 + (x+h)(y+k)^2 - x^3 - xy^2 - (3x^2+y^2)h - 2xyk$$

$$= 3xh^2 + h^3 + 2yhk + hk^2 + xk^2.$$

Observe that the result above is a polynomial in h and k with no term of less than second degree in these variables. Evidently this difference approaches zero like the *square* of the distance $\sqrt{h^2+k^2}$ from (x,y) to $(x+h, y+k)$ as $(h,k) \to (0,0)$, so the condition for differentiability is certainly satisfied. This quadratic behavior is the case for any function f with continuous *second* partial derivatives. (See Exercise 9 at the end of this section.)

Proof of the Chain Rule

We are now able to give a formal statement and proof of a simple but representative case of the Chain Rule for multivariate functions.

THEOREM 2.5.7   *(A Chain Rule)* Let $z = f(x,y)$, where $x = u(s,t)$ and $y = v(s,t)$. Suppose that

i) $u(a,b) = p$ and $v(a,b) = q$,

ii) the first partial derivatives of u and v exist at the point (a,b), and

iii) f is differentiable at the point (p,q).

Then $z = w(s,t) = f(u(s,t), v(s,t))$ has first partial derivatives with respect to s and t at (a,b) and

$$w_1(a,b) = f_1(p,q)u_1(a,b) + f_2(p,q)v_1(a,b),$$

$$w_2(a,b) = f_1(p,q)u_2(a,b) + f_2(p,q)v_2(a,b),$$

that is,

$$\frac{\partial z}{\partial s} = \frac{\partial z}{\partial x}\frac{\partial x}{\partial s} + \frac{\partial z}{\partial y}\frac{\partial y}{\partial s}, \qquad \frac{\partial z}{\partial t} = \frac{\partial z}{\partial x}\frac{\partial x}{\partial t} + \frac{\partial z}{\partial y}\frac{\partial y}{\partial t}.$$

PROOF   Define a function E of two variables by:

$$E(0,0) = 0,$$

$$E(h,k) = \frac{f(p+h,q+k) - f(p,q) - hf_1(p,q) - kf_2(p,q)}{\sqrt{h^2 + k^2}} \quad \text{if } (h,k) \neq (0,0).$$

Then $E(h,k)$ is continuous at $(0,0)$, because f is differentiable at (p,q). Now

$$f(p+h,q+k) - f(p,q) = hf_1(p,q) + kf_2(p,q) + \sqrt{h^2 + k^2}\, E(h,k).$$

In this formula put $h = u(a+\sigma,b) - u(a,b)$ and $k = v(a+\sigma,b) - v(a,b)$ and divide by σ to obtain

$$\frac{w(a+\sigma,b) - w(a,b)}{\sigma} = \frac{f(u(a+\sigma,b), v(a+\sigma,b)) - f(u(a,b), v(a,b))}{\sigma}$$

$$= \frac{f(p+h,q+k) - f(p,q)}{\sigma}$$

$$= f_1(p,q)\frac{h}{\sigma} + f_2(p,q)\frac{k}{\sigma} + \sqrt{\left(\frac{h}{\sigma}\right)^2 + \left(\frac{k}{\sigma}\right)^2}\, E(h,k).$$

We want to let σ approach 0 in this formula. Since

$$\lim_{\sigma \to 0}\frac{h}{\sigma} = \lim_{\sigma \to 0}\frac{u(a+\sigma,b) - u(a,b)}{\sigma} = u_1(a,b),$$

and similarly $\lim_{\sigma \to 0}(k/\sigma) = v_1(a,b)$ we have

$$w_1(a,b) = f_1(p,q)u_1(a,b) + f_2(p,q)v_1(a,b).$$

The proof for w_2 is similar. $\square$

Differentials

If the first partial derivatives of a function $z = f(x_1, \ldots, x_n)$ exist at a point we may construct a **differential** dz of the function at that point in a manner similar to that used for functions of one variable:

$$dz = \frac{\partial z}{\partial x_1}\, dx_1 + \frac{\partial z}{\partial x_2}\, dx_2 + \cdots + \frac{\partial z}{\partial x_n}\, dx_n$$

$$= f_1(x_1, \ldots, x_n)\, dx_1 + \cdots + f_n(x_1, \ldots, x_n)\, dx_n.$$

Here the differential dz is considered to be a function of the $2n$ independent variables $x_1, x_2, \ldots, x_n, dx_1, dx_2, \ldots, dx_n$.

For a differentiable function f, the differential df is an approximation to the change Δf in value of the function given by

$$\Delta f = f(x_1 + dx_1, \ldots, x_n + dx_n) - f(x_1, \ldots, x_n).$$

The error in this approximation is small compared to the distance between the two points in the domain of f, that is,

$$\frac{\Delta f - df}{\sqrt{(dx_1)^2 + \cdots + (dx_n)^2}} \to 0 \quad \text{if all } dx_i \to 0,\ (1 \leq i \leq n).$$

REMARK: The equations $x = u(s,t)$ and $y = v(s,t)$ define a *transformation* (that is, a function) from $I\!\!R^2$ (the st-plane) to $I\!\!R^2$ (the xy-plane). At the point (a, b) the corresponding *differentials* ds and dt are transformed to differentials dx and dy via a *linear transformation* whose representative matrix involves the four first partial derivatives of x and y with respect to s and t:

$$\begin{pmatrix} dx \\ dy \end{pmatrix} = \begin{pmatrix} \dfrac{\partial x}{\partial s} & \dfrac{\partial x}{\partial t} \\[2mm] \dfrac{\partial y}{\partial s} & \dfrac{\partial y}{\partial t} \end{pmatrix} \begin{pmatrix} ds \\ dt \end{pmatrix}.$$

Similarly, $z = f(x, y)$ defines a function from $I\!\!R^2$ (the xy-plane) to $I\!\!R^1$ (the z-axis) and the corresponding differentials are related by a linear transformation whose representative matrix is the 1×2 matrix of first partial derivatives of z with respect to x and y:

$$dz = \begin{pmatrix} \dfrac{\partial z}{\partial x} & \dfrac{\partial z}{\partial y} \end{pmatrix} \begin{pmatrix} dx \\ dy \end{pmatrix}.$$

The composite function $z = f\Big(u(s,t), v(s,t)\Big)$ is a transformation from $I\!\!R^2$ (the st-plane) to $I\!\!R^1$ (the z-axis), so the differential dz is given in terms of ds and dt by the matrix equation

$$dz = \begin{pmatrix} \dfrac{\partial z}{\partial s} & \dfrac{\partial z}{\partial t} \end{pmatrix} \begin{pmatrix} ds \\ dt \end{pmatrix}.$$

The Chain Rule merely asserts that this linear transformation is the composition of the two transformations above. That is,

$$\begin{pmatrix} \dfrac{\partial z}{\partial s} & \dfrac{\partial z}{\partial t} \end{pmatrix} \begin{pmatrix} ds \\ dt \end{pmatrix} = dz = \begin{pmatrix} \dfrac{\partial z}{\partial x} & \dfrac{\partial z}{\partial y} \end{pmatrix} \begin{pmatrix} dx \\ dy \end{pmatrix}$$

$$= \begin{pmatrix} \dfrac{\partial z}{\partial x} & \dfrac{\partial z}{\partial y} \end{pmatrix} \begin{pmatrix} \dfrac{\partial x}{\partial s} & \dfrac{\partial x}{\partial t} \\[2mm] \dfrac{\partial y}{\partial s} & \dfrac{\partial y}{\partial t} \end{pmatrix} \begin{pmatrix} ds \\ dt \end{pmatrix}.$$

It follows that

$$\begin{pmatrix} \dfrac{\partial z}{\partial s} & \dfrac{\partial z}{\partial t} \end{pmatrix} = \begin{pmatrix} \dfrac{\partial z}{\partial x} & \dfrac{\partial z}{\partial y} \end{pmatrix} \begin{pmatrix} \dfrac{\partial x}{\partial s} & \dfrac{\partial x}{\partial t} \\[2mm] \dfrac{\partial y}{\partial s} & \dfrac{\partial y}{\partial t} \end{pmatrix}.$$

EXERCISES

In Exercises 1–6 use suitable tangent planes to find approximate values for the given functions at the points indicated.

1. $f(x,y) = x^2y^3$ at $(3.1, 0.9)$

2. $f(x,y) = \tan^{-1}\left(\dfrac{y}{x}\right)$ at $(3.01, 2.99)$

3. $f(x,y) = \sin(\pi xy + \ln y)$ at $(0.01, 1.05)$

4. $f(x,y) = \dfrac{24}{x^2 + xy + y^2}$ at $(2.1, 1.8)$

5. $f(x,y,z) = \sqrt{x + 2y + 3z}$ at $(1.9, 1.8, 1.1)$

6. $f(x,y) = x\,e^{y+x^2}$ at $(2.05, -3.92)$

7. By approximately what percentage will the value of $w = \dfrac{x^2y^3}{z^4}$ increase or decrease if x increases by 1%, y increases by 2%, and z and increases by 3%?

8.*Prove the following version of the Mean-Value Theorem: if $f(x,y)$ has first partial derivatives continuous near every point of the straight line segment joining the points (a,b) and $(a+h, b+k)$ then there exists a number θ satisfying $0 < \theta < 1$ such that

$$f(a + h, b + k) = f(a,b) + hf_1(a + \theta h, b + \theta k) + kf_2(a + \theta h, b + \theta k).$$

Hint: apply the single-variable Mean-Value Theorem to $g(t) = f(a + th, b + tk)$. Why could we not have used this result in place of Theorem 2.5.4 to prove Theorem 2.5.5 and hence the version of the Chain Rule given in this section?

9.*Generalize the previous exercise as follows: show that if $f(x,y)$ has continuous partial derivatives of second order near the point (a,b) then there exists a number θ satisfying $0 < \theta < 1$ such that for h and k sufficiently small in absolute value,

$$\begin{aligned}
f(a + h, b + k) = {} & f(a,b) + hf_1(a,b) + kf_2(a,b) \\
& + h^2 f_{11}(a + \theta h, b + \theta k) \\
& + 2hk f_{12}(a + \theta h, b + \theta k) \\
& + k^2 f_{22}(a + \theta h, b + \theta k).
\end{aligned}$$

Hence show that there is a constant K such that for all sufficiently small h and k,

$$\begin{aligned}
\big| f(a + h, b + k) &- f(a,b) - hf_1(a,b) - kf_2(a,b) \big| \\
&\leq K(h^2 + k^2).
\end{aligned}$$

▨ 2.6   GRADIENTS AND DIRECTIONAL DERIVATIVES

A first partial derivative of a function of several variables gives the rate of change of that function with respect to distance measured in the direction of one of the coordinate axes. In this section we will develop a method for finding the rate of change of such a function with respect to distance measured in *any direction* in the domain of the function.

To begin, it is useful to combine the first partial derivatives of a function into a single *vector function* called a **gradient**. For simplicity, we will develop and interpret the gradient for functions of two variables. Extension to functions of three or more variables is straightforward and will be discussed later in the section.

2.6.1

Definition of the
Gradient Vector

At any point (x, y) where the first partial derivatives of the function $f(x, y)$ exist we define the **gradient vector** $\nabla f(x, y)$ by

$$\nabla f(x, y) = f_1(x, y)\mathbf{i} + f_2(x, y)\mathbf{j}.$$

(Recall that $\mathbf{i}$ and $\mathbf{j}$ denote the unit basis vectors from the origin to the points $(1,0)$ and $(0,1)$ respectively.)

EXAMPLE 2.6.2   If $f(x,y) = x^2 + y^2$ then $\nabla f(x,y) = 2x\mathbf{i} + 2y\mathbf{j}$. In particular, $\nabla f(1,2) = 2\mathbf{i} + 4\mathbf{j}$. Observe that this vector is perpendicular to the straight line $x + 2y = 5$ which is tangent at $(1,2)$ to the circle $x^2 + y^2 = 5$. This circle is the level curve of f which passes through the point $(1,2)$. (See Fig. 2.6.1..) As the following theorem shows, this perpendicularity is not a coincidence.

THEOREM 2.6.3   If $f(x,y)$ is differentiable at the point (a,b) and $\nabla f(a,b) \neq \mathbf{0}$, then $\nabla f(a,b)$ is a normal vector to the level curve of f which passes through (a,b).

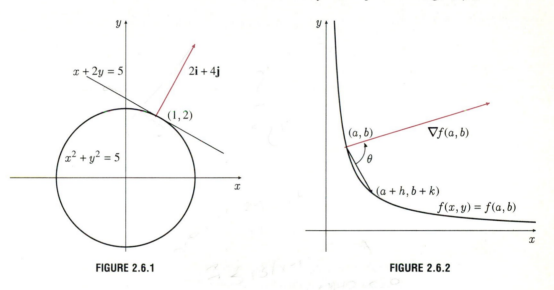

FIGURE 2.6.1   FIGURE 2.6.2

PROOF   The angle θ between the vector $\nabla f(a,b)$ and the vector $h\mathbf{i} + k\mathbf{j}$ from the point (a,b) to the point $(a+h, b+k)$ (see Fig. 2.6.2) satisfies

$$\cos\theta = \frac{\nabla f(a,b) \bullet (h\mathbf{i} + k\mathbf{j})}{|\nabla f(a,b)|\sqrt{h^2 + k^2}} = \frac{1}{|\nabla f(a,b)|} \frac{hf_1(a,b) + kf_2(a,b)}{\sqrt{h^2 + k^2}}.$$

If $(a+h, b+k)$ lies on the level curve of f which passes through (a,b), then $f(a+h, b+k) = f(a,b)$, and so, since f is differentiable at (a,b), we have

$$\lim_{h,k\to 0} \frac{hf_1(a,b) + kf_2(a,b)}{\sqrt{h^2 + k^2}}$$

$$= -\lim_{h,k\to 0} \frac{f(a+h, b+k) - f(a,b) - hf_1(a,b) - kf_2(a,b)}{\sqrt{h^2 + k^2}} = 0.$$

Hence $\cos\theta \to 0$ and $\theta \to \pi/2$ as $h, k \to 0$, and $\nabla f(a,b)$ is perpendicular to the tangent to the level curve $f(x,y) = f(a,b)$. $\square$

Directional Derivatives

The first partial derivatives $f_1(a, b)$ and $f_2(a, b)$ give the rates of change of $f(x, y)$ at (a, b) measured in the directions of the positive x- and y-axes respectively. If we want to know how fast $f(x, y)$ changes value as we move through the domain of f at (a, b) in some other direction we require a more general *directional derivative*. We can specify the direction by means of a nonzero vector. It is most convenient to use a *unit vector*.

2.6.4
Definition of
Directional Derivative

Let **u** be a unit vector, that is,

$$\mathbf{u} = u\mathbf{i} + v\mathbf{j}, \qquad \text{where} \quad u^2 + v^2 = 1.$$

The **directional derivative** of $f(x, y)$ at (a, b) in the direction of **u** is the rate of change of $f(x, y)$ with respect to distance measured at (a, b) along a line in the direction of **u** in the xy-plane. This directional derivative is given by

$$D_{\mathbf{u}}f(a, b) = \lim_{h \to 0} \frac{f(a + hu, b + hv) - f(a, b)}{h},$$

or, equivalently,

$$D_{\mathbf{u}}f(a, b) = \frac{d}{dt}f(a + tu, b + tv)\Big|_{t=0}.$$

Observe that directional derivatives in directions parallel to the coordinate axes are given directly by first partials: $D_{\mathbf{i}}f(a, b) = f_1(a, b)$, $D_{\mathbf{j}}f(a, b) = f_2(a, b)$, $D_{-\mathbf{i}}f(a, b) = -f_1(a, b)$, $D_{-\mathbf{j}}f(a, b) = -f_2(a, b)$. The following theorem shows how the gradient can be used to calculate any directional derivative.

THEOREM 2.6.5   If f is differentiable at (a, b) and $\mathbf{u} = u\mathbf{i} + v\mathbf{j}$ is a unit vector, then the directional derivative of f at (a, b) in the direction of **u** is given by

2.6.6
Formula for the
Directional Derivative

$$D_{\mathbf{u}}f(a, b) = \mathbf{u} \bullet \nabla f(a, b).$$

PROOF   By the Chain Rule:

$$D_{\mathbf{u}}f(a, b) = \frac{d}{dt}f(a + tu, b + tv)\Big|_{t=0}$$
$$= u f_1(a, b) + v f_2(a, b) = \mathbf{u} \bullet \nabla f(a, b). \quad \square$$

Given any nonzero vector $\mathbf{v}$, we can always obtain a unit vector in the same direction by dividing $\mathbf{v}$ by its length. The directional derivative of f at (a, b) in the direction of $\mathbf{v}$ is therefore given by

$$D_{\mathbf{v}/|\mathbf{v}|} f(a, b) = \frac{\mathbf{v}}{|\mathbf{v}|} \bullet \nabla f(a, b).$$

EXAMPLE 2.6.7 Find the rate of change of $f(x, y) = y^4 + 2xy^3 + x^2 y^2$ at $(0, 1)$ measured in each of the following directions:

a) $\mathbf{i} + 2\mathbf{j}$, b) $\mathbf{j} - 2\mathbf{i}$,
c) $3\mathbf{i}$, d) $\mathbf{i} + \mathbf{j}$.

SOLUTION We calculate

$$\nabla f(x, y) = (2y^3 + 2xy^2)\mathbf{i} + (4y^3 + 6xy^2 + 2x^2 y)\mathbf{j},$$
$$\nabla f(0, 1) = 2\mathbf{i} + 4\mathbf{j}.$$

Therefore,

a) the directional derivative of f at $(0, 1)$ in the direction of $\mathbf{i} + 2\mathbf{j}$ is

$$\frac{\mathbf{i} + 2\mathbf{j}}{|\mathbf{i} + 2\mathbf{j}|} \bullet (2\mathbf{i} + 4\mathbf{j}) = \frac{2 + 8}{\sqrt{5}} = 2\sqrt{5}.$$

(Observe that $\mathbf{i} + 2\mathbf{j}$ points in the same direction as $\nabla f(0, 1)$ so the directional derivative is positive and equal to the length of $\nabla f(0, 1)$.)

b) the directional derivative of f at $(0, 1)$ in the direction of $\mathbf{j} - 2\mathbf{i}$ is

$$\frac{-2\mathbf{i} + \mathbf{j}}{|-2\mathbf{i} + \mathbf{j}|} \bullet (2\mathbf{i} + 4\mathbf{j}) = \frac{-4 + 4}{\sqrt{5}} = 0.$$

(Since $\mathbf{j} - 2\mathbf{i}$ is perpendicular to $\nabla f(0, 1)$, it is tangent to the level curve of f through $(0, 1)$ and so the directional derivative in that direction must be zero.)

c) the directional derivative of f at $(0, 1)$ in the direction of $3\mathbf{i}$ is

$$\mathbf{i} \bullet (2\mathbf{i} + 4\mathbf{j}) = 2.$$

(As noted previously, the directional derivative of f in the direction of the positive x-axis is just $f_1(0, 1)$.)

d) the directional derivative of f at $(0, 1)$ in the direction of $\mathbf{i} + \mathbf{j}$ is

$$\frac{\mathbf{i} + \mathbf{j}}{|\mathbf{i} + \mathbf{j}|} \bullet (2\mathbf{i} + 4\mathbf{j}) = \frac{2 + 4}{\sqrt{2}} = 3\sqrt{2}.$$

(If we move along the surface $z = f(x, y)$ through the point $(0, 1, 1)$ in a direction making horizontal angles of 45 degrees with the positive directions of the x- and y-axes, we would be rising at a rate of $3\sqrt{2}$ vertical units per horizontal unit moved.)

REMARK: A direction in the plane can be specified by a polar angle. The direction making angle ϕ with the positive direction of the x-axis corresponds to the unit vector

$$\mathbf{u}_\phi = \cos\phi\,\mathbf{i} + \sin\phi\,\mathbf{j}$$

so the directional derivative of f at (x, y) in that direction is

$$D_\phi f(x, y) = D_{\mathbf{u}_\phi} f(x, y) = \mathbf{u}_\phi \bullet \nabla f(x, y) = f_1(x, y)\cos\phi + f_2(x, y)\sin\phi.$$

Note the use of the symbol $D_\phi f(x, y)$ to denote a derivative of f with respect to *distance* measured in the direction ϕ.

As observed in the previous example, Theorem 2.6.5 provides a useful interpretation for the gradient vector. For any unit vector $\mathbf{u}$ we have

$$D_{\mathbf{u}} f(a, b) = \mathbf{u} \bullet \nabla f(a, b) = |\nabla f(a, b)|\,\cos\theta,$$

where θ is the angle between the vectors $\mathbf{u}$ and $\nabla f(a, b)$. Since $\cos\theta$ only takes on values between -1 and 1, $D_{\mathbf{u}} f(a, b)$ only takes on values between $-|\nabla f(a, b)|$ and $|\nabla f(a, b)|$. Moreover, $D_{\mathbf{u}} f(a, b) = -|\nabla f(a, b)|$ if and only if $\mathbf{u}$ points in the opposite direction to $\nabla f(a, b)$ (so that $\cos\theta = -1$), and $D_{\mathbf{u}} f(a, b) = |\nabla f(a, b)|$ if and only if $\mathbf{u}$ points in the same direction as $\nabla f(a, b)$ (so that $\cos\theta = 1$). The directional derivative is zero in the direction $\theta = \pi/2$; this is the direction of the (tangent line to the) level curve of f through (a, b).

We summarize these properties of the gradient as follows:

i) At (a, b), $f(x, y)$ increases most rapidly in the direction of the gradient vector $\nabla f(a, b)$. The maximum rate of increase is $|\nabla f(a, b)|$.

ii) At (a, b), $f(x, y)$ decreases most rapidly in the direction of $-\nabla f(a, b)$. The maximum rate of decrease is $|\nabla f(a, b)|$.

iii) The rate of change of $f(x, y)$ at (a, b) is zero in directions tangent to the level curve of f which passes through (a, b).

Look again at the topographic map in Fig. 2.1.5. The streams on the map flow in the direction of steepest descent, that is, in the direction of $-\nabla f$ where f measures the elevation of land. The streams therefore cross the contours (the level curves of f) at right angles.

EXAMPLE 2.6.8   In what direction at the point $(2, 1)$ does the function $f(x, y) = x^2 e^{-y}$ increase most rapidly? What is the rate of increase of f in that direction?

SOLUTION   We have

$$\nabla f(x, y) = 2x\, e^{-y}\mathbf{i} - x^2\, e^{-y}\mathbf{j},$$

$$\nabla f(2, 1) = \frac{4}{e}\mathbf{i} - \frac{4}{e}\mathbf{j} = \frac{4}{e}(\mathbf{i} - \mathbf{j}).$$

At $(2, 1)$, $f(x, y)$ increases most rapidly in the direction of the vector $\mathbf{i} - \mathbf{j}$. The rate of increase in this direction is $|\nabla f(2, 1)| = 4\sqrt{2}/e$.

EXAMPLE 2.6.9   A hiker is standing beside a stream on the side of a hill, examining her map of the region. The height of land (in km) at any point (x, y) is given by

$$h(x, y) = \frac{20}{3 + x^2 + 2y^2},$$

where x and y (also in km) denote the coordinates of the point on the hiker's map. The hiker is at the point $(3, 2)$.

a) In what horizontal direction is the stream flowing near the hiker? How fast is the stream descending there?

b) Find the equation of the path of the stream on the hiker's map of the region.

c) At what angle to the path of the stream (on the map) should the hiker set out if she wishes to ascend the hill at a 15 degree inclination to the horizontal?

d) Make a sketch of the hiker's map, showing some curves of constant elevation, and showing the stream.

SOLUTION   a) We begin by calculating the gradient of h and its length at $(3, 2)$:

$$\nabla h(x, y) = -\frac{20}{(3 + x^2 + 2y^2)^2}(2x\mathbf{i} + 4y\mathbf{j}),$$

$$\nabla h(3, 2) = -\frac{1}{20}(6\mathbf{i} + 8\mathbf{j}) = -\frac{1}{10}(3\mathbf{i} + 4\mathbf{j}),$$

$$|\nabla h(3, 2)| = 0.5.$$

The stream is flowing in the direction whose horizontal projection at $(3, 2)$ is $-\nabla h(3, 2)$, that is, in the horizontal direction of the vector $3\mathbf{i} + 4\mathbf{j}$. The stream is descending at a rate of 0.5 vertical units per horizontal unit travelled.

b) Coordinates on the map are the coordinates (x, y) in the domain of the height function h. We can find an equation of the path of the stream on a map of the region by setting up a differential equation for a change of position along the stream. If the vector $d\mathbf{r} = dx\,\mathbf{i} + dy\,\mathbf{j}$ is tangent to the path of the stream at point (x, y) on the map then $d\mathbf{r}$ is parallel to $\nabla h(x, y)$. Hence the components of these two vectors are proportional:

$$\frac{dx}{2x} = \frac{dy}{4y}, \qquad \text{or} \qquad \frac{dy}{y} = \frac{2dx}{x}.$$

Integrating both sides of this latter equation we get $\ln y = 2\ln x + \ln C$, or $y = Cx^2$. Since the stream passes through $(3, 2)$, we have $C = 2/9$ and the equation is $9y = 2x^2$.

c) Suppose the hiker moves away from $(3, 2)$ in the direction of the unit vector $\mathbf{u}$. She will be ascending at an inclination of 15 degrees if the directional derivative of h in the direction of $\mathbf{u}$ is $\tan 15° \approx 0.268$. If θ is the angle between $\mathbf{u}$ and the upstream direction then

$$0.5\cos\theta = |\nabla h(3, 2)|\cos\theta = D_{\mathbf{u}}h(3, 2) \approx 0.268.$$

Hence $\cos\theta \approx 0.536$ and $\theta \approx 57.6°$. She should set out in a direction making a horizontal angle of about $58°$ with the upstream direction.

d) A suitable sketch of the map is given in Fig. 2.6.3.

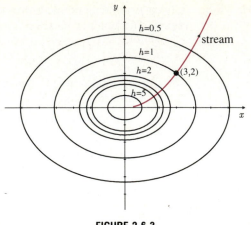

FIGURE 2.6.3

EXAMPLE 2.6.10 Find the second directional derivative of $f(x, y)$ in the direction making angle ϕ with the positive x-axis.

SOLUTION As observed earlier, the first directional derivative is

$$D_\phi f(x, y) = (\cos \phi \mathbf{i} + \sin \phi \mathbf{j}) \bullet \nabla f(x, y) = f_1(x, y) \cos \phi + f_2(x, y) \sin \phi.$$

The second directional derivative is therefore

$$
\begin{aligned}
D_\phi^2 f(x, y) &= D_\phi \left(D_\phi f(x, y) \right) \\
&= (\cos \phi \mathbf{i} + \sin \phi \mathbf{j}) \bullet \nabla \left(f_1(x, y) \cos \phi + f_2(x, y) \sin \phi \right) \\
&= \left(f_{11}(x, y) \cos \phi + f_{21}(x, y) \sin \phi \right) \cos \phi \\
&\quad + \left(f_{12}(x, y) \cos \phi + f_{22}(x, y) \sin \phi \right) \sin \phi \\
&= f_{11}(x, y) \cos^2 \phi + 2 f_{12}(x, y) \cos \phi \sin \phi + f_{22}(x, y) \sin^2 \phi.
\end{aligned}
$$

Note that if $\phi = 0$ or $\phi = \pi$ (so the directional derivative is in a direction parallel to the x-axis) then $D_\phi^2 f(x, y) = f_{11}(x, y)$. Similarly, $D_\phi^2 f(x, y) = f_{22}(x, y)$ if $\phi = \pi/2$ or $3\pi/2$.

Rates Perceived by a Moving Observer

We have used the symbol $D_\mathbf{u} f(a, b)$ to represent the directional derivative of f at (a, b) in the direction of $\mathbf{u}$ only if $\mathbf{u}$ is a unit vector: in this case

$$D_\mathbf{u} f(a, b) = \mathbf{u} \bullet \nabla f(a, b).$$

If we define

$$D_\mathbf{v} f(a, b) = \mathbf{v} \bullet \nabla f(a, b)$$

for an arbitrary nonzero vector $\mathbf{v}$, then the directional derivative of f at (a, b) in the direction of $\mathbf{v}$ is not $D_{\mathbf{v}}f(a, b)$, but rather $D_{\mathbf{v}/|\mathbf{v}|}f(a, b)$. However, the rate of change of f as perceived by a *moving observer* passing through (a, b) with velocity $\mathbf{v}$ will be the product of this directional derivative with the speed $|\mathbf{v}|$ of the observer. Hence it is $D_{\mathbf{v}}f(a, b)$. This rate of change will be equal to the directional derivative if the observer is moving at unit speed. If the hiker in Example 2.6.9 moves away from $(3, 2)$ with horizontal velocity $\mathbf{v} = -\mathbf{i} - \mathbf{j}$ km/h, then she will be rising at a rate

$$\mathbf{v} \bullet \nabla h(3, 2) = (-\mathbf{i} - \mathbf{j}) \bullet \left(-\frac{1}{5}(6\mathbf{i} + 8\mathbf{j})\right) = \frac{14}{5} \text{ km/h.}$$

As defined here, $D_{\mathbf{v}}f$ is the spatial component of the derivative of f following the motion. See Example 2.4.7. The rate of change of the reading on the moving thermometer in that example can be expressed as

$$\frac{dT}{dt} = D_{\mathbf{v}}T(x, y, z, t) + \frac{\partial T}{\partial t}$$

where $\mathbf{v}$ is the velocity of the moving thermometer and $D_{\mathbf{v}}T = \mathbf{v} \bullet \nabla T$, the gradient being taken with respect to the three spatial variables only.

The Gradient in Higher Dimensions

By analogy with the two-dimensional case, a function $f(x_1, x_2, \ldots, x_n)$ of n variables possessing first partial derivatives has gradient given by

$$\nabla f(x_1, x_2, \ldots, x_n) = \frac{\partial f}{\partial x_1}\mathbf{e_1} + \frac{\partial f}{\partial x_2}\mathbf{e_2} + \cdots + \frac{\partial f}{\partial x_n}\mathbf{e_n}$$

where $\mathbf{e}_j$ is the unit vector from the origin to the unit point on the jth coordinate axis. In particular, for a function of three variables,

$$\nabla f(x, y, z) = \frac{\partial f}{\partial x}\mathbf{i} + \frac{\partial f}{\partial y}\mathbf{j} + \frac{\partial f}{\partial z}\mathbf{k}.$$

For functions of any number of variables the vector $\nabla f(P_0)$ is normal to the "level surface" of f passing through the point P_0 (that is, the (hyper)surface with equation $f(x_1, \ldots, x_n) = f(P_0)$), and, if f is differentiable at P_0, the rate of change of f at P_0 in the direction of the unit vector $\mathbf{u}$ is given by $\mathbf{u} \bullet \nabla f(P_0)$. Equations of tangent planes to surfaces in 3-space can be found easily with the aid of gradients.

EXAMPLE 2.6.11 Find ∇f where $f(x, y, z) = x^2 + y^2 + z^2$ and use it to find an equation of the tangent plane to the sphere $x^2 + y^2 + z^2 = 6$ at the point $(1, -1, 2)$. What is the maximum rate of increase of f at that point? What is the rate of change with respect to distance of f at $(1, -1, 2)$ measured in the direction from that point towards the point $(3, 1, 1)$?

SOLUTION $\nabla f(x, y, z) = 2x\mathbf{i} + 2y\mathbf{j} + 2z\mathbf{k}$ so $\nabla f(1, -1, 2) = 2\mathbf{i} - 2\mathbf{j} + 4\mathbf{k}$. The required tangent plane has this vector as normal. (See Fig. 2.6.4.) Therefore its equation is given by $2(x - 1) - 2(y + 1) + 4(z - 2) = 0$ or, more simply, $x - y + 2z = 6$. The maximum rate of increase of f at $(1, -1, 2)$ is $|\nabla f(1, -1, 2)| = \sqrt{24} = 2\sqrt{6}$, and it occurs in the direction of the vector $\mathbf{i} - \mathbf{j} + 2\mathbf{k}$. The direction from $(1, -1, 2)$ towards $(3, 1, 1)$ is specified by the vector $2\mathbf{i} + 2\mathbf{j} - \mathbf{k}$. The rate of change of f with respect to distance in this direction is

$$\frac{2\mathbf{i} + 2\mathbf{j} - \mathbf{k}}{\sqrt{4 + 4 + 1}} \bullet (2\mathbf{i} - 2\mathbf{j} + 4\mathbf{k}) = \frac{4 - 4 - 4}{3} = -\frac{4}{3},$$

that is, f decreases at rate $4/3$ of a unit per horizontal unit moved.

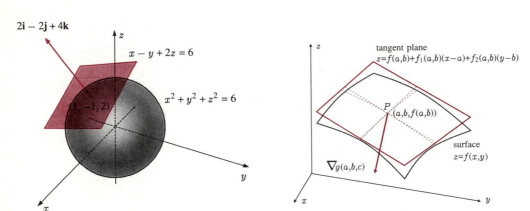

FIGURE 2.6.4   FIGURE 2.6.5

EXAMPLE 2.6.12   The graph of a *function* $f(x, y)$ of two variables is the graph of the *equation* $z = f(x, y)$ in 3-space. This surface is the level surface $g(x, y, z) = 0$ of the 3-variable function

$$g(x, y, z) = f(x, y) - z.$$

If f is differentiable at (a, b) and $c = f(a, b)$ then g is differentiable at (a, b, c) and

$$\nabla g(a, b, c) = f_1(a, b)\mathbf{i} + f_2(a, b)\mathbf{j} - \mathbf{k}$$

is normal to $g(x, y, z) = 0$ at (a, b, c) (Note that $\nabla g(a, b, c) \neq \mathbf{0}$, since its z component is -1.) It follows that the graph of f has nonvertical tangent plane at (a, b) given by

$$f_1(a, b)(x - a) + f_2(a, b)(y - b) - (z - c) = 0,$$

or

$$z = f(a, b) + f_1(a, b)(x - a) + f_2(a, b)(y - b).$$

(See Fig. 2.6.5.) This result was obtained by a different argument in Section 2.2.

Students frequently confuse graphs of functions with level curves or surfaces of those functions. In the above example we are talking about a *level surface* of the function $g(x, y, z)$ which happens to coincide with the *graph* of a different function, $f(x, y)$. Do not confuse that surface with the graph of g, which is a three dimensional "hypersurface" in 4-space having equation $w = g(x, y, z)$. Similarly, do not confuse the tangent *plane* to the graph of $f(x, y)$, (that is, the plane obtained in the above example), with the tangent *line* to the level curve of $f(x, y)$ passing through (a, b) and lying in the xy-plane. This line has equation $f_1(a, b)(x - a) + f_2(a, b)(y - b) = 0$.

EXAMPLE 2.6.13   Find a vector tangent to the curve of intersection of the two surfaces

$$z = x^2 - y^2 \qquad \text{and} \qquad xyz + 30 = 0$$

at the point $(-3, 2, 5)$.

SOLUTION   Evidently the given point lies on both surfaces and so on their curve of intersection. A vector tangent to this curve there will be perpendicular to the normals to both surfaces, that is to the vectors

$$\mathbf{n}_1 = \nabla(x^2 - y^2 - z)\Big|_{(-3,2,5)} = 2x\mathbf{i} - 2y\mathbf{j} - \mathbf{k}\Big|_{(-3,2,5)} = -6\mathbf{i} - 4\mathbf{j} - \mathbf{k},$$

$$\mathbf{n}_2 = \nabla(xyz + 30)\Big|_{(-3,2,5)} = (yz\mathbf{i} + xz\mathbf{j} + xy\mathbf{k})\Big|_{(-3,2,5)} = 10\mathbf{i} - 15\mathbf{j} - 6\mathbf{k}.$$

For the tangent vector $\mathbf{T}$ we can therefore use

$$\mathbf{T} = \mathbf{n}_1 \times \mathbf{n}_2 = \begin{vmatrix} \mathbf{i} & \mathbf{j} & \mathbf{k} \\ -6 & -4 & -1 \\ 10 & -15 & -6 \end{vmatrix} = 9\mathbf{i} - 46\mathbf{j} + 130\mathbf{k}.$$

EXERCISES

In Exercises 1–8 find

a) the gradient of the given function at the point indicated,

b) an equation of the plane tangent to the graph of the given function at the point whose x and y coordinates are given,

c) an equation of the straight line tangent, at the given point, to the level curve of the given function passing through that point.

1. $f(x, y) = x^2 - y^2$ at $(2, -1)$

2. $f(x, y) = \dfrac{x - y}{x + y}$ at $(1, 1)$

3. $f(x, y) = \cos(x/y)$ at $(\pi, 4)$

4. $f(x, y) = e^{xy}$ at $(2, 0)$

5. $f(x, y) = \dfrac{x}{x^2 + y^2}$ at $(1, 2)$

6. $f(x, y) = \dfrac{2xy}{x^2 + y^2}$ at $(0, 2)$

7. $f(x, y) = \ln(x^2 + y^2)$ at $(1, -2)$

8. $f(x, y) = \sqrt{1 + xy^2}$ at $(2, -2)$

In Exercises 9–11 find an equation of the tangent plane to the level surface of the given function which passes through the given point.

9. $f(x, y, z) = x^2 y + y^2 z + z^2 x$ at $(1, -1, 1)$

10. $f(x, y, z) = \cos(x + 2y + 3z)$ at $(\frac{\pi}{2}, \pi, \pi)$

11. $f(x, y, z) = y e^{-x^2} \sin z$ at $(0, 1, \pi/3)$

In Exercises 12–17 find the rate of change of the given function at the given point in the specified direction.

12. $f(x, y) = 3x - 4y$ at $(0, 2)$ in the direction of the vector $-2\mathbf{i}$.

13. $f(x, y) = x^2 y$ at $(-1, -1)$ in the direction of the vector $\mathbf{i} + 2\mathbf{j}$.

14. $f(x, y) = \dfrac{x}{1 + y}$ at $(0, 0)$ in the direction of the vector $\mathbf{i} - \mathbf{j}$.

15. $f(x, y) = x^2 + y^2$ at $(1, -2)$ in the direction making a (positive) angle of $60°$ with the positive x-axis.

16. $f(x, y, z) = (y^2 + \sin z)e^{-x}$ at $(0, 2, \pi)$ in the direction towards the point $(1, 1, 0)$.

17. $f(x, y, z) = \dfrac{1}{x} + \dfrac{1}{y} + \dfrac{1}{z}$ at $(2, -3, 4)$ in the direction of the vector $\mathbf{i} + \mathbf{j} + \mathbf{k}$.

18. Let $f(x, y) = \ln |\mathbf{r}|$ where $\mathbf{r} = x\mathbf{i} + y\mathbf{j}$. Show that
$$\nabla f = \frac{\mathbf{r}}{|\mathbf{r}|^2}.$$

19. Let $f(x, y, z) = |\mathbf{r}|^{-n}$ where $\mathbf{r} = x\mathbf{i} + y\mathbf{j} + z\mathbf{k}$. Show that
$$\nabla f = \frac{-n\mathbf{r}}{|\mathbf{r}|^{n+2}}.$$

20. Show that, in terms of polar coordinates (r, θ) (where $x = r\cos\theta$, and $y = r\sin\theta$), the gradient of a function $f(r, \theta)$ is given by
$$\nabla f = \frac{\partial f}{\partial r}\hat{\mathbf{r}} + \frac{1}{r}\frac{\partial f}{\partial \theta}\hat{\boldsymbol\theta},$$
where $\hat{\mathbf{r}}$ is a unit vector in the direction of the position vector $\mathbf{r} = x\mathbf{i} + y\mathbf{j}$, and $\hat{\boldsymbol\theta}$ is a unit vector at right angles to $\hat{\mathbf{r}}$ in the direction of increasing θ.

21. In what directions at the point $(2, 0)$ does the function $f(x, y) = xy$ have rate of change -1? Are there directions in which the rate is -3? How about -2?

22. In what directions at the point (a, b, c) does the function $f(x, y, z) = x^2 + y^2 - z^2$ increase at half of its maximal rate at that point?

23. Find $\nabla f(a, b)$ for the differentiable function $f(x, y)$ given the directional derivatives
$$D_{(\mathbf{i}+\mathbf{j})/\sqrt{2}}f(a, b) = 3\sqrt{2}, \quad \text{and} \quad D_{(3\mathbf{i}-4\mathbf{j})/5}f(a, b) = 5.$$

24. If $f(x, y)$ is differentiable at (a, b), what condition should angles ϕ_1 and ϕ_2 satisfy in order that the gradient $\nabla f(a, b)$ can be determined from the values of the directional derivatives $D_{\phi_1}f(a, b)$ and $D_{\phi_2}f(a, b)$?

25. The temperature $T(x, y)$ at points of the xy-plane is given by $T(x, y) = x^2 - 2y^2$.

a) Draw a contour diagram for T showing some isotherms (curves of constant temperature).

b) In what direction should an ant at position $(2, -1)$ move if it wishes to cool off as quickly as possible?

c) If the ant moves in that direction at speed k (units distance per unit time), at what rate does it experience the decrease of temperature?

d) At what rate would the ant experience the decrease of temperature if it moved from $(2, -1)$ at speed k in the direction of the vector $-\mathbf{i} - 2\mathbf{j}$?

e) Along what curve through $(2, -1)$ should the ant move in order to continue to experience maximum rate of cooling?

26. Find an equation of the curve in the xy-plane which passes through the point $(1, 1)$ and intersects all level curves of the function $f(x, y) = x^4 + y^2$ at right angles.

27. Find an equation of the curve in the xy-plane which passes through the point $(2, -1)$ and which intersects every curve with equation of the form $x^2 y^3 = K$ at right angles.

28. Find the second directional derivative of $e^{-x^2-y^2}$ at the point $(a, b) \neq (0, 0)$ in the direction directly away from the origin.

29. Find the second directional derivative of $f(x, y, z) = xyz$ at $(2, 3, 1)$ in the direction of the vector $\mathbf{i} - \mathbf{j} - \mathbf{k}$.

30. Find a vector tangent to the curve of intersection of the two cylinders $x^2 + y^2 = 2$ and $y^2 + z^2 = 2$ at the point $(1, -1, 1)$

31. Repeat the previous exercise for the surfaces $x+y+z = 6$ and $x^2 + y^2 + z^2 = 14$ and the point $(1, 2, 3)$

32. The temperature in 3-space is given by
$$T(x, y, z) = x^2 - y^2 + z^2 + xz^2.$$

At time $t = 0$ a fly passes through the point $(1, 1, 2)$, flying along the curve of intersection of the surfaces $z = 3x^2 - y^2$ and $2x^2 + 2y^2 - z^2 = 0$. If the fly's speed is 7, at what rate does it experience temperature changing at $t = 0$?

33. State and prove a version of Theorem 2.6.3 for a function of three variables.

34. What is the level surface of $f(x, y, z) = \cos(x + 2y + 3z)$ which passes through (π, π, π)? What is the tangent plane to that level surface at that point? (Compare this exercise with Exercise 10 above.)

35. If $\nabla f(x, y) = 0$ throughout the disc $x^2 + y^2 < r^2$ prove that $f(x, y)$ is constant throughout the disc.

36. Theorem 2.6.3 implies that the level curve of $f(x, y)$ passing through (a, b) is smooth (has a tangent line) at (a, b) provided f is differentiable at (a, b) and sat-

isfies $\nabla f(a, b) \neq \mathbf{0}$. Show that the level curve need not be smooth at (a, b) if $\nabla f(a, b) = \mathbf{0}$. (Hint: consider $f(x, y) = y^3 - x^2$ at $(0, 0)$.)

37. If $\mathbf{v}$ is a nonzero vector, express $D_{\mathbf{v}}(D_{\mathbf{v}}f)$ in terms of the components of $\mathbf{v}$ and the second partials of f. What is the interpretation of this quantity for a moving observer?

38.* An observer moves so that his position, velocity and acceleration at time t are given by $\mathbf{r}(t) = x(t)\mathbf{i} + y(t)\mathbf{j} + z(t)\mathbf{k}$, $\mathbf{v}(t) = d\mathbf{r}/dt$ and $\mathbf{a}(t) = d\mathbf{v}/dt$. If the temperature in the vicinity of the observer depends only on position, $T = T(x, y, z)$, express the second time derivative of temperature as measured by the observer in terms of $D_{\mathbf{v}}$ and $D_{\mathbf{a}}$.

39.* Repeat the previous exercise but with T depending explicitly on time as well as position: $T = T(x, y, z, t)$.

2.7 IMPLICIT FUNCTIONS

When we study the calculus of functions of one variable we encounter examples of functions defined implicitly as solutions of equations in two variables. Suppose, for example, that

$$F(x, y) = 0$$

is such an equation. Suppose that the point (a, b) satisfies the equation, and that F has continuous first partial derivatives (and so is differentiable) at all points near (a, b). Can the equation be solved for y as a function of x near (a, b)? That is, does there exist a function $y(x)$ defined in some interval $I = (a - h, a + h)$ (where $h > 0$) satisfying $y(a) = b$ and such that

$$F\Big(x, y(x)\Big) = 0$$

holds for all x in the interval I? If there is such a function $y(x)$ we can try to find its derivative at $x = a$ by differentiating the equation $F(x, y) = 0$ implicitly with respect to x, and evaluating the result at (a, b):

$$F_1(x, y) + F_2(x, y)\frac{dy}{dx} = 0,$$

so that

$$\frac{dy}{dx}\Big|_{x=a} = -\frac{F_1(a, b)}{F_2(a, b)} \qquad \text{provided} \qquad F_2(a, b) \neq 0.$$

Observe, however, that the condition $F_2(a, b) \neq 0$ required for the calculation of $y'(a)$ will itself guarantee that the solution $y(x)$ exists. This condition, together with the differentiability of $F(x, y)$ near (a, b) implies that the level curve $F(x, y) = F(a, b)$ has *nonvertical* tangent lines near (a, b), so some part of the level curve near (a, b) must be the graph of a function of x. This is a special case of the Implicit Function Theorem, which we will state more generally later in this section.

A similar situation holds for equations involving several variables. We may, for example, ask whether the equation

$$F(x, y, z) = 0$$

defines z as a function of x and y (say $z = z(x, y)$) near some point $P_0 = (x_0, y_0, z_0)$ satisfying the equation. If so, and if F has continuous first partials near P_0, then the partial derivatives of z can be found at (x_0, y_0) by implicit differentiation of the equation $F(x, y, z) = 0$ with respect to x and y:

$$F_1(x, y, z) + F_3(x, y, z)\frac{\partial z}{\partial x} = 0, \qquad F_2(x, y, z) + F_3(x, y, z)\frac{\partial z}{\partial y} = 0,$$

so that

$$\frac{\partial z}{\partial x}\bigg|_{(x_0, y_0)} = -\frac{F_1(x_0, y_0, z_0)}{F_3(x_0, y_0, z_0)}, \qquad \frac{\partial z}{\partial y}\bigg|_{(x_0, y_0)} = -\frac{F_2(x_0, y_0, z_0)}{F_3(x_0, y_0, z_0)},$$

provided $F_3(x_0, y_0, z_0) \neq 0$. This condition implies that the level surface of F through P_0 is not vertical (that is, not parallel to the z-axis), and so part of it near P_0 must indeed be the graph of a function $z = z(x, y)$. Similarly, $F(x, y, z) = 0$ can be solved for x as a function of y and z near points where $F_1 \neq 0$, and for $y = y(x, z)$ near points where $F_2 \neq 0$.

EXAMPLE 2.7.1   Let $P_0 = (x_0, y_0, z_0)$ be a point on the sphere

$$F(x, y, z) = x^2 + y^2 + z^2 - 1 = 0.$$

The above equation can be solved for $z = z(x, y)$ near P_0 provided that P_0 is not on the "equator" of the sphere: $x^2 + y^2 = 1$, $z = 0$. Specifically, if P_0 is on the upper hemisphere, then $z = z(x, y) = \sqrt{1 - x^2 - y^2}$ and if P_0 is on the lower hemisphere then $z = z(x, y) = -\sqrt{1 - x^2 - y^2}$. The equator, the set of points P_0 for which such a solution is not possible, satisfies $F_3(x, y, z) = 2z = 0$. If $z \neq 0$, we may calculate the partial derivatives of the solution $z = z(x, y)$ by implicitly differentiating the equation of the sphere: $x^2 + y^2 + z^2 = 1$:

$$2x + 2z\frac{\partial z}{\partial x} = 0, \qquad \text{so} \qquad \frac{\partial z}{\partial x} = -\frac{x}{z},$$

$$2y + 2z\frac{\partial z}{\partial y} = 0, \qquad \text{so} \qquad \frac{\partial z}{\partial y} = -\frac{y}{z}.$$

Systems of Equations

Experience with linear equations shows us that systems of such equations can generally be solved for as many variables as there are equations in the system. We would expect, therefore, that a pair of equations in several variables might determine two of those variables as functions of the remaining ones. For instance we might expect the equations

$$\begin{cases} F(x, y, z, w) = 0 \\ G(x, y, z, w) = 0 \end{cases}$$

to possess, nearby some point satisfying them, solutions of one or more of the forms

$$\begin{cases} x = x(z, w) \\ y = y(z, w), \end{cases} \qquad \begin{cases} x = x(y, w) \\ z = z(y, w), \end{cases} \qquad \begin{cases} x = x(y, z) \\ w = w(y, z), \end{cases}$$

$$\begin{cases} y = y(x, w) \\ z = z(x, w), \end{cases} \qquad \begin{cases} y = y(x, z) \\ w = w(x, z), \end{cases} \qquad \begin{cases} z = z(x, y) \\ w = w(x, y). \end{cases}$$

Where such solutions exist, we should be able to differentiate the given system of equations implicitly to find partial derivatives of the solutions.

If you are given a single equation $F(x, y, z) = 0$ and asked to find $\partial x / \partial z$, you would understand that x is intended to be a function of the remaining variables y and z, so there would be no chance of misinterpreting which variable is to be held constant in calculating the partial derivative. Suppose, however, that you are asked to calculate $\partial x / \partial z$ given the system $F(x, y, z, w) = 0$, $\quad G(x, y, z, w) = 0$. The question implies that x is one of the dependent variables and z is one of the independent variables, but does not imply which of y and w is the other dependent variable and which is the other independent variable. That is, which of the situations

$$\begin{cases} x = x(z, w) \\ y = y(z, w) \end{cases} \qquad \text{and} \qquad \begin{cases} x = x(y, z) \\ w = w(y, z) \end{cases}$$

are we dealing with? As it stands, the question is ambiguous. To avoid this ambiguity we can specify *in the notation for the partial derivative* which variable is to be regarded as the other independent variable and therefore *held fixed* during the differentiation. Thus

$$\left(\frac{\partial x}{\partial z} \right)_w \quad \text{implies the interpretation} \quad \begin{cases} x = x(z, w) \\ y = y(z, w), \end{cases}$$

$$\left(\frac{\partial x}{\partial z} \right)_y \quad \text{implies the interpretation} \quad \begin{cases} x = x(y, z) \\ w = w(y, z). \end{cases}$$

EXAMPLE 2.7.2 Given the equations $F(x, y, z, w) = 0$ and $G(x, y, z, w) = 0$, where F and G have continuous first partial derivatives, calculate $\left(\dfrac{\partial x}{\partial z} \right)_w$.

SOLUTION We differentiate the two equations with respect to z, regarding x and y as functions of z and w, and holding w fixed:

$$F_1 \frac{\partial x}{\partial z} + F_2 \frac{\partial y}{\partial z} + F_3 = 0$$

$$G_1 \frac{\partial x}{\partial z} + G_2 \frac{\partial y}{\partial z} + G_3 = 0$$

(Note that the terms $F_4 \dfrac{\partial w}{\partial z}$ and $G_4 \dfrac{\partial w}{\partial z}$ are not present because w and z are independent variables, and w is being held fixed during the differentiation.) The pair of equations above is linear in $\partial x/\partial z$ and $\partial y/\partial z$. Eliminating $\partial y/\partial z$ (or using Cramer's Rule, Theorem 1.5.10) we obtain

$$\left(\frac{\partial x}{\partial z}\right)_w = -\frac{F_3 G_2 - F_2 G_3}{F_1 G_2 - F_2 G_1}.$$

In the light of the examples considered above, you should not be too surprised to learn that the nonvanishing of the denominator $F_1 G_2 - F_2 G_1$ at some point $P_0 = (x_0, y_0, z_0, w_0)$ satisfying the system $F = 0$, $G = 0$ is sufficient to guarantee that the system does indeed have a solution of the form $x = x(z, w)$, $y = y(z, w)$ near P_0. We will not, however, attempt to prove this fact here.

EXAMPLE 2.7.3   Let x, y, u and v be related by the equations

$$\begin{cases} u = x^2 + xy - y^2 \\ v = 2xy + y^2 \end{cases}$$

Find $(\partial x/\partial u)_v$ and $(\partial x/\partial u)_y$ at the point where $x = 2$ and $y = -1$.

SOLUTION   a) To calculate $(\partial x/\partial u)_v$ we regard x and y as functions of u and v, and differentiate the given equations with respect to u, holding v constant:

$$1 = \frac{\partial u}{\partial u} = (2x + y)\frac{\partial x}{\partial u} + (x - 2y)\frac{\partial y}{\partial u}$$

$$0 = \frac{\partial v}{\partial u} = 2y\frac{\partial x}{\partial u} + (2x + 2y)\frac{\partial y}{\partial u}$$

At $x = 2$, $y = -1$ we have

$$1 = 3\frac{\partial x}{\partial u} + 4\frac{\partial y}{\partial u}$$

$$0 = -2\frac{\partial x}{\partial u} + 2\frac{\partial y}{\partial u}.$$

Eliminating $\partial y/\partial u$ leads to the result $(\partial x/\partial u) = 1/7$.

b) To calculate $(\partial x/\partial u)_y$ we regard x and v as functions of y and u, and differentiate the given equations with respect to u, holding y constant:

$$1 = \frac{\partial u}{\partial u} = (2x + y)\frac{\partial x}{\partial u}$$

$$\frac{\partial v}{\partial u} = 2y\frac{\partial x}{\partial u}.$$

At $x = 2$, $y = -1$ the first equation immediately gives $(\partial x/\partial u)_y = 1/3$.

It often happens that the independent variables in a problem are either clear from the context or can be chosen at the outset. In either case, ambiguity is not likely to occur and we can safely omit subscripts showing which variables are being held constant. The following example is taken from the thermodynamics of ideal gases.

EXAMPLE 2.7.4   *Reversible changes in an ideal gas:* The state of a closed system containing n moles of an ideal gas is characterized by three state variables, pressure, volume and temperature (P, V and T respectively), which satisfy the equation of state for an ideal gas:

$$PV = nRT,$$

where R is a universal constant. The internal energy, E, and the entropy, S, of the system are thermodynamic quantities which depend on the state variables and hence may be expressed as functions of any two of P, V and T. Let us choose T and V for the independent variables and so write $E = E(V,T)$ and $S = S(V,T)$. For reversible processes in the system, the first and second laws of thermodynamics imply that infinitesimal changes in these quantities satisfy the differential equation

$$T\,dS = dE + P\,dV.$$

Deduce that for such processes, E is independent of V and so depends only on the temperature T.

SOLUTION   We calculate the differentials dS and dE and substitute them into the differential equation to obtain

$$T\left(\frac{\partial S}{\partial V}\,dV + \frac{\partial S}{\partial T}\,dT\right) = \frac{\partial E}{\partial V}\,dV + \frac{\partial E}{\partial T}\,dT + P\,dV.$$

Divide by T, substitute nR/V for P/T (from the equation of state), and collect coefficients of dV and dT on opposite sides of the equation to get

$$\left(\frac{\partial S}{\partial V} - \frac{1}{T}\frac{\partial E}{\partial V} - \frac{nR}{V}\right)dV = \left(\frac{1}{T}\frac{\partial E}{\partial T} - \frac{\partial S}{\partial T}\right)dT.$$

Since dV and dT are independent variables, both coefficients must vanish. Hence

$$\frac{\partial S}{\partial V} = \frac{1}{T}\frac{\partial E}{\partial V} + \frac{nR}{V}$$
$$\frac{\partial S}{\partial T} = \frac{1}{T}\frac{\partial E}{\partial T}.$$

Now differentiate the first of these equations with respect to T and the second with respect to V. Using equality of mixed partials for both S and E, we obtain the desired result:

$$\frac{\partial}{\partial T}\left(\frac{1}{T}\frac{\partial E}{\partial V} + \frac{nR}{V}\right) = \frac{\partial^2 S}{\partial T\,\partial V} = \frac{\partial^2 S}{\partial V\,\partial T} = \frac{\partial}{\partial V}\left(\frac{1}{T}\frac{\partial E}{\partial T}\right),$$

$$\frac{-1}{T^2}\frac{\partial E}{\partial V} + \frac{1}{T}\frac{\partial^2 E}{\partial T\,\partial V} = \frac{1}{T}\frac{\partial^2 E}{\partial V\,\partial T},$$

$$\frac{-1}{T^2}\frac{\partial E}{\partial V} = 0.$$

It follows that $\partial E/\partial V = 0$ and so E is independent of V.

Jacobian Determinants

Partial derivatives obtained by implicit differentiation of systems of equations are fractions, the numerators and denominators of which are conveniently expressed in terms of certain determinants called Jacobians.

2.7.5
Jacobian
Determinants

The **Jacobian** of two functions, $u = u(x, y)$ and $v = v(x, y)$, with respect to two variables, x and y, is the determinant

$$\frac{\partial(u, v)}{\partial(x, y)} = \begin{vmatrix} \dfrac{\partial u}{\partial x} & \dfrac{\partial u}{\partial y} \\ \dfrac{\partial v}{\partial x} & \dfrac{\partial v}{\partial y} \end{vmatrix}.$$

Similarly, the Jacobian of two functions, $F(x, y)$ and $G(x, y)$, with respect to the variables, x and y, is the determinant

$$\frac{\partial(F, G)}{\partial(x, y)} = \begin{vmatrix} \dfrac{\partial F}{\partial x} & \dfrac{\partial F}{\partial y} \\ \dfrac{\partial G}{\partial x} & \dfrac{\partial G}{\partial y} \end{vmatrix} = \begin{vmatrix} F_1 & F_2 \\ G_1 & G_2 \end{vmatrix}.$$

The definition above can be extended in the obvious way to give the Jacobian of n functions (or variables) with respect to n variables. For example the Jacobian of three functions, F, G and H, with respect to three variables, x, y and z, is the determinant

$$\frac{\partial(F, G, H)}{\partial(x, y, z)} = \begin{vmatrix} F_1 & F_2 & F_3 \\ G_1 & G_2 & G_3 \\ H_1 & H_2 & H_3 \end{vmatrix}.$$

In terms of Jacobians, the value of $(\partial x/\partial z)_w$, obtained from the system of equations

$$F(x, y, z, w) = 0, \qquad G(x, y, z, w) = 0$$

in Example 2.7.2, can be expressed in the form

$$\left(\frac{\partial x}{\partial z} \right)_w = - \frac{\dfrac{\partial(F, G)}{\partial(z, y)}}{\dfrac{\partial(F, G)}{\partial(x, y)}}.$$

Observe the pattern here. The denominator is the Jacobian of F and G with respect to the two *dependent* variables, x and y. The numerator is the same Jacobian except that the dependent variable x is replaced with the independent variable z.

The pattern observed above is general. Given n equations in $n + m$ variables

$$\begin{cases} F_{(1)}(x_1, x_2, \ldots, x_m, y_1, y_2, \ldots, y_n) = 0 \\ F_{(2)}(x_1, x_2, \ldots, x_m, y_1, y_2, \ldots, y_n) = 0 \\ \quad \vdots \\ F_{(n)}(x_1, x_2, \ldots, x_m, y_1, y_2, \ldots, y_n) = 0 \end{cases}$$

we can calculate, for instance,

$$\left(\frac{\partial y_i}{\partial x_j} \right)_{x_1, \ldots, x_{j-1}, x_{j+1}, \ldots, x_m} = -\frac{\dfrac{\partial(F_{(1)}, F_{(2)}, \ldots, F_{(n)})}{\partial(y_1, \ldots, x_j, \ldots, y_n)}}{\dfrac{\partial(F_{(1)}, F_{(2)}, \ldots, F_{(n)})}{\partial(y_1, \ldots, y_i, \ldots, y_n)}}.$$

This is a consequence of Cramer's Rule (Theorem 1.5.10) applied to the n linear equations in the n unknowns $\partial y_1/\partial x_j, \ldots, \partial y_n/\partial x_j$ obtained by differentiating each of the equations in the given system with respect to x_j.

EXAMPLE 2.7.6   If the equations

$$x = u^2 + v^2, \qquad y = uv$$

are solved for u and v in terms of x and y find, where possible,

$$\frac{\partial u}{\partial x}, \quad \frac{\partial u}{\partial y}, \quad \frac{\partial v}{\partial x}, \quad \frac{\partial v}{\partial y}.$$

Hence show that

$$\frac{\partial(u, v)}{\partial(x, y)} = \frac{1}{\dfrac{\partial(x, y)}{\partial(u, v)}}$$

provided the denominator does not vanish.

SOLUTION   The given equations can be rewritten in the form

$$F(u, v, x, y) = u^2 + v^2 - x = 0$$
$$G(u, v, x, y) = uv - y = 0.$$

Let

$$J = \frac{\partial(F, G)}{\partial(u, v)} = \begin{vmatrix} 2u & 2v \\ v & u \end{vmatrix} = 2(u^2 - v^2) = \frac{\partial(x, y)}{\partial(u, v)}.$$

If $u^2 \neq v^2$, then $J \neq 0$ and we can calculate the required partial derivatives:

$$\frac{\partial u}{\partial x} = -\frac{1}{J} \frac{\partial(F, G)}{\partial(x, v)} = -\frac{1}{J} \begin{vmatrix} -1 & 2v \\ 0 & u \end{vmatrix} = \frac{u}{2(u^2 - v^2)}$$

$$\frac{\partial u}{\partial y} = -\frac{1}{J} \frac{\partial(F, G)}{\partial(y, v)} = -\frac{1}{J} \begin{vmatrix} 0 & 2v \\ -1 & u \end{vmatrix} = \frac{-2v}{2(u^2 - v^2)}$$

$$\frac{\partial v}{\partial x} = -\frac{1}{J} \frac{\partial(F, G)}{\partial(u, x)} = -\frac{1}{J} \begin{vmatrix} 2u & -1 \\ v & 0 \end{vmatrix} = \frac{-v}{2(u^2 - v^2)}$$

$$\frac{\partial v}{\partial y} = -\frac{1}{J} \frac{\partial(F, G)}{\partial(u, y)} = -\frac{1}{J} \begin{vmatrix} 2u & 0 \\ v & -1 \end{vmatrix} = \frac{2u}{2(u^2 - v^2)}.$$

Thus

$$\frac{\partial(u,v)}{\partial(x,y)} = \frac{1}{J^2}\begin{vmatrix} u & -2v \\ -v & 2u \end{vmatrix} = \frac{1}{J} = \frac{1}{\dfrac{\partial(x,y)}{\partial(u,v)}}.$$

REMARK: Note in the above example that $\partial u/\partial x \neq \dfrac{1}{\partial x/\partial u}$. This should be contrasted with the single-variable situation where, if $y = f(x)$ and $dy/dx \neq 0$ then $x = f^{-1}(y)$ and $dx/dy = \dfrac{1}{dy/dx}$. This is another reason for distinguishing between "∂" and "d". It is the Jacobian rather than any single partial derivative which takes the place of the ordinary derivative in such situations.

REMARK: Let us look briefly at the general case of invertible transformations from $\mathbb{R}^n$ to $\mathbb{R}^n$. Suppose that $\mathbf{y} = \mathbf{F(x)}$ and $\mathbf{z} = \mathbf{G(y)}$ are both functions from $\mathbb{R}^n$ to $\mathbb{R}^n$ (that is, both n-vector functions of an n-vector variable) whose components have continuous first partial derivatives. Separate applications of the Chain Rule for each of the partial derivatives $\partial z_i/\partial x_j$, $i,j = 1,\ldots,n$ show that

$$\begin{pmatrix} \dfrac{\partial z_1}{\partial x_1} & \cdots & \dfrac{\partial z_1}{\partial x_n} \\ \vdots & \ddots & \vdots \\ \dfrac{\partial z_n}{\partial x_1} & \cdots & \dfrac{\partial z_n}{\partial x_n} \end{pmatrix} = \begin{pmatrix} \dfrac{\partial z_1}{\partial y_1} & \cdots & \dfrac{\partial z_1}{\partial y_n} \\ \vdots & \ddots & \vdots \\ \dfrac{\partial z_n}{\partial y_1} & \cdots & \dfrac{\partial z_n}{\partial y_n} \end{pmatrix} \begin{pmatrix} \dfrac{\partial y_1}{\partial x_1} & \cdots & \dfrac{\partial y_1}{\partial x_n} \\ \vdots & \ddots & \vdots \\ \dfrac{\partial y_n}{\partial x_1} & \cdots & \dfrac{\partial y_n}{\partial x_n} \end{pmatrix}.$$

(This is just the Chain Rule for the composition $\mathbf{z} = \mathbf{G(F(x))}$. It follows from Theorem 1.5.6 that the determinants of these matrices satisfy a similar equation:

$$\frac{\partial(z_1 \cdots z_n)}{\partial(x_1 \cdots x_n)} = \frac{\partial(z_1 \cdots z_n)}{\partial(y_1 \cdots y_n)} \frac{\partial(y_1 \cdots y_n)}{\partial(x_1 \cdots x_n)}.$$

If $\mathbf{F}$ is one-to-one and $\mathbf{G}$ is the inverse of $\mathbf{F}$, then $\mathbf{z} = \mathbf{G(F(x))} = \mathbf{x}$, and $\partial(z_1 \cdots z_n)/\partial(x_1 \cdots x_n) = 1$, the determinant of the identity matrix. Thus

$$\frac{\partial(x_1 \cdots x_n)}{\partial(y_1 \cdots y_n)} = \frac{1}{\dfrac{\partial(y_1 \cdots y_n)}{\partial(x_1 \cdots x_n)}}.$$

In fact, the nonvanishing of either of these determinants is sufficient to guarantee that $\mathbf{F}$ is one-to-one and so has an inverse. This is a special case of the Implicit Function Theorem stated below.

We will encounter Jacobians again when we study transformations of coordinates in multiple integrals in Chapter 4.

The Implicit Function Theorem

The Implicit Function Theorem guarantees that systems of equations can be solved for certain variables as functions of other variables under certain circumstances. Before stating it we consider a simple illustrative example.

EXAMPLE 2.7.7 Consider the system of linear equations

$$F(x, y, s, t) = a_1 x + b_1 y + c_1 s + d_1 t + e_1 = 0$$
$$G(x, y, s, t) = a_2 x + b_2 y + c_2 s + d_2 t + e_2 = 0.$$

This system can be written in matrix form:

$$\mathcal{A}\begin{pmatrix} x \\ y \end{pmatrix} + C\begin{pmatrix} s \\ t \end{pmatrix} + \mathcal{E} = \begin{pmatrix} 0 \\ 0 \end{pmatrix},$$

where

$$\mathcal{A} = \begin{pmatrix} a_1 & b_1 \\ a_2 & b_2 \end{pmatrix}, \qquad C = \begin{pmatrix} c_1 & d_1 \\ c_2 & d_2 \end{pmatrix}, \quad \text{and} \quad \mathcal{E} = \begin{pmatrix} e_1 \\ e_2 \end{pmatrix}.$$

The equations can be solved for x and y as functions of s and t provided $\det(\mathcal{A}) \neq 0$, for this implies the existence of the inverse matrix $\mathcal{A}^{-1}$ (Theorem 1.5.7), so

$$\begin{pmatrix} x \\ y \end{pmatrix} = -\mathcal{A}^{-1}\left(C\begin{pmatrix} s \\ t \end{pmatrix} + \mathcal{E}\right).$$

Observe that $\det(\mathcal{A}) = \dfrac{\partial(F, G)}{\partial(x, y)}$, so the nonvanishing of this Jacobian guarantees that the equations can be solved for x and y.

We conclude this section with a statement, without proof, of a general form of the Implicit Function Theorem.

THEOREM 2.7.8 *(The Implicit Function Theorem)* Consider a system of n equations in $n + m$ variables,

$$\begin{cases} F_{(1)}(x_1, x_2, \ldots, x_m, y_1, y_2, \ldots, y_n) = 0 \\ F_{(2)}(x_1, x_2, \ldots, x_m, y_1, y_2, \ldots, y_n) = 0 \\ \quad\vdots \\ F_{(n)}(x_1, x_2, \ldots, x_m, y_1, y_2, \ldots, y_n) = 0, \end{cases}$$

and a point $P_0 = (a_1, a_2, \ldots, a_m, b_1, b_2, \ldots, b_n)$ satisfying the system. Suppose each of the functions $F_{(i)}$ has continuous first partial derivatives with respect to each of the variables x_j and y_k, $(i = 1, \ldots, n, \ j = 1, \ldots, m, \ k = 1, \ldots, n)$, near P_0. Finally, suppose that

$$\left.\frac{\partial(F_{(1)}, F_{(2)}, \ldots, F_{(n)})}{\partial(y_1, y_2, \ldots, y_n)}\right|_{P_0} \neq 0.$$

Then the system can be solved for $y_1, y_2, \ldots, y_n$ as functions of $x_1, x_2, \ldots, x_m$ near P_0. That is, there exist functions

$$\phi_1(x_1, \ldots, x_m), \ldots, \phi_n(x_1, \ldots, x_m)$$

such that

$$\phi_j(a_1, \ldots, a_m) = b_j, \qquad (j = 1, \ldots, n),$$

and such that the equations

$$F_{(1)}\Big(x_1,\ldots,x_m,\phi_1(x_1,\ldots,x_m),\ldots,\phi_n(x_1,\ldots,x_m)\Big)=0,$$
$$F_{(2)}\Big(x_1,\ldots,x_m,\phi_1(x_1,\ldots,x_m),\ldots,\phi_n(x_1,\ldots,x_m)\Big)=0,$$
$$\vdots$$
$$F_{(n)}\Big(x_1,\ldots,x_m,\phi_1(x_1,\ldots,x_m),\ldots,\phi_n(x_1,\ldots,x_m)\Big)=0,$$

hold for all $(x_1,\ldots,x_m)$ sufficiently near $(a_1,\ldots,a_m)$.

EXERCISES

In Exercises 1–12 calculate the indicated derivative from the given equation(s). What condition on the variables will guarantee the existence of a solution having the indicated derivative? Assume any general functions F, G, H appearing have continuous first partial derivatives.

1. $\dfrac{dx}{dy}$ if $xy^3 + x^4y = 2$

2. $\dfrac{\partial x}{\partial y}$ if $xy^3 = y - z$

3. $\dfrac{\partial z}{\partial y}$ if $z^2 + xy^3 = \dfrac{xz}{y}$

4. $\dfrac{\partial y}{\partial z}$ if $e^{yz} - x^2z \ln y = \pi$

5. $\dfrac{\partial x}{\partial w}$ if $x^2y^2 + y^2z^2 + z^2t^2 + t^2w^2 - xw = 0$

6. $\dfrac{dy}{dx}$ if $F(x, y, x^2 - y^2) = 0$

7. $\dfrac{\partial u}{\partial x}$ if $G(x, y, z, u, v) = 0$

8. $\dfrac{\partial z}{\partial x}$ if $F(x^2 - z^2, y^2 + xz) = 0$

9. $\dfrac{\partial w}{\partial t}$ if $H(u^2w, v^2t, wt) = 0$

10. $\left(\dfrac{\partial y}{\partial x}\right)_u$ if $xyuv = 1$ and $x + y + u + v = 0$

11. $\left(\dfrac{\partial x}{\partial y}\right)_z$ if $x^2 + y^2 + z^2 + w^2 = 1$, and $x + 2y + 3z + 4w = 2$

12. $\dfrac{du}{dx}$ if $x^2y + y^2u - u^3 = 0$ and $x^2 + yu = 1$

13. If $x = u^3 + v^3$ and $y = uv - v^2$ are solved for u and v in terms of x and y evaluate

$$\frac{\partial u}{\partial x},\quad \frac{\partial u}{\partial y},\quad \frac{\partial v}{\partial x},\quad \frac{\partial v}{\partial y},\quad \text{and}\quad \frac{\partial(u,v)}{\partial(x,y)}$$

at the point where $u = 1$ and $v = 1$.

14. Near what points (r, s) can the transformation

$$x = r^2 + 2s,\quad y = s^2 - 2r$$

be solved for r and s as functions of x and y? Calculate the values of the first partial derivatives of the solution at the origin.

15. Evaluate the Jacobian $\partial(x, y)/\partial(r, \theta)$ for the transformation to polar coordinates: $x = r\cos\theta$, $y = r\sin\theta$. Near what points (r, θ) is the transformation one-to-one and therefore invertible to give r and θ as functions of x and y?

16. Evaluate the Jacobian $\partial(x, y, z)/\partial(\rho, \phi, \theta)$ where

$$x = \rho\sin\phi\cos\theta,\qquad y = \rho\sin\phi\sin\theta,\qquad z = \rho\cos\phi.$$

This is the transformation from Cartesian to spherical polar coordinates in 3-space which we will be considering in Section 4.5. Near what points is the transformation one-to-one and hence invertible to give ρ, ϕ and θ as functions of x, y and z?

17. Find dx/dy from the system

$$F(x, y, z, w) = 0,\quad G(x, y, z, w) = 0,\quad H(x, y, z, w) = 0.$$

18. Given the system

$$F(x, y, z, u, v) = 0$$
$$G(x, y, z, u, v) = 0$$
$$H(x, y, z, u, v) = 0,$$

how many possible interpretations are there for $\partial x/\partial y$? Evaluate them.

19. Given the system

$$F(x_1, x_2, \ldots, x_8) = 0$$
$$G(x_1, x_2, \ldots, x_8) = 0$$
$$H(x_1, x_2, \ldots, x_8) = 0,$$

how many possible interpretations are there for the partial $\partial x_1/\partial x_2$? Evaluate $\left(\partial x_1/\partial x_2\right)_{x_4, x_6, x_7, x_8}$.

20. If $F(x, y, z) = 0$ determines z as a function of x and y calculate $\partial^2 z/\partial x^2$, $\partial^2 z/\partial x \partial y$ and $\partial^2 z/\partial y^2$ in terms of the partial derivatives of F.

21. If $x = u+v$, $y = uv$ and $z = u^2+v^2$ define z as a function of x and y, find $\partial z/\partial x$, $\partial z/\partial y$ and $\partial^2 z/\partial x \partial y$.

22. A certain gas satisfies the law

$$pV = T - \frac{4p}{T^2},$$

where p = pressure, V = volume, and T = temperature.

a) Calculate $\dfrac{\partial T}{\partial p}$ and $\dfrac{\partial T}{\partial V}$ at the point where $p = V = 1$ and $T = 2$.

b) If measurements of p and V yield the values $p = 1 \pm 0.001$ and $V = 1 \pm 0.002$, find the approximate maximum error in the calculated value $T = 2$.

23. If $F(x, y, z) = 0$ show that

$$\left(\frac{\partial x}{\partial y}\right)_z \left(\frac{\partial y}{\partial z}\right)_x \left(\frac{\partial z}{\partial x}\right)_y = -1.$$

Derive analogous results for $F(x, y, z, u) = 0$ and for $F(x, y, z, u, v) = 0$. What is the general case?

24.*If the equations $F(x, y, u, v) = 0$ and $G(x, y, u, v) = 0$ are solved for x and y as functions of u and v show that

$$\frac{\partial(x, y)}{\partial(u, v)} = \frac{\partial(F, G)}{\partial(u, v)} \bigg/ \frac{\partial(F, G)}{\partial(x, y)}.$$

25.*If the equations $x = f(u, v)$, $y = g(u, v)$ can be solved for u and v in terms of x and y show that

$$\frac{\partial(u, v)}{\partial(x, y)} = 1 \bigg/ \frac{\partial(x, y)}{\partial(u, v)}.$$

(Hint: use the result of the previous exercise.)

26.*If $x = f(u, v)$, $y = g(u, v)$, $u = h(r, s)$ and $v = k(r, s)$ then x and y can be expressed as functions of r and s. Verify by direct calculation that

$$\frac{\partial(x, y)}{\partial(r, s)} = \frac{\partial(x, y)}{\partial(u, v)} \frac{\partial(u, v)}{\partial(r, s)}.$$

This is a special case of the Chain Rule for Jacobians.

27.*Two functions, $f(x, y)$ and $g(x, y)$, are said to be functionally dependent if one is a function of the other; that is, if there exists a single-variable function $k(t)$ such that $f(x, y) = k\left(g(x, y)\right)$ for all x and y. Show that in this case $\partial(f, g)/\partial(x, y)$ vanishes identically. Assume all necessary derivatives exist.

28.*Prove the converse of the previous exercise as follows: Let $u = f(x, y)$ and $v = g(x, y)$, and suppose that $\partial(u, v)/\partial(x, y) = \partial(f, g)/\partial(x, y)$ is identically zero for all x and y. Show that $(\partial u/\partial x)_v$ is identically zero. Hence u, considered as a function of x and v, is independent of x; that is, $u = k(v)$ for some function k of one variable. Why does this imply that f and g are functionally dependent?

2.8 TAYLOR SERIES AND APPROXIMATIONS

As is the case for functions of one variable, power series representations and their partial sums (Taylor polynomials) can provide an efficient method for determining the behavior of a smooth function of several variables near a point in its domain. In this section we shall look briefly at the extension of Taylor series to such functions. As usual we will develop the machinery for functions of two variables but the extension to more variables will be obvious.

As a starting point, recall Taylor's formula for a function $F(x)$ with continuous partial derivatives of order up to $n+1$ on the interval $[a, a+h]$:

$$F(a+h) = F(a) + F'(a)h + \frac{F''(a)}{2!}h^2 + \cdots + \frac{F^{(n)}(a)}{n!}h^n + \frac{F^{(n+1)}(X)}{(n+1)!}h^{n+1},$$

where X is some number between a and $a+h$. (The last term in the formula is the *Lagrange* form of the remainder.) In the special case where $a = 0$ and $h = 1$, this formula becomes

$$F(1) = F(0) + F'(0) + \frac{F''(0)}{2!} + \cdots + \frac{F^{(n)}(0)}{n!} + \frac{F^{(n+1)}(\theta)}{(n+1)!}$$

for some θ between 0 and 1.

Now suppose that $f(x, y)$ has continuous partial derivatives up to order $n+1$ at all points nearby the line segment joining the points (a, b) and $(a+h, b+k)$ in its domain. We can find the Taylor Formula for $f(a+h, b+k)$ in powers of h and k by applying the one-variable formula above to the function

$$F(t) = f(a+th, b+tk), \qquad 0 \le t \le 1.$$

Clearly $F(0) = f(a, b)$ and $F(1) = f(a+h, b+k)$. Let us calculate some derivatives of F:

$$F'(t) = hf_1(a+th, b+tk) + kf_2(a+th, b+tk),$$
$$F''(t) = h^2 f_{11}(a+th, b+tk) + 2hkf_{12}(a+th, b+tk) + k^2 f_{22}(a+th, b+tk),$$
$$F'''(t) = \left(h^3 f_{111} + 3h^2 k f_{112} + 3hk^2 f_{122} + k^3 f_{222} \right)\Big|_{(a+th, b+tk)}.$$

The pattern of binomial coefficients is pretty obvious here, but the notation, involving subscripts to denote partial derivatives of f, gets more and more unwieldy for higher derivatives. The notation can be simplified greatly by using $D_1 f$ and $D_2 f$ to denote the first partials of f with respect to its first and second variables. Since h and k are constant, and mixed partials commute ($D_1 D_2 f = D_2 D_1 f$), we have

$$(h^2 D_1^2 f + 2hk D_1 D_2 f + k^2 D_2^2 f = (hD_1 + kD_2)^2 f,$$

and so on. Therefore

$$F'(t) = \left(hD_1 + kD_2 \right) f(a+th, b+tk),$$
$$F''(t) = \left(hD_1 + kD_2 \right)^2 f(a+th, b+tk),$$
$$F'''(t) = \left(hD_1 + kD_2 \right)^3 f(a+th, b+tk),$$
$$\vdots$$
$$F^{(m)}(t) = \left(hD_1 + kD_2 \right)^m f(a+th, b+tk).$$

In particular, $F^{(m)}(0) = (hD_1 + kD_2)^m f(a,b)$. Hence the Taylor formula for $f(a+h,b+k)$ is

$$f(a+h,b+k) = \sum_{m=0}^{n} \frac{1}{m!} (hD_1 + kD_2)^m f(a,b) + R_n(h,k)$$

$$= \sum_{m=0}^{n} \sum_{j=0}^{m} C_{mj} D_1^j D_2^{m-j} f(a,b) \, h^j \, k^{m-j} + R_n(h,k),$$

where, using the binomial expansion, we have

$$C_{mj} = \frac{1}{m!} \binom{m}{j} = \frac{1}{m!} \frac{m!}{j!(m-j)!} = \frac{1}{j!(m-j)!},$$

and where the remainder term is given by

$$R_n(h,k) = \frac{1}{(n+1)!} (hD_1 + kD_2)^{n+1} f(a+\theta h, b+\theta k)$$

for some θ between 0 and 1. If f has partial derivatives of all orders and

$$\lim_{n\to\infty} R_n(h,k) = 0,$$

then $f(a+h,b+k)$ can be expressed as a Taylor series in powers of h and k:

$$f(a+h,b+k) = \sum_{m=0}^{\infty} \sum_{j=0}^{m} \frac{1}{j!(m-j)!} D_1^j D_2^{m-j} f(a,b) \, h^j \, k^{m-j}.$$

As for functions of one variable, the Taylor polynomial of degree n:

$$P_n(x,y) = \sum_{m=0}^{n} \sum_{j=0}^{m} \frac{1}{j!(m-j)!} D_1^j D_2^{m-j} f(a,b) (x-a)^j (y-b)^{m-j},$$

provides the "best" nth degree polynomial approximation for $f(x,y)$ near (a,b). For $n = 1$ this approximation reduces to the tangent plane approximation

$$f(x,y) \approx f(a,b) + f_1(a,b)(x-a) + f_2(a,b)(y-b).$$

EXAMPLE 2.8.1 Find a second degree approximation to $f(x,y) = \sqrt{x^2 + y^3}$ near the point $(1,2)$ and use it to estimate the value of $\sqrt{(1.02)^2 + (1.97)^3}$.

SOLUTION   For the second degree approximation we need the values of the partial derivatives of f up to second order at (1,2). We have

$$f(x, y) = \sqrt{x^2 + y^3} \qquad\qquad f(1, 2) = 3$$

$$f_1(x, y) = \frac{x}{\sqrt{x^2 + y^3}} \qquad\qquad f_1(1, 2) = \frac{1}{3}$$

$$f_2(x, y) = \frac{3y^2}{2\sqrt{x^2 + y^3}} \qquad\qquad f_2(1, 2) = 2$$

$$f_{11}(x, y) = \frac{y^3}{(x^2 + y^3)^{3/2}} \qquad\qquad f_{11}(1, 2) = \frac{8}{27}$$

$$f_{12}(x, y) = \frac{-3xy^2}{2(x^2 + y^3)^{3/2}} \qquad\qquad f_{12}(1, 2) = -\frac{2}{9}$$

$$f_{22}(x, y) = \frac{12x^2 y + 3y^4}{4(x^2 + y^3)^{3/2}} \qquad\qquad f_{22}(1, 2) = \frac{2}{3}.$$

Thus

$$f(1 + h, 2 + k) = 3 + \frac{1}{3}h + 2k + \frac{1}{2!}\left(\frac{8}{27}h^2 + 2(-\frac{2}{9})hk + \frac{2}{3}k^2\right)$$

or, setting $x = 1 + h$ and $y = 2 + k$,

$$f(x, y) = 3 + \frac{1}{3}(x - 1) + 2(y - 2) + \frac{4}{27}(x - 1)^2 - \frac{2}{9}(x - 1)(y - 2) + \frac{1}{3}(y - 2)^2.$$

This is the required second degree Taylor polynomial for f near (1,2). Therefore

$$\sqrt{(1.02)^2 + (1.97)^3} = f(1 + .02, 2 - .03)$$

$$\approx 3 + \frac{1}{3}(.02) + 2(-.03) + \frac{4}{27}(.02)^2 - \frac{2}{9}(.02)(-.03)$$

$$+ \frac{1}{3}(-.03)^2$$

$$\approx 2.9471593 \,.$$

(For comparison purposes: the true value is $2.9471636\cdots$. The approximation is accurate to six significant figures.)

As observed for functions of one variable, one does not usually have to calculate derivatives in order to determine coefficients in a Taylor series or Taylor polynomial. It is often much easier to perform algebraic manipulations on known series. For instance, the above example could have been done by writing f in the form

$$f(1 + h, 2 + k) = \sqrt{(1 + h)^2 + (2 + k)^3}$$

$$= \sqrt{9 + 2h + h^2 + 12k + 6k^2 + k^3}$$

$$= 3\sqrt{1 + \frac{2h + h^2 + 12k + 6k^2 + k^3}{9}}$$

and then applying the binomial expansion

$$\sqrt{1 + t} = 1 + \frac{1}{2}t + \frac{1}{2!}\left(\frac{1}{2}\right)\left(-\frac{1}{2}\right)t^2 + \cdots$$

to obtain the terms up to second degree in h and k.

EXAMPLE 2.8.2 Find the Taylor polynomial of degree 3 for the function $f(x, y) = e^{x-2y}$ in powers of x and y.

SOLUTION The required Taylor polynomial will be the Taylor polynomial of degree 3 for e^t evaluated at $t = x - 2y$:

$$P_3(x, y) = 1 + (x - 2y) + \frac{1}{2!}(x - 2y)^2 + \frac{1}{3!}(x - 2y)^3$$

$$= 1 + x - 2y + \frac{1}{2}x^2 - 2xy + 2y^2 + \frac{1}{6}x^3 - x^2y + 2xy^2 - \frac{4}{3}y^3.$$

Approximating Implicit Functions

In the previous section we saw how to determine whether an equation in several variables could be solved for one of those variables as a function of the others. Even when such a solution is known to exist, it is not usually possible to find an exact formula for it. However, where the equation involves only smooth functions, the solution will have a Taylor series. We can determine at least the first several coefficients in that series, and thus obtain a useful approximation to the solution. The following example shows the technique.

EXAMPLE 2.8.3 Show that the equation

$$\sin(x + y) = xy + 2x$$

has a solution of the form $y = f(x)$ near $x = 0$ satisfying $f(0) = 0$, and find the terms up to fourth degree for the Taylor series for $f(x)$ in powers of x.

SOLUTION The given equation can be written in the form $F(x, y) = 0$, where

$$F(x, y) = \sin(x + y) - xy - 2x.$$

Since $F(0, 0) = 0$ and $F_2(0, 0) = \cos(0) - 0 = 1$, the equation has a solution $y = f(x)$ near $x = 0$ satisfying $f(0) = 0$ by the implicit function theorem. It is not possible to calculate $f(x)$ exactly, but it will have a Maclaurin series of the form

$$y = f(x) = a_1 x + a_2 x^2 + a_3 x^3 + a_4 x^4 + \cdots.$$

(There is no constant term because $f(0) = 0$.) We can substitute this series into the given equation and keep track of terms up to degree 4 in order to calculate the coefficients a_1, a_2, a_3 and a_4. For the left hand side we use the Maclaurin series for sin to obtain

$$\sin(x + y) = \sin\left((1 + a_1)x + a_2 x^2 + a_3 x^3 + a_4 x^4 + \cdots\right)$$

$$= (1 + a_1)x + a_2 x^2 + a_3 x^3 + a_4 x^4 + \cdots$$

$$- \frac{1}{3!}\left((1 + a_1)x + a_2 x^2 + \cdots\right)^3 + \cdots$$

$$= (1 + a_1)x + a_2 x^2 + \left(a_3 - \frac{1}{6}(1 + a_1)^3\right)x^3$$

$$+ \left(a_4 - \frac{3}{6}(1 + a_1)^2 a_2\right)x^4 + \cdots.$$

The right hand side is

$$xy + 2x = 2x + a_1 x^2 + a_2 x^3 + a_3 x^4 + \cdots.$$

Equating coefficients of like powers of x we obtain

$$
\begin{aligned}
1 + a_1 &= 2 & a_1 &= 1 \\
a_2 &= a_1 & a_2 &= 1 \\
a_3 - \frac{1}{6}(1 + a_1)^3 &= a_2 & a_3 &= \frac{7}{3} \\
a_4 - \frac{1}{2}(1 + a_1)^2 a_2 &= a_3 & a_4 &= \frac{13}{3}.
\end{aligned}
$$

Thus

$$y = f(x) = x + x^2 + \frac{7}{3}x^3 + \frac{13}{3}x^4 + \cdots.$$

(We could have obtained more terms in the series by keeping track of higher powers of x in the substitution process.)

REMARK: From the series for $f(x)$ obtained above we can determine the values of the first four derivatives of f at $x = 0$. Remember that

$$a_k = \frac{f^{(k)}(0)}{k!}.$$

We have therefore

$$
\begin{aligned}
f'(0) &= a_1 = 1 & f''(0) &= 2!a_2 = 2 \\
f'''(0) &= 3!a_3 = 14 & f^{(4)}(0) &= 4!a_4 = 104.
\end{aligned}
$$

We could have done the example by first calculating these derivatives by implicit differentiation of the given equation and then determined the series coefficients from them. This would have been much the more difficult way to do it. (Try it and see.)

EXERCISES

In Exercises 1–6 find the Taylor series for the given function about the indicated point.

1. $f(x, y) = \dfrac{1}{2 + xy^2};\quad (0,0)$

2. $f(x, y) = \ln(1 + x + y + xy);\quad (0,0)$

3. $f(x, y) = \tan^{-1}(x + xy);\quad (0, -1)$

4. $f(x, y) = x^2 + xy + y^3;\quad (1, -1)$

5. $f(x, y) = e^{x^2 + y^2};\quad (0,0)$

6. $f(x, y) = \sin(2x + 3y);\quad (0,0)$

In Exercises 7–12 find Taylor polynomials of the indicated degree for the given functions near the given point.

7. $f(x, y) = \dfrac{1}{2 + x - 2y}$, degree 3, near $(2,1)$

8. $f(x, y) = \ln(x^2 + y^2)$, degree 3, near $(1,0)$

9. $f(x, y) = \displaystyle\int_0^{x+y^2} e^{-t^2}\, dt$, degree 3, near $(0,0)$

10. $f(x, y) = \cos(x + \sin y)$, degree 4, near $(0,0)$

11. $f(x,y) = \dfrac{\sin x}{y}$, degree 2, near $(\frac{\pi}{2}, 1)$

12. $f(x,y) = \dfrac{1+x}{1+x^2+y^4}$, degree 2, near $(0,0)$

In Exercises 13–16 show that the given equation has a solution of the form $y = f(x)$ for x near the indicated point $x = a$, and taking on the indicated value at that point. Find the first three nonzero terms of the Taylor series for $f(x)$ in powers of $x - a$.

13.*$x \sin y = y + \sin x$, near $x = 0$, with $f(0) = 0$

14.*$e^{x+y-1} = 2y + 1$, near $x = 1$, with $f(1) = 0$

15.*$\ln(x^2 + y^2) = y - 1$, near $x = 0$, with $f(0) = 1$

16.*$\sqrt{1 + xy} = 1 + x + \ln(1 + y)$, near $x = 0$, with $f(0) = 0$

17.*Show that the equation $x + 2y + z + e^{2z} = 1$ has a solution of the form $z = f(x,y)$ near $x = 0$, $y = 0$, where $f(0,0) = 0$. Find the Taylor polynomial of degree 2 for $f(x,y)$ in powers of x and y.

18.*Use series methods to find the value of the partial derivative $f_{112}(0,0)$ given that $f(x,y) = \tan^{-1}(x+y)$.

19.*Use series methods to evaluate

$$\left. \frac{\partial^{4n}}{\partial x^{2n} \partial y^{2n}} \frac{1}{1+x^2+y^2} \right|_{(0,0)} .$$

CHAPTER 3

Applications of
Partial Derivatives

In this chapter we shall discuss some of the ways partial derivatives contribute to the understanding and solution of problems in applied mathematics. Many such problems can be put in the context of determining maximum or minimum values for functions of several variables, and the first four sections of this chapter deal with that subject. The remaining sections discuss some miscellaneous problems involving the differentiation of functions with respect to parameters, and also Newton's method for approximating solutions of systems of nonlinear equations. Much of the material in this chapter may be considered "optional." Only Sections 3.1–3.3 contain "core material," and even parts of those sections can be omitted (for example, the discussion of Linear Programming in Section 3.2).

3.1   EXTREME VALUES

The determination of maximum and minimum values of functions of several variables is, like its single-variable counterpart, the crux of many applications of advanced calculus to problems arising in other disciplines. Unfortunately, the determination and classification of such extreme values is often much more complicated than in the single-variable case. Our discussion will begin with developing the techniques for functions of two variables. Some of the techniques extend to functions of more variables in obvious ways. The extension of those that do not will be discussed later in the section.

Let us begin by reviewing what we know about the single-variable case. Recall that a function $f(x)$ has a *local maximum value* (or a *local minimum value*) at a point a in its domain if $f(x) \leq f(a)$ (or $f(x) \geq f(a)$) for all x in the domain of f which are *sufficiently close* to a. If the appropriate inequality holds *for all x* in the domain of f then we say that f has an *absolute maximum* (or *absolute minimum*) value at a. Moreover, such local or absolute extreme values can occur only at points of one of the following three types:

a) critical points – where $f'(x) = 0$, or

b) singular points – where $f'(x)$ does not exist, or

c) endpoints of the domain of f.

A similar situation exists for functions of several variables. For example, we say that a function of two variables has a **local maximum** (or **minimum**) value at the point (a, b) in its domain if $f(x, y) \leq f(a, b)$ (or $f(x, y) \geq f(a, b)$) for all points (x, y) in the domain of f which are *sufficiently close* to the point (a, b). If the inequality holds *for all (x, y)* in the domain of f then we say f has an **absolute maximum** (or **minimum**) value at (a, b). In practice, the word "absolute" is usually omitted, and we refer simply to *the maximum* or *the minimum* value of f. The following theorem shows that there are three possibilities for points where extreme values can occur, analogous to those for the single-variable case.

THEOREM 3.1.1   A function $f(x, y)$ can have a local or absolute extreme value at a point (a, b) in its domain only if (a, b) is

a) a **critical point** of f, that is, a point satisfying $\nabla f(a, b) = \mathbf{0}$, *or*

b) a **singular point** of f, that is, a point where $\nabla f(a, b)$ does not exist, *or*

c) a **boundary point** of the domain of f.

Before we can prove this theorem we have to make precise what we mean by a *boundary point* of the domain. If S is a set of points in the plane, then we say that a point P is a **boundary point** of S if every disc of positive radius centred at P contains at least one point of S and at least one point not in S. The boundary point P itself may or may not belong to S. If *all* of the boundary points of a set S belong to S, then we say that S is a **closed** set. If *none* of the boundary points of S belong to S, then S is called an **open** set. The set of all boundary points of S is called **the boundary** of S. Points of S which are not boundary points of S are called **interior points** of S. The interior of any set is open. The empty set and the whole plane are regarded as both open and closed.

For example, if S is the set of points (x, y) in the plane which satisfy the inequality $x^2 + y^2 \leq 1$, then the boundary of S is the circle $x^2 + y^2 = 1$ and the interior of S is the open disc $x^2 + y^2 < 1$. The reader should also compare these notions of open and closed sets and boundary points with the similar one-dimensional notions of open and closed intervals and endpoints.

Proof of Theorem 3.1.1. Suppose (a, b) belongs to the domain of f. If (a, b) is not on the boundary of the domain of f, then it must belong to the interior of that and if (a, b) is not a singular point of f then $\nabla f(a, b)$ exists. Finally, if (a, b) a critical point of f, then $\nabla f(a, b) \neq \mathbf{0}$ and so f has a positive directional derivative in the direction of $\nabla f(a, b)$ and a negative directional derivative in the direction of $-\nabla f(a, b)$. That is, f is increasing as we move from (a, b) in one direction and decreasing as we move in the opposite direction. Hence f cannot have either a maximum or minimum value at (a, b). Therefore, any point where an extreme value occurs must be either a critical point or a singular point of f or a boundary point of the domain of f. $\square$

The definitions of boundary and interior can easily be extended to sets in $\mathbb{R}^3$ (or even $\mathbb{R}^n$); the word "disc" in the definition of boundary point should be replaced with "ball". Theorem 3.1.1 remains valid with unchanged proof for functions of any number of variables. Of course, Theorem 3.1.1 does not guarantee that a given function will have any extreme values. It only tells us where to look to find any which may exist. Theorem 3.1.2 below provides conditions which guarantee the existence of absolute maximum and minimum values for a continuous function. The proof is beyond the scope of this book; an interested student should consult an elementary text on mathematical analysis. A set in $\mathbb{R}^n$ is **bounded** if it is contained inside some "ball" $x_1^2 + x_2^2 + \cdots + x_n^2 \leq R^2$ of finite radius R. A set on the real line is bounded if it is contained in an interval of finite length.

THEOREM 3.1.2   If f is a *continuous* function of n variables whose domain is a *closed* and *bounded* set in $\mathbb{R}^n$, then the range of f is a bounded set of real numbers, and there are points in its domain where f takes on absolute maximum and minimum values.

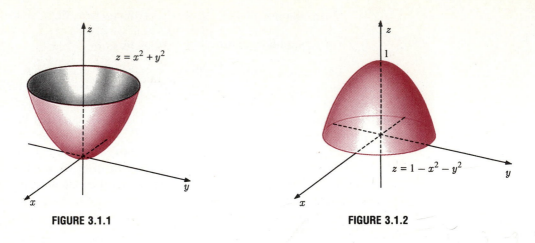

FIGURE 3.1.1   **FIGURE 3.1.2**

EXAMPLE 3.1.3   The function $f(x, y) = x^2 + y^2$ has a critical point at $(0,0)$ since $\nabla f = 2x\mathbf{i} + 2y\mathbf{j}$ and both components of ∇f vanish at $(0,0)$. Evidently

$$f(x, y) > 0 = f(0, 0) \quad \text{if} \quad (x, y) \neq (0, 0),$$

so f has the (absolute) minimum value 0 at that point. (See Fig. 3.1.1.) If the domain of f is not restricted f has no maximum value. Similarly, $g(x, y) = 1 - x^2 - y^2$ has (absolute) maximum value 1 at its critical point $(0,0)$. (See Fig. 3.1.2.)

EXAMPLE 3.1.4   The function $h(x, y) = x^2 - y^2$ also has a critical point at $(0,0)$ but has neither a local maximum nor a local minimum value at that point. Observe that $h(0,0) = 0$ but $h(x, 0) > 0$ and $h(0, y) < 0$ for all nonzero values of x and y. (See Fig. 3.1.3.) The graph of h is a hyperbolic paraboloid. In view of its shape we call the critical point $(0,0)$ a *saddle point* of h.

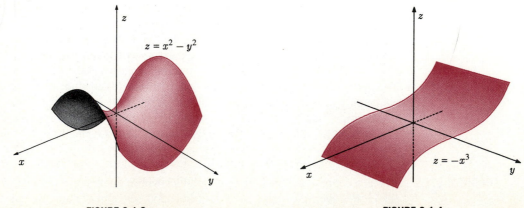

FIGURE 3.1.3   **FIGURE 3.1.4**

In general we shall somewhat loosely call any *interior critical* point of the domain of a function f of several variables a **saddle point** if f does not have a local maximum or minimum value there. Even for functions of two variables, the graph will not always look like a saddle near a saddle point. For instance, the function $f(x,y) = -x^3$ has a whole line of "saddle points" along the y-axis (see Fig. 3.1.4) though its graph does not resemble a saddle anywhere. Saddle points are higher dimensional analogues of the horizontal inflection points of functions of one variable.

EXAMPLE 3.1.5   The function $f(x,y) = \sqrt{x^2 + y^2}$ has no critical points, but does have a singular point at (0,0) where it has a local (and absolute) minimum value, zero. The graph of f is a circular cone. (See Fig. 3.1.5.)

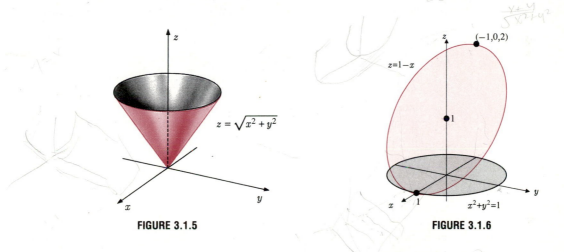

FIGURE 3.1.5   FIGURE 3.1.6

EXAMPLE 3.1.6   The function $f(x,y) = 1 - x$ is defined everywhere in the xy-plane and has no critical or singular points. ($\nabla f(x,y) = -\mathbf{i}$ at every point (x,y).) Therefore f has no extreme values. However, if we restrict the domain of f to the points in the disc $x^2 + y^2 \le 1$ (a closed bounded set in the xy-plane) then f does have absolute maximum and minimum values, as it must by Theorem 3.1.2. The maximum value is 2 at the boundary point $(-1, 0)$ and the minimum value is 0 at $(1,0)$. (See Fig. 3.1.6.)

Classifying Critical Points

The above examples were very simple ones; it was immediately obvious in each case whether the function had a local maximum or local minimum or a saddle point at the critical or singular point. For more complicated functions, classifying the interior critical points can be harder. In theory it can always be done by considering the difference

$$\Delta f = f(a + h, b + k) - f(a, b)$$

for small values of h and k, where (a, b) is the critical point in question. If the difference is always nonnegative (or nonpositive) for small h and k then f must have a local minimum (or maximum) at (a, b); if the difference is negative for some points (h, k) arbitrarily near (0,0), and positive for others, then f must have a saddle point at (a, b).

EXAMPLE 3.1.7   Find and classify the critical points of $f(x, y) = 2x^3 - 6xy + 3y^2$.

SOLUTION   The critical points must satisfy the system of equations:

$$0 = f_1(x, y) = 6x^2 - 6y \quad \Longleftrightarrow \quad x^2 = y$$
$$0 = f_2(x, y) = -6x + 6y \quad \Longleftrightarrow \quad x = y.$$

Together these equations imply $x^2 = x$ so that $x = 0, 1$. Evidently the critical points are (0,0) and (1,1).

Consider (0,0):

$$\Delta f = f(h, k) - f(0, 0) = 2h^3 - 6hk + 3k^2.$$

Since $f(h, 0) - f(0, 0) = 2h^3$ is positive for small positive h and negative for small negative h, f cannot have a maximum or minimum value at (0,0). Therefore (0,0) is a saddle point.

Now consider (1,1):

$$\begin{aligned}
\Delta f &= f(1 + h, 1 + k) - f(1, 1) \\
&= 2(1 + h)^3 - 6(1 + h)(1 + k) + 3(1 + k)^2 - (-1) \\
&= 2 + 6h + 6h^2 + 2h^3 - 6 - 6h - 6k - 6hk + 3 + 6k + 3k^2 + 1 \\
&= 6h^2 - 6hk + 3k^2 + 2h^3 \\
&= 3(h - k)^2 + h^2(3 + 2h)
\end{aligned}$$

Both terms in the latter expression are nonnegative if $|h| < 3/2$, and they are not both zero unless $h = k = 0$. Hence $\Delta f > 0$ for small h and k, and f has a local minimum value -1 at (1,1).

The method used to classify critical points in the above example takes on a "brute force" aspect if the function involved is more complicated. However, it provides a basis for developing a *second derivative test* similar to that for functions of one variable. The two-variable version is the subject of the following theorem.

THEOREM 3.1.8   *(A second derivative test)* Suppose that (a, b) is a critical point of $f(x, y)$ interior to the domain of f. Suppose also that the second partial derivatives of f are continuous near (a, b) and have at that point the values

$$A = f_{11}(a, b), \quad B = f_{12}(a, b) = f_{21}(a, b), \quad C = f_{22}(a, b).$$

If $B^2 < AC$ and $A > 0$ then f has a local minimum value at (a, b).

If $B^2 < AC$ and $A < 0$ then f has a local maximum value at (a, b).

If $B^2 > AC$ then f has a saddle point at (a, b).

(If $B^2 = AC$ this test provides no information.)

PROOF   Since $f_1(a, b) = f_2(a, b) = 0$, and the second partial derivatives of f are continuous near (a, b), the case $n = 1$ of Taylor's formula (see Section 2.8) gives

$$f(a + h, b + k) - f(a, b) = \frac{1}{2}\left(\bar{A}h^2 + 2\bar{B}hk + \bar{C}k^2\right) = \frac{1}{2}\bar{Q}(h, k),$$

where $\bar{A}$, $\bar{B}$, and $\bar{C}$ are, respectively, the values of the partial derivatives f_{11}, f_{12}, and f_{22} at some point $(a+\theta h, b+\theta k)$ on the line segment from (a, b) to $(a+h, b+k)$ (i.e., θ is between 0 and 1), and where $\bar{Q}(h, k) = \bar{A}h^2 + 2\bar{B}hk + \bar{C}k^2$. In order to prove that f has a local minimum (or a local maximum) at (a, b), we need to show that $\bar{Q}(h, k) \geq 0$ (or $\bar{Q}(h, k) \leq 0$) at *all* points (h, k) sufficiently close to $(0, 0)$. If $\bar{Q}(h, k) > 0$ at some points (h, k) arbitrarily close to $(0, 0)$ and $\bar{Q}(h, k) < 0$ at other such points, then f will have a saddle point at (a, b).

Let $Q(h, k) = Ah^2 + 2Bhk + Ck^2$. Since the second partial derivatives of f are continuous at (a, b), any of the inequalities $A > 0$, $A < 0$, $B^2 < AC$, or $B^2 > AC$ satisfied by the coefficients A, B, and C of Q will imply the same inequalities for the coefficients $\bar{A}$, $\bar{B}$, and $\bar{C}$ of $\bar{Q}$, provided (h, k) is close to $(0, 0)$, and therefore $(a + \theta h, b + \theta k)$ is sufficiently close to (a, b). Hence it suffices to consider the sign of $Q(h, k)$ under the conditions stated in the theorem.

If $A \neq 0$, then completing the square in the quadratic function Q, we obtain

$$Q(h, k) = A\left[\left(h + \frac{B}{A}k\right)^2 + \frac{AC - B^2}{A^2}k^2\right].$$

If $B^2 < AC$ then the expression in the square brackets above is a sum of positive expressions, so, for all $(h, k) \neq (0, 0)$, $g''(0)$ will have the same sign as A and f will have a local minimum or maximum at (a, b) according as $A > 0$ or $A < 0$. If $B^2 > AC$ then the expression in the square brackets is a difference of positive quantities which can be either positive (at points $(h, 0)$ say), or negative (at points $(-Bk/A, k)$), so f must have a saddle point at (a, b).

If $A = 0$ but $B^2 \neq AC$, then $B \neq 0$ and $g''(0) = k(2Bh + Ck)$, which has both positive and negative values in the four angular regions lying between the lines $k = 0$ and $2Bh + Ck = 0$. In this case f must have a saddle point.

Consideration of the functions $f(x, y) = x^4 + y^4$, $g(x, y) = -x^4 - y^4$ and $h(x, y) = x^4 - y^4$ will readily convince you that if $B^2 = AC$ then a function can have a minimum, a maximum or a saddle point. $\square$

EXAMPLE 3.1.9   We reconsider Example 3.1.7, and use the second derivative test to classify the two critical points $(0, 0)$ and $(1, 1)$. We have

$$f_{11}(x, y) = 12x, \quad f_{12}(x, y) = -6, \quad f_{22}(x, y) = 6.$$

At (0,0) we therefore have

$$A = 0, \quad B = -6, \quad C = 6, \quad B^2 - AC = 36 > 0$$

so (0,0) is a saddle point. At (1,1) we have

$$A = 12, \quad B = -6, \quad C = 6, \quad B^2 - AC = -36 < 0$$

so f must have a local minimum at (1,1).

EXAMPLE 3.1.10   Find and classify the critical points of

$$f(x,y) = xy\, e^{-(x^2+y^2)/2}.$$

Does f have absolute maximum and minimum values? Why?

SOLUTION   We begin by calculating the first and second order partial derivatives of f:

$$f_1(x,y) = y(1 - x^2)\, e^{-(x^2+y^2)/2},$$
$$f_2(x,y) = x(1 - y^2)\, e^{-(x^2+y^2)/2},$$
$$f_{11}(x,y) = xy(x^2 - 3)\, e^{-(x^2+y^2)/2},$$
$$f_{12}(x,y) = (1 - x^2)(1 - y^2)\, e^{-(x^2+y^2)/2},$$
$$f_{22}(x,y) = xy(y^2 - 3)\, e^{-(x^2+y^2)/2}.$$

At any critical point $f_1 = 0$ and $f_2 = 0$ so the critical points are the solutions of the system

$$y(1 - x^2) = 0$$
$$x(1 - y^2) = 0.$$

There are five of them: $(0,0)$, $(1,1)$, $(1,-1)$, $(-1,1)$ and $(-1,-1)$. We classify them using the second derivative test.

At $(0,0)$ we have $A = C = 0$, $B = 1$ so $B^2 - AC = 1 > 0$. Thus f has a saddle point at $(0,0)$.

At $(1,1)$ and $(-1,-1)$ we have $A = C = -2/e < 0$, $B = 0$ so $B^2 - AC = -4/e^2 < 0$. Thus f has local maximum values at these points. The value of f is $1/e$ at each.

At $(1,-1)$ and $(-1,1)$ we have $A = C = 2/e > 0$, $B = 0$ so $B^2 - AC = -4/e^2 < 0$. Thus f has local minimum values at these points. The value of f at each of them is $-1/e$.

Indeed, f has absolute maximum and minimum values—namely the values obtained above as local extrema. To see why, observe that $f(x,y)$ approaches 0 as the point (x,y) recedes to infinity in any direction, because the negative exponential dominates the power factor xy for large x^2+y^2. Accordingly, for some R, we must have $|f(x,y)| \leq 1/(2e)$ whenever $x^2 + y^2 \geq R^2$. On the closed disc $x^2 + y^2 \leq R^2$ f must have absolute maximum and minimum values by Theorem 3.1.2. These cannot occur on the circle $x^2 + y^2 = R^2$ because $|f|$ is smaller there than it is at the critical points considered above. Since f has no singular points, the absolute maximum and minimum values for the disc, and therefore for the whole plane, must occur at those critical points.

Quadratic Forms

It is not immediately apparent how Theorem 3.1.8 can be extended to functions of more than two variables. In order to make such an extension we shall rephrase that theorem in terms of *quadratic forms*.

If $\mathbf{u} = u\mathbf{i} + v\mathbf{j}$ is a unit vector then the *second directional derivative* of $f(x,y)$ at (a,b) in the direction of $\mathbf{u}$ is given by

$$D_{\mathbf{u}}^2 f(a,b) = \mathbf{u} \bullet \nabla\left(\mathbf{u} \bullet \nabla f\right)(a,b)$$
$$= Au^2 + 2Buv + Cv^2.$$

(See Example 2.6.10, where $\mathbf{u} = \cos\phi\,\mathbf{i} + \sin\phi\,\mathbf{j}$.) Being a homogeneous polynomial of degree two, the expression

$$Q(u,v) = Au^2 + 2Buv + Cv^2$$

is called a **quadratic form** in the variables u and v. Such a quadratic form is said to be **positive definite** (or **negative definite**) if $Q(u,v) > 0$ (or $Q(u,v) < 0$) for *all* nonzero vectors $\mathbf{u}$. Otherwise it is said to be **indefinite**.

Theorem 3.1.8 says that f has a local minimum or a local maximum at the critical point (a,b) according as the second directional derivative $Q(u,v) = D_{\mathbf{u}}^2 f(a,b)$ is a positive definite or negative definite in the components of $\mathbf{u}$. It says also that f has a saddle point at (a,b) if $Q(u,v)$ is positive for some vectors $\mathbf{u}$ and negative for others. This is not the same as saying Q is indefinite. For instance Q might satisfy $Q(u,v) \geq 0$ (or $Q(u,v) \leq 0$) for all nonzero vectors $\mathbf{u}$, with equality holding for some such vectors, or it can even happen that $Q(u,v)$ vanishes for all vectors $\mathbf{u}$. Such things can happen only in the indeterminate case $B^2 = AC$ of Theorem 3.1.8.

An extension of Theorem 3.1.8 to functions of any number of variables can be phrased in terms of quadratic forms. For a function $f(x,y,z)$ with continuous second partial derivatives, the second directional derivative at (a,b,c) in the direction of the unit vector $\mathbf{u} = u\mathbf{i} + v\mathbf{j} + w\mathbf{k}$ is the quadratic form

$$Q(u,v,w) = D_{\mathbf{u}}^2 f(a,b,c) = Au^2 + Bv^2 + Cw^2 + 2Duv + 2Euw + 2Fvw$$

where

$$A = f_{11}(a,b,c), \quad B = f_{22}(a,b,c), \quad C = f_{33}(a,b,c),$$
$$D = f_{12}(a,b,c), \quad E = f_{13}(a,b,c), \quad F = f_{23}(a,b,c).$$

Again f will have a local minimum, a local maximum, or a saddle point at the critical point (a,b,c) if $Q(u,v,w)$ is positive definite, negative definite, or has positive values for some vectors $\mathbf{u}$ and negative values for others. This can frequently be determined by a process of successive completion of squares as the example below shows. If Q does not satisfy one of these conditions, then no *second derivative test* can determine the nature of the critical point. One can still resort to "brute force" methods as in Example 3.1.7.

EXAMPLE 3.1.11   Find and classify the critical points of $f(x, y, z) = x^2 y + y^2 z + z^2 - 2x$.

SOLUTION   The equations which determine the critical points are

$$0 = f_1(x, y, z) = 2xy - 2$$
$$0 = f_2(x, y, z) = x^2 + 2yz$$
$$0 = f_3(x, y, z) = y^2 + 2z.$$

The third equation implies $z = -y^2/2$ and the second then implies $y^3 = x^2$. From the first equation we get $y^{5/2} = 1$. Thus $y = 1$ and $z = -\frac{1}{2}$. Since $xy = 1$, we must have $x = 1$. The only critical point is $P = (1, 1, -\frac{1}{2})$. Evaluating the second partial derivatives of f at this point we get

$$A = 2, \quad B = -1, \quad C = 2, \quad D = 2, \quad E = 0, \quad F = 2.$$

Hence the second directional derivative of f at P in the direction of the unit vector **u** is

$$Q(u, v, w) = 2u^2 - v^2 + 2w^2 + 4uv + 4vw$$
$$= 2(u^2 + 2uv + v^2) + 2(w^2 + 2vw + v^2) - 5v^2$$
$$= 2(u + v)^2 + 2(w + v)^2 - 5v^2.$$

Evidently $Q(1, 0, 0) > 0$ and $Q(0, 1, 0) < 0$, so P must be a saddle point of f.

REMARK: There is an orderly procedure for determining whether a quadratic form in any number of variables is positive definite. We shall describe it for the three-variable case but the extension should be obvious. The quadratic form

$$Q(u, v, w) = Au^2 + Bv^2 + Cw^2 + 2Duv + 2Euw + 2Fvw$$

can be written as

$$Q(u, v, w) = \mathbf{u}^T \mathcal{Q} \mathbf{u}$$

where

$$\mathbf{u} = \begin{pmatrix} u \\ v \\ w \end{pmatrix}, \quad \text{and} \quad \mathcal{Q} = \begin{pmatrix} A & D & E \\ D & B & F \\ E & F & C \end{pmatrix}.$$

Q is positive definite if

$$A > 0, \quad \begin{vmatrix} A & D \\ D & B \end{vmatrix} > 0, \quad \text{and} \quad \begin{vmatrix} A & D & E \\ D & B & F \\ E & F & C \end{vmatrix} > 0.$$

The reader is encouraged to prove this (see Exercise 29 below) by using suitable square-completion techniques. We can deduce an equivalent test for negative definiteness. Evidently Q is negative definite if $-Q(u, v, w)$ is positive definite. Thus Q is negative definite if

$$A < 0, \quad \begin{vmatrix} A & D \\ D & B \end{vmatrix} > 0, \quad \text{and} \quad \begin{vmatrix} A & D & E \\ D & B & F \\ E & F & C \end{vmatrix} < 0.$$

If $\det(\mathcal{Q}) \neq 0$ but neither Q nor $-Q$ is positive definite then Q will be positive for some values of (u, v, w) and negative for others.

EXERCISES

In Exercises 1–4 specify the boundary and the interior of the plane sets S whose points (x, y) satisfy the given conditions. Is S open, closed or neither? Is S bounded?

1. $0 < x^2 + y^2 < 1$ **2.** $x \geq 0, \quad y < 0$

3. $x + y = 1$ **4.** $|x| + |y| \leq 1$

In Exercises 5–19 find and classify the critical points of the given functions.

5. $f(x, y) = x^2 + 2y^2 - 4x + 4y$

6. $f(x, y) = xy - x + y$ **7.** $f(x, y) = x^3 + y^3 - 3xy$

8. $f(x, y) = x^4 + y^4 - 4xy$ **9.** $f(x, y) = \dfrac{x}{y} + \dfrac{8}{x} - y$

10. $f(x, y) = \cos(x + y)$ **11.** $f(x, y) = x \sin y$

12. $f(x, y) = \cos x + \cos y$ **13.** $f(x, y) = x^2 y \, e^{-(x^2 + y^2)}$

14. $f(x, y) = \dfrac{xy}{2 + x^4 + y^4}$ **15.** $f(x, y) = x \, e^{-x^3 + y^3}$

16. $f(x, y) = \dfrac{1}{1 - x + y + x^2 + y^2}$

17. $f(x, y) = \left(1 + \dfrac{1}{x}\right)\left(1 + \dfrac{1}{y}\right)\left(\dfrac{1}{x} + \dfrac{1}{y}\right)$

18.*$f(x, y, z) = xyz - x^2 - y^2 - z^2$

19.*$f(x, y, z) = xy + x^2 z - x^2 - y - z^2$

20.*Show that $f(x, y, z) = 4xyz - x^4 - y^4 - z^4$ has a local maximum value at the point $(1,1,1)$.

21. Find the maximum and minimum values of $f(x, y) = xy \, e^{-x^2 - y^4}$.

22. Find the maximum and minimum values of $f(x, y) = x/(1 + x^2 + y^2)$.

23.*Find the maximum and minimum values of $f(x, y, z) = xyz \, e^{-x^2 - y^2 - z^2}$. How do you know that such extreme values exist?

24. Find the minimum value of $f(x, y) = x + 8y + \dfrac{1}{xy}$ in the first quadrant $x > 0$, $y > 0$. How do you know that a minimum exists?

25. Find the critical points of the function $z = g(x, y)$ which satisfies the equation

$$e^{2zx - x^2} - 3e^{2zy + y^2} = 2.$$

26.*Classify the critical points of the function g in the previous exercise.

27.*Let $f(x, y) = (y - x^2)(y - 3x^2)$. Show that the origin is a critical point of f and that the restriction of f to every straight line through the origin has a local minimum value at the origin. (That is, show $f(x, kx)$ has a local minimum value at $x = 0$ for every k, and $f(0, y)$ has a local minimum value at $y = 0$.) Does $f(x, y)$ have a local minimum value at the origin? What happens to f on the curve $y = 2x^2$? What does the Second Derivative Test say about this situation?

28.*Prove the determinant tests for the positive and negative definiteness of three-variable quadratic forms given in the remark at the end of this section.

29.*State conditions on the coefficients $A, B, \ldots, J$ which will guarantee that the quadratic form

$$Q(w, x, y, z) = Aw^2 + Bx^2 + Cy^2$$
$$+ Dz^2 + 2Ewx + 2Fwy$$
$$+ 2Gwz + 2Hxy + 2Ixz + 2Jyz$$

is positive definite. (Generalize the assertion made for three-variable forms in the text.)

▨ 3.2   EXTREME VALUES OF FUNCTIONS DEFINED ON RESTRICTED DOMAINS

The previous section was concerned mainly with techniques for determining whether a critical point of a function provided a local maximum or minimum value, or was a saddle point. In this section we address the problem of determining absolute maximum and minimum values for functions which have them — usually functions whose domains are restricted to subsets of $\mathbb{R}^2$ (or $\mathbb{R}^n$) having nonempty interiors. In the Example 3.1.10 we had to *prove* that the given function had absolute extreme values. If, however, we are dealing with a function which is continuous on a domain which is closed and bounded, then we can rely on Theorem 3.1.2 to guarantee the existence of such extreme values, but we will always have to check boundary points as well as any interior critical or singular points to find them. The following examples illustrate the technique.

EXAMPLE 3.2.1   Find the maximum and minimum values of the function $f(x, y) = 2xy$ on the closed disc $x^2 + y^2 \leq 4$.

SOLUTION   Since f is continuous and the disc is closed, f must have absolute maximum and minimum values at some points of the disc. The first partial derivatives of f are

$$f_1(x, y) = 2y, \qquad f_2(x, y) = 2x,$$

so there are no singular points and the only critical point is (0,0), where f has the value 0.

We must still consider values of f on the boundary circle $x^2 + y^2 = 4$. We can express f as a function of a single variable on this circle, by using a convenient parametrization of the circle, say

$$x = 2\cos t, \quad y = 2\sin t, \qquad -\pi \leq t \leq \pi.$$

We have

$$f\left(2\cos t, 2\sin t\right) = 8\cos t \sin t = g(t).$$

We must find any extreme values of $g(t)$. We can do this in either of two ways. If we rewrite $g(t) = 4\sin 2t$, it is clear that $g(t)$ has maximum value 4 (at $t = \frac{\pi}{4}$ and $-\frac{3\pi}{4}$), and minimum value -4 (at $t = -\frac{\pi}{4}$ and $\frac{3\pi}{4}$). Alternately, we can differentiate g to find its critical points:

$$0 = g'(t) = -8\sin^2 t + 8\cos^2 t \quad \Longleftrightarrow \quad \tan^2 t = 1$$
$$\Longleftrightarrow \quad t = \pm\frac{\pi}{4} \text{ or } \pm\frac{3\pi}{4},$$

which again yield the maximum value 4 and the minimum value -4. (It is not necessary to check the endpoints $t = 0$ and $t = 2\pi$; since g is everywhere differentiable and is periodic with period π, any absolute maximum or minimum will occur at a critical point.)

In any event, f has maximum value 4 at the boundary points $(\sqrt{2}, \sqrt{2})$ and $(-\sqrt{2}, -\sqrt{2})$, and minimum value -4 at the boundary points $(\sqrt{2}, -\sqrt{2})$ and $(-\sqrt{2}, \sqrt{2})$. It is easily shown by the second derivative test or otherwise that the interior critical point (0,0) is a saddle point.

EXAMPLE 3.2.2   Find the extreme values of the function $f(x, y) = x^2 y e^{-(x+y)}$ on the triangular region $x \geq 0$, $y \geq 0$, $x + y \leq 4$.

SOLUTION   First we look for critical points:

$$0 = f_1(x, y) = xy(2 - x)e^{-(x+y)} \quad \Longleftrightarrow \quad x = 0, \ y = 0, \text{ or } x = 2,$$
$$0 = f_2(x, y) = x^2(1 - y)e^{-(x+y)} \quad \Longleftrightarrow \quad x = 0 \text{ or } y = 1.$$

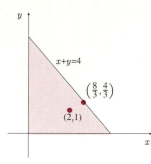

FIGURE 3.2.1

The critical points are $(0, y)$ for any y and $(2,1)$. Only $(2,1)$ is interior to the triangular region. (See Fig. 3.2.1.) $f(2, 1) = 4/e^3 \approx 0.199$. The boundary of the region consists of three straight line segments. On two of these, the coordinate axes, f is identically zero. The third segment is given by

$$y = 4 - x, \qquad 0 \le x \le 4,$$

so the values of f on it can be expressed as a function of x alone:

$$g(x) = f(x, 4 - x) = x^2(4 - x)e^{-4}, \qquad 0 \le x \le 4.$$

Clearly $g(0) = g(4) = 0$ and $g(x) > 0$ if $0 < x < 4$. The critical points of g are given by $0 = g'(x) = (8x - 3x^2)e^{-4}$, so they are $x = 0$ and $x = 8/3$. We have

$$g\left(\frac{8}{3}\right) = f\left(\frac{8}{3}, \frac{4}{3}\right) = \frac{256}{27}e^{-4} \approx 0.174 < f(2, 1).$$

We conclude that the maximum value of f over the triangular region is $4/e^3$ and it occurs at the interior critical point $(2,1)$. The minimum value of f is zero and occurs at all points of the two perpendicular boundary segments. Note that f has neither a local maximum nor a local minimum at the boundary point $(8/3, 4/3)$ although g has a local maximum there. Of course that point is not a saddle point of f either. It is not a critical point of f.

EXAMPLE 3.2.3   Among all triangles with vertices on the unit circle $x^2 + y^2 = 1$ find those which have largest area.

SOLUTION   Intuition tells us that the equilateral triangles must have the largest area. However proving this can be quite difficult unless you make a good choice of variables in which to set up the problem analytically. Let one vertex of the triangle be the point P with coordinates $(1,0)$ and let the other two vertices, Q and R, be as shown in Fig. 3.2.2. There is clearly no harm in assuming that Q lies on the upper semicircle and R on the lower. Let PQ and PR make angles θ and ϕ respectively with the negative direction of the x-axis. Clearly $0 \le \theta \le \pi/2$ and $0 \le \phi \le \pi/2$. The lines from the origin O to Q and R make equal angles ψ with the line QR, where $2\theta + 2\phi + 2\psi = \pi$. Dropping perpendiculars from O to the three sides of the triangle PQR, we can write the area A of triangle as the sum of the areas of six small, right-angled triangles:

$$A = 2 \times \frac{1}{2}\sin\theta\cos\theta + 2 \times \frac{1}{2}\sin\phi\cos\phi + 2 \times \frac{1}{2}\sin\psi\cos\psi$$

$$= \frac{1}{2}\left(\sin 2\theta + \sin 2\phi + \sin 2\psi\right)$$

$$= \frac{1}{2}\left(\sin 2\theta + \sin 2\phi + \sin 2(\theta + \phi)\right), \qquad \text{(since } 2\psi = \pi - 2(\theta + \phi)\text{)}.$$

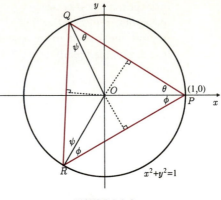

FIGURE 3.2.2

The domain of A is the square $0 \le \theta \le \pi/2$, $0 \le \phi \le \pi/2$. $A > 0$ everywhere inside the square and $A = 0$ along the sides $\theta = \pi/2$ and $\phi = \pi/2$ and at the vertex where $\theta = 0$ and $\phi = 0$. Although we can have $A > 0$ at other boundary points (where either $\theta = 0$ or $\phi = 0$ but not both), nevertheless the largest triangle cannot arise in this way. (If, for example, $\theta = 0$, then Q is $(-1, 0)$, and the triangle can be made larger by letting Q rise along the upper semicircle, thus increasing the altitude of the triangle PQR perpendicular to the base PR.) Therefore the maximum area must occur at an interior critical point. There are no singular points. We have

$$0 = \frac{\partial A}{\partial \theta} = \cos 2\theta + \cos(2\theta + 2\phi)$$

$$0 = \frac{\partial A}{\partial \phi} = \cos 2\phi + \cos(2\theta + 2\phi)$$

so the critical points satisfy $\cos 2\theta = \cos 2\phi$, and hence $\theta = \phi$. We now substitute into either of the above equations to determine θ:

$$\cos 2\theta + \cos 4\theta = 0$$

$$2\cos^2 2\theta + \cos 2\theta - 1 = 0$$

$$(2\cos 2\theta - 1)(\cos 2\theta + 1) = 0$$

$$\cos 2\theta = \frac{1}{2}, \quad \text{or} \quad \cos 2\theta = -1$$

The only solution arising here which lies interior to the domain of A is $\theta = \pi/6$. Hence also $\phi = \pi/6$, $\psi = \pi/6$, and the triangle is equilateral as suspected.

REMARK: Since the area A of the inscribed triangle must have a maximum value, (A is continuous and its domain is closed and bounded), a strictly geometric argument can be used to show that the largest triangle is equilateral. If an inscribed triangle has two unequal sides, its area can be made larger by moving the common vertex of these two sides along the circle to increase its perpendicular distance from the opposite side of the triangle.

Linear Programming

Linear programming is a branch of linear algebra which develops systematic techniques for solving problems that ask for the maximum or minimum value of a *linear function* subject to several *linear inequality constraints.* Such problems arise frequently in management science and operations research. Because of their linear nature they do not usually involve calculus in their solution; the topic of linear programming is frequently presented in courses on "finite mathematics." We will not attempt any formal study of linear programming here, but will make a few observations for comparison with the more general nonlinear extreme value problems considered above which involve calculus in their solution.

The inequality $ax + by \leq c$ is an example of a linear inequality in two variables. The *solution set* of this inequality consists of a half-plane lying on one side of the straight line $ax + by = c$. The solution set of a system of several 2-variable linear inequalities is an intersection of such half-planes, so it is a *convex* region of the plane bounded by a "polygonal line." If it is a bounded set then it is a convex polygon together with its interior. (A set is called **convex** if it contains the entire line segment between any two of its points. On the real line the convex sets are intervals.)

Let us examine a simple concrete example which involves only two variables and a few constraints.

EXAMPLE 3.2.4   Find the maximum value of $F(x, y) = 2x + 7y$ subject to the constraints

$$x + 2y \leq 6,$$
$$2x + y \leq 6,$$
$$x \geq 0,$$
$$y \geq 0.$$

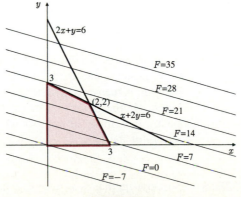

FIGURE 3.2.3

SOLUTION   The solution set S of the system of four constraint equations is shown in Fig. 3.2.3. It is the quadrilateral region with vertices (0,0), (3,0), (2,2) and (0,3). Several level curves of the linear function F are also shown in the figure. They are parallel straight lines with slope $-\frac{2}{7}$. We want the line which gives F the greatest value and which still intersects S. Evidently this is the line $F = 21$ which passes through the vertex (0,3) of S. The maximum value of F subject to the constraints is 21.

As this simple example illustrates, a *linear* function with domain restricted by *linear inequalities* does not achieve maximum or minimum values at points in the interior of its domain (if that set has an interior). Any such extreme value occurs at a boundary point of the domain, or a set of such boundary points. Where an extreme value occurs at a set of boundary points that set will *always* contain at least one vertex. This phenomenon holds in general for extreme value problems for linear functions in any number of variables with domains restricted by any number of linear inequalities. For problems involving 3 variables the domain will be a convex region of $\mathbb{R}^3$ bounded by planes. For a problem involving n variables the domain will be a convex region in $\mathbb{R}^n$ bounded by $(n-1)$-dimensional hyperplanes. Such "polyhedral" regions still have vertices (where n hyperplanes intersect) and maximum or minimum values of linear functions subject to the constraints will still occur at subsets of the boundary containing such vertices. These problems can therefore be solved by evaluating the linear function to be extremized (it is called the **objective function**) at all the vertices and selecting the greatest or least value.

In practice, linear programming problems can involve hundreds or even thousands of variables and even more constraints. Such problems need to be solved with computers, but even then it is extremely inefficient if not impossible to calculate all the vertices of the constraint solution set and the values of the objective function at them. Much of the study of linear programming therefore centres on devising techniques for getting to (or at least near) the optimizing vertex in as few steps as possible. Usually this involves criteria whereby large numbers of vertices can be rejected on geometric grounds. We will not delve into such techniques here, but will content ourselves with one more example to illustrate, in a very simple case, how the underlying geometry of a problem can be used to reduce the number of vertices which must be considered.

EXAMPLE 3.2.5   A tailor has 230 metres of a certain fabric and has orders for up to 20 suits, up to 30 jackets, and up to 40 pairs of slacks to be made from the fabric. Each suit requires 6 metres, each jacket 3 metres and each pair of slacks 2 metres of the fabric. If the tailor's profit is $20 per suit, $14 per jacket and $12 per pair of slacks, how many of each should he make to realize the maximum profit from his supply of the fabric?

SOLUTION   Suppose he makes x suits, y jackets and z pairs of slacks. Then his profit will be

$$P = 20x + 14y + 12z.$$

The constraints posed in the problem are

$$x \geq 0, \qquad x \leq 20,$$
$$y \geq 0, \qquad y \leq 30,$$
$$z \geq 0, \qquad z \leq 40,$$

$$6x + 3y + 2z \leq 230.$$

The last inequality is due to the limited supply of fabric. The solution set is shown

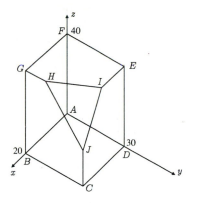

FIGURE 3.2.4

in Fig. 3.2.4. It has ten vertices, $A, B, \ldots, J$. Since P increases in the direction of the vector $\nabla P = 20\mathbf{i} + 14\mathbf{j} + 12\mathbf{k}$ which points into the first octant, its maximum value cannot occur at any of the vertices $A, B, \ldots, G$. (Think about why.) Thus we need look only at the vertices H, I and J.

$$H = (20, 10, 40), \qquad P = 1020 \text{ at } H.$$
$$I = (10, 30, 40), \qquad P = 1100 \text{ at } I.$$
$$J = (20, 30, 10), \qquad P = 940 \ \text{ at } J.$$

Thus the tailor should make 10 suits, 30 jackets and 40 pairs of slacks to realize the maximum profit, \$1,100, from the fabric.

EXERCISES

1. Find the maximum and minimum values of $f(x, y) = x - x^2 + y^2$ on the rectangle $0 \leq x \leq 2, 0 \leq y \leq 1$.

2. Find the maximum and minimum values of $f(x, y) = xy - 2x$ on the rectangle $-1 \leq x \leq 1, 0 \leq y \leq 1$.

3. Find the maximum and minimum values of $f(x, y) = xy - y^2$ on the disc $x^2 + y^2 \leq 1$.

4. Find the maximum and minimum values of $f(x, y) = x + 2y$ on the disc $x^2 + y^2 \leq 1$.

5. Find the maximum value of $f(x, y) = xy - x^3 y^2$ over the square $0 \leq x \leq 1, 0 \leq y \leq 1$.

6. Find the maximum and minimum values of $f(x, y) = xy(1 - x - y)$ over the triangle with vertices $(0,0)$, $(1,0)$ and $(0,1)$.

7. Find the maximum and minimum values of $f(x, y) = \sin x \cos y$ on the closed triangular region bounded by the coordinate axes and the line $x + y = 2\pi$.

8. Find the maximum value of

$$f(x,y) = \sin x \sin y \sin(x+y)$$

over the triangle bounded by the coordinate axes and the line $x+y=\pi$.

9. The temperature at all points in the disc $x^2+y^2 \le 1$ is given by

$$T = (x+y)\,e^{-x^2-y^2}.$$

Find the maximum and minimum temperatures at points of the disc.

10. Find the maximum and minimum values of

$$f(x,y) = \frac{x-y}{1+x^2+y^2}$$

on the upper half-plane $y \ge 0$.

11. Consider the function $f(x,y) = xy\,e^{-xy}$ with domain the first quadrant $x \ge 0$, $y \ge 0$. Show that $\lim_{x\to\infty} f(x,kx) = 0$. Does f have a limit as (x,y) recedes arbitrarily far from the origin in the first quadrant? Does f have a maximum value in the first quadrant?

12. Repeat the previous exercise for the function $f(x,y) = xy^2\,e^{-xy}$.

13. In a certain community there are two breweries in competition, so that sales of each negatively affect the profits of the other. If brewery A produces x litres of beer per month and brewery B produces y litres per month, then brewery A's monthly profit $\$P$ and brewery B's monthly profit $\$Q$ will be given by

$$P = 2x - \frac{2x^2+y^2}{10^6},$$

$$Q = 2y - \frac{4y^2+x^2}{2\times 10^6}.$$

Find the sum of the profits of the two breweries if each brewery independently sets its own production level to maximize its own profit, and assumes its competitor does likewise. Find the sum of the profits if the two breweries cooperate to determine their respective productions to maximize that sum.

14. Equal angle bends are made at equal distances from the two ends of a 100 metre long straight length of fence so the resulting three segment fence can be placed along an existing wall to make an enclosure of trapezoidal shape. What is the largest possible area for such an enclosure?

15. Maximize $Q(x,y) = 2x + 3y$ subject to the constraints $x \ge 0$, $y \ge 0$, $y \le 5$, $x+2y \le 12$, and $4x+y \le 12$.

16. Minimize $F(x,y,z) = 2x + 3y + 4z$ subject to $x \ge 0$, $y \ge 0$, $z \ge 0$, $x+y \ge 2$, $y+z \ge 2$ and $x+z \ge 2$.

17. A textile manufacturer produces two grades of wool-cotton-polyester fabric. The deluxe grade has composition (by weight) 20% wool, 50% cotton and 30% polyester, and it sells for 3 dollars per kilogram. The standard grade has composition 10% wool, 40% cotton and 50% polyester, and sells for $2 per kilogram. If he has in stock 2000 kg of wool and 6000 kg each of cotton and polyester, how many kilograms of fabric of each grade should he manufacture to maximize his revenue?

18. A 10 hectare parcel of land is zoned for building densities of 6 detached houses per hectare, 8 duplex units per hectare or 12 apartments per hectare. The developer who owns the land can make a profit of $40,000 per house, $20,000 per duplex unit and $16,000 per apartment that he builds. Municipal bylaws require him to build at least as many apartments as houses or duplex units. How many of each type of dwelling should he build to maximize his profit?

3.3 EXTREME VALUE PROBLEMS WITH EQUALITY CONSTRAINTS

A constrained extreme value problem is one in which the variables of the function to be maximized or minimized are not completely independent of one another, but must satisfy one or more constraint equations or inequalities. For instance the problems

$$\textbf{maximize}\quad f(x,y)\quad \textbf{subject to}\quad g(x,y)=C,$$

and

$$\text{minimize} \quad f(x, y, z, w) \quad \textbf{subject to} \quad g(x, y, z, w) = C_1,$$
$$\textbf{and} \quad h(x, y, z, w) = C_2$$

have, respectively, one and two constraint equations, while the problem

$$\textbf{maximize} \quad f(x, y, z) \quad \textbf{subject to} \quad g(x, y, z) \le C$$

has a single constraint inequality.

Generally, inequality constraints may be regarded as restricting the domain of the function to be extremized to a smaller set which still has interior points. Section 3.2 was devoted to such problems. In each of the first three examples of that section we looked for *free* (that is, unconstrained) extreme values in the interior of the domain, and then examined the boundary of the domain, which was specified by one or more *constraint equations*. In Example 3.2.1 we parametrized the boundary and expressed the function to be extremized as a function of the parameter, thus reducing the boundary case to a free problem in one variable instead of a constrained problem in two variables. In Example 3.2.2 the boundary consisted of three line segments, on two of which the function was obviously zero. We solved the equation for the third boundary segment for y in terms of x, again in order to express the values of $f(x, y)$ on that segment as a function of one free variable. In Example 3.2.3 we used geometric circumstances of the problem to convince ourselves that the maximum area being sought could not possibly occur on the boundary of the domain of the area function.

The techniques used to deal with the boundary in those three examples are frequently useful. In particular, one should always consider the possibility of reducing problems with equation constraints to free (unconstrained) problems in fewer variables by solving the constraint equations for some variables. We give another example.

EXAMPLE 3.3.1   Find the volume of the largest rectangular box (with faces parallel to the coordinate planes) which can be inscribed in the ellipsoid

$$\frac{x^2}{a^2} + \frac{y^2}{b^2} + \frac{z^2}{c^2} = 1.$$

SOLUTION   If the first octant corner of the box has coordinates (X, Y, Z) then by symmetry the diagonally opposite corner has coordinates $(-X, -Y, -Z)$ so the volume of the box is $V = 8XYZ$. This volume must be maximized subject to the constraint that the corners lie on the ellipsoid:

$$\frac{X^2}{a^2} + \frac{Y^2}{b^2} + \frac{Z^2}{c^2} = 1.$$

Fig. 3.3.1 shows the first octant part of the ellipsoid and of the box. Since X, Y and Z are nonnegative we can solve this constraint equation for one of the variables, say Z:

$$Z = c\sqrt{1 - \frac{X^2}{a^2} - \frac{Y^2}{b^2}}$$

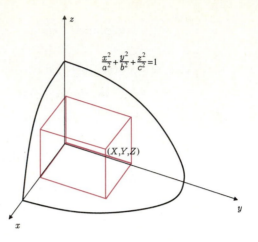

$$\frac{x^2}{a^2} + \frac{y^2}{b^2} + \frac{z^2}{c^2} = 1$$

(X,Y,Z)

FIGURE 3.3.1

and so write the volume as a function of two variables:

$$V = 8cXY\sqrt{1 - \frac{X^2}{a^2} - \frac{Y^2}{b^2}}.$$

Note that X and Y are still constrained, but only by inequalities: the domain of V satisfies

$$X \geq 0, \quad Y \geq 0, \quad \frac{X^2}{a^2} + \frac{Y^2}{b^2} \leq 1.$$

Evidently $V = 0$ on the boundary of this domain, so the maximum of V, which must exist by Theorem 3.1.2, must occur at an interior critical point. We find any such points:

$$0 = \frac{\partial V}{\partial X} = 8cY\left(\sqrt{1 - \frac{X^2}{a^2} - \frac{Y^2}{b^2}} - \frac{X^2}{a^2}\frac{1}{\sqrt{1 - \frac{X^2}{a^2} - \frac{Y^2}{b^2}}}\right)$$

$$= 8cY\,\frac{1 - \frac{2X^2}{a^2} - \frac{Y^2}{b^2}}{\sqrt{1 - \frac{X^2}{a^2} - \frac{Y^2}{b^2}}}$$

$$0 = \frac{\partial V}{\partial Y} = 8cX\left(\sqrt{1 - \frac{X^2}{a^2} - \frac{Y^2}{b^2}} - \frac{Y^2}{b^2}\frac{1}{\sqrt{1 - \frac{X^2}{a^2} - \frac{Y^2}{b^2}}}\right)$$

$$= 8cX\,\frac{1 - \frac{2Y^2}{b^2} - \frac{X^2}{a^2}}{\sqrt{1 - \frac{X^2}{a^2} - \frac{Y^2}{b^2}}}.$$

Since $X > 0$ and $Y > 0$ in the interior of the domain of V, we must have

$$1 - \frac{2X^2}{a^2} - \frac{Y^2}{b^2} = 0 = 1 - \frac{2Y^2}{b^2} - \frac{X^2}{a^2}$$

at a critical point. Thus $X/a = Y/b = 1/\sqrt{3}$, which does give a point interior to the domain of V. It follows that $Z = c/\sqrt{3}$ and the largest box has volume $8abc/(3\sqrt{3})$ cubic units.

The Method of Lagrange Multipliers

The reduction of extremization problems with equation constraints to free problems with fewer independent variables is only feasible when the constraint equations can be solved either explicitly for some variables in terms of others, or parametrically for all variables in terms of some parameters. It is often very difficult or impossible to solve the constraint equations, so we need another technique. We begin with a geometric analysis of the problem:

minimize (or maximize) $f(x, y)$ subject to $g(x, y) = 0$.

Suppose this problem has a solution, that is, there exists a point $P_0 = (x_0, y_0)$ on the curve C with equation $g(x, y) = 0$, such that $f(x, y)$, restricted to C, has an extreme value at P_0. We also assume that

(i) P_0 is not an endpoint of C, and

(ii) $\nabla g(P_0) \neq \mathbf{0}$.

Together, (i) and (ii) imply that C is smooth enough to have a tangent line at P_0, and $\nabla g(P_0)$ is normal to that tangent line. (See Theorem 2.6.3 and Exercise 36 in Section 2.6.)

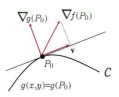

If $\nabla f(P_0)$ is not parallel to $\nabla g(P_0)$, then $\nabla f(P_0)$ has a nonzero vector projection $\mathbf{v}$ along the tangent line to C at P_0. (See Fig. 3.3.2.) Therefore f has a positive directional derivative at P_0 in the direction of $\mathbf{v}$, and a negative directional derivative in the opposite direction. Thus $f(x, y)$ increases or decreases as we move away from P_0 along C in the direction of $\mathbf{v}$ or $-\mathbf{v}$, and f cannot have a maximum or minimum value at P_0. Since we are assuming that f *does* have an extreme value at P_0, it must be that $\nabla f(P_0)$ is parallel to $\nabla g(P_0)$. Since $\nabla g(P_0) \neq \mathbf{0}$, there must exist a real number λ such that $\nabla f(P_0) = -\lambda \nabla g(P_0)$, or $\nabla(f + \lambda g)(P_0) = \mathbf{0}$. This suggests that to find candidates for points on the curve $g(x, y) = 0$ at which $f(x, y)$ is maximum or minimum, we should look for critical points of the **Lagrangian function**

FIGURE 3.3.2

$$L(x, y, \lambda) = f(x, y) + \lambda g(x, y).$$

At any critical point of L we must have

$$\left. \begin{array}{l} 0 = \dfrac{\partial L}{\partial x} = f_1(x, y) + \lambda g_1(x, y), \\[2mm] 0 = \dfrac{\partial L}{\partial y} = f_2(x, y) + \lambda g_2(x, y), \end{array} \right\} \quad \text{i.e., } \nabla f \text{ is parallel to } \nabla g,$$

and $0 = \dfrac{\partial L}{\partial \lambda} = g(x, y)$ the constraint equation.

Let us put the method to a concrete test:

EXAMPLE 3.3.2 Find the shortest distance from the origin to the curve $x^2 y = 16$.

SOLUTION It is sufficient to minimize the square of the distance from the point (x, y) on the curve $x^2 y = 16$ to the origin, that is, to solve the problem

$$\textbf{minimize} \quad f(x, y) = x^2 + y^2 \quad \textbf{subject to} \quad g(x, y) = x^2 y - 16 = 0.$$

Let $L(x, y, \lambda) = x^2 + y^2 + \lambda(x^2 y - 16)$. For critical points of L we want

$$0 = \frac{\partial L}{\partial x} = 2x + 2\lambda xy = 2x(1 + \lambda y) \tag{A}$$

$$0 = \frac{\partial L}{\partial y} = 2y + \lambda x^2 \tag{B}$$

$$0 = \frac{\partial L}{\partial \lambda} = x^2 y - 16 \tag{C}$$

Equation (A) requires that either $x = 0$ or $\lambda y = -1$. However, $x = 0$ is inconsistent with equation (C). Therefore $\lambda y = -1$. From equation (B) we now have

$$0 = 2y^2 + \lambda y x^2 = 2y^2 - x^2.$$

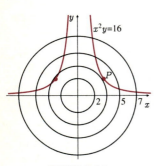

FIGURE 3.3.3

Thus $x = \pm\sqrt{2}y$, and (C) now gives $2y^3 = 16$, so $y = 2$. There are, therefore, two candidates for points on $x^2 y = 16$ closest to the origin, $(\pm 2\sqrt{2}, 2)$. Both of these points are at distance $\sqrt{8 + 4} = 2\sqrt{3}$ units from the origin, so this is the minimum distance from the origin to the curve. The constraint curve $x^2 y = 16$ and some level curves of $x^2 + y^2$ are shown in Fig. 3.3.3. Observe how the constraint curve is tangent to the level curve passing through the minimizing points $(\pm 2\sqrt{2}, 2)$, reflecting the fact that the two curves have parallel normals there.

In the above example we could, of course, have solved the constraint equation for $y = 16/x^2$, substituted into f, and thus reduced the problem to one of finding the (unconstrained) minimum value of

$$F(x) = f\left(x, \frac{16}{x^2}\right) = x^2 + \frac{256}{x^4}.$$

The reader is invited to verify that this gives the same result.

The number λ occurring in the Lagrangian function in Example 3.3.2 is called a **Lagrange multipler**. The technique for solving an extreme value problem with equation constraints by looking for critical points of an unconstrained problem with more variables (the original variables plus a Lagrange multiplier corresponding to each constraint equation) is called **the method of Lagrange multipliers.** It can be expected to give results so long as the constraint equations have "smooth" graphs near the extremizing points, and these points are not on "edges" of those graphs. See Example 3.3.4 and Exercise 24 at the end of this section.

EXAMPLE 3.3.3   Find the points on the curve $17x^2 + 12xy + 8y^2 = 100$ which are closest to and farthest away from the origin.

SOLUTION   The quadratic form on the left side of the equation above is positive definite as can be seen by completing a square. Hence the curve is bounded and must have points closest and farthest from the origin. (In fact, the curve is an ellipse with centre at the origin and oblique principal axes. The problem asks us to find the ends of the major and minor axes.)

Again we want to extremize $x^2 + y^2$ subject to an equation constraint. The Lagrangian in this case is

$$L(x, y, \lambda) = x^2 + y^2 + \lambda(17x^2 + 12xy + 8y^2 - 100),$$

and its critical points are given by

$$0 = \frac{\partial L}{\partial x} = 2x + \lambda(34x + 12y) \tag{A}$$

$$0 = \frac{\partial L}{\partial y} = 2y + \lambda(12x + 16y) \tag{B}$$

$$0 = \frac{\partial L}{\partial \lambda} = 17x^2 + 12xy + 8y^2 - 100. \tag{C}$$

Elimination of λ from equations (A) and (B) leads to

$$\frac{-2x}{34x + 12y} = \frac{-2y}{12x + 16y}, \qquad \text{or} \qquad 12x^2 + 16xy = 34xy + 12y^2.$$

This equation simplifies to

$$2x^2 - 3xy - 2y^2 = 0, \tag{D}$$

and multiplying this latter equation by 4 and adding it to equation (C) we get $25x^2 = 100$ so that $x = \pm 2$. Finally we substitute each of these values of x into (D) and obtain (for each) two values of y from the resulting quadratics:

$$y^2 + 3y - 4 = 0 \qquad\qquad y^2 - 3y - 4 = 0$$
$$(y - 1)(y + 4) = 0, \qquad\qquad (y + 1)(y - 4) = 0.$$

We therefore obtain four candidate points: $(2, 1)$, $(-2, -1)$, $(2, -4)$ and $(-2, 4)$. The first two points are closest to the origin (they are the ends of the minor axis of the ellipse); the second pair are farthest from the origin (the ends of the major axis). (See Fig. 3.3.4.)

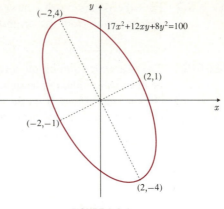

FIGURE 3.3.4

Considering the geometric underpinnings of the method of Lagrange multipliers, we would not expect the method to work if the level curves of the functions involved are not smooth, or if the maximum or minimum occurs at an endpoint of the constraint curve. One of the pitfalls of the method is that the level curves of functions may not be smooth, even though the functions themselves are differentiable. Problems can occur where a gradient vanishes, as the following example shows.

EXAMPLE 3.3.4   Find the minimum value of $f(x, y) = y$ subject to the constraint equation $g(x, y) = y^3 - x^2 = 0$.

SOLUTION   The semicubical parabola $y^3 = x^2$ has a cusp at the origin. (See Fig. 3.3.5.) Clearly $f(x, y) = y$ has minimum value 0 at that point. Suppose, however, that we try to solve the problem using the method of Lagrange multipliers to find this solution. The Lagrangian here is

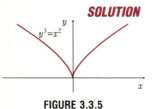

FIGURE 3.3.5

$$L(x, y, \lambda) = y + \lambda(y^3 - x^2),$$

which has critical points given by

$$-2\lambda x = 0$$
$$1 + 3\lambda y^2 = 0$$
$$y^3 - x^2 = 0.$$

Observe that $y = 0$ cannot satisfy the second equation, and, in fact, the three equations have *no solution* (x, y, λ).

The method of Lagrange multipliers breaks down in the above example because $\nabla g = \mathbf{0}$ at the solution point, and therefore the curve $g(x, y) = 0$ need not be smooth there. (In this case, it isn't smooth!) The geometric condition that ∇f should be parallel to ∇g at the solution point is meaningless in this case. When you apply the method of Lagrange multipliers, be aware that an extreme value may occur at

i) a critical point of the Lagrangian,

ii) a point where $\nabla g = \mathbf{0}$,

iii) a point where ∇f or ∇g does not exist, or

iv) an "endpoint" of the constraint set.

This situation is similar to that for extreme values of a function f of one variable, which may occur at a critical point of f, a singular point of f, or an endpoint of the domain of f.

Next consider a three-dimensional problem requiring us to find a maximum or minimum value of a function of three variables subject to two equation constraints:

extremize $f(x, y, z)$ **subject to** $g(x, y, z) = 0$ and $h(x, y, z) = 0$.

Again we assume that the problem has a solution, say at the point $P_0 = (x_0, y_0, z_0)$, that the functions f, g and h have continuous first partial derivatives near P_0, and that $\mathbf{T} = \nabla g(P_0) \times \nabla h(P_0) \neq \mathbf{0}$. These conditions imply that the surfaces $g(x, y, z) = 0$ and $h(x, y, z) = 0$ intersect in a smooth curve C near P_0, and that that the curve has tangent vector $\mathbf{T}$ at P_0. The same geometric argument used to set up the Method of Lagrange Multipliers for the two-dimensional problem considered earlier again shows that $\nabla f(P_0)$ must be perpendicular to $\mathbf{T}$; otherwise it would have a nonzero vector projection along $\mathbf{T}$, f would have a nonzero directional derivative along $\mathbf{T}$ and would therefore increase and decrease as we moved away from P_0 along C in opposite directions. Since $\nabla g(P_0)$ and $\nabla h(P_0)$ are nonzero and both perpendicular to $\mathbf{T}$, $\nabla f(P_0)$ must lie in the plane spanned by these two vectors and hence must be a linear combination of them:

$$\nabla f(x, y, z) = -\lambda \nabla g(x, y, z) - \mu \nabla h(x, y, z)$$

for some constants λ and μ. Thus we should look for critical points of the Lagrangian function

$$L(x, y, z, \lambda, \mu) = f(x, y, z) + \lambda g(x, y, z) + \mu h(x, y, z),$$

and therefore solve the system of equations

$$f_1(x, y, z) + \lambda g_1(x, y, z) + \mu h_1(x, y, z) = 0,$$
$$f_2(x, y, z) + \lambda g_2(x, y, z) + \mu h_2(x, y, z) = 0,$$
$$f_3(x, y, z) + \lambda g_3(x, y, z) + \mu h_3(x, y, z) = 0,$$
$$g(x, y, z) = 0,$$
$$h(x, y, z) = 0.$$

Solving such a system can present a considerable obstacle. It should be noted that in using the method of Lagrange multipliers instead of solving the constraint equations, we have traded the problem of solving two equations for two variables as functions of a third to one of solving five equations for numerical values of five unknowns.

EXAMPLE 3.3.5   Find the maximum and minimum values of the function $f(x,y,z) = xy + 2z$ on the circle which is the intersection of the plane $x + y + z = 0$ and the sphere $x^2 + y^2 + z^2 = 24$.

SOLUTION   The function f is continuous and the circle is a closed bounded set in 3-space. Therefore maximum and minimum values must exist. We look for critical points of the Lagrangian

$$L = xy + 2z + \lambda(x + y + z) + \mu(x^2 + y^2 + z^2 - 24).$$

Setting the first partial derivatives of L equal to zero we obtain

$$y + \lambda + 2\mu x = 0 \tag{A}$$
$$x + \lambda + 2\mu y = 0 \tag{B}$$
$$2 + \lambda + 2\mu z = 0 \tag{C}$$
$$x + y + z = 0 \tag{D}$$
$$x^2 + y^2 + z^2 - 24 = 0, \tag{E}$$

Subtracting (A) from (B) we get $(x - y)(1 - 2\mu) = 0$. Therefore either $\mu = \frac{1}{2}$ or $x = y$. We analyze both possibilities.

If $\mu = \frac{1}{2}$ we obtain from (B) and (C)

$$x + \lambda + y = 0, \qquad 2 + \lambda + z = 0.$$

Thus $x + y = 2 + z$. Combining this with D we get $z = -1$ and $x + y = 1$. Now by (E), $x^2 + y^2 = 24 - z^2 = 23$. Since $x^2 + y^2 + 2xy = (x + y)^2 = 1$ we have $2xy = 1 - 23 = -22$ and $xy = -11$. Now $(x - y)^2 = x^2 + y^2 - 2xy = 23 + 22 = 45$, so $x - y = \pm 3\sqrt{5}$. Combining this with $x + y = 1$ we obtain two critical points arising from $\mu = \frac{1}{2}$, namely $\left((1 + 3\sqrt{5})/2, (1 - 3\sqrt{5})/2, -1\right)$ and $\left((1 - 3\sqrt{5})/2, (1 + 3\sqrt{5})/2, -1\right)$. At both of these points we find that $f(x,y,z) = xy + 2z = -11 - 2 = -13$.

If $x = y$ then (D) implies that $z = -2x$, and (E) then gives $6x^2 = 24$, so $x = \pm 2$. Therefore points $(2, 2, -4)$ and $(-2, -2, 4)$ must be considered. We have $f(2, 2, -4) = 4 - 8 = -4$ and $f(-2, -2, 4) = 4 + 8 = 12$.

We conclude that the maximum value of f on the circle is 12 and the minimum value is -13.

The method of Lagrange multipliers may be applied to find extreme values of a function of n variables,

$$f(x_1, x_2, \ldots, x_n),$$

subject to $m \le n - 1$ constraints,

$$g_{(1)}(x_1, x_2, \ldots, x_n) = 0$$
$$g_{(2)}(x_1, x_2, \ldots, x_n) = 0$$
$$\vdots$$
$$g_{(m)}(x_1, x_2, \ldots, x_n) = 0.$$

Assuming that the problem has a solution at the point P_0, that f and all of the functions $g_{(j)}$ have continuous first partial derivatives at all points near P_0, and that the intersection of the constraint (hyper)surfaces is smooth near P_0, then we should look for P_0 among the critical points of the $(n+m)$-variable Lagrangian function

$$L(x_1, \ldots, x_n, \lambda_1, \ldots, \lambda_m) = f(x_1, \ldots, x_n) + \lambda_1 g_{(1)}(x_1, \ldots, x_n)$$
$$+ \lambda_2 g_{(2)}(x_1, \ldots, x_n) + \cdots + \lambda_m g_{(m)}(x_1, \ldots, x_n).$$

We will not attempt to prove this general assertion. (A proof can be based on the implicit function theorem.)

EXERCISES

1. Rework Example 3.3.1 using the method of Lagrange multipliers.

2. Find the shortest distance from the point $(3,0)$ to the parabola $y = x^2$,

   a) by reducing to an unconstrained problem in one variable, and

   b) by using the method of Lagrange multipliers.

3. Find the distance from the origin to the plane $x + 2y + 2z = 3$,

   a) by a geometric argument (no calculus),

   b) by reducing the problem to an unconstrained problem in two variables, and

   c) by using the method of Lagrange multipliers.

4. Find the maximum and minimum values of the function $f(x, y, z) = x + y - z$ over the sphere $x^2 + y^2 + z^2 = 1$.

5. Use the Lagrange multiplier method to find the greatest and least distances from the point $(2, 1, -2)$ to the sphere with equation $x^2 + y^2 + z^2 = 1$. (Of course, the answer could be obtained more easily by using a simple geometric argument.)

6. Find the shortest distance from the origin to the surface $xyz^2 = 2$.

7. Find a, b and c so that the volume $V = 4\pi abc/3$ of an ellipsoid $\dfrac{x^2}{a^2} + \dfrac{y^2}{b^2} + \dfrac{z^2}{c^2} = 1$ passing through the point $(1, 2, 1)$ is as small as possible.

8. Find the ends of the major and minor axes of the ellipse $3x^2 + 2xy + 3y^2 = 16$.

9. Find the maximum and minimum values of the function $f(x, y, z) = x$ over the curve of intersection of the plane $z = x + y$ and the ellipsoid $x^2 + 2y^2 + 2z^2 = 8$.

10. Find the maximum and minimum values of $f(x, y, z) = x^2 + y^2 + z^2$ on the ellipse formed by the intersection of the cone $z^2 = x^2 + y^2$ and the plane $x - 2z = 3$.

11. Find the maximum and minimum values of $f(x, y, z) = 4 - z$ on the ellipse formed by the intersection of the cylinder $x^2 + y^2 = 8$ and the plane $x + y + z = 1$.

12. Find the maximum and minimum values of $f(x, y, z) = x + y^2z$ subject to the constraints $y^2 + z^2 = 2$ and $z = x$.

13. *Use the method of Lagrange multipliers to find the shortest distance between the straight lines $x = y = z$ and $x = -y$, $z = 2$. (There are, of course, much easier ways to get the answer. This is an object lesson in not trying to shoot sparrows with cannons.)

14. Find the maximum and minimum values of the n-variable function $x_1 + x_2 + \cdots + x_n$ subject to the constraint $x_1^2 + x_2^2 + \cdots + x_n^2 = 1$.

15. Repeat the previous exercise for the function $x_1 + 2x_2 + 3x_3 + \cdots + nx_n$ with the same constraint.

16. Find the most economical shape of a rectangular box with no top.

17. Find the maximum volume of a rectangular box with faces parallel to the coordinate planes if one corner is at the origin and the diagonally opposite corner lies on the plane $4x + 2y + z = 2$.

18. Find the volume of the largest rectangular box with faces parallel to the coordinate planes which has one corner at the origin and diagonally opposite corner on the first octant part of the surface $xy + 2yz + 3xz = 18$.

19. A rectangular box having no top and having a prescribed volume $V\,\mathrm{m}^3$ is to be constructed using two different materials. The material used for the bottom and front of the box is five times as costly (per square metre) as the material used for the back and the other two sides.

What should be the dimensions of the box to make the cost of materials a minimum?

20.*Find the maximum and minimum values of $xy + z^2$ on the ball $x^2 + y^2 + z^2 \leq 1$. Use Lagrange multipliers to treat the boundary case.

21.*Repeat the previous exercise but handle the boundary case by parametrizing the sphere $x^2 + y^2 + z^2 = 1$ using

$$x = \sin \phi \cos \theta,$$
$$y = \sin \phi \sin \theta,$$
$$z = \cos \phi,$$

where $0 \leq \phi \leq \pi$ and $0 \leq \theta \leq 2\pi$.

22.*If α, β and γ are the angles of a triangle show that

$$\sin \frac{\alpha}{2} \sin \frac{\beta}{2} \sin \frac{\gamma}{2} \leq \frac{1}{8}.$$

For what triangles does equality occur?

23.*Suppose that f and g have continuous first partial derivatives throughout the xy-plane, and suppose that $g_2(a, b) \neq 0$. This implies that the equation $g(x, y) = g(a, b)$ defines y implicitly as a function of x nearby the point (a, b). Use the chain rule to show that if $f(x, y)$ has a local extreme value at (a, b) subject to the constraint $g(x, y) = g(a, b)$, then for some number λ the point (a, b, λ) is a critical point of the function

$$L(x, y, \lambda) = f(x, y) + \lambda g(x, y).$$

This constitutes a more formal justification of the Method of Lagrange multipliers in this case.

24. What is the shortest distance from the point $(0, -1)$ to the curve $y = \sqrt{1 - x^2}$? Can this problem be solved by the Lagrange multiplier method? Why?

25. Example 3.3.4 showed that the Method of Lagrange Multipliers might fail to find a point which extremizes $f(x, y)$ subject to the constraint $g(x, y) = 0$ if $\nabla g = \mathbf{0}$ at the extremizing point. Can the method also fail if $\nabla f = \mathbf{0}$ at the extremizing point? Why?

3.4   THE METHOD OF LEAST SQUARES

Important optimization problems arise in the statistical analysis of experimental data. Frequently experiments are designed to measure the values of one or more quantities supposed constant, or to demonstrate a supposed functional relationship among variable quantities. Experimental error is usually present in the measurements, and experiments need to be repeated several times in order to arrive at "mean" or "average" values of the quantities being measured.

Consider a very simple example. An experiment to measure a certain physical constant c is repeated n times, yielding the values $c_1, c_2, \ldots, c_n$. If none of the measurements is suspected of being faulty, intuition tells us that we should use the mean value $\bar{c} = (c_1 + c_2 + \cdots + c_n)/n$ as the value of c determined by the experiments. Let us see how this intuition can be justified.

Various methods for determining c from the data values are possible. We could, for instance, choose c to minimize the sum T of its distances from the data points:

$$T = |c - c_1| + |c - c_2| + \cdots + |c - c_n|.$$

This is unsatisfactory for a number of reasons. Since absolute values have singular points it is difficult to determine the minimizing value of c. More importantly, c may not be determined uniquely. If $n = 2$ any point in the interval between c_1 and c_2 will give the same minimum value to T. (See Exercise 20 at the end of this section.)

A more promising approach is to minimize the sum S of *squares* of the distances from c to the data points:

$$S = (c - c_1)^2 + (c - c_2)^2 + \cdots + (c - c_n)^2 = \sum_{i=1}^{n}(c - c_i)^2.$$

This function of c is smooth and its (unconstrained) minimum value will occur at a critical point $\bar{c}$ given by

$$0 = \left.\frac{dS}{dc}\right|_{c=\bar{c}} = \sum_{i=1}^{n} 2(\bar{c} - c_i) = 2n\bar{c} - 2\sum_{i=1}^{n} c_i.$$

Thus $\bar{c}$ is the *mean* of the data values:

$$\bar{c} = \frac{1}{n}\sum_{i=1}^{n} c_i = \frac{c_1 + c_2 + \cdots + c_n}{n}.$$

The technique used to obtain $\bar{c}$ above is an example of what is called **the method of least squares.** It has the following geometric interpretation. If the data values $c_1, c_2, \ldots, c_n$ are regarded as components of a vector $\mathbf{c}$ in $\mathbb{R}^n$ and $\mathbf{w}$ is the vector with components $1, 1, \ldots, 1$ then the vector projection of $\mathbf{c}$ in the direction of $\mathbf{w}$,

$$\mathbf{c_w} = \frac{\mathbf{c} \bullet \mathbf{w}}{|\mathbf{w}|^2}\,\mathbf{w} = \frac{c_1 + c_2 + \cdots + c_n}{n}\,\mathbf{w}$$

has all its components equal to the average of the data values. Thus determining c from the data by the method of least squares corresponds to finding the vector projection of the data vector onto the one-dimensional subspace of $\mathbb{R}^n$ spanned by $\mathbf{w}$. Had there been no error in the measurements c_i, then $\mathbf{c}$ would have been equal to $c\mathbf{w}$.

Linear Regression

It often happens in scientific investigations that the response of a system is believed to be a certain kind of function of one or more input variables. An investigator can set up an experiment to measure the response of the system for various values of those variables in order to determine the parameters of the function.

For example, suppose that the response y of a system is suspected to depend on the input x according to the linear relationship

$$y = ax + b,$$

where the values of a and b are unknown. An experiment set up to measure values of y corresponding to several values of x yields n data points, (x_i, y_i), $i = 1, 2, \ldots, n$. If the supposed linear relationship is valid, these data points should lie "approximately" along a straight line, but not exactly on one because of experimental error. Suppose the points are as shown in Fig. 3.4.1. The linear

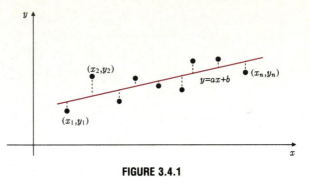

FIGURE 3.4.1

relationship seems reasonable in this case. We want to find values of a and b so that the straight line $y = ax + b$ "best" fits the data.

In this situation the method of least squares requires that a and b be chosen to minimize the sum S of the squares of the vertical displacements of the data points from the line:

$$S = \sum_{i=1}^{n}(y_i - ax_i - b)^2.$$

This is an unconstrained minimum problem in two variables, a and b. The minimum will occur at a critical point of S:

$$0 = \frac{\partial S}{\partial a} = -2\sum_{i=1}^{n} x_i(y_i - ax_i - b),$$

$$0 = \frac{\partial S}{\partial b} = -2\sum_{i=1}^{n}(y_i - ax_i - b).$$

These equations can be rewritten

$$\left(\sum_{i=1}^{n} x_i^2\right)a \; + \; \left(\sum_{i=1}^{n} x_i\right)b \; = \; \sum_{i=1}^{n} x_i y_i,$$

$$\left(\sum_{i=1}^{n} x_i\right)a \; + \; n\,b \; = \; \sum_{i=1}^{n} y_i.$$

Solving this pair of linear equations we obtain the desired parameters

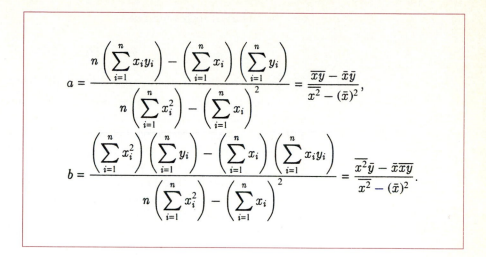

$$a = \frac{n\left(\sum_{i=1}^{n} x_i y_i\right) - \left(\sum_{i=1}^{n} x_i\right)\left(\sum_{i=1}^{n} y_i\right)}{n\left(\sum_{i=1}^{n} x_i^2\right) - \left(\sum_{i=1}^{n} x_i\right)^2} = \frac{\overline{xy} - \bar{x}\bar{y}}{\overline{x^2} - (\bar{x})^2},$$

$$b = \frac{\left(\sum_{i=1}^{n} x_i^2\right)\left(\sum_{i=1}^{n} y_i\right) - \left(\sum_{i=1}^{n} x_i\right)\left(\sum_{i=1}^{n} x_i y_i\right)}{n\left(\sum_{i=1}^{n} x_i^2\right) - \left(\sum_{i=1}^{n} x_i\right)^2} = \frac{\overline{x^2}\bar{y} - \bar{x}\overline{xy}}{\overline{x^2} - (\bar{x})^2}.$$

In the latter formulas we have used a bar to indicate the mean value of a quantity; thus $\overline{xy} = (1/n)\sum_{i=0}^{n} x_i y_i$ and so on.

The procedure of fitting the "best" straight line through data points by the method of least squares is called **linear regression** and the line $y = ax + b$ obtained in this way is called the **empirical regression line** corresponding to the data. Some scientific calculators with statistical features provide for linear regression by accumulating the sums of x_i, y_i, x_i^2 and $x_i y_i$ in various registers, and keeping track of the number n of data points entered in another register. At any time it has available the information necessary to calculate a and b, and the value of y corresponding to any given x.

EXAMPLE 3.4.1   Find the empirical regression line for the data $(x, y) = (0, 2.10)$, $(1,1.92)$, $(2,1.84)$, $(3,1.71)$, $(4,1.64)$. What is the predicted value of y at $x = 5$?

SOLUTION   We have

$$\bar{x} = \frac{0 + 1 + 2 + 3 + 4}{5} = 2,$$

$$\bar{y} = \frac{2.10 + 1.92 + 1.84 + 1.71 + 1.64}{5} = 1.842,$$

$$\overline{xy} = \frac{(0)(2.10) + (1)(1.92) + (2)(1.84) + (3)(1.71) + (4)(1.64)}{5} = 3.458,$$

$$\overline{x^2} = \frac{0^2 + 1^2 + 2^2 + 3^2 + 4^2}{5} = 6.$$

Therefore

$$a = \frac{3.458 - (2)(1.842)}{6 - 2^2} = -0.113,$$

$$b = \frac{(6)(1.842) - (2)(3.458)}{6 - 2^2} = 2.068,$$

and the empirical regression line is

$$y = 2.068 - 0.113x.$$

The predicted value of y at $x = 5$ is $2.068 - 0.113 \times 5 = 1.503$.

Linear regression can also be interpreted in terms of vector projection. The data points define two vectors $\mathbf{x}$ and $\mathbf{y}$ in $\mathbb{R}^n$ with components $x_1, x_2, \ldots, x_n$ and $y_1, y_2, \ldots, y_n$ respectively. Let $\mathbf{w}$ be the vector with components $1, 1, \ldots, 1$. Finding the coefficients a and b for the regression line corresponds to finding the orthogonal projection of $\mathbf{y}$ onto the two-dimensional subspace (plane) of $\mathbb{R}^n$ spanned by $\mathbf{x}$ and $\mathbf{w}$. (See Fig. 3.4.2.) This projection is $\mathbf{p} = a\mathbf{x} + b\mathbf{w}$. In fact, the two equations obtained above by setting the partial derivatives of S equal to zero are just the two conditions

$$(\mathbf{y} - \mathbf{p}) \bullet \mathbf{x} = 0,$$
$$(\mathbf{y} - \mathbf{p}) \bullet \mathbf{w} = 0,$$

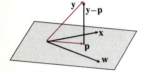

FIGURE 3.4.2

stating that $\mathbf{y}$ minus its projection onto the subspace is perpendicular to the subspace. The angle between $\mathbf{y}$ and this $\mathbf{p}$ provides a measure of how well the empirical regression line fits the data; the smaller the angle the better the fit.

Linear regression can be used to find specific functional relationships of types other than linear if suitable transformations are applied to the data.

EXAMPLE 3.4.2   Find the values of constants K and s for which the curve

$$y = Kx^s$$

best fits the experimental data points (x_i, y_i), $i = 1, 2, \ldots, n$. (Assume all data values are positive.)

SOLUTION   Observe that the required functional form corresponds to a linear relationship between $\ln y$ and $\ln x$:

$$\ln y = \ln K + s \ln x.$$

If we determine the parameters a and b of the empirical regression line $\eta = a\xi + b$ corresponding to the transformed data $(\xi_i, \eta_i) = (\ln x_i, \ln y_i)$ then $s = a$ and $K = e^b$ are the required values.

REMARK: It should be stressed that the constants K and s obtained by the method used in the solution above are not the same as those that would be obtained by direct application of the least squares method to the untransformed problem, that is, by minimizing $\sum_{i=1}^{n}(y_i - Kx_i^s)^2$. This latter problem cannot readily be solved. (Try it!)

Generally, the method of least squares is applied to fit an equation in which the response is expressed as a sum of constants times functions of one or more input variables. The constants are determined as critical points of the sum of squared deviations of the actual response values from the values predicted by the equation.

Applications of Least Squares to Integrals

The method of least squares can be used to find approximations to reasonably well-behaved (say, piecewise continuous) functions as sums of constants times specified functions. The idea is to choose the constants to minimize the *integral* of the square of the difference.

For example, suppose we want to approximate the continuous function $f(x)$ over the interval $[0,1]$ by a linear function $g(x) = px + q$. The method of least squares would require that p and q be chosen to minimize the integral

$$I(p, q) = \int_0^1 \Big(f(x) - px - q \Big)^2 dx.$$

Assuming that we can "differentiate through the integral" (we will verify the validity of this in Section 3.5) the critical point of $I(p, q)$ can be found from

$$0 = \frac{\partial I}{\partial p} = -2 \int_0^1 x \Big(f(x) - px - q \Big) dx,$$

$$0 = \frac{\partial I}{\partial q} = -2 \int_0^1 \Big(f(x) - px - q \Big) dx.$$

Thus

$$\frac{p}{3} + \frac{q}{2} = \int_0^1 x f(x) dx,$$

$$\frac{p}{2} + q = \int_0^1 f(x) dx,$$

and solving this linear system for p and q we get

$$p = \int_0^1 (12x - 6) f(x) dx,$$

$$q = \int_0^1 (4 - 6x) f(x) dx.$$

The following example concerns the approximation of a function by a "trigonometric polynomial." Such approximations form the basis for the study of Fourier series, which are of fundamental importance in the solution of boundary-value problems for the Laplace, heat and wave equations, and other partial differential equations which arise in applied mathematics.

EXAMPLE 3.4.3   Use a least squares integral to approximate $f(x)$ by the sum

$$\sum_{k=1}^{n} b_k \sin kx$$

on the interval $0 \leq x \leq \pi$.

SOLUTION We want to choose the constants to minimize

$$I = \int_0^\pi \left(f(x) - \sum_{k=1}^n b_k \sin kx \right)^2 dx.$$

For each $1 \le j \le n$ we have

$$0 = \frac{\partial I}{\partial b_j} = -2 \int_0^\pi \left(f(x) - \sum_{k=1}^n b_k \sin kx \right) \sin jx \, dx.$$

Thus

$$\sum_{k=1}^n b_k \int_0^\pi \sin kx \sin jx \, dx = \int_0^\pi f(x) \sin jx \, dx.$$

However, if $j \ne k$, then $\sin kx \sin jx$ is an even function, so

$$\int_0^\pi \sin kx \sin jx \, dx = \frac{1}{2} \int_{-\pi}^\pi \sin kx \sin jx \, dx$$

$$= \frac{1}{4} \int_{-\pi}^\pi \left(\cos(k-j)x - \cos(k+j)x \right) dx = 0.$$

If $j = k$, then we have

$$\int_0^\pi \sin^2 jx \, dx = \frac{1}{2} \int_0^\pi (1 - \cos 2jx) \, dx = \frac{\pi}{2},$$

so that

$$b_j = \frac{2}{\pi} \int_0^\pi f(x) \sin jx \, dx.$$

REMARK: If f is continuous on $0 \le x \le \pi$, it can be shown that

$$\lim_{n \to \infty} \int_0^\pi \left(f(x) - \sum_{k=1}^n b_k \sin kx \right)^2 dx = 0,$$

with the coefficients b_k given as above. It follows that

$$f(x) = \sum_{k=1}^\infty b_k \sin kx, \qquad 0 < x < \pi.$$

This is known as a Fourier sine series representation of $f(x)$ on the interval $(0, \pi)$. The function f can also be approximated using a sum of cosines (see Exercise 17 below), and such approximations lead to an exact representation of f as a Fourier cosine series:

$$f(x) = \frac{a_0}{2} + \sum_{k=1}^\infty a_k \cos kx, \qquad 0 < x < \pi,$$

where

$$a_j = \frac{2}{\pi} \int_0^\pi f(x) \cos jx \, dx.$$

REMARK: Representing a function as the sum of a Fourier series is analogous to representing a vector as a sum of basis vectors. If we think of continuous functions on the interval $[0, \pi]$ as "vectors" with addition and scalar multiplication defined pointwise:

$$(f + g)(x) = f(x) + g(x), \qquad (cf)(x) = cf(x),$$

and with "dot product" defined as

$$f \bullet g = \int_0^\pi f(x)g(x)\, dx,$$

then the functions $e_k(x) = \sqrt{2/\pi}\, \sin kx$ form a "basis." As shown in the example above, $e_j \bullet e_j = 1$, and if $k \neq j$ then $e_k \bullet e_j = 0$. Thus these "basis vectors" are "mutually perpendicular unit vectors." The Fourier coefficients b_j of a function f are the components of f with respect to that basis.

EXERCISES

1. A power plant must be installed in a factory to supply power to n machines located at positions (x_i, y_i), $i = 1, 2, \ldots, n$. Where should the plant be located to minimize the sum of the squares of its distances from the machines?

2. The relationship $y = ax^2$ is known to hold between certain variables. Given the experimental data (x_i, y_i), $i = 1, 2, \ldots, n$ determine a value for a by the method of least squares.

3. Repeat the above exercise but with the relationship $y = ae^x$.

4. Use the method of least squares to find the plane $z = ax + by + c$ which best fits the data (x_i, y_i, z_i), $i = 1, 2, \ldots, n$.

5. Resolve the above exercise using a vector projection argument instead of the method of least squares.

In Exercises 6–11 show how to adapt linear regression to determine the two parameters p and q so that the given relationship fits the experimental data (x_i, y_i), $i = 1, 2, \ldots, n$. In which of these are the values of p and q obtained identical to those obtained by direct application of the method of least squares with no change of variable?

6. $y = p + qx^2$ 7. $y = pe^{qx}$

8. $y = \ln(p + qx)$ 9. $y = px + qx^2$

10. $y = \sqrt{px + q}$ 11. $y = pe^x + qe^{-x}$

12. Find the parabola of the form $y = p + qx^2$ which best fits the data $(x, y) = (1, 0.11)$, $(2, 1.62)$, $(3, 4.07)$, $(4, 7.55)$, $(6, 17.63)$, $(7, 24.20)$. No value of y was measured at $x = 5$. What value would you predict at this point?

13. Use the method of least squares to find constants a, b and c so that the relationship $y = ax^2 + bx + c$ best describes the experimental data (x_i, y_i), $i = 1, 2, \ldots, n$, $(n \geq 3)$. How is this situation interpreted in terms of vector projection?

14. How can the result of the previous exercise be used to fit a curve of the form $y = pe^x + q + re^{-x}$ through the same data points?

15.*Find a and b to minimize $\displaystyle\int_0^\pi (\sin x - ax^2 - bx)^2\, dx$.

16.*Find a, b and c to minimize $\displaystyle\int_0^1 (x^3 - ax^2 - bx - c)^2\, dx$. What is the minimum value of the integral?

17.*Find constants a_j, $j = 0, 1, \ldots, n$ to minimize

$$\int_0^\pi \left(f(x) - \frac{a_0}{2} - \sum_{k=1}^n a_k \cos kx \right)^2 dx.$$

18. Find the Fourier sine series for the function $f(x) = x$ on $0 < x < \pi$. To what function would you expect the series to converge in the interval $-\pi < x < 0$?

19. Repeat the above exercise, but obtaining instead a Fourier cosine series.

20. Suppose $x_1, x_2, \ldots, x_n$ satisfy $x_i \leq x_j$ whenever $i < j$. Find x which minimizes $\sum_{i=1}^n |x - x_i|$. Treat the cases n odd and n even separately. For what values of n is x unique? (Hint: do not use calculus in this problem.)

21.*The problem of finding a point in the plane (or a higher dimensional space) which minimizes the sum of its distances from n given points is very difficult. The case $n = 3$ is known as *Steiner's Problem*. If $P_1 P_2 P_3$ is a triangle whose largest angle is less than $120°$, there is a point Q inside the triangle so that the lines QP_1, QP_2 and QP_3 make equal $120°$ angles with one another. Show that the sum of the distances from the vertices of the triangle to a point P is minimum when $P = Q$. Hint: first show that if $P = (x, y)$ and $P_i = (x_i, y_i)$ then

$$\frac{d|PP_i|}{dx} = \cos\theta_i, \qquad \frac{d|PP_i|}{dy} = \sin\theta_i,$$

where θ_i is the angle between $\overrightarrow{P_iP}$ and the positive direction of the x-axis. Hence show that the minimal point P satisfies two trigonometric equations involving θ_1, θ_2 and θ_3. Then try to show that any two of those angles differ by $\pm 2\pi/3$. Where should P be taken if the triangle has an angle of $120°$ or greater?

3.5   PARAMETRIC PROBLEMS

In this section we shall briefly examine three unrelated situations in which one wants to differentiate a function with respect to a parameter rather than one of the basic variables of the function. Such situations arise frequently in mathematics and its applications.

Differentiating Integrals with Parameters

The fundamental theorem of calculus shows how to differentiate a definite integral with respect to the upper limit of integration:

$$\frac{d}{dx} \int_a^x f(t)\,dt = f(x).$$

We are going to look at a different problem about differentiating integrals. If the integrand of a definite integral also depends on variables other than the variable of integration then the integral will be a function of those other variables. How are we to find the derivative of such a function? For instance, consider the function $F(x)$ defined by

$$F(x) = \int_a^b f(x, t)\,dt.$$

We would like to be able to calculate $F'(x)$ by "taking the derivative inside the integral:"

$$F'(x) = \frac{d}{dx} \int_a^b f(x, t)\,dt = \int_a^b \frac{\partial}{\partial x} f(x, t)\,dt.$$

Observe that we use "d/dx" outside the integral and "$\partial/\partial x$" inside because the integral is a function of x only, but the integrand f is a function of both x and t. If the integrand depends on more than one parameter, then partial derivatives would be needed inside and outside the integral:

$$\frac{\partial}{\partial x} \int_a^b f(x, y, t)\,dt = \int_a^b \frac{\partial}{\partial x} f(x, y, t)\,dt.$$

The operation of taking a derivative with respect to a parameter inside the integral, or "differentiating through the integral" as it is usually called, seems plausible. We differentiate sums term by term, and integrals are the limits of sums. However, both the differentiation and integration operations involve the taking of limits, (limits of Newton quotients for derivatives, limits of Riemann sums for integrals). Differentiating through the integral requires changing the order in which the two limits are taken, and therefore requires justification.

We have already seen another example of change of order of limits. When we assert that two mixed partial derivatives with respect to the same variables are equal,

$$\frac{\partial^2 f}{\partial x \partial y} = \frac{\partial^2 f}{\partial y \partial x},$$

we are, in fact, saying that limits corresponding to differentiation with respect to x and y can be taken in either order with the same result. This is not true in general; we proved it under the assumption that both of the mixed partials were *continuous*. (See Theorem 2.3.5 and Exercise 18 of Section 2.3.) In general, some assumptions are required to justify the interchange of limits. The following theorem gives some conditions which justify the interchange of limits involved in differentiating through the integral.

THEOREM 3.5.1   Suppose that for every x satisfying $c < x < d$ the following conditions hold:

i) the integrals

$$\int_a^b f(x,t)\,dt \qquad \text{and} \qquad \int_a^b f_1(x,t)\,dt$$

both exist (either as proper or convergent improper integrals).

ii) $f_{11}(x,t)$ exists and satisfies

$$|f_{11}(x,t)| \le g(t), \qquad \text{for } a < t < b$$

where

$$\int_a^b g(t)\,dt = K < \infty.$$

Then for each x satisfying $c < x < d$ we have

$$\frac{d}{dx}\int_a^b f(x,t)\,dt = \int_a^b \frac{\partial}{\partial x} f(x,t)\,dt.$$

PROOF   Let

$$F(x) = \int_a^b f(x,t)\,dt.$$

If $c < x < d$, $h \neq 0$ and $|h|$ is sufficiently small that $c < x+h < d$ then by Taylor's formula

$$f(x+h,t) = f(x,t) + h f_1(x,t) + \frac{h^2}{2} f_{11}(x+\theta h, t)$$

for some θ between 0 and 1. Therefore

$$\left| \frac{F(x+h)-F(x)}{h} - \int_a^b f_1(x,t)\,dt \right|$$

$$= \left| \int_a^b \frac{f(x+h,t)-f(x,t)}{h}\,dt - \int_a^b f_1(x,t)\,dt \right|$$

$$\le \int_a^b \left| \frac{f(x+h,t)-f(x,t)}{h} - f_1(x,t) \right| dt$$

$$= \int_a^b \left| \frac{h}{2} f_{11}(x+\theta h,t) \right| dt$$

$$\le \frac{h}{2} \int_a^b g(t)\,dt = \frac{Kh}{2} \;\to\; 0 \text{ as } h \to 0.$$

Therefore

$$F'(x) = \lim_{h \to 0} \frac{F(x+h)-F(x)}{h} = \int_a^b f_1(x,t)\,dt$$

which is the desired result. $\square$

REMARK: It can be shown that the conclusion of Theorem 3.5.1 also holds under the sole assumption that $f_1(x,t)$ is continuous on the *closed, bounded* rectangle $c \le x \le d$, $a \le t \le b$. We cannot prove this here—the proof depends on a subtle property called *uniform continuity* possessed by continuous functions on closed bounded sets in $\mathbf{R}^n$. In any event, Theorem 3.5.1 is more useful for our purposes because it allows for improper integrals.

EXAMPLE 3.5.2 Evaluate $\int_0^\infty t^n e^{-t}\,dt$.

SOLUTION Starting with the convergent improper integral

$$\int_0^\infty e^{-s}\,ds = \lim_{R \to \infty} \left. \frac{e^{-s}}{-1} \right|_0^R = \lim_{R \to \infty} (1 - e^{-R}) = 1$$

we introduce a parameter by substituting $s = xt$, $ds = x\,dt$ (where $x > 0$) and get

$$\int_0^\infty e^{-xt}\,dt = \frac{1}{x}.$$

Now differentiate n times (each resulting integral converges):

$$\int_0^\infty -t\,e^{-xt}\,dt = -\frac{1}{x^2},$$

$$\int_0^\infty (-t)^2 e^{-xt}\,dt = (-1)^2 \frac{2}{x^3},$$

$$\vdots$$

$$\int_0^\infty (-t)^n e^{-xt}\,dt = (-1)^n \frac{n!}{x^{n+1}}.$$

Putting $x = 1$ we get

$$\int_0^\infty t^n \, e^{-t} \, dt = n!.$$

Note that this result could be obtained by integration by parts (n times) or a reduction formula. This method is a little easier.

REMARK: The reader should check that for $x > 0$, and $k \geq 0$ the function $f(x,t) = t^k \, e^{-xt}$ satisfies the conditions of Theorem 3.5.1. We will normally not make a point of this.

EXAMPLE 3.5.3   Evaluate $F(x,y) = \displaystyle\int_0^\infty \frac{e^{-xt} - e^{-yt}}{t} \, dt$ for $x > 0$, $y > 0$.

SOLUTION   We have

$$\frac{\partial F}{\partial x} = -\int_0^\infty e^{-xt} \, dt = -\frac{1}{x}, \qquad \frac{\partial F}{\partial y} = \int_0^\infty e^{-yt} \, dt = \frac{1}{y}.$$

It follows that

$$F(x,y) = -\ln x + C_1(y), \quad \text{and} \quad F(x,y) = \ln y + C_2(x).$$

Comparing these two formulas for F, we are forced to conclude that $C_1(y) = \ln y + C$ for some constant C. Therefore

$$F(x,y) = \ln y - \ln x + C = \ln \frac{y}{x} + C.$$

Since $F(1,1) = 0$ we must have $C = 0$ and $F(x,y) = \ln(y/x)$.

If we wish to differentiate a definite integral with respect to a parameter appearing in the limits of integration as well as in the integrand then the chain rule comes into play. For instance, if $a = a(x)$ and $b = b(x)$ are differentiable functions of x then under the conditions of Theorem 3.5.1 we have

$$\frac{d}{dx} \int_{a(x)}^{b(x)} f(x,t) \, dt = \int_{a(x)}^{b(x)} \frac{\partial}{\partial x} f(x,t) \, dt + f\big(x, b(x)\big) b'(x) - f\big(x, a(x)\big) a'(x).$$

EXAMPLE 3.5.4   Solve the *integral equation*

$$f(x) = a - \int_b^x (x - t) f(t) \, dt.$$

SOLUTION   Assume, for the moment, that the equation has a solution sufficiently well behaved to allow for differentiation through the integral. Differentiating twice we get

$$f'(x) = -(x - x)f(x) - \int_b^x f(t) \, dt = -\int_b^x f(t) \, dt,$$

$$f''(x) = -f(x).$$

The latter equation is the differential equation of simple harmonic motion. Observe that the given equation for f and that for f' imply the initial conditions

$$f(b) = a, \qquad \text{and} \qquad f'(b) = 0.$$

Accordingly we write the general solution of $f''(x) = -f(x)$ in the form

$$f(x) = A\cos(x - b) + B\sin(x - b).$$

The initial conditions then imply $A = a$ and $B = 0$ so the required solution is $f(x) = a\cos(x - b)$. Finally, we note that this function is indeed smooth enough to allow the differentiations through the integral, so is the solution of the given integral equation. (If you wish, verify it in the integral equation.)

Envelopes

An equation $f(x, y, c) = 0$ which involves a parameter c as well as the variables x and y represents a family of curves in the xy-plane. Consider, for instance, the family

$$f(x, y, c) = \frac{x}{c} + cy - 2 = 0$$

which consists of straight lines with intercepts $\left(2c, \dfrac{2}{c}\right)$ on the coordinate axes.

Several of these lines are sketched in Fig. 3.5.1. It appears that there is a curve to which all these lines are tangent. This curve is called the *envelope* of the family of lines.

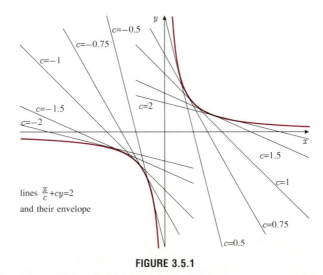

lines $\frac{x}{c}+cy=2$
and their envelope

FIGURE 3.5.1

In general, a curve C is called the **envelope** of the family of curves with equations $f(x, y, c) = 0$ if, for each value of c, the curve $f(x, y, c) = 0$ is tangent to C at some point depending on c.

For the family of lines in Fig. 3.5.1 it appears that the envelope may be the rectangular hyperbola $xy = 1$. We will verify this after developing a method for determining the equation of the envelope of a family of curves. We assume that the function $f(x, y, c)$ has continuous first partials, and that the envelope is a smooth curve.

For each c, the curve $f(x, y, c) = 0$ is tangent to the envelope at a point (x, y) which depends on c. Let us express this dependence in the explicit form $x = g(c)$, $y = h(c)$; these equations are parametric equations of the envelope. Since (x, y) lies on the curve $f(x, y, c) = 0$ we have

$$f\big(g(c), h(c), c\big) = 0.$$

Differentiating this equation with respect to c, we obtain

$$f_1 g'(c) + f_2 h'(c) + f_3 = 0,$$

where the partials of f are evaluated at $\big(g(c), h(c), c\big)$. Assuming (without loss of generality) that f_2 is not zero at that point, we can differentiate the equation $f(x, y, c) = 0$ with respect to x to obtain the slope of this curve at $\big(g(c), h(c), c\big)$:

$$\frac{dy}{dx} = -\frac{f_1}{f_2}.$$

Since this curve is tangent to the envelope, which has slope h'/g', we must have

$$f_1 g'(c) + f_2 h'(c) = 0.$$

It follows that $f_3(x, y, c)$ must vanish at all points of the envelope. The equation of the envelope can therefore be found by eliminating c between the two equations

$$f(x, y, c) = 0,$$
$$\frac{\partial}{\partial c} f(x, y, c) = 0.$$

For the family of straight lines we were considering above, these equations become

$$\frac{x}{c} + cy - 2 = 0, \qquad \text{and} \qquad -\frac{x}{c^2} + y = 0,$$

which can be solved for $x = c$, $y = 1/c$ and hence imply that $xy = 1$ is the envelope, as we conjectured.

EXAMPLE 3.5.5   Find the envelope of the family of circles

$$(x - c)^2 + y^2 = c.$$

SOLUTION   Here $f(x,y,c) = (x - c)^2 + y^2 - c$. The equation of the envelope is obtained by eliminating c from the pair of equations

$$f(x,y,c) = (x - c)^2 + y^2 - c = 0,$$

$$\frac{\partial}{\partial c} f(x,y,c) = -2(x - c) - 1 = 0.$$

From the second equation, $x = c - \frac{1}{2}$, and then from the first, $y^2 = c - \frac{1}{4}$. Hence the envelope is the parabola

$$x^2 = y + \frac{1}{4}.$$

This envelope and some of the circles in the family are sketched in Fig. 3.5.2.

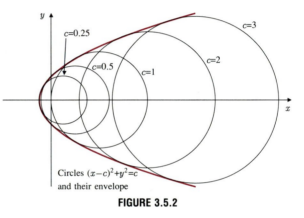

Circles $(x-c)^2+y^2=c$
and their envelope

FIGURE 3.5.2

A similar technique can be used to find the envelope of a family of surfaces. This will be a surface tangent to each member of the family.

EXAMPLE 3.5.6   Identify the envelope of the family of spheres

$$x^2 + y^2 + (z - 2c)^2 = c^2.$$

SOLUTION   The equation of the envelope will be found by eliminating c from the pair of equations

$$f(x,y,z,c) = x^2 + y^2 + (z - 2c)^2 - c^2 = 0,$$

$$\frac{\partial}{\partial c} f(x,y,z,c) = -4(z - 2c) - 2c = 0.$$

Solving the second equation for $c = 2z/3$ and substituting into the first equation, we find that the envelope is the cone

$$z^2 = 3(x^2 + y^2).$$

Equations with Perturbations

In applied mathematics one frequently encounters intractable equations for which at least approximate solutions are desired. Sometimes such equations are the result of adding an extra term to what would otherwise be a simple and easily solved equation. This extra term is called a *perturbation* of the simpler equation. Often the perturbation has coefficient smaller than the other terms in the equation, that is, it is a *small perturbation*. When this is the case one can find approximate solutions to the perturbed equation by replacing the small coefficient by a parameter and calculating Maclaurin polynomials in that parameter. One example should serve to clarify the method.

EXAMPLE 3.5.7   Consider the equation

$$y + \frac{1}{50} \ln(1+y) = x^2.$$

Without the logarithm term the equation would have the solution $y = x^2$. Let us replace the coefficient $1/50$ with the parameter ϵ and look for a solution to the equation

$$y + \epsilon \ln(1+y) = x^2$$

in the form

$$y = y(x, \epsilon) = y(x, 0) + \epsilon y_\epsilon(x, 0) + \frac{\epsilon^2}{2!} y_{\epsilon\epsilon}(x, 0) + \cdots,$$

where subscripts ϵ denote derivatives with respect to ϵ. We shall calculate the terms up to second order in ϵ. Evidently $y(x, 0) = x^2$. Differentiating the equation twice with respect to ϵ and evaluating the results at $\epsilon = 0$ we obtain

$$\frac{\partial y}{\partial \epsilon} + \ln(1+y) + \frac{\epsilon}{1+y} \frac{\partial y}{\partial \epsilon} = 0,$$

$$\frac{\partial^2 y}{\partial \epsilon^2} + \frac{2}{1+y} \frac{\partial y}{\partial \epsilon} + \epsilon \frac{\partial}{\partial \epsilon} \left(\frac{1}{1+y} \frac{\partial y}{\partial \epsilon} \right) = 0,$$

$$y_\epsilon(x, 0) = -\ln(1 + x^2),$$

$$y_{\epsilon\epsilon}(x, 0) = \frac{2}{1+x^2} \ln(1 + x^2).$$

Hence

$$y(x, \epsilon) = x^2 - \epsilon \ln(1 + x^2) + \frac{\epsilon^2}{1+x^2} \ln(1 + x^2) + \cdots,$$

and the given equation has approximate solution

$$y \approx x^2 - \frac{\ln(1 + x^2)}{50} + \frac{\ln(1 + x^2)}{2500(1 + x^2)}.$$

Similar perturbation techniques can be used for systems of equations and even for differential equations.

EXERCISES

1. Let $F(x) = \int_0^1 t^x \, dt = \dfrac{1}{x+1}$ for $x > -1$. By repeated differentiation of F evaluate the integral

$$\int_0^1 t^x (\ln t)^n \, dt.$$

2. By replacing t with xt in the well-known integral

$$\int_{-\infty}^{\infty} e^{-t^2} \, dt = \sqrt{\pi},$$

and differentiating with respect to x, evaluate

$$\int_{-\infty}^{\infty} t^2 e^{-t^2} \, dt, \quad \text{and} \quad \int_{-\infty}^{\infty} t^4 e^{-t^2} \, dt.$$

3. Evaluate $\displaystyle\int_{-\infty}^{\infty} \dfrac{e^{-xt^2} - e^{-yt^2}}{t^2} \, dt$ for $x > 0$, $y > 0$.

4. Evaluate $\displaystyle\int_0^1 \dfrac{t^x - t^y}{\ln t} \, dt$ for $x > -1$, $y > -1$.

5. Given that $\displaystyle\int_0^{\infty} e^{-xt} \sin t \, dt = \dfrac{1}{1+x^2}$ for $x > 0$ (which can be shown by integration by parts) evaluate

$$\int_0^{\infty} te^{-xt} \sin t \, dt \quad \text{and} \quad \int_0^{\infty} t^2 e^{-xt} \sin t \, dt.$$

6.* Referring to the previous example, for $x > 0$ evaluate

$$F(x) = \int_0^{\infty} e^{-xt} \dfrac{\sin t}{t} \, dt.$$

Show that $\lim_{x \to \infty} F(x) = 0$ and hence evaluate the integral

$$\int_0^{\infty} \dfrac{\sin t}{t} \, dt = \lim_{x \to 0} F(x).$$

7. Evaluate $\displaystyle\int_0^{\infty} \dfrac{dt}{x^2 + t^2}$ and use the result to help you evaluate

$$\int_0^{\infty} \dfrac{dt}{(x^2 + t^2)^2}, \quad \text{and} \quad \int_0^{\infty} \dfrac{dt}{(x^2 + t^2)^3}.$$

8.* Evaluate $\displaystyle\int_0^x \dfrac{dt}{x^2 + t^2}$ and use the result to help you evaluate

$$\int_0^x \dfrac{dt}{(x^2 + t^2)^2}, \quad \text{and} \quad \int_0^x \dfrac{dt}{(x^2 + t^2)^3}.$$

9. Find $f^{(n+1)}(a)$ if $f(x) = 1 + \displaystyle\int_a^x (x - t)^n f(t) \, dt$.

In Exercises 10–12 solve the given integral equations.

10. $f(x) = Cx + D + \displaystyle\int_0^x (x - t) f(t) \, dt$

11. $f(x) = x + \displaystyle\int_0^x (x - 2t) f(t) \, dt$

12. $f(x) = 1 + \displaystyle\int_0^1 (x + t) f(t) \, dt$

Find the envelopes of the families of curves in Exercises 13–18.

13. $y = 2cx - c^2$

14. $y - (x - c) \cos c = \sin c$

15. $x \cos c + y \sin c = 1$

16. $\dfrac{x}{\cos c} + \dfrac{y}{\sin c} = 1$

17. $y = c + (x - c)^2$

18. $(x - c)^2 + (y - c)^2 = 1$

19. Does every one-parameter family of curves in the plane have an envelope? Try to find the envelope of $y = x^2 + c$.

20. For what values of k does the family of curves $x^2 + (y - c)^2 = kc^2$ have an envelope?

21. Try to find the envelope of the family $y^3 = (x + c)^2$. Are the curves of the family tangent to the envelope? What have you actually found in this case? Compare with Example 3.3.4.

22.* Show that if a two parameter family of surfaces $f(x, y, z, \lambda, \mu) = 0$ has an envelope then the equation of that envelope can be obtained by eliminating λ and μ from the three equations

$$f(x, y, z, \lambda, \mu) = 0,$$

$$\dfrac{\partial}{\partial \lambda} f(x, y, z, \lambda, \mu) = 0,$$

$$\dfrac{\partial}{\partial \mu} f(x, y, z, \lambda, \mu) = 0.$$

23. Find the envelope of the two-parameter family of planes

$$x \sin \lambda \cos \mu + y \sin \lambda \sin \mu + z \cos \lambda = 1.$$

24. Find the envelope of the two-parameter family of spheres

$$(x - \lambda)^2 + (y - \mu)^2 + z^2 = \frac{\lambda^2 + \mu^2}{2}.$$

In Exercises 25–27 find the terms up to second power in ϵ in the solution y of the given equation.

25. $y + \epsilon \sin \pi y = x$ **26.** $y^2 + \epsilon e^{-y^2} = 1 + x^2$

27. $2y + \dfrac{\epsilon x}{1 + y^2} = 1$

28. Use perturbation methods to evaluate y with error less than 10^{-8} given

$$y + \frac{y^5}{100} = \frac{1}{2}.$$

29.*Use perturbation methods to find approximate values for x and y from the system

$$x + 2y + \frac{1}{100} e^{-x} = 3$$

$$x - y + \frac{1}{100} e^{-y} = 0.$$

Calculate all terms up to second order in $\epsilon = 1/100$.

⧉ 3.6   NEWTON'S METHOD

A frequently encountered problem in applied mathematics is to determine, to some desired degree of accuracy, a root (that is, a solution r) of an equation of the form

$$f(r) = 0.$$

Such a root is called a **zero** of the function f. Usually encountered in single-variable calculus courses, Newton's method is a simple but powerful technique for determining roots of functions which are sufficiently "smooth." The method involves "guessing" an approximate value x_0 for a root r of the function f, and then calculating successive approximations $x_1, x_2, \ldots$ by using the formula

$$x_{n+1} = x_n - \frac{f(x_n)}{f'(x_n)}, \qquad n = 0, 1, 2, \cdots.$$

If the initial guess x_0 is not too far from r, and if $|f'(x)|$ is "not too small" and $|f''(x)|$ is "not too large" near r then the successive approximations $x_1, x_2, \ldots$ will converge very rapidly to r. Each new approximation x_{n+1} is obtained as the x-intercept of the tangent line drawn to the graph of f at the previous approximation, x_n. For instance, the tangent line to the graph $y = f(x)$ at $x = x_0$ has equation

$$y - f(x_0) = f'(x_0)(x - x_0).$$

The x-intercept, x_1, of this line is determined by setting $y = 0$, $x = x_1$ in this equation, so is given by the formula for x_{n+1} above with $n = 0$. (See Fig. 3.6.1.)

Newton's method can be extended to finding solutions of systems of m equations in m variables. We will show here how to adapt the method to find approximations to a solution (x, y) of the pair of equations

$$\begin{cases} f(x, y) = 0 \\ g(x, y) = 0 \end{cases}$$

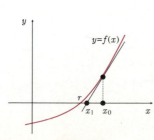

FIGURE 3.6.1

starting from an initial "guess" (x_0, y_0). We will observe the same rapid convergence of approximations to the root that typifies the single-variable case.

The idea is as follows. The two surfaces $z = f(x, y)$ and $z = g(x, y)$ intersect in a curve which itself intersects the xy-plane at the point whose coordinates are the desired solution. If (x_0, y_0) is near that point then the tangent planes to the two surfaces at (x_0, y_0) will intersect in a straight line which meets the xy-plane at a point (x_1, y_1) which should be even closer to the solution point than was (x_0, y_0). We can easily determine (x_1, y_1). The tangent planes to $z = f(x, y)$ and $z = g(x, y)$ at (x_0, y_0) have equations

$$z = f(x_0, y_0) + f_1(x_0, y_0)(x - x_0) + f_2(x_0, y_0)(y - y_0),$$
$$z = g(x_0, y_0) + g_1(x_0, y_0)(x - x_0) + g_2(x_0, y_0)(y - y_0).$$

The line of intersection of these two planes meets the xy-plane at the point (x_1, y_1) satisfying

$$f_1(x_0, y_0)(x_1 - x_0) + f_2(x_0, y_0)(y_1 - y_0) + f(x_0, y_0) = 0,$$
$$g_1(x_0, y_0)(x_1 - x_0) + g_2(x_0, y_0)(y_1 - y_0) + g(x_0, y_0) = 0.$$

Solving these two equations for x_1 and y_1 we obtain

$$x_1 = x_0 - \left.\frac{fg_2 - f_2g}{f_1g_2 - f_2g_1}\right|_{(x_0,y_0)} = x_0 - \left.\frac{\begin{vmatrix} f & f_2 \\ g & g_2 \end{vmatrix}}{\begin{vmatrix} f_1 & f_2 \\ g_1 & g_2 \end{vmatrix}}\right|_{(x_0,y_0)},$$

$$y_1 = y_0 - \left.\frac{f_1g - fg_1}{f_1g_2 - f_2g_1}\right|_{(x_0,y_0)} = y_0 - \left.\frac{\begin{vmatrix} f_1 & f \\ g_1 & g \end{vmatrix}}{\begin{vmatrix} f_1 & f_2 \\ g_1 & g_2 \end{vmatrix}}\right|_{(x_0,y_0)}.$$

Observe that the denominator in each of these expressions is the Jacobian determinant $\partial(f, g)/\partial(x, y)\big|_{(x_0,y_0)}$. This is another instance where the Jacobian is the appropriate multi-variable analogue of the derivative of a function of one variable.

Continuing in this way we generate successive approximations (x_n, y_n) according to the formulas

$$x_{n+1} = x_n - \left.\frac{\begin{vmatrix} f & f_2 \\ g & g_2 \end{vmatrix}}{\begin{vmatrix} f_1 & f_2 \\ g_1 & g_2 \end{vmatrix}}\right|_{(x_n,y_n)},$$

$$y_{n+1} = y_n - \left.\frac{\begin{vmatrix} f_1 & f \\ g_1 & g \end{vmatrix}}{\begin{vmatrix} f_1 & f_2 \\ g_1 & g_2 \end{vmatrix}}\right|_{(x_n,y_n)}.$$

We stop when the desired accuracy has been achieved.

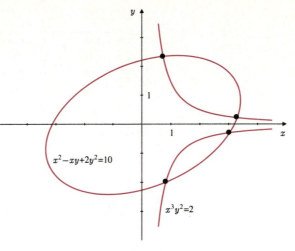

FIGURE 3.6.2

EXAMPLE 3.6.1   Find the four roots of the system

$$x^2 - xy + 2y^2 - 10 = 0, \qquad x^3y^2 - 2 = 0$$

with sufficient accuracy to ensure that the left hand sides of the equations vanish to the sixth decimal place.

SOLUTION   A sketch of the graphs of the two equations (see Fig. 3.6.2) in the xy-plane indicates that there are roots near the points $(1, 2.5)$, $(3.5, 0.5)$, $(3, -0.5)$ and $(1, -2)$. Application of Newton's method requires successive computations of the quantities

$$f(x, y) = x^2 - xy + 2y^2 - 10 \qquad f_1(x, y) = 2x - y \qquad f_2(x, y) = -x + 4y$$
$$g(x, y) = x^3y^2 - 2 \qquad\qquad g_1(x, y) = 3x^2y^2 \qquad g_2(x, y) = 2x^3y.$$

Using a calculator or computer we can calculate successive values of (x_n, y_n) starting from each of the four points (x_0, y_0) mentioned above:

n	x_n	y_n	$f(x_n, y_n)$	$g(x_n, y_n)$
0	1.000000	2.500000	1.000000	4.250000
1	0.805839	2.378102	0.043749	0.959420
2	0.721568	2.365659	0.006363	0.102502
3	0.710233	2.363735	0.000114	0.001708
4	0.710038	2.363701	0.000000	0.000001
5	0.710038	2.363701	0.000000	0.000000

n	x_n	y_n	$f(x_n, y_n)$	$g(x_n, y_n)$
0	3.500000	0.500000	1.000000	8.718750
1	3.308687	0.337643	0.058259	2.129355
2	3.273924	0.255909	0.011728	0.298145
3	3.266437	0.240187	0.000433	0.010584
4	3.266148	0.239587	0.000001	0.000015
5	3.266148	0.239586	0.000000	0.000000

n	x_n	y_n	$f(x_n, y_n)$	$g(x_n, y_n)$
0	3.000000	−0.500000	1.000000	4.750000
1	2.977072	−0.329806	0.062360	0.870022
2	3.004434	−0.275270	0.005205	0.054976
3	3.006167	−0.271350	0.000027	0.000318
4	3.006178	−0.271327	0.000000	0.000000

n	x_n	y_n	$f(x_n, y_n)$	$g(x_n, y_n)$
0	1.000000	−2.000000	1.000000	2.000000
1	0.847826	−1.956522	0.033554	0.332865
2	0.803190	−1.971447	0.001772	0.013843
3	0.801180	−1.972071	0.000004	0.000028
4	0.801176	−1.972072	0.000000	0.000000

The desired approximations to the four roots of the system are the x_n and y_n values in the last lines of the above tables. Note the rapidity of convergence in each case. However, many function evaluations are needed for each iteration of the method. For large systems Newton's method is computationally too inefficient to be practical. Other methods requiring more iterations but many fewer calculations per iteration are used in practice.

REMARK: While a detailed analysis of the convergence of Newton's method approximations is beyond the scope of this book, a few observations can be made. At each step in the approximation process we must divide by J, the Jacobian determinant of f and g with respect to x and y evaluated at the most recently obtained approximation. Assuming that the functions and partial derivatives involved in the formulas are continuous, the larger the value of J at the actual solution, the more likely are the approximations to converge to the solution, and to do so rapidly. If J vanishes (or is very small) at the solution, the successive "approximations" may not converge, even if our initial guess is quite close to the solution. Even if the first partials of f and g are large at the solution, their Jacobian may be small if their gradients are nearly parallel there. Thus we cannot expect as rapid convergence when the curves $f(x, y) = 0$ and $g(x, y) = 0$ intersect at a very small angle.

Newton's method can be applied to systems of m equations in m variables; the formulas are the obvious generalizations of those for two functions given above.

EXERCISES

Find the solutions of the systems in Exercises 1–6 so that the left-hand sides of the equations vanish up to 6 decimal places. These can be done with the aid of a scientific calculator, but that approach will be very time consuming. It is much easier to program the Newton's method formulas on a computer to generate the required approximations. In each case try to determine reasonable "initial guesses" by sketching graphs of the equations.

1. $y - e^x = 0$, $x - \sin y = 0$

2. $x^2 + y^2 - 1 = 0$, $y - e^x = 0$ (two solutions)

3. $x^4 + y^2 - 16 = 0$, $xy - 1 = 0$ (four solutions)

4. $x(1 + y^2) - 1 = 0$, $y(1 + x^2) - 2 = 0$ (one solution)

5. $y - \sin x = 0$, $x^2 + (y + 1)^2 - 2 = 0$ (two solutions)

6. $\sin x + \sin y - 1 = 0$, $y^2 - x^3 = 0$ (two solutions)

7.*Write formulas for obtaining successive Newton's method approximations to a solution of the system

$$f(x, y, z) = 0, \quad g(x, y, z) = 0, \quad h(x, y, z) = 0$$

starting from an initial guess (x_0, y_0, z_0).

8.*Use the formulas from Exercise 7 to find the first octant intersection point of the surfaces $y^2 + z^2 = 3$, $x^2 + z^2 = 2$ and $x^2 - z = 0$.

9. The equations $y - x^2 = 0$ and $y - x^3 = 0$ evidently have the solutions $x = y = 0$ and $x = y = 1$. Try to obtain these solutions by using the two variable form of Newton's method with starting values (a) $x_0 = y_0 = 0.1$, and (b) $x_0 = y_0 = 0.9$. How many iterations are required to obtain 6 decimal place accuracy for the appropriate solution in each case? How do you account for the difference in behavior of Newton's method for these equations near $(0, 0)$ and $(1, 1)$?

CHAPTER 4

Multiple Integration

In this chapter we extend the concept of definite integral to functions of several variables. Defined as limits of Riemann sums, like the one-dimensional definite integral, such multiple integrals can be evaluated using successive single definite integrals. They are used to represent and calculate quantities specified in terms of densities in regions of the plane or higher dimensional spaces. In the simplest instance, the volume of a three dimensional region is given by a *double integral* of its height over the two dimensional plane region which is its base.

4.1   DOUBLE INTEGRALS

The definition of the definite integral, $\int_a^b f(x)\,dx$, is motivated by the *standard area problem*, namely the problem of finding the area of the plane region bounded by the curve $y = f(x)$, the x-axis, and the lines $x = a$ and $x = b$. Similarly, we can motivate the double integral of a function of two variables over a domain D in the plane by means of the *standard volume problem* of finding the volume of the three dimensional region S bounded by the surface $z = f(x, y)$, the xy-plane, and the cylinder parallel to the z-axis passing through the boundary of D. (See Fig. 4.1.1.)   We shall call such a three dimensional region S a "solid" though we

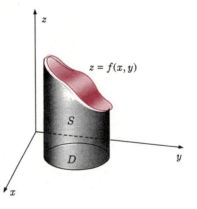

FIGURE 4.1.1

are not implying that it is filled with any particular substance. We shall define the double integral of $f(x, y)$ over the domain D,

$$\iint_D f(x, y)\,dA,$$

in such a way that its value will give the volume of the solid S whenever D is a "reasonable" domain and f is a "reasonable" function with positive values.

What is a *reasonable* domain D? For simplicity, we will use this term to denote a *bounded* region of the xy-plane which has well-defined *area* and whose boundary consists of finitely many curves with finite length. We will not try to be more precise than this. For example, the rectangle $a \le x \le b$, $c \le y \le d$, and the circular disc $x^2 + y^2 < a^2$ are both reasonable domains.

By a **partition** P of a reasonable domain D we mean a collection of non-overlapping subdomains of D, each of which is itself a reasonable domain, whose union is D: $P = \{D_1, D_2, \ldots, D_n\}$, where

$$D = D_1 \cup D_2 \cup \cdots \cup D_n,$$

and where every pair of the subdomains, D_j and D_k say, do not overlap one another, (that is, their interiors have empty intersection, though the two subdomains may share boundary points.) (See Fig. 4.1.2.) The number n of subdomains in a particular partition P is denoted $n(P)$.

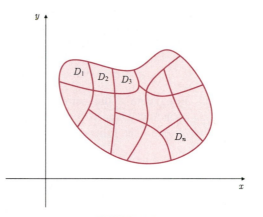

FIGURE 4.1.2

Each subdomain D_j in a partition P has finite area ΔA_j and finite *diameter*

$$d_j = \max_{P,Q \in D_j} |\overrightarrow{PQ}|.$$

(The diameter of a set is the maximum distance between two points in that set.) The quantity

$$\|P\| = \max_{1 \le j \le n(P)} d_j$$

is called the *mesh* of the partition P. If the mesh is small, all the subdomains in P have small diameters.

Given a partition P of D, let us choose a point (x_j, y_j) in each subdomain D_j, $(1 \le j \le n(P))$. For a given *bounded* function $f(x,y)$ defined on D we can then form the sum

$$R(f, P) = \sum_{j=1}^{n(P)} f(x_j, y_j)\, \Delta A_j.$$

Such a sum (which, we stress, depends on the particular choices made for the points (x_j, y_j)) is called a **Riemann sum** for f. The volume of the vertical "column" in Figure 4.1.3 represents the jth term in $R(f, P)$. We will call the function f

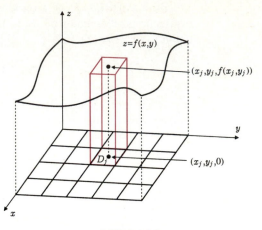

FIGURE 4.1.3

integrable if the numbers $R(f, P)$ have a limit as $n(P)$ approaches infinity in such a way that $\|P\|$ approaches zero, independently of how the points (x_j, y_j) are chosen. The following definition makes this more precise.

4.1.1
The Double Ingegral

> Suppose there exists a real number I satisfying the following condition: for every positive, real number ϵ there exists a positive number $\delta = \delta(\epsilon)$ such that for every partition P of D satisfying $\|P\| < \delta$ and every choice of points (x_j, y_j) in D_j, $(1 \le j \le n(P))$, we have $|R(f, P) - I| < \epsilon$. Then we say that f is **integrable** on D, and call the number I the double integral of f over D, writing
>
> $$I = \iint_D f(x, y)\, dA \qquad \text{or} \qquad I = \iint_D f(x, y)\, dx\, dy.$$

The following theorem, which we state without proof, guarantees an ample supply of integrable functions.

THEOREM 4.1.2   If f is a continuous function defined on a *closed, reasonable* domain D, then f is integrable on D. $\square$

According to Theorem 3.1.2, a continuous function is bounded if its domain is closed and bounded. Generally, however, it is not necessary to restrict our domains to be closed. If D is a reasonable domain and $\text{int}(D)$ is its interior, and if f is integrable on D, then

$$\iint_D f(x, y)\, dA = \iint_{\text{int}(D)} f(x, y)\, dA.$$

Properties of the Double Integral

Some properties of double integrals are analogous to properties of the one-dimensional definite integral and require little comment: if f and g are integrable over D, and if L and M are constants, then

a) $\iint_D f(x,y)\,dA = 0$ if D has zero area.

b) If $f(x,y) \geq 0$ on D, then $\iint_D f(x,y)\,dA = V \geq 0$, where V is the volume of the solid lying vertically above D and below the surface $z = f(x,y)$.

c) If $f(x,y) \leq 0$ on D, then $\iint_D f(x,y)\,dA = -V \leq 0$, where V is the volume of the solid lying vertically below D and above the surface $z = f(x,y)$.

d) $\iint_D 1\,dA = $ area of D.

e) $\iint_D \left(Lf(x,y) + Mg(x,y) \right) dA = L \iint_D f(x,y)\,dA + M \iint_D g(x,y)\,dA.$

f) If $f(x,y) \leq g(x,y)$ on D then $\iint_D f(x,y)\,dA \leq \iint_D g(x,y)\,dA.$

g) $\left| \iint_D f(x,y)\,dA \right| \leq \iint_D |f(x,y)|\,dA.$

Moreover, if $D_1, D_2, \ldots, D_k$ are non-overlapping domains on each of which f is integrable, then f is integrable over the union $D = D_1 \cup D_2 \cup \cdots \cup D_k$ and

$$\iint_D f(x,y)\,dA = \sum_{j=1}^k \iint_{D_j} f(x,y)\,dA.$$

Double Integrals by Inspection

If $f(x,y)$ is everywhere positive and integrable over the domain D then the double integral $\iint_D f(x,y)\,dA$ gives the volume of the solid bounded by the surface $z = f(x,y)$, the xy-plane and the vertical cylinder through the boundary of D. If f is everywhere negative over D then $\iint_D f(x,y)\,dA$ is the negative of that volume. These facts, combined with symmetry, ensure that some double integrals can be evaluated by inspection without any calculation necessary.

EXAMPLE 4.1.3   a) If R is the rectangle $a \leq x \leq b,\ c \leq y \leq d$ then

$$\iint_R 3\,dA = 3 \times \text{area of } R = 3(b-a)(d-c).$$

Here the integrand is $f(x,y) = 3$ and the integral is equal to the volume of the solid box of height 3 whose base is the rectangle R.

b) $$\iint_{x^2+y^2 \leq 1} (\sin x + y + 3)\,dA = 3\pi.$$

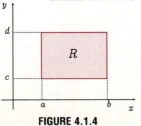

FIGURE 4.1.4

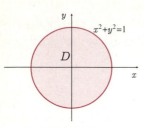

FIGURE 4.1.5

Here the domain D is a circular disc centred at the origin. Since this disc is symmetric about the y-axis, and since the function $\sin x$ is an *odd* function of x, its graph bounds as much volume below the xy-plane in the region $x < 0$ as it does above the xy-plane in the region $x > 0$. These two contributions to the double integral cancel, and so

$$\iint_D \sin x \, dA = 0.$$

Note that symmetry of *both* the domain *and* the integrand is necessary for this argument. Similarly, $\iint_D y \, dA = 0$ because of the oddness of y and the symmetry of D about the x-axis. Finally,

$$\iint_D 3 \, dA = 3 \times \text{area of } D = 3\pi.$$

c) If D is the disc of part (b), the integral

$$\iint_D \sqrt{1 - x^2 - y^2} \, dA$$

represents the volume of a hemisphere of radius 1, so has the value $2\pi/3$.

When evaluating double integrals, always be alert for situations such as those in the above example. You can save much time by not trying to calculate an integral whose value should be obvious without calculation.

Iteration of Double Integrals in Cartesian Coordinates

The existence of the double integral $\iint_D f(x, y) \, dA$ depends on f and the domain D. As we shall see, evaluation of double integrals is easiest when the domain of integration is of *simple* type.

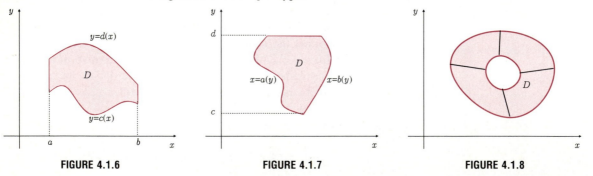

FIGURE 4.1.6   FIGURE 4.1.7   FIGURE 4.1.8

We say that the domain D in the xy-plane is y-**simple** if it is bounded by two vertical lines $x = a$ and $x = b$ and two continuous graphs $y = c(x)$ and $y = d(x)$ between these lines. (See Fig. 4.1.6.) Lines parallel to the y-axis intersect a y-simple domain in an *interval* if at all. Similarly D is x-**simple** if it is bounded by horizontal lines $y = c$ and $y = d$ and two continuous graphs $x = a(y)$ and $x = b(y)$ between these lines. (See Fig. 4.1.7.) Many of the domains over which we will take integrals are y-simple or x-simple, or both. For example, rectangles, triangles and discs are both x-simple and y-simple. Those domains which are not one or the other will usually be unions of finitely many non-overlapping subdomains which are both x-simple and y-simple. We will call such domains **regular**. The shaded region in Fig. 4.1.8 is shown divided into four subregions each of which is both x-simple and y-simple.

It can be shown that a bounded, continuous function $f(x, y)$ is integrable over a bounded x-simple or y-simple domain, and therefore over any regular domain.

Unlike those in Example 4.1.3, most double integrals cannot be evaluated by staring at them until the value occurs to you. We need a technique for evaluating double integrals similar to the technique for evaluating single definite integrals in terms of antiderivatives. Since the double integral represents a volume we can evaluate it for simple domains by a slicing technique.

Suppose, for instance, that D is y-simple, and is bounded by $x = a$, $x = b$, $y = c(x)$ and $y = d(x)$ as shown in Fig. 4.1.9. Then $\iint_D f(x, y)\, dA$ represents the volume of the solid S. Consider the cross-section of S with the vertical plane

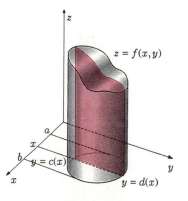

FIGURE 4.1.9

perpendicular to the x-axis at position x. Note that x is constant in that plane. If we use the projections of the y- and z-axes onto the plane as coordinate axes there, the cross-section is a plane region bounded by vertical lines $y = c(x)$ and $y = d(x)$, by the horizontal line $z = 0$, and by the curve $z = f(x, y)$. The area of the cross-section is therefore given by

$$A(x) = \int_{c(x)}^{d(x)} f(x, y)\, dy.$$

The double integral, $\iint_D f(x, y)\, dA$, that is, the volume of S, is obtained by summing the volumes of "thin" slices of area $A(x)$ and thickness dx between $x = a$ and $x = b$ and is therefore given by

$$\iint_D f(x, y)\, dA = \int_a^b A(x)\, dx = \int_a^b \left(\int_{c(x)}^{d(x)} f(x, y)\, dy \right) dx.$$

Notationally, it is common to omit the large parentheses and write

$$\iint_D f(x,y)\,dA = \int_a^b \int_{c(x)}^{d(x)} f(x,y)\,dy\,dx,$$

or

$$\iint_D f(x,y)\,dA = \int_a^b dx \int_{c(x)}^{d(x)} f(x,y)\,dy.$$

The latter form shows better which variable corresponds to which limits of integration.

The expressions on the right-hand sides of the above formulas are called **iterated** integrals. **Iteration** is the process of reducing the problem of evaluating a double (or multiple) integral to one of evaluating two (or more) successive single definite integrals. In the above iteration, the integral

$$\int_{c(x)}^{d(x)} f(x,y)\,dy$$

is called the *inner* integral since it must be evaluated first. It is evaluated using standard techniques, treating x as a constant. The result of this evaluation is a function of x alone (note that both the integrand and the limits of the inner integral can depend on x), and is the integrand of the *outer* integral in which x is the variable of integration.

We summarize and extend the above discussion in the following theorem.

THEOREM 4.1.4 *(Iteration of Double Integrals)* If $f(x,y)$ is continuous on the bounded y-simple domain D given by $a \leq x \leq b$, $c(x) \leq y \leq d(x)$, then

$$\iint_D f(x,y)\,dA = \int_a^b dx \int_{c(x)}^{d(x)} f(x,y)\,dy.$$

Similarly, if f is continuous on the x-simple domain D given by $c \leq y \leq d$, $a(y) \leq x \leq b(y)$, then (see Fig. 4.1.10)

$$\iint_D f(x,y)\,dA = \int_c^d dy \int_{a(y)}^{b(y)} f(x,y)\,dx. \quad \square$$

REMARK: The symbol dA in the double integral is replaced in the iterated integrals by the dx and the dy. Accordingly, dA is frequently written $dx\,dy$ or $dy\,dx$ even in the double integral. The three expressions

$$\iint_D f(x,y)\,dx\,dy, \qquad \iint_D f(x,y)\,dy\,dx, \quad \text{and} \quad \iint_D f(x,y)\,dA$$

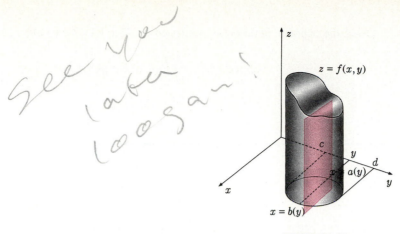

FIGURE 4.1.10

all stand for the double integral of f over D. Only when the double integral is iterated does the order of dx and dy become important. Later in this chapter we will iterate double integrals in polar coordinates and dA will take the form $r\,dr\,d\theta$.

It is not always necessary to make a three-dimensional sketch of the solid volume represented by a double integral. In order to iterate the integral properly (in one direction or the other) it is usually sufficient to make a sketch of the domain D over which the integral is taken. The direction of iteration can be shown by a line along which the inner integral is taken. The following examples will illustrate this.

EXAMPLE 4.1.5   Find the volume of the solid lying above the square Q defined by $0 \le x \le 1$, $1 \le y \le 2$ and below the plane $z = 4 - x - y$.

SOLUTION   The square Q is both x-simple and y-simple, so the double integral giving the volume can be iterated in either direction. We will do it both ways. The horizontal line at height y in Fig. 4.1.11 suggests that we first integrate with respect to x along this line (from 0 to 1) and then integrate the result with respect to y from 1 to 2. Iterating the double integral in this direction we calculate

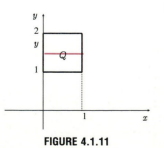

FIGURE 4.1.11

$$\text{Volume of } Q = \iint_Q (4 - x - y)\,dA$$

$$= \int_1^2 dy \int_0^1 (4 - x - y)\,dx$$

$$= \int_1^2 dy \left(4x - \frac{x^2}{2} - xy\right)\bigg|_0^1$$

$$= \int_1^2 \left(\frac{7}{2} - y\right) dy$$

$$= \left(\frac{7y}{2} - \frac{y^2}{2}\right)\bigg|_1^2 = 2 \text{ units}^3.$$

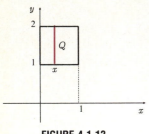

FIGURE 4.1.12

Using the opposite iteration as suggested by Fig. 4.1.12 we calculate

$$\text{Volume of } Q = \iint_Q (4 - x - y)\, dA$$

$$= \int_0^1 dx \int_1^2 (4 - x - y)\, dy$$

$$= \int_0^1 dx \left(4y - xy - \frac{y^2}{2} \right)\Big|_1^2$$

$$= \int_0^1 \left(\frac{5}{2} - x \right) dx$$

$$= \left(\frac{5x}{2} - \frac{x^2}{2} \right)\Big|_0^1 = 2 \text{ units}^3.$$

It is comforting to get the same answer both ways. Note that because Q is a rectangle with sides parallel to the coordinate axes, the limits of the inner integrals do not depend on the variables of the outer integrals in either iteration. This cannot be expected to happen with more general domains.

EXAMPLE 4.1.6 Evaluate

$$\iint_T xy\, dA$$

where T is the triangle with vertices (0,0), (1,0) and (1,1).

SOLUTION The triangle T is shown in Fig. 4.1.13. It is both x-simple and y-simple. Using the iteration corresponding to slicing in the direction shown in the figure, we obtain:

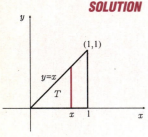

FIGURE 4.1.13

$$\iint_T xy\, dA = \int_0^1 dx \int_0^x xy\, dy$$

$$= \int_0^1 dx \left(\frac{xy^2}{2} \right)\Big|_{y=0}^{y=x}$$

$$= \int_0^1 \frac{x^3}{2}\, dx = \frac{x^4}{8}\Big|_0^1 = \frac{1}{8}.$$

Iteration in the other direction leads to the same value:

$$\iint_T xy\, dA = \int_0^1 dy \int_y^1 xy\, dx$$

$$= \int_0^1 dy \left(\frac{yx^2}{2} \right)\Big|_{x=y}^{x=1}$$

$$= \int_0^1 \frac{y}{2}(1 - y^2)\, dy$$

$$= \left(\frac{y^2}{4} - \frac{y^4}{8} \right)\Big|_0^1 = \frac{1}{8}.$$

In both of the examples above the double integral could be evaluated easily using either possible iteration. (We did them both ways just to illustrate that fact.) It often occurs, however, that a double integral is easily evaluated if iterated in one direction, and very difficult, or impossible, if iterated in the other direction. Sometimes you will even encounter iterated integrals whose evaluation requires that they be expressed as double integrals and then reiterated in the opposite direction.

EXAMPLE 4.1.7   Evaluate the iterated integral

$$I = \int_0^1 dx \int_{\sqrt{x}}^1 e^{y^3}\, dy.$$

SOLUTION   We cannot antidifferentiate e^{y^3} to evaluate the inner integral in this iteration, so we express I as a double integral and identify the region over which it is taken:

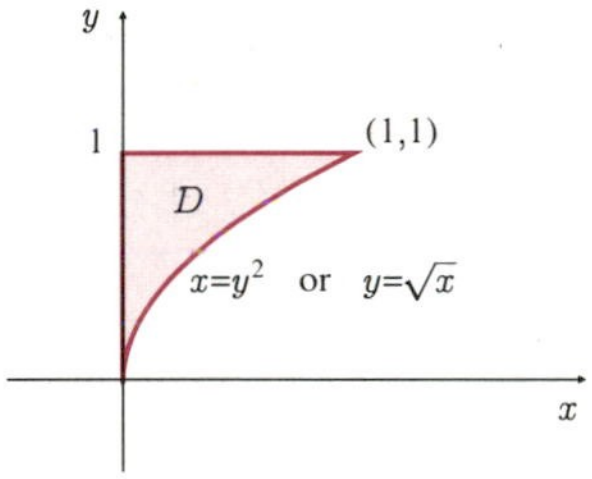

$$I = \iint_D e^{y^3}\, dA$$

where D is the region shown in Fig. 4.1.14. Reiterating with the x integration on the inside we get

$$I = \int_0^1 dy \int_0^{y^2} e^{y^3}\, dx$$

$$= \int_0^1 e^{y^3} dy \int_0^{y^2} dx$$

$$= \int_0^1 y^2 e^{y^3}\, dy = \frac{e^{y^3}}{3}\Big|_0^1 = \frac{e-1}{3}.$$

FIGURE 4.1.14

The following is an example of the calculation of the volume of a somewhat awkward solid. Even though it is not always necessary to sketch solids to find their volumes, the student is encouraged to sketch them whenever possible. When we encounter triple integrals over three-dimensional regions later in this chapter it will usually be necessary to sketch the regions. Get as much practice as you can.

EXAMPLE 4.1.8   Sketch and find the volume of the solid bounded by the planes $y = 0$, $z = 0$ and $z = a - x + y$, and the parabolic cylinder $y = a - (x^2/a)$, where a is a positive constant.

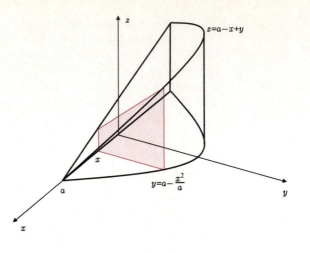

FIGURE 4.1.15

SOLUTION   The solid is shown in Fig. 4.1.15. Its base is the parabolic segment D in the xy-plane bounded by $y = 0$ and $y = a - (x^2/a)$, so the volume of the solid is given by

$$V = \iint_D (a - x + y)\, dA = \iint_D (a + y)\, dA.$$

(Note how we used symmetry to drop the x term from the integrand. This term is an odd function of x and D is symmetric about the y-axis.) Iterating the double integral in the direction suggested by the slice shown in the figure, we obtain

$$V = \int_{-a}^{a} dx \int_0^{a-(x^2/a)} (a + y)\, dy$$

$$= \int_{-a}^{a} \left(ay + \frac{y^2}{2} \right) \Bigg|_0^{a-(x^2/a)} dx$$

$$= \int_{-a}^{a} \left[a^2 - x^2 + \frac{1}{2}\left(a^2 - 2x^2 + \frac{x^4}{a^2} \right) \right] dx$$

$$= 2 \int_0^{a} \left[\frac{3}{2}a^2 - 2x^2 + \frac{x^4}{2a^2} \right] dx$$

$$= \left(3a^2 x - \frac{4x^3}{3} + \frac{x^5}{5a^2} \right) \Bigg|_0^{a}$$

$$= 3a^3 - \frac{4}{3}a^3 + \frac{1}{5}a^3 = \frac{28}{15}a^3 \text{ units}^3.$$

EXERCISES

In Exercises 1–10 evaluate the given double integral without using iteration.

1. $\displaystyle\iint_R dA$, where R is the rectangle $-1 \leq x \leq 3$, $-4 \leq y \leq 1$.

2. $\displaystyle\iint_D (x+3)\, dA$, where D is the half disc $0 \leq y \leq \sqrt{4-x^2}$.

3. $\displaystyle\iint_T (x+y)\, dA$, where T is the parallelogram having the points $(2,2)$, $(1,-1)$, $(-2,-2)$, and $(-1,1)$ as vertices.

4. $\displaystyle\iint_{|x|+|y|\leq 1} \left(x^3 \cos(y^2) + 3 \sin y - \pi\right) dA$.

5. $\displaystyle\iint_{x^2+y^2\leq 1} (4x^2 y^3 - x + 5)\, dA$.

6. $\displaystyle\iint_{x^2+y^2\leq a^2} \sqrt{a^2 - x^2 - y^2}\, dA$.

7. $\displaystyle\iint_{x^2+y^2\leq a^2} (a - \sqrt{x^2+y^2})\, dA$.

8. $\displaystyle\iint_S (x+y)\, dA$, where S is the square $0 \leq x \leq a$, $0 \leq y \leq a$.

9. $\displaystyle\iint_T (1-x-y)\, dA$, where T is the triangle with vertices $(0,0)$, $(1,0)$, and $(0,1)$.

10. $\displaystyle\iint_R \sqrt{b^2 - y^2}\, dA$, where R is the rectangle $0 \leq x \leq a$, $0 \leq y \leq b$.

In Exercises 11–20 evaluate the double integrals by iteration.

11. $\displaystyle\iint_R (x^2 + y^2)\, dA$, where R is the rectangle $0 \leq x \leq a$, $0 \leq y \leq b$.

12. $\displaystyle\iint_R x^2 y^2\, dA$, where R is the rectangle of the previous exercise.

13. $\displaystyle\iint_S (\sin x + \cos y)\, dA$, where S is the square $0 \leq x \leq \pi/2$, $0 \leq y \leq \pi/2$.

14. $\displaystyle\iint_T (x - 3y)\, dA$, where T is the triangle with vertices $(0,0)$, $(a,0)$ and $(0,b)$.

15. $\displaystyle\iint_R xy^2\, dA$, where R is the finite region in the first quadrant bounded by the curves $y = x^2$ and $x = y^2$.

16. $\displaystyle\iint_D x \cos y\, dA$, where D is the finite region in the first quadrant bounded by the coordinate axes and the curve $y = 1 - x^2$.

17. $\displaystyle\iint_D \ln x\, dA$, where D is the finite region in the first quadrant bounded by the line $2x + 2y = 5$ and the hyperbola $xy = 1$.

18. $\displaystyle\iint_T \sqrt{a^2 - y^2}\, dA$, where T is the triangle with vertices $(0,0)$, $(a,0)$ and (a,a).

19. $\displaystyle\iint_R \frac{x}{y}\, e^y\, dA$, where R is the region $0 \leq x \leq 1$, $x^2 \leq y \leq x$.

20. $\displaystyle\iint_T \frac{xy}{1 + x^4}\, dA$, where T is the triangle with vertices $(0,0)$, $(0,1)$ and $(1,1)$.

In Exercises 21–24 sketch the domain of integration and evaluate the given iterated integrals.

21. $\displaystyle\int_0^1 dy \int_y^1 e^{-x^2}\, dx$ 22. $\displaystyle\int_0^{\pi/2} dy \int_y^{\pi/2} \frac{\sin x}{x}\, dx$

23. $\displaystyle\int_0^1 dx \int_x^1 \frac{y^\lambda}{x^2 + y^2}\, dy$ $(\lambda > 0)$

24. $\displaystyle\int_0^1 dx \int_x^{x^{1/3}} \sqrt{1 - y^4}\, dy$

In Exercises 25–28 find the volumes of the indicated solids.

25. Above the xy-plane and under the surface $z = 1 - x^2 - 2y^2$.

26. Above the triangle with vertices $(0,0)$, $(a,0)$ and $(0,b)$ and under the plane $z = 2 - (x/a) - (y/b)$.

27. Inside the two cylinders $x^2 + y^2 = a^2$ and $y^2 + z^2 = a^2$.

28. Inside the cylinder $x^2 + 2y^2 = 8$, above the plane $z = y - 4$ and below the plane $z = 8 - x$.

29.*Suppose that $f(x,t)$ and $f_1(x,t)$ are continuous on the rectangle $a \leq x \leq b$ and $c \leq t \leq d$. Let

$$g(x) = \int_c^d f(x,t)\, dt, \quad \text{and} \quad G(x) = \int_c^d f_1(x,t)\, dt.$$

Show that $g'(x) = G(x)$ for $a < x < b$. (Hint: Evaluate $\int_a^x G(u)\,du$ by reversing the order of iteration. Then differentiate the result. This is a different version of Theorem 3.5.1.)

30.*Let $F'(x) = f(x)$ and $G'(x) = g(x)$ on the interval $a \leq x \leq b$. Let T be the triangle with vertices (a, a), (b, a) and (b, b). By iterating $\iint_T f(x)g(y)\,dA$ in both directions, show that

$$\int_a^b f(x)G(x)\,dx$$

$$= F(b)G(b) - F(a)G(a) - \int_a^b g(y)F(y)\,dy.$$

(This is an alternate derivation of the formula for integration by parts.)

4.2   IMPROPER INTEGRALS AND A MEAN-VALUE THEOREM

In order to simplify matters, the definition of the double integral given in the previous section required that the domain D be bounded, and that the integrand f be bounded on D. As in the single variable case, **improper double integrals** can arise if either the domain of integration is unbounded or the integrand is unbounded near any part of the boundary of the domain. If $f(x, y) \geq 0$ on the domain D then such an improper integral must either exist (that is, converge to a finite value) or be infinite (diverge to infinity). Convergence or divergence of improper double integrals of such *positive* functions can be determined by iterating them and determining the convergence or divergence of any single improper integrals which result.

EXAMPLE 4.2.1   If D is the region lying above the x-axis, under the curve $y = 1/x$, and to the right of the line $x = 1$, determine whether the double integral

$$\iint_D \frac{dA}{x + y}$$

converges or not.

SOLUTION   The region D is sketched in Fig. 4.2.1. We have

$$\iint_D \frac{dA}{x + y} = \int_1^\infty dx \int_0^{1/x} \frac{dy}{x + y}$$

$$= \int_1^\infty \ln(x + y)\Big|_{y=0}^{y=1/x}\,dx$$

$$= \int_1^\infty \left(\ln\left(x + \frac{1}{x}\right) - \ln x\right)\,dx$$

$$= \int_1^\infty \ln\left(\frac{x + \frac{1}{x}}{x}\right)\,dx = \int_1^\infty \ln\left(1 + \frac{1}{x^2}\right)\,dx.$$

Since $0 < \ln(1 + u) < u$ if $u > 0$ we have

$$0 < \iint_D \frac{dA}{x + y} < \int_1^\infty \frac{1}{x^2}\,dx = 1.$$

Therefore the given integral converges and its value lies between 0 and 1.

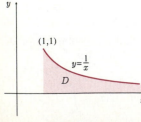

y

$(1,1)$

$y = \frac{1}{x}$

D

x

FIGURE 4.2.1

EXAMPLE 4.2.2 Determine the convergence or divergence of

$$\iint_D \frac{dA}{xy},$$

where D is the bounded region in the first quadrant lying between the line $y = x$ and the parabola $y = x^2$.

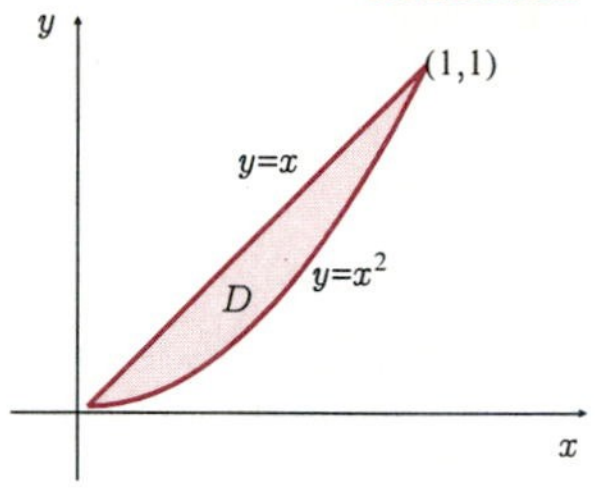

SOLUTION The domain D is shown in Fig. 4.2.2. The integral is improper because the integrand $\frac{1}{xy}$ is unbounded as we approach the boundary point $(0,0)$. We have

$$\iint_D \frac{dA}{xy} = \int_0^1 \frac{dx}{x} \int_{x^2}^x \frac{dy}{y}$$

$$= \int_0^1 \frac{1}{x}(\ln x - \ln x^2)\,dx = \int_0^1 \frac{\ln(1/x)}{x}\,dx > \int_0^{1/e} \frac{dx}{x},$$

since $\ln(1/x) \geq 1$ if $(1/x) > e$, i.e. if $0 < x \leq 1/e$. The latter integral diverges to infinity, and so, therefore, does the given integral.

We cannot deal here with the convergence of general improper double integrals with integrands $f(x,y)$ which do not have constant sign on the domain D of the integral. We remark, however, that such an integral cannot converge unless

$$\iint_E f(x,y)\,dA$$

is finite for every bounded, reasonable subdomain E of D. We cannot, in general, determine the convergence of the given integral by looking at the convergence of iterations. The double integral may diverge even if its iterations converge. (See Exercise 19 at the end of this section. In fact, opposite iterations may even give different values.) This happens because of cancellation of infinite volumes of opposite sign. (Similar behavior in one dimension is exemplified by the integral $\int_{-1}^1 dx/x$ which does not exist, although it represents the difference of "equal" but infinite areas.) It can be shown that an improper double integral of $f(x,y)$ over D converges if the integral of $|f(x,y)|$ over D converges:

$$\int_D |f(x,y)|\,dA \text{ converges} \quad \Rightarrow \quad \int_D f(x,y)\,dA \text{ converges}.$$

In this case any iterations will converge to the same value. Such double integrals are called **absolutely convergent** by analogy with absolutely convergent infinite series.

A Mean-Value Theorem for Double Integrals

Let D be a set in the xy-plane which is closed and bounded and has positive area $A = \iint_D dA$. Suppose that $f(x,y)$ is continuous on D. Then there exist points (x_1,y_1) and (x_2,y_2) in D where f assumes minimum and maximum values, (see Theorem 3.1.2), that is

$$f(x_1,y_1) \leq f(x,y) \leq f(x_2,y_2)$$

FIGURE 4.2.2

for all points (x, y) in D. If we integrate this inequality over D we obtain

$$f(x_1, y_1)A = \iint_D f(x_1, y_1)\, dA \leq \iint_D f(x, y)\, dA$$
$$\leq \iint_D f(x_2, y_2)\, dA = f(x_2, y_2)A.$$

Therefore the *number*

$$\bar{f} = \frac{1}{A} \iint_D f(x, y)\, dA$$

lies between the minimum and maximum values of f on D:

$$f(x_1, y_1) \leq \bar{f} \leq f(x_2, y_2).$$

A set D in the plane is said to be **connected** if any two points in it can be joined by a continuous parametric curve $x = x(t)$, $y = y(t)$, $(0 \leq t \leq 1)$, lying in D. Suppose this curve joins (x_1, y_1) (where $t = 0$) and (x_2, y_2) (where $t = 1$). Let $g(t)$ be defined by

$$g(t) = f(x(t), y(t)), \quad 0 \leq t \leq 1.$$

Then g is continuous and takes the values $f(x_1, y_1)$ at $t = 0$ and $f(x_2, y_2)$ at $t = 1$. By the Intermediate-Value Theorem there exists a number t_0 between 0 and 1 such that $\bar{f} = g(t_0) = f(x_0, y_0)$ where $x_0 = x(t_0)$ and $y_0 = y(t_0)$. Thus we have found a point (x_0, y_0) in D such that

$$\frac{1}{\text{area of } D} \iint_D f(x, y)\, dA = f(x_0, y_0).$$

We have therefore proved the following version of the Mean-Value Theorem.

THEOREM 4.2.3   *(A Mean-Value Theorem for Double Integrals)* If the function $f(x, y)$ is continuous on a closed, bounded, connected set D in the xy-plane then there exists a point (x_0, y_0) in D such that

$$\iint_D f(x, y)\, dA = f(x_0, y_0) \times (\text{area of } D).$$

The above theorem is the two-variable analogue of the Mean-Value theorem for definite integrals. By analogy with the definition of average value for one-variable functions, we make the following definition.

4.2.4
Average Value
of a Function

The **average value** or **mean value** of an integrable function $f(x, y)$ over the set D is the number

$$\bar{f} = \frac{1}{\text{area of } D} \iint_D f(x, y)\, dA.$$

If $f(x, y) \geq 0$ on D, then the cylinder with base D and constant height $\bar{f}$ has volume equal to that of the solid region lying above D and below the surface $z = f(x, y)$. It is often very useful to interpret a double integral in terms of the average value of the function which is its integrand.

EXAMPLE 4.2.5   The average value of x over a domain D having area A is

$$\bar{x} = \frac{1}{A} \iint_D x \, dA.$$

Of course, $\bar{x}$ is just the x-coordinate of the centroid (or centre of gravity) of the region D.

EXAMPLE 4.2.6   A large number of points (x, y) are chosen at random in the triangle T with vertices $(0,0)$, $(1,0)$, and $(1,1)$. What is the approximate average value of $x^2 + y^2$ for these points?

SOLUTION   The approximate average value of $x^2 + y^2$ for the randomly chosen points will be the average value of that function over the triangle, namely

$$\frac{1}{2} \iint_T (x^2 + y^2) \, dA = \frac{1}{2} \int_0^1 dx \int_0^x (x^2 + y^2) \, dy$$

$$= \frac{1}{2} \int_0^1 \left(x^2 y + \frac{1}{3} y^3 \right) \Big|_0^x dx = \frac{2}{3} \int_0^1 x^3 \, dx = \frac{1}{6}.$$

EXAMPLE 4.2.7   Let (a, b) be an interior point of a domain D on which $f(x, y)$ is continuous. For sufficiently small positive r, the closed circular disc D_r with centre at (a, b) and radius r is contained in D. Show that

$$\lim_{r \to 0} \frac{1}{\pi r^2} \iint_{D_r} f(x, y) \, dA = f(a, b).$$

SOLUTION   If D_r is contained in D then by the Mean-Value Theorem given above (Theorem 4.2.3)

$$\frac{1}{\pi r^2} \iint_{D_r} f(x, y) \, dA = f(x_0, y_0)$$

for some point (x_0, y_0) in D_r. As $r \to 0$ we must have $(x_0, y_0) \to (a, b)$. Since f is continuous at (a, b) therefore $f(x_0, y_0) \to f(a, b)$. Thus

$$\lim_{r \to 0} \frac{1}{\pi r^2} \iint_{D_r} f(x, y) \, dA = f(a, b).$$

EXERCISES

In Exercises 1–8 determine whether the given integral converges or not. Try to evaluate those which do.

1. $\iint_{I\!R^2} e^{-(|x|+|y|)}\, dA$ **2.** $\iint_{I\!R^2} e^{-|x+y|}\, dA$

3. $\iint_T \dfrac{1}{x^3} e^{-y/x}\, dA$, where T is the region satisfying $x \ge 1,\ 0 \le y \le x$.

4. $\iint_T \dfrac{dA}{x^2 + y^2}$, where T is the region in the previous Exercise.

5. $\iint_R \dfrac{dA}{x^2 + y^2}$ where R satisfies $1 \le x < \infty$, $1 \le y < \infty$

6. $\iint_R \dfrac{dA}{x^4 + y^2}$ where R satisfies $1 \le x < \infty$, $0 \le y \le x^2$.

7. $\iint_Q e^{-xy}\, dA$, where Q is the first quadrant of the xy-plane.

8. $\iint_R \dfrac{1}{x}\sin\dfrac{1}{x}\, dA$, where R is the region $2/\pi \le x < \infty$, $0 \le y \le 1/x$.

9. Evaluate

$$I = \iint_S \frac{dA}{x+y},$$

where S is the square $0 \le x \le 1,\ 0 \le y \le 1$

   a) by direct iteration of the double integral.

   b) by using the symmetry of the integrand and the domain to write

$$I = 2 \iint_T \frac{dA}{x+y},$$

where T is the triangle with vertices $(0,0)$, $(1,0)$ and $(1,1)$.

10. Find the volume of the solid lying above the square S of the previous exercise, and under the surface $z = 2xy/(x^2 + y^2)$.

In Exercises 11–16 a and b are given real numbers. D_k is the region $0 \le x \le 1,\ 0 \le y \le x^k$, and R_k is the region $1 \le x < \infty,\ 0 \le y \le x^k$. Find all real values of k for which the given integral converges.

11. $\iint_{D_k} \dfrac{dA}{x^a}$ **12.** $\iint_{D_k} y^b\, dA$

13. $\iint_{R_k} x^a\, dA$ **14.** $\iint_{R_k} \dfrac{dA}{y^b}$

15. $\iint_{D_k} x^a y^b\, dA$ **16.** $\iint_{R_k} x^a y^b\, dA$

17. *Evaluate both iterations of the improper integral

$$\iint_S \frac{x-y}{(x+y)^3}\, dA,$$

where S is the square $0 < x < 1,\ 0 < y < 1$. Show that the above improper double integral does not exist by considering

$$\iint_T \frac{x-y}{(x+y)^3}\, dA,$$

where T is that part of the square S lying under the line $x = y$.

In Exercises 18–20 find the average value of the given function over the given region.

18. x^2 over the rectangle $a \le x \le b,\ c \le y \le d$.

19. $x^2 + y^2$ over the triangle $0 \le x \le a,\ 0 \le y \le a - x$.

20. $1/x$ over the region $0 \le x \le 1,\ x^2 \le y \le \sqrt{x}$.

21. *Find the average distance from points in the quarter-disc $x^2 + y^2 \le a^2,\ x \ge 0,\ y \ge 0$ to the line $x + y = 0$.

22. *Let (a, b) be an interior point of a domain D on which the function $f(x, y)$ is continuous. For small enough $h^2 + k^2$ the rectangle R_{hk} with vertices $(a, b),\ (a+h, b),\ (a, b+k)$ and $(a+h, b+k)$ is contained in D. Show that

$$\lim_{(h,k)\to(0,0)} \frac{1}{hk} \iint_{R_{hk}} f(x, y) = f(a, b).$$

(Hint. See Example 4.2.7.)

23.*Suppose that $f_{12}(x,y)$ and $f_{21}(x,y)$ are continuous in a neighbourhood of the point (a,b). Without assuming the equality of these mixed partial derivatives, show that

$$\iint_R f_{12}(x,y)\,dA = \iint_R f_{21}(x,y)\,dA,$$

where R is the rectangle with vertices (a,b), $(a+h,b)$, $(a,b+k)$ and $(a+h,b+k)$ and h^2+k^2 is sufficiently small. Now use the result of the previous exercise to show that $f_{12}(a,b) = f_{21}(a,b)$. (This reproves Theorem 2.3.5. However, in that theorem we only assumed continuity of the mixed partials *at* (a,b). Here we assume the continuity *at all points sufficiently near* (a,b).)

4.3 DOUBLE INTEGRALS IN POLAR COORDINATES

For many applications of double integrals either the domain of integration or the integrand function or both may be more easily expressed in terms of polar coordinates than in terms of Cartesian coordinates. Recall that a point P with Cartesian coordinates (x,y) can also be located by its polar coordinates (r,θ), where r is the distance from P to the origin O, and θ is the angle OP makes with the positive direction of the x-axis. (Positive angles θ are measured counterclockwise.) The polar and Cartesian coordinates of P are related by the transformations

4.3.1
Polar
Coordinates

$$x = r\cos\theta \qquad\qquad r^2 = x^2 + y^2$$
$$y = r\sin\theta \qquad\qquad \tan\theta = y/x$$

The volume of the solid region lying above the xy-plane and beneath the surface $z = 1 - x^2 - y^2$ is given in Cartesian coordinates by

$$V = \iint_{x^2+y^2\le 1} (1 - x^2 - y^2)\,dA.$$

We can express the same volume in terms of polar coordinates as

$$V = \iint_{r\le 1} (1 - r^2)\,dA,$$

where dA represents a suitable *area element*.

In the Cartesian formula for V, the area element $dA = dx\,dy$ represents the area of the "infinitesimal" region bounded by the coordinate lines at x, $x+dx$, y and $y+dy$. (See Fig. 4.3.1.) In the polar formula, the area element dA represents

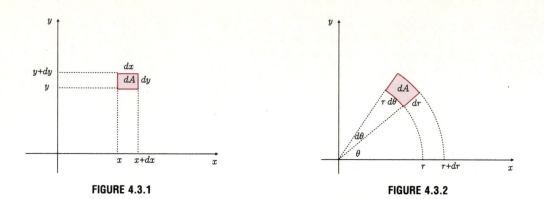

FIGURE 4.3.1

FIGURE 4.3.2

the area of the "infinitesimal" region bounded by the coordinate circles with radii r and $r + dr$, and coordinate rays from the origin at angles θ and $\theta + d\theta$. (See Fig. 4.3.2.) Evidently dA is approximately the area of a rectangle with dimensions dr and $r\, d\theta$. The error in this approximation becomes negligible *compared to the size of dA* as dr and $d\theta$ approach zero. Thus, in transforming a double integral between Cartesian and polar coordinates the area element transforms according to the formula

4.3.2
Area Element in
Polar Coordinates

$$dA = dx\, dy = r\, dr\, d\theta.$$

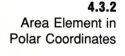

FIGURE 4.3.3

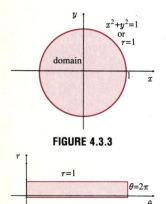

FIGURE 4.3.4

In order to iterate the polar form of the double integral for V we may regard the domain of integration as a set in a plane having *Cartesian coordinates* r and θ. In the xy Cartesian plane the domain is a disc $r \leq 1$ (see Fig. 4.3.3) but in the $r\theta$ Cartesian plane (with perpendicular r- and θ-axes) the domain is the rectangle R specified by $0 \leq r \leq 1$, $0 \leq \theta \leq 2\pi$. (See Fig. 4.3.4.) The area element in the $r\theta$-plane is $dA^* = dr\, d\theta$, so area is not preserved under the transformation to polar coordinates. ($dA = r\, dA^*$) Thus the polar integral for V is really a Cartesian integral in the $r\theta$-plane, with integrand modified by the inclusion of an extra factor r to compensate for the change of area. It can be evaluated by standard iteration methods:

$$V = \iint_R (1 - r^2) r\, dA^* = \int_0^{2\pi} d\theta \int_0^1 (1 - r^2) r\, dr$$

$$= \int_0^{2\pi} \left. \left(\frac{r^2}{2} - \frac{r^4}{4} \right) \right|_0^1 d\theta = \frac{\pi}{2} \text{ units}^3.$$

REMARK: It is not necessary to sketch the region R in the $r\theta$-plane. We are used to thinking of polar coordinates in terms of distances and angles in the xy-plane, and can easily understand from looking at the disc in Fig. 4.3.3 that the iteration of the integral in polar coordinates corresponds to $0 \le \theta \le 2\pi$ and $0 \le r \le 1$. That is, we should be able to write the iteration

$$V = \int_0^{2\pi} d\theta \int_0^1 (1 - r^2) r \, dr$$

directly from consideration of the domain of integration in the xy-plane.

EXAMPLE 4.3.3   Evaluate

$$I = \iint_R \frac{y^2}{x^2} \, dA$$

where R is that part of the annulus $0 < a^2 \le x^2 + y^2 \le b^2$ lying in the first quadrant and below the line $y = x$.

SOLUTION   Fig. 4.3.5 shows the region R. Evidently it is specified in polar coordinates by $0 \le \theta \le \pi/4$ and $a \le r \le b$. Since

$$\frac{y^2}{x^2} = \frac{r^2 \sin^2 \theta}{r^2 \cos^2 \theta} = \tan^2 \theta$$

we have

$$I = \int_0^{\pi/4} \tan^2\theta \, d\theta \int_a^b r \, dr$$

$$= \frac{1}{2}(b^2 - a^2) \int_0^{\pi/4} \left(\sec^2\theta - 1 \right) d\theta$$

$$= \frac{1}{2}(b^2 - a^2)(\tan\theta - \theta) \Big|_0^{\pi/4}$$

$$= \frac{1}{2}(b^2 - a^2) \left(1 - \frac{\pi}{4} \right) = \frac{4 - \pi}{8}(b^2 - a^2).$$

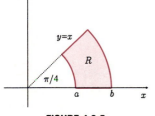

FIGURE 4.3.5

EXAMPLE 4.3.4   Derive the formula for the area of the polar region R bounded by the curve $r = f(\theta)$ and the rays $\theta = \alpha$ and $\theta = \beta$. (See Fig. 4.3.6.)

SOLUTION   The area A of R is numerically equal to the volume of a cylinder of height 1 above the region R:

$$A = \iint_R dx \, dy = \iint_R r \, dr \, d\theta$$

$$= \int_\alpha^\beta d\theta \int_0^{f(\theta)} r \, dr = \frac{1}{2} \int_\alpha^\beta \left(f(\theta) \right)^2 d\theta.$$

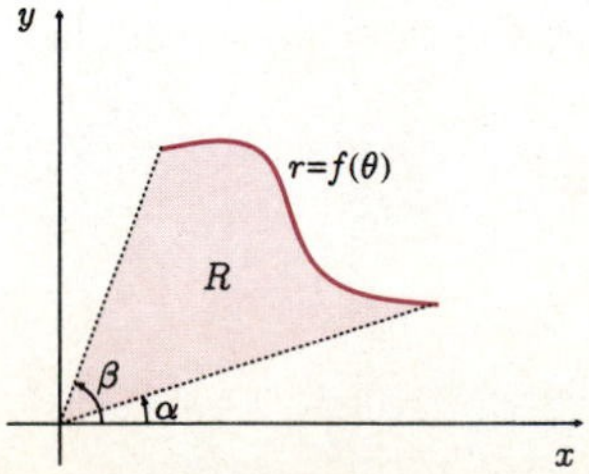

FIGURE 4.3.6

Observe that the inner integral in the iteration involves integrating r along the ray specified by θ from 0 to $f(\theta)$.

There is no firm rule as to when one should or should not convert a double integral from Cartesian to polar coordinates. In Example 4.3.3 above, the conversion was strongly suggested by the shape of the domain, but was also indicated by the fact that the integrand, y^2/x^2, becomes a function of θ alone when converted to polar coordinates. It is usually wise to switch to polar coordinates if the switch simplifies the iteration (that is, if the *domain* is "simpler" when expressed in terms of polar coordinates), even if the form of the integrand is made more complicated.

EXAMPLE 4.3.5 Find the volume of the solid lying in the first octant, inside the cylinder $x^2+y^2 = a^2$, and under the plane $z = y$.

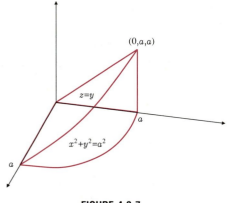

FIGURE 4.3.7

SOLUTION The solid is shown in Fig. 4.3.7. The base is a quarter disc, easily expressed in polar coordinates by the inequalities $0 \le \theta \le \pi/2$, $0 \le r \le a$. The height is given by $z = y = r \sin\theta$. The solid has volume

$$V = \int_0^{\pi/2} d\theta \int_0^a (r\sin\theta)r\,dr = \int_0^{\pi/2} \sin\theta\,d\theta \int_0^a r^2\,dr = \frac{1}{3}a^3 \text{ units}^3.$$

The following example establishes the value of a definite integral which plays a very important role in probability theory and statistics.

EXAMPLE 4.3.6 Show that

$$\int_{-\infty}^{\infty} e^{-x^2}\,dx = \sqrt{\pi}.$$

SOLUTION   The improper integral converges, and its value does not depend on what symbol we use for the variable of integration. Therefore we can express the square of the integral as a product of two identical integrals, but with their variables of integration named differently. We then interpret this product as an improper double integral and reiterate it in polar coordinates:

$$\left(\int_{-\infty}^{\infty} e^{-x^2} \, dx \right)^2 = \int_{-\infty}^{\infty} e^{-x^2} \, dx \int_{-\infty}^{\infty} e^{-y^2} \, dy$$

$$= \iint_{\mathbb{R}^2} e^{-(x^2+y^2)} \, dA$$

$$= \int_{0}^{2\pi} d\theta \int_{0}^{\infty} e^{-r^2} r \, dr$$

$$= 2\pi \lim_{R \to \infty} \left(-\frac{1}{2} e^{-r^2} \right) \bigg|_{0}^{R} = \pi.$$

The r integral, a convergent improper integral, was evaluated with the aid of the substitution $u = r^2$.

As our final example on integration in polar coordinates let us try something a little more demanding.

EXAMPLE 4.3.7   Find the volume of the solid region lying inside both the sphere $x^2 + y^2 + z^2 = 4a^2$ and the cylinder $x^2 + (y - a)^2 = a^2$.

SOLUTION   The sphere is centred at the origin and has radius $2a$. The cylinder is vertical and has axis along the vertical line through $(0, a, 0)$. Since its radius is a, the z-axis lies on the cylinder. One quarter of the required volume lies in the first octant. This part is sketched in Fig. 4.3.8.   If we use polar coordinates in the xy-plane,

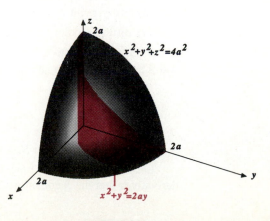

FIGURE 4.3.8

the sphere has equation $r^2 + z^2 = 4a^2$ and the equation of the cylinder, which can be written $x^2 + y^2 = 2ay$ becomes $r^2 = 2ar \sin \theta$ or, more simply, $r = 2a \sin \theta$. The first octant portion of the volume lies above the region specified by the inequalities $0 \le \theta \le \pi/2$, $0 \le r \le 2a \sin \theta$. Therefore the total volume is

$$V = 4 \int_0^{\pi/2} d\theta \int_0^{2a \sin \theta} \sqrt{4a^2 - r^2}\, r\, dr \qquad [\text{let } u = 4a^2 - r^2]$$

$$= 2 \int_0^{\pi/2} d\theta \int_{4a^2 \cos^2 \theta}^{4a^2} \sqrt{u}\, du$$

$$= \frac{4}{3} \int_0^{\pi/2} (8a^3 - 8a^3 \cos^3 \theta)\, d\theta \qquad [\text{let } v = \sin \theta]$$

$$= \frac{16}{3} \pi a^3 - \frac{32}{3} a^3 \int_0^1 (1 - v^2)\, dv$$

$$= \frac{16}{3} \pi a^3 - \frac{64}{9} a^3 = \frac{16}{9} (3\pi - 4) a^3 \text{ units}^3.$$

Transformations of Variables in Double Integrals

The transformation of a double integral to polar coordinates is just a special case of a general change of variables formula for double integrals. Suppose that x and y are expressed as functions of two other variables u and v by the equations

$$x = x(u, v)$$
$$y = y(u, v).$$

We regard these equations as defining a **transformation** (or mapping) from points (u, v) in a uv-Cartesian plane to points (x, y) in the xy-plane. We say that the transformation is *one-to-one* from the set S in the uv-plane *onto* the set D in the xy-plane provided:

  i) every point in S gets mapped to a point in D,

  ii) every point in D is the image of a point in S, and

  iii) different points in S get mapped to different points in D.

If the transformation is one-to-one, the defining equations can be solved for u and v as functions of x and y, and the resulting *inverse transformation*

$$u = u(x, y)$$
$$v = v(x, y)$$

is one-to-one from D onto S.

Let us assume that the functions $x(u, v)$ and $y(u, v)$ have continuous first partial derivatives and the Jacobian determinant

$$\frac{\partial(x, y)}{\partial(u, v)} \neq 0$$

at (u, v). As stated in Section 2.7, the Implicit Function Theorem implies that the transformation is one-to-one near (u, v) and the inverse transformation also has continuous first partial derivatives and nonzero Jacobian satisfying

$$\frac{\partial(u, v)}{\partial(x, y)} = \frac{1}{\dfrac{\partial(x, y)}{\partial(u, v)}}$$

on D.

For example, the transformation $x = r\cos\theta$, $y = r\sin\theta$ to polar coordinates has Jacobian

$$\frac{\partial(x, y)}{\partial(r, \theta)} = \begin{vmatrix} \cos\theta & -r\sin\theta \\ \sin\theta & r\cos\theta \end{vmatrix} = r.$$

Near any point except the origin (where $r = 0$), the transformation is one-to-one. (In fact it is one-to-one from any set in the $r\theta$-plane which does not contain the axis $r = 0$ and lies in, say, the strip $0 \le \theta < 2\pi$.)

A one-to-one transformation can be used to transform the double integral

$$\iint_D f(x, y)\, dA$$

to a double integral over the corresponding set S in the uv-plane. Under the transformation, the integrand $f(x, y)$ becomes $g(u, v) = f(x(u, v), y(u, v))$. We must discover how to express the area element $dA = dx\, dy$ in terms of the area element $du\, dv$ in the uv-plane.

For any fixed value of u, (say $u = c$), the equations

$$x = x(u, v), \quad \text{and} \quad y = y(u, v)$$

define a parametric curve (with v as parameter) in the xy-plane. This curve is called a u-curve corresponding to the value c. Similarly, for fixed v the equations define a parametric curve (with parameter u) called a v-curve. Consider the differential area element bounded by the u-curves corresponding to nearby values u and $u + du$ and the v-curves corresponding to nearby values v and $v + dv$. Since these curves are smooth, for small values of du and dv the area element is approximately a parallelogram, and its area is approximately

$$dA = |\overrightarrow{PQ} \times \overrightarrow{PR}|,$$

where P, Q and R are the points shown in Fig. 4.3.9.   The error in this

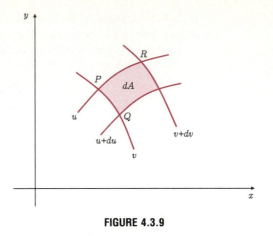

FIGURE 4.3.9

approximation becomes negligible compared to dA as du and dv approach zero.

Now $\overrightarrow{PQ} = dx\,\mathbf{i} + dy\,\mathbf{j}$ where

$$dx = \frac{\partial x}{\partial u}du + \frac{\partial x}{\partial v}dv \quad \text{and} \quad dy = \frac{\partial y}{\partial u}du + \frac{\partial y}{\partial v}dv.$$

However, $dv = 0$ along the v-curve PQ so

$$\overrightarrow{PQ} = \frac{\partial x}{\partial u}du\,\mathbf{i} + \frac{\partial y}{\partial u}du\,\mathbf{j}.$$

Similarly

$$\overrightarrow{PR} = \frac{\partial x}{\partial v}dv\,\mathbf{i} + \frac{\partial y}{\partial v}dv\,\mathbf{j}.$$

Hence

$$dA = \left\|\begin{vmatrix} \mathbf{i} & \mathbf{j} & \mathbf{k} \\ \frac{\partial x}{\partial u}du & \frac{\partial y}{\partial u}du & 0 \\ \frac{\partial x}{\partial v}dv & \frac{\partial y}{\partial v}dv & 0 \end{vmatrix}\right\| = \left|\frac{\partial(x,y)}{\partial(u,v)}\right| du\,dv;$$

that is, the absolute value of the Jacobian $\partial(x,y)/\partial(u,v)$ is the ratio between corresponding area elements in the xy-plane and the uv-plane:

**4.3.8
Area Element
for Transformed
Coordinates**

$$dA = dx\,dy = \left|\frac{\partial(x,y)}{\partial(u,v)}\right| du\,dv.$$

We summarize the change of variables procedure for a double integral as follows:

THEOREM 4.3.9   *(Change of variables formula for double integrals.)* Let $x = x(u, v)$, $y = y(u, v)$ be a one-to-one transformation from a domain S in the uv-plane onto a domain D in the xy-plane. Suppose that the functions x and y and their first partial derivatives with respect to u and v are continuous in S. If $f(x, y)$ is integrable on D, and if $g(u, v) = f(x(u, v), y(u, v))$, then g is integrable on S and

$$\iint_D f(x, y)\, dx\, dy = \iint_S g(u, v) \left| \frac{\partial(x, y)}{\partial(u, v)} \right| du\, dv.$$

REMARK: It is not necessary that S or D be closed, or that the transformation be one-to-one on the boundary of S. The transformation to polar coordinates maps the rectangle $0 < r < 1$, $0 \le \theta < 2\pi$ one-to-one onto the punctured disc $0 < x^2 + y^2 < 1$ and, as in the first example in this section, we can transform an integral over the closed disc $x^2 + y^2 \le 1$ to one over the closed rectangle $0 \le r \le 1$, $0 \le \theta \le 2\pi$.

It is always tempting to try to use the change of variable formula to transform the domain of a double integral into a rectangle so that iteration will be easy. As the following example shows, this usually involves defining the inverse transformation (u and v in terms of x and y). Remember that inverse transformations have reciprocal Jacobians.

EXAMPLE 4.3.10   Find the area of the finite plane region bounded by the four parabolas $y = x^2$, $y = 2x^2$, $x = y^2$ and $x = 3y^2$.

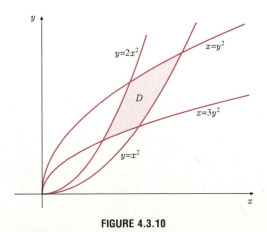

FIGURE 4.3.10

SOLUTION   The region, call it D, is sketched in Fig. 4.3.10. Let

$$u = \frac{y}{x^2}, \qquad v = \frac{x}{y^2}.$$

Evidently the region D corresponds to the rectangle R in the uv-plane given by $1 \le u \le 2$, $1 \le v \le 3$. Since

$$\frac{\partial(u,v)}{\partial(x,y)} = \begin{vmatrix} -2y/x^3 & 1/x^2 \\ 1/y^2 & -2x/y^3 \end{vmatrix} = \frac{3}{x^2 y^2} = 3u^2 v^2,$$

it follows that

$$\left| \frac{\partial(x,y)}{\partial(u,v)} \right| = \frac{1}{3u^2 v^2}$$

and the area of D is given by

$$\iint_D dx\, dy = \iint_R \frac{1}{3u^2 v^2}\, du\, dv$$
$$= \frac{1}{3} \int_1^2 \frac{du}{u^2} \int_1^3 \frac{dv}{v^2} = \frac{1}{3} \times \frac{1}{2} \times \frac{2}{3} = \frac{1}{9} \text{ units}^2.$$

The following example shows what can happen if the transformation of a double integral is not one-to-one.

EXAMPLE 4.3.11   Let D be the square $0 \le x \le 1$, $0 \le y \le 1$ in the xy-plane, and let S be the square $0 \le u \le 1$, $0 \le v \le 1$ in the uv-plane. Show that the transformation

$$x = 4u - 4u^2, \qquad y = v$$

maps S onto D, and use it to transform the integral $I = \iint_D dx\, dy$. Compare the value of I with that of the transformed integral.

SOLUTION   Since $x = 4u - 4u^2 = 1 - (1 - 2u)^2$, the minimum value of x on the interval $0 \le u \le 1$ is 0 (at $u = 0$ and $u = 1$), and the maximum value is 1 (at $u = \frac{1}{2}$). Therefore, $x = 4u - 4u^2$ maps the interval $0 \le u \le 1$ onto the interval $0 \le x \le 1$. Since $y = v$ clearly maps $0 \le v \le 1$ onto $0 \le y \le 1$, the given transformation maps S onto D. Since

$$dx\, dy = \left| \frac{\partial(x,y)}{\partial(u,v)} \right| du\, dv = \left| \begin{matrix} 4 - 8u & 0 \\ 0 & 1 \end{matrix} \right| du\, dv = |4 - 8u|\, du\, dv,$$

transforming I leads to the integral

$$J = \iint_S |4 - 8u|\, du\, dv = 4 \int_0^1 dv \int_0^1 |1 - 2u|\, du = 8 \int_0^{1/2} (1 - 2u)\, du = 2.$$

However, $I = \iint_D dx\, dy$ = area of D = 1. The reason that $J \ne I$ is that the transformation is not one-to-one from S onto D; it actually maps S onto D twice. The rectangle R defined by $0 \le u \le \frac{1}{2}$, $0 \le v \le 1$ is mapped one-to-one onto D by the transformation, so the appropriate transformed integral is $\iint_R |4 - 8u|\, du\, dv$, which is equal to I.

EXERCISES

1. Evaluate $\iint_S (x + y)\, dA$, where S is the region in the first quadrant lying inside the disc $x^2 + y^2 \leq a^2$ and under the line $y = \sqrt{3}x$.

2. Find $\iint_S x\, dA$, where S is the disc segment $x^2 + y^2 \leq 2$, $x \geq 1$.

3. Evaluate $\iint_T (x^2 + y^2)\, dA$, where T is the triangle with vertices $(0,0)$, $(1,0)$ and $(1,1)$.

4. Evaluate $\iint_{x^2+y^2 \leq 1} \ln(x^2 + y^2)\, dA$.

5. Find the average distance from the origin to points in the disc $x^2 + y^2 \leq a^2$.

6. Find the average value of $e^{-(x^2+y^2)}$ over the annular region $0 < a \leq \sqrt{x^2 + y^2} \leq b$.

7. For what values of k, and to what value, does the integral $\iint_{x^2+y^2 \leq 1} \dfrac{dA}{(x^2 + y^2)^k}$ converge?

8. For what values of k, and to what value, does the integral $\iint_{\mathbb{R}^2} \dfrac{dA}{(1 + x^2 + y^2)^k}$ converge?

9. Evaluate $\iint_D xy\, dA$, where D is the plane region satisfying $x \geq 0$, $0 \leq y \leq x$, and $x^2 + y^2 \leq a^2$.

10. Evaluate $\iint_C y\, dA$, where C is the upper half of the cardioid disc $r \leq 1 + \cos\theta$.

11. Find the volume lying between the paraboloids $z = x^2 + y^2$ and $3z = 4 - x^2 - y^2$.

12. Find the volume lying inside both the sphere $x^2 + y^2 + z^2 = a^2$ and the cylinder $x^2 + y^2 = ax$.

13. Find the volume lying inside both the sphere $x^2 + y^2 + z^2 = 2a^2$ and the cylinder $x^2 + y^2 = a^2$.

14. *Find the volume lying outside the cone $z^2 = x^2 + y^2$ and inside the sphere $x^2 + (y - a)^2 + z^2 = a^2$.

15. Find the volume lying inside the cylinder $x^2 + (y - a)^2 = a^2$ and between the upper and lower halves of the cone $z^2 = x^2 + y^2$.

16. Find the volume of the region lying above the xy-plane, inside the cylinder $x^2 + y^2 = 4$ and below the plane $z = x + y + 4$.

17. *Find the volume of the region lying inside all three of the circular cylinders $x^2 + y^2 = a^2$, $x^2 + z^2 = a^2$ and $y^2 + z^2 = a^2$. Hint: Make a good sketch of the first octant part of the region and use symmetry whenever possible.

18. Find the volume of the region lying inside the circular cylinder $x^2 + y^2 = 2y$ and inside the parabolic cylinder $z^2 = y$.

19. *Many points are chosen at random in the disc $x^2 + y^2 \leq 1$. Find the approximate average value of the distance from these points to the nearest side of the smallest square which contains the disc.

20. *Find the average value of x over the segment of the disc $x^2 + y^2 \leq 4$ lying to the right of $x = 1$. What is the centroid of the segment?

21. Find the volume enclosed by the ellipsoid

$$\frac{x^2}{a^2} + \frac{y^2}{b^2} + \frac{z^2}{c^2} = 1.$$

22. Find the volume of the region in the first octant below the paraboloid

$$z = 1 - \frac{x^2}{a^2} - \frac{y^2}{b^2}.$$

Hint: use the change of variables $x = au$, $y = bv$.

23. *Evaluate $\iint_{|x|+|y| \leq a} e^{x+y}\, dA$.

24. Find $\iint_P (x^2 + y^2)\, dA$, where P is the parallelogram bounded by the lines $x + y = 1$, $x + y = 2$, $3x + 4y = 5$ and $3x + 4y = 6$.

25. Find the area of the region in the first quadrant bounded by the curves $xy = 1$, $xy = 4$, $y = x$ and $y = 2x$.

26. Evaluate $\iint_R (x^2 + y^2)\, dA$, where R is the region in the first quadrant bounded by $y = 0$, $y = x$, $xy = 1$ and $x^2 - y^2 = 1$.

27. *Let T be the triangle with vertices $(0,0)$, $(1,0)$ and $(0,1)$. Evaluate the integral $\iint_T e^{(y-x)/(y+x)}\, dA$,

a) by transforming to polar coordinates, and

b) by using the change of variable $u = y - x$, $v = y + x$.

28. *The error function, Erf(x), is defined for $x \geq 0$ by

$$\text{Erf}(x) = \frac{2}{\sqrt{\pi}} \int_0^x e^{-t^2} \, dt.$$

Show that

$$\left(\text{Erf}(x)\right)^2 = \frac{4}{\pi} \int_0^{\pi/4} \left(1 - e^{-x^2/\cos^2\theta}\right) d\theta.$$

Hence deduce that $\text{Erf}(x) \geq \sqrt{1 - e^{-x^2}}$.

29. *The Gamma and Beta functions are defined by

$$\Gamma(x) = \int_0^\infty t^{x-1} e^{-t} \, dt, \quad (x > 0),$$

$$B(x, y) = \int_0^1 t^{x-1}(1-t)^{y-1} \, dt, \quad (x > 0, \ y > 0).$$

Deduce the following properties of these functions.

a) $\Gamma(x+1) = x\Gamma(x), \qquad (x > 0)$,

b) $\Gamma(n+1) = n!, \qquad (n = 0, 1, 2, \ldots)$,

c) $\Gamma(x) = 2 \int_0^\infty s^{2x-1} e^{-s^2} \, ds, \qquad (x > 0)$,

d) $\Gamma\left(\frac{1}{2}\right) = \sqrt{\pi}, \qquad \Gamma\left(\frac{3}{2}\right) = \frac{1}{2}\sqrt{\pi}$,

e) $B(x, y) = 2 \int_0^{\pi/2} \cos^{2x-1}\theta \sin^{2y-1}\theta \, d\theta$,

$(x > 0, \ y > 0)$,

f) $B(x, y) = \dfrac{\Gamma(x)\Gamma(y)}{\Gamma(x+y)}$.

In view of b), $\Gamma(x+1)$ is frequently denoted $x!$.

4.4 TRIPLE INTEGRALS

Now that we have seen how to extend definite integration to two dimensional domains the extension to three (or more) dimensions is straightforward. Given a bounded function $f(x, y, z)$ defined in a "reasonable" domain D in 3-space, the **triple integral** of f over D,

$$\iiint_D f(x, y, z) \, dV, \qquad \text{or} \qquad \iiint_D f(x, y, z) \, dx \, dy \, dz,$$

can be defined as a suitable limit of Riemann sums. We omit the details.

All the properties of double integrals mentioned in Section 4.1 have analogues for triple integrals. In particular, a continuous function is integrable over a closed, bounded domain. If $f(x, y, z) = 1$ on D then the triple integral gives the volume of D:

$$\text{Volume of } D = \iiint_D dV.$$

The triple integral of a positive function $f(x, y, z)$ can be interpreted has the "hypervolume" (that is, the four-dimensional volume) of a region in 4-space having the set D as three-dimensional base and having top on the hypersurface $w = f(x, y, z)$. This is not a particularly useful interpretation; many more useful ones arise in applications. For instance, if $\rho(x, y, z)$ represents the density (mass per unit volume) at position (x, y, z) in a substance occupying the domain D in 3-space then the mass m of the solid is the "sum" of mass elements $dm = \rho(x, y, z) \, dV$ occupying volume elements dV:

$$\text{mass} = \iiint_D \rho(x, y, z) \, dV.$$

Some triple integrals can be evaluated by inspection, using symmetry and known volumes.

EXAMPLE 4.4.1   We have

$$\iiint_{x^2+y^2+z^2\le a^2} (2 + x - \sin z)\, dV = \frac{8}{3}\pi a^3.$$

The domain of integration is the ball of radius a centred at the origin. The integral of 2 over this domain is twice the volume of that ball, that is $8\pi a^3/3$. The integrals of x and $\sin z$ over the ball are both zero since both functions are odd in one of the variables and the domain is symmetric about the origin in each variable. (For instance, corresponding to every volume element dV in the half of the ball where $x > 0$ there is a corresponding element in the other half where x has the same size but the opposite sign. The contribution from these to elements cancel one another.)

Most triple integrals are evaluated by an iteration procedure similar to that used for double integrals. We slice the domain D with a plane parallel to one of the coordinate planes, double integrate the function with respect to two variables over that slice, and then integrate the result with respect to the remaining variable. Some examples should serve to make the procedure clear.

EXAMPLE 4.4.2   Let B be the rectangular box $0 \le x \le a$, $0 \le y \le b$, $0 \le z \le c$. Evaluate

$$I = \iiint_B xy^2z^3 \, dV$$

SOLUTION   As indicated in Fig. 4.4.1 we will slice with planes normal to the z-axis, so the z integral will be outermost in the iteration. The slices are rectangles, so the double integrals over them can be immediately iterated also. We do it with the y integral outer and the x integral inner as suggested by the line shown in the slice.

$$I = \int_0^c dz \int_0^b dy \int_0^a xy^2z^3 \, dx$$
$$= \int_0^c z^3\, dz \int_0^b y^2\, dy \int_0^a x\, dx = \frac{c^4}{4} \times \frac{b^3}{3} \times \frac{a^2}{2} = \frac{1}{24}a^2b^3c^4.$$

EXAMPLE 4.4.3   Evaluate

$$I = \iiint_T y \, dV$$

over the tetrahedron T with vertices (0,0,0), (1,0,0), (0,1,0) and (0,0,1).

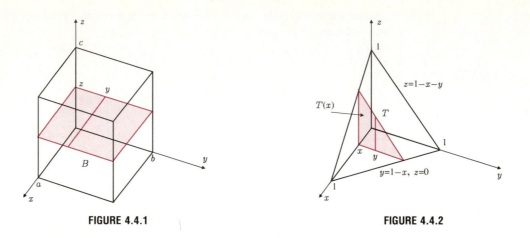

FIGURE 4.4.1   FIGURE 4.4.2

SOLUTION   The tetrahedron is shown in Fig. 4.4.2. The plane slice in the plane normal to the x-axis at position x is the triangle $T(x)$ shown in that Figure. x is constant and y and z are variables in this slice. The double integral of y over $T(x)$ is a function of x. We evaluate it by integrating first in the z direction and then in the y direction as suggested by the vertical line shown in the slice:

$$\iint_{T(x)} y \, dA = \int_0^{1-x} dy \int_0^{1-x-y} y \, dz$$

$$= \int_0^{1-x} y(1 - x - y) \, dy$$

$$= \left((1-x)\frac{y^2}{2} - \frac{y^3}{3} \right)\Bigg|_0^{1-x} = \frac{1}{6}(1-x)^3.$$

The value of I is the integral of this expression with respect to the remaining variable x, to sum the contributions from all such slices between $x = 0$ and $x = 1$:

$$I = \int_0^1 \frac{1}{6}(1-x)^3 \, dx = -\frac{1}{24}(1-x)^4 \Bigg|_0^1 = \frac{1}{24}.$$

In the above solution we carried out the iteration in two steps in order to show the procedure clearly. In practice, triple integrals are iterated in one step, with no explicit mention made of the double integral over the slice. Thus, using the iteration suggested by Fig. 4.4.2 we would immediately write

$$I = \int_0^1 dx \int_0^{1-x} dy \int_0^{1-x-y} y \, dz.$$

The evaluation proceeds as above, starting with the rightmost (that is, *innermost*) integral, followed by the middle integral and then the leftmost (outermost) integral. The triple integral represents the "summation" of elements $y \, dV$ over the three-dimensional region T. The above iteration corresponds to "summing" (that is, integrating) first along a vertical line (the z integral), then summing these one-dimensional "sums" in the y direction to get the "double sum" of all elements in the plane slice, and finally "summing" these double sums in the x direction to add up the contributions from all the slices. The iteration can be carried out in other directions; there are six possible iterations corresponding to different orders of doing the x, y and z integrals. The other five are

$$I = \int_0^1 dx \int_0^{1-x} dz \int_0^{1-x-z} y\,dy,$$

$$I = \int_0^1 dy \int_0^{1-y} dx \int_0^{1-x-y} y\,dz,$$

$$I = \int_0^1 dy \int_0^{1-y} dz \int_0^{1-y-z} y\,dx,$$

$$I = \int_0^1 dz \int_0^{1-z} dx \int_0^{1-x-z} y\,dy,$$

$$I = \int_0^1 dz \int_0^{1-z} dy \int_0^{1-y-z} y\,dx.$$

The student should verify these by drawing diagrams analogous to Fig. 4.4.2. Of course, all six iterations give the same result.

It is sometimes difficult to visualize the region of 3-space over which a given triple integral is taken. In such situations try to determine the *projection* of that region on one or other of the coordinate planes. For instance, if a region R is bounded by two surfaces with given equations, combining these equations to eliminate one variable will yield the equation of a cylinder (not necessarily circular) with axis parallel to the axis of the eliminated variable. This cylinder will then determine the projection of R onto the coordinate plane perpendicular to that axis. The following example illustrates the use of this technique to find the volume bounded by two surfaces. The volume is expressed as a triple integral with unit integrand.

EXAMPLE 4.4.4   Find the volume of the region R lying below the plane $z = 3 - 2y$ and above the paraboloid $z = x^2 + y^2$.

SOLUTION   The region R is shown in Fig. 4.4.3. It is evidently symmetric about the yz-plane, and so its volume V may be found by doubling that part lying in the half-space $x > 0$. Note that the two surfaces bounding R intersect on the vertical cylinder $x^2 + y^2 = 3 - 2y$, or $x^2 + (y+1)^2 = 4$, which lies between $y = -1$ and $y = 3$. Thus

$$V = \iiint_R dV = 2 \int_{-3}^{1} dy \int_0^{\sqrt{3-2y-y^2}} dx \int_{x^2+y^2}^{3-2y} dz$$

$$= 2 \int_{-3}^{1} dy \int_0^{\sqrt{3-2y-y^2}} (3 - 2y - x^2 - y^2)\,dx$$

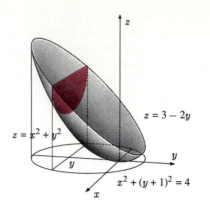

FIGURE 4.4.3

$$= 2 \int_{-3}^{1} \left((3 - 2y - y^2)x - \frac{x^3}{3} \right) \Bigg|_{0}^{\sqrt{3-2y-y^2}} dy$$

$$= \frac{4}{3} \int_{-3}^{1} \left(3 - 2y - y^2 \right)^{3/2} dy$$

$$= \frac{4}{3} \int_{-3}^{1} \left(4 - (y + 1)^2 \right)^{3/2} dy.$$

In the last integral we make the change of variable $y + 1 = 2 \sin \theta$ and obtain

$$V = \frac{64}{3} \int_{-\pi/2}^{\pi/2} \cos^4 \theta \, d\theta$$

$$= \frac{128}{3} \int_{0}^{\pi/2} \left(\frac{1 + \cos 2\theta}{2} \right)^2 d\theta$$

$$= \frac{32}{3} \int_{0}^{\pi/2} \left(1 + 2 \cos 2\theta + \frac{1 + \cos 4\theta}{2} \right) d\theta = 8\pi \text{ units}^3.$$

It is sometimes essential to sketch the region over which a triple integral is taken. As the following example shows, it is not always easy to sketch the region even if the triple integral is already given in iterated form. The ability to deduce the shape of the region from the limits in the iterated integral is a skill that one acquires with practice. Again you should first determine the projection of the region on a coordinate plane — the plane of the two variables in the outer integrals of the given iteration.

EXAMPLE 4.4.5   Express the iterated integral

$$I = \int_{0}^{1} dy \int_{y}^{1} dz \int_{0}^{z} f(x, y, z) \, dx$$

as a triple integral and sketch the region over which it is taken.   Reiterate the integral in such a way that the integrations are performed in the order: first y, then z, then x (that is, the opposite order to the given iteration).

SOLUTION   We have

$$I = \iiint_R f(x, y, z) \, dV.$$

It is clear from the outer integral in the given iteration that the region R lies between the planes $y = 0$ and $y = 1$. For each such value of y, z must lie between y and 1. Therefore R lies below the plane $z = 1$ and above the plane $z = y$ and the projection of R onto the yz-plane must be the triangle with vertices $(0,0,0)$, $(0,0,1)$ and $(0,1,1)$. Through any point $(0, y, z)$ in this triangle, a line parallel to the x-axis intersects R between $x = 0$ and $x = z$. Thus the solid is bounded by the five planes $x = 0$, $y = 0$, $z = 1$, $y = z$ and $z = x$. It is sketched in Fig. 4.4.4, with slice and line corresponding to the given iteration.

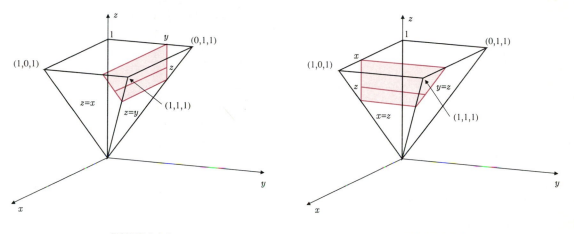

FIGURE 4.4.4   FIGURE 4.4.5

The required iteration corresponds to the slice and line shown in Fig. 4.4.5. Therefore it is

$$I = \int_0^1 dx \int_x^1 dz \int_0^z f(x, y, z) \, dy.$$

EXERCISES

In Exercises 1–10 evaluate the triple integrals over the indicated region R. Be alert for simplifications and auspicious orders of iteration.

1. $\displaystyle\iiint_R (1 + 2x - 3y) \, dV$, over the box $-a \le x \le a$, $-b \le y \le b$, $-c \le z \le c$.

2. $\displaystyle\iiint_R x \, dV$, over the tetrahedron bounded by the coordinate planes and the plane $\dfrac{x}{a} + \dfrac{y}{b} + \dfrac{z}{c} = 1$.

3. $\displaystyle\iiint_R (x^2 + y^2) \, dV$ over the cube $0 \le x, y, z \le 1$.

4. $\displaystyle\iiint_R (x^2 + y^2 + z^2) \, dV$ over the cube of the previous exercise.

5. $\displaystyle\iiint_R (xy + z^2) \, dV$, over the set $0 \le z \le 1 - |x| - |y|$.

6. $\displaystyle\iiint_R yz^2 e^{-xyz} \, dV$, over the cube $0 \le x, y, z \le 1$.

7. $\iiint_R \sin(\pi y^3)\,dV$, over the pyramid with vertices (0,0,0), (0,1,0), (1,1,0), (1,1,1) and (0,1,1).

8. $\iiint_R y\,dV$, over that portion of the cube $0 \le x, y, z \le 1$ lying above the plane $y + z = 1$ and below the plane $x + y + z = 2$.

9. $\iiint_R \dfrac{1}{(x+y+z)^3}\,dV$, over the region bounded by the six planes $z = 1$, $z = 2$, $y = 0$, $y = z$, $x = 0$ and $x = y + z$.

10. $\iiint_R \cos x \cos y \cos z\,dV$, over the tetrahedron defined by $x, y, z \ge 0$, $x + y + z \le \pi$.

11. Evaluate $\iiint_{\mathbb{R}^3} e^{-x^2-2y^2-3z^2}\,dV$. Hint: use the result of Example 4.3.6.

12. Find the volume of the region lying inside the cylinder $x^2 + 4y^2 = 4$, above the xy-plane and below the plane $z = 2 + x$.

13. *Find the volume of the region inside the ellipsoid $\dfrac{x^2}{a^2} + \dfrac{y^2}{b^2} + \dfrac{z^2}{c^2} = 1$ and above the plane $z = b - y$.

14. Find $\iiint_T x\,dV$ where T is the tetrahedron bounded by the planes $x = 1$, $y = 1$, $z = 1$ and $x + y + z = 2$.

In Exercises 15–18 express the given iterated integral as a triple integral and sketch the region over which it is taken. Reiterate the integral so that the integrations are performed in the order: first z, then y, then x.

15.* $\displaystyle\int_0^1 dz \int_0^{1-z} dy \int_0^1 f(x,y,z)\,dx$

16.* $\displaystyle\int_0^1 dz \int_z^1 dy \int_0^y f(x,y,z)\,dx$

17.* $\displaystyle\int_0^1 dz \int_z^1 dx \int_0^{x-z} f(x,y,z)\,dy$

18.* $\displaystyle\int_0^1 dy \int_0^{\sqrt{1-y^2}} dz \int_{y^2+z^2}^1 f(x,y,z)\,dx$

In Exercises 19–20 evaluate the given iterated integral by reiterating it in a different order. (You will need to make a good sketch of the region.)

19.* $\displaystyle\int_0^1 dz \int_z^1 dx \int_0^x e^{x^3}\,dy$

20.* $\displaystyle\int_0^1 dx \int_0^{1-x} dy \int_y^1 \dfrac{\sin(\pi z)}{z(2-z)}\,dz$

21. Define the average value of an integrable function $f(x,y,z)$ over a region R of 3-space. Find the average value of $x^2 + y^2 + z^2$ over the cube $0 \le x \le 1$, $0 \le y \le 1$, $0 \le z \le 1$.

22. *State a Mean-Value Theorem for triple integrals analogous to Theorem 4.2.3. Use it to prove that if $f(x,y,z)$ is continuous near the point (a,b,c) and if $B_\epsilon(a,b,c)$ is the ball of radius ϵ centred at (a,b,c) then

$$\lim_{\epsilon \to 0} \frac{3}{4\pi\epsilon^3} \iiint_{B_\epsilon(a,b,c)} f(x,y,z)\,dV = f(a,b,c).$$

4.5 CHANGE OF VARIABLES IN TRIPLE INTEGRALS

The change of variables formula for a double integral extends in the obvious way to triple (or higher order) integrals. Consider the transformation

$$x = x(u, v, w)$$
$$y = y(u, v, w)$$
$$z = z(u, v, w)$$

where x, y and z have continuous first partial derivatives with respect to u, v and w. Near any point where the Jacobian $\partial(x,y,z)/\partial(u,v,w)$ is nonzero, the transformation scales volume elements according to the formula

4.5.1
Change of Variables
in a Triple Integral

$$dV = dx\,dy\,dz = \left|\frac{\partial(x,y,z)}{\partial(u,v,w)}\right|\,du\,dv\,dw.$$

Thus, if the transformation is one-to-one from a domain S in uvw-space onto a domain D in xyz-space, and if

$$g(u,v,w) = f\big(x(u,v,w), y(u,v,w), z(u,v,w)\big),$$

then

$$\iiint_D f(x,y,z)\,dx\,dy\,dz = \iiint_S g(u,v,w)\left|\frac{\partial(x,y,z)}{\partial(u,v,w)}\right|\,du\,dv\,dw.$$

The proof is similar to the two dimensional case given in the previous section. (See Exercise 24 at the end of this section.)

EXAMPLE 4.5.2 Under the change of variable $x = au$, $y = bv$, $z = cw$ the solid ellipsoid E given by

$$\frac{x^2}{a^2} + \frac{y^2}{b^2} + \frac{z^2}{c^2} \le 1$$

becomes the ball B given by $u^2 + v^2 + w^2 \le 1$. Since the Jacobian of this transformation is

$$\frac{\partial(x,y,z)}{\partial(u,v,w)} = \begin{vmatrix} a & 0 & 0 \\ 0 & b & 0 \\ 0 & 0 & c \end{vmatrix} = abc$$

the volume of the ellipsoid is

$$\begin{aligned} \text{Volume of } E &= \iiint_E dx\,dy\,dz \\ &= \iiint_B abc\,du\,dv\,dw = abc \times (\text{Volume of } B) = \frac{4}{3}\pi abc. \end{aligned}$$

Cylindrical Coordinates

Among the most useful alternatives to Cartesian coordinates in 3-space are two coordinate systems which generalize plane polar coordinates. The simpler of these systems is called the system of **cylindrical coordinates** and uses ordinary plane polar coordinates in the xy-plane while retaining the Cartesian z coordinate for measuring vertical distances. Thus each point in 3-space has cylindrical coordinates (r, θ, z) related to its Cartesian coordinates (x, y, z) by the transformation

4.5.3
Cylindrical
Coordinates

$$x = r\cos\theta, \quad y = r\sin\theta, \quad z = z.$$

The coordinate surfaces in this system are the r-surfaces (vertical circular cylinders centred on the z-axis), θ-surfaces (vertical planes containing the z-axis) and z-surfaces (planes perpendicular to the z-axis). (See Fig. 4.5.1.) Cylindrical coordinates lend themselves to representing domains which are bounded by such surfaces, and in general to problems with axial symmetry (around the z-axis).

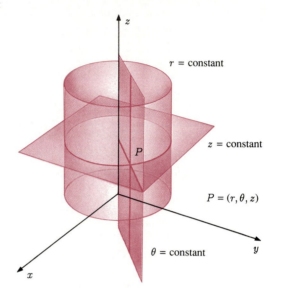

FIGURE 4.5.1

The volume element in cylindrical coordinates is

4.5.4
Volume Element for
Cylindrical
Coordinates

$$dV = r\, dr\, d\theta\, dz,$$

which is easily seen by examining the infinitesimal "box" bounded by the coordinate surfaces corresponding to values r, $r + dr$, θ, $\theta + d\theta$, z and $z + dz$, (see Fig. 4.5.2), or by calculating the Jacobian

$$\frac{\partial(x,y,z)}{\partial(r,\theta,z)} = \begin{vmatrix} \cos\theta & -r\sin\theta & 0 \\ \sin\theta & r\cos\theta & 0 \\ 0 & 0 & 1 \end{vmatrix} = r.$$

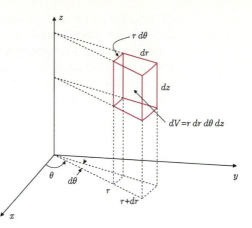

FIGURE 4.5.2

EXAMPLE 4.5.5   Evaluate

$$\iiint_D (x^2 + y^2)\, dV$$

over the first octant region bounded by the cylinders $x^2 + y^2 = 1$ and $x^2 + y^2 = 4$ and the planes $z = 0$, $z = 1$, $x = 0$ and $x = y$.

SOLUTION   In terms of cylindrical coordinates the region is bounded by $r = 1$, $r = 2$, $\theta = \pi/4$, $\theta = \pi/2$, $z = 0$ and $z = 1$. (That is, it is a rectangular coordinate box in $r\theta z$-space.) Since the integrand is $x^2 + y^2 = r^2$ the integral is

$$\iiint_D (x^2 + y^2)\, dV = \int_0^1 dz \int_{\pi/4}^{\pi/2} d\theta \int_1^2 r^2\, r\, dr$$

$$= (1 - 0)(\frac{\pi}{2} - \frac{\pi}{4})(\frac{2^4}{4} - \frac{1^4}{4}) = \frac{15}{16}\pi.$$

The above example would have been much more difficult to solve in Cartesian coordinates.

Spherical Coordinates

In the system of **spherical coordinates** a point P in 3-space is represented by the ordered triple (R, ϕ, θ) where R is the distance from P to the origin O, ϕ is the angle the radial line OP makes with the positive direction of the z-axis, and θ is the angle between the plane containing P and the z-axis and the xz-plane. (See Fig. 4.5.3.) The R-surfaces (R = constant) are spheres centred at the origin; the ϕ-surfaces (ϕ = constant) are circular cones with the z-axis as axis; the θ-surfaces (θ = constant) are vertical half-planes with edge along the z-axis. If we take a coordinate system with origin at the centre of the earth, z-axis through the north pole, and x-axis through the intersection of the Greenwich meridian and the equator, then the intersection of the surface of the earth with the ϕ-surfaces are the *parallels of latitude*, and the intersection with the θ-surfaces are the *meridians of longitude*. Since latitude is measured from $90°$ at the north pole to $-90°$ at the south pole while ϕ is measured from 0 at the north pole to π $(= 180°)$ at the south pole, the coordinate ϕ is frequently referred to as the **colatitude** coordinate. θ is the **longitude** coordinate. Observe that θ has the same significance in spherical coordinates as it does in cylindrical coordinates.

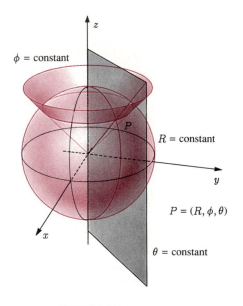

FIGURE 4.5.3

It is conventional to consider spherical coordinates restricted in such a way that $R \geq 0$, $0 \leq \phi \leq \pi$ and $0 \leq \theta < 2\pi$ (or $-\pi < \theta \leq \pi$). Every point not on the z-axis then has exactly one spherical coordinate representation, and the transformation from Cartesian coordinates (x, y, z) to spherical coordinates (R, ϕ, θ) is one-to-one off the z-axis. This transformation is given by

4.5.6
Spherical Coordinates

$$x = R \sin \phi \cos \theta$$
$$y = R \sin \phi \sin \theta$$
$$z = R \cos \phi.$$

The r coordinate in cylindrical coordinates is related to R and ϕ by

$$r = \sqrt{x^2 + y^2} = R \sin \phi$$

If $\phi = 0$ or $\phi = \pi$ then $r = 0$ so the θ coordinate is irrelevant at points on the z-axis.

The volume element in spherical coordinates is

4.5.7
Volume Element in
Spherical Coordinates

$$dV = R^2 \sin \phi \, dR \, d\phi \, d\theta.$$

To see this observe that the infinitesimal coordinate box bounded by the coordinate surfaces corresponding to values R, $R+dR$, ϕ, $\phi+d\phi$, θ and $\theta+d\theta$ has dimensions dR, $R \, d\phi$ and $R \sin \phi \, d\theta$. (See Fig. 4.5.4.)   Alternatively, the Jacobian of the transformation can be calculated:

$$\frac{\partial(x,y,z)}{\partial(R,\phi,\theta)} = \begin{vmatrix} \sin \phi \cos \theta & R \cos \phi \cos \theta & -R \sin \phi \sin \theta \\ \sin \phi \sin \theta & R \cos \phi \sin \theta & R \sin \phi \cos \theta \\ \cos \phi & -R \sin \phi & 0 \end{vmatrix}$$

$$= \cos \phi \begin{vmatrix} R \cos \phi \cos \theta & -R \sin \phi \sin \theta \\ R \cos \phi \sin \theta & R \sin \phi \cos \theta \end{vmatrix} + R \sin \phi \begin{vmatrix} \sin \phi \cos \theta & -R \sin \phi \sin \theta \\ \sin \phi \sin \theta & R \sin \phi \cos \theta \end{vmatrix}$$

$$= \cos \phi (R^2 \sin \phi \cos \phi) + R \sin \phi (R \sin^2 \phi) = R^2 \sin \phi.$$

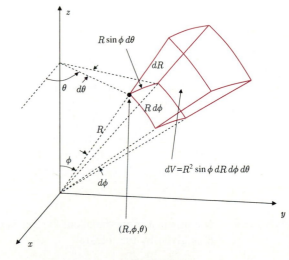

$R \sin \phi \, d\theta$

dR

θ $d\theta$

$R \, d\phi$

R

$dV = R^2 \sin \phi \, dR \, d\phi \, d\theta$

ϕ

$d\phi$

(R,ϕ,θ)

y

x

FIGURE 4.5.4

Spherical coordinates are suited to problems involving spherical symmetry, and in particular, to regions bounded by spheres centred at the origin, circular cones with axes along the z-axis, and vertical planes containing the z-axis.

EXAMPLE 4.5.8   A solid hemisphere H of radius a has density depending on the distance R from the centre (of the base disc) and given by $\rho = k(2a - R)$ where k is a constant. Find the mass of the hemisphere.

SOLUTION   Choosing coordinates with origin at the centre of the base and, so that the hemisphere lies above the xy-plane, we calculate the mass m of the hemisphere:

$$m = \iiint_H k(2a - R)\, R^2 \sin\phi\, dR\, d\phi\, d\theta$$

$$= k \int_0^{2\pi} d\theta \int_0^{\pi/2} \sin\phi\, d\phi \int_0^a (2a - R)\, R^2\, dR$$

$$= 2k\pi \times 1 \times \left(\frac{2a}{3}R^3 - \frac{1}{4}R^4 \right) \Big|_0^a = \frac{5}{6}\pi k a^4 \text{ units.}$$

REMARK: In the above example both the integrand and the region of integration exhibited spherical symmetry, so that the choice of spherical coordinates to carry out the integration was obvious. The mass could have been evaluated in cylindrical coordinates. The iteration in that system is

$$m = \int_0^{2\pi} d\theta \int_0^a r\, dr \int_0^{\sqrt{a^2 - r^2}} k(2a - \sqrt{r^2 + z^2})\, dz$$

and is much harder to evaluate. It is still more difficult in Cartesian coordinates:

$$m = 4 \int_0^a dx \int_0^{\sqrt{a^2 - x^2}} dy \int_0^{\sqrt{a^2 - x^2 - y^2}} k(2a - \sqrt{x^2 + y^2 + z^2})\, dz.$$

The choice of coordinate system can greatly affect the difficulty of computation of a multiple integral.

Frequently a problem will have elements of spherical and axial symmetry. In such cases it may not be clear whether using spherical or cylindrical coordinates is the better choice. In such doubtful cases the integrand is usually the best guide. Use cylindrical or spherical coordinates according to whether the integrand involves $x^2 + y^2$ or $x^2 + y^2 + z^2$.

EXAMPLE 4.5.9   The moment of inertia about the z-axis of a solid of density ρ occupying the region R is given by the integral

$$I = \iiint_R (x^2 + y^2)\rho\, dV.$$

(See Section 4.6.) Calculate that moment of inertia for a solid of unit density occupying the region inside the sphere $x^2 + y^2 + z^2 = 4a^2$ and outside the cylinder $x^2 + y^2 = a^2$.

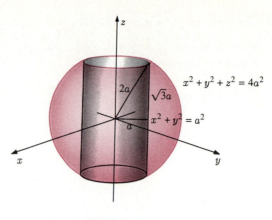

FIGURE 4.5.5

SOLUTION   See Fig. 4.5.5. In terms of spherical coordinates the required moment of inertia is

$$I = 2 \int_0^{2\pi} d\theta \int_{\pi/6}^{\pi/2} \sin\phi \, d\phi \int_{a/\sin\phi}^{2a} R^2 \sin^2\phi \, R^2 \, dR.$$

In terms of cylindrical coordinates it is

$$I = 2 \int_0^{2\pi} d\theta \int_a^{2a} r \, dr \int_0^{\sqrt{4a^2 - r^2}} r^2 \, dz.$$

Evidently the latter formula will be more easily evaluated. We continue with it. Evaluating the θ and z integrals we get

$$I = 4\pi \int_a^{2a} r^3 \sqrt{4a^2 - r^2} \, dr.$$

Making the substitution $u = 4a^2 - r^2$, $du = -2r \, dr$, we obtain

$$I = 2\pi \int_0^{3a^2} (4a^2 - u)\sqrt{u} \, du = 2\pi \left(4a^2 \frac{u^{3/2}}{3/2} - \frac{u^{5/2}}{5/2} \right)\Bigg|_0^{3a^2} = \frac{44}{5}\sqrt{3}\pi a^5.$$

EXERCISES

In Exercises 1–9 find the volumes of the indicated regions.

1. Inside the cone $z = \sqrt{x^2 + y^2}$ and inside the sphere $x^2 + y^2 + z^2 = a^2$.

2. Above the surface $z = (x^2 + y^2)^{1/4}$ and inside the sphere $x^2 + y^2 + z^2 = 2$.

3. Between the paraboloids $z = 10 - x^2 - y^2$ and $z = 2(x^2 + y^2 - 1)$.

4. Inside the paraboloid $z = x^2 + y^2$ and inside the sphere $x^2 + y^2 + z^2 = 12$.

5. Above the xy-plane, inside the cone $z = 2a - \sqrt{x^2 + y^2}$ and inside the cylinder $x^2 + y^2 = 2ay$.

6. Above the xy-plane, under the paraboloid $z = 1 - x^2 - y^2$ and in the wedge $-x \le y \le \sqrt{3}x$.

7. In the first octant, between the planes $y = 0$ and $y = x$ and inside the ellipsoid $\dfrac{x^2}{a^2} + \dfrac{y^2}{b^2} + \dfrac{z^2}{c^2} = 1$. Hint: use the change of variables suggested in Example 4.5.2

8.*Bounded by the hyperboloid $\dfrac{x^2}{a^2} + \dfrac{y^2}{b^2} - \dfrac{z^2}{c^2} = 1$ and the planes $z = -c$ and $z = c$.

9. Above the xy-plane and below the paraboloid
$$z = 1 - \frac{x^2}{a^2} - \frac{y^2}{b^2}.$$

10.*Find the volume of the region lying above the cone $z = 2\sqrt{x^2 + y^2}$ and beneath the plane $z = 1 - x$. Hint: this is rather difficult to do with integrals but can be done by a geometric argument. The region is itself a cone with elliptical base and central axis oblique to the base. The volume of *any* cone is one-third the base area times the height measured perpendicular to the base.

11. Evaluate $\displaystyle\iiint_R z(x^2 + y^2)\,dV$, where R is the solid cylinder $0 \le x^2 + y^2 \le a^2$, $0 \le z \le h$.

12. Evaluate $\displaystyle\iiint_R (x^2 + y^2 + z^2)\,dV$, where R is the same cylinder as in the previous exercise.

13. Find $\displaystyle\iiint_B (x^2 + y^2)\,dV$, where B is the ball given by $x^2 + y^2 + z^2 \le a^2$.

14. Find $\displaystyle\iiint_B (x^2 + y^2 + z^2)\,dV$, where B is the ball of the previous exercise.

15. Find $\displaystyle\iiint_R (x^2 + y^2 + z^2)\,dV$, where R is the region which lies above the cone $z = c\sqrt{x^2 + y^2}$ and inside the sphere $x^2 + y^2 + z^2 = a^2$.

16. Evaluate $\displaystyle\iiint_R (x^2 + y^2)\,dV$ over the region R of the previous exercise.

17. Find $\displaystyle\iiint_R z\,dV$ over the region R satisfying
$$x^2 + y^2 \le z \le \sqrt{2 - x^2 - y^2}.$$

18. Find $\displaystyle\iiint_R x\,dV$ and $\displaystyle\iiint_R z\,dV$ over that part of the hemisphere $0 \le z \le \sqrt{a^2 - x^2 - y^2}$ which lies in the first octant.

19.*Find $\displaystyle\iiint_R x\,dV$ and $\displaystyle\iiint_R z\,dV$ over that part of the cone
$$0 \le z \le h\left(1 - \frac{\sqrt{x^2 + y^2}}{a}\right)$$
which lies in the first octant.

20.*For what real values of λ and μ does the integral
$$\iiint_{\mathbb{R}^3} \frac{dV}{(x^2 + y^2)^\lambda (1 + x^2 + y^2 + z^2)^\mu}$$
converge?

21.*For what real values of λ and μ does the integral
$$\iiint_{\mathbb{R}^3} \frac{dV}{(x^2 + y^2 + z^2)^\lambda (1 + x^2 + y^2 + z^2)^\mu}$$
converge?

22.*Show that for cylindrical coordinates the Laplace operator
$$\Delta u = \frac{\partial^2 u}{\partial x^2} + \frac{\partial^2 u}{\partial y^2} + \frac{\partial^2 u}{\partial z^2}$$
is given by
$$\frac{\partial^2 u}{\partial r^2} + \frac{1}{r}\frac{\partial u}{\partial r} + \frac{1}{r^2}\frac{\partial^2 u}{\partial \theta^2} + \frac{\partial^2 u}{\partial z^2}.$$

23.*Show that in spherical coordinates the Laplace operator is given by
$$\frac{\partial^2 u}{\partial R^2} + \frac{2}{R}\frac{\partial u}{\partial R} + \frac{\cot\phi}{R^2}\frac{\partial u}{\partial \phi} + \frac{1}{R^2}\frac{\partial^2 u}{\partial \phi^2} + \frac{1}{R^2 \sin^2\phi}\frac{\partial^2 u}{\partial \theta^2}.$$

24.*If x, y and z are functions of u, v and w with continuous first partial derivatives and nonvanishing Jacobian at (u, v, w) show that they map an infinitesimal volume element in uvw-space bounded by the coordinate planes u, $u + du$, v, $v + dv$, w and $w + dw$ into an infinitesimal "parallelepiped" in xyz-space having volume

$$dx \, dy \, dz = \left| \frac{\partial(x, y, z)}{\partial(u, v, w)} \right| du \, dv \, dw.$$

Hint: adapt the two-dimensional argument given in Section 4.3. What three vectors from the point $P = (x(u, v, w), y(u, v, w), z(u, v, w))$ span the parallelepiped?

4.6 APPLICATIONS OF MULTIPLE INTEGRALS IN MECHANICS

When we express the volume V of a region R in 3-space as an integral,

$$V = \iiint_R dV,$$

we are regarding V as a "sum" of infinitely many *infinitesimal elements of volume*, that is, as the limit of the sum of volumes of smaller and smaller, nonoverlapping subregions into which we subdivide R. This idea of representing sums of infinitesimal elements of quantities by integrals has many applications in mechanics.

For example, if a rigid body of constant density ρ g/cm^3 occupies a volume V cm^3 then its mass is $m = \rho V$ grams. If the density is not constant but varies continuously over the region R of 3-space occupied by the rigid body, say $\rho = \rho(x, y, z)$, we can still regard the density as being constant on an infinitesimal element of R having volume dV. The mass of this element is therefore $dm = \rho(x, y, z) \, dV$ and the mass of the whole body is calculated by integrating these mass elements over R:

$$m = \iiint_R \rho(x, y, z) \, dV.$$

Similar formulas apply when the rigid body is one or two-dimensional and its density is given in units of mass per unit length or per unit area. In such cases single or double integrals are needed to sum the individual elements of mass. All this works because mass is "additive," that is, the mass of a composite object is the sum of the masses of the parts which comprise the object. The gravitational forces, moments, and energies we consider in this section all have this additivity property.

The Gravitational Attraction of a Disc

Newton's universal law of gravitation asserts that two point masses m_1 and m_2, separated by a distance s, attract one another with a force

$$F = \frac{k m_1 m_2}{s^2},$$

k being a universal constant. The force on each mass is directed towards the other, along the line joining the two masses. Suppose that a flat disc D of radius a, occupying the region $x^2 + y^2 = a^2$ of the xy-plane, has constant *area density* σ (units of mass per unit area). Let us calculate the total force of attraction that this disc exerts upon a mass m located at the point $(0, 0, b)$ on the positive z-axis. The total force is a vector quantity. Although the various mass elements on the disc are in different directions from the mass m, symmetry indicates that the net force will be in the direction towards the centre of the disc, that is, towards the origin. Thus the total force will be $-F\mathbf{k}$ where F is the magnitude of the force.

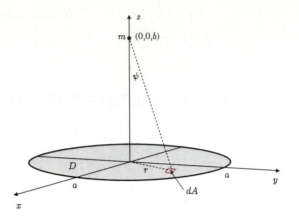

FIGURE 4.6.1

We will calculate F by integrating the vertical component dF of the force of attraction on m due to the mass $\sigma \, dA$ in an area element dA on the disc. If the area element contains the point with polar coordinates (r, θ), and if the line from this point to $(0, 0, b)$ makes angle ψ with the z-axis as shown in Fig. 4.6.1, then the vertical component of the force of attraction of the mass element $\sigma \, dA$ on m is

$$dF = \frac{km\sigma \, dA}{r^2 + b^2} \cos \psi = km\sigma b \, \frac{dA}{(r^2 + b^2)^{3/2}}.$$

Accordingly, the total vertical force of attraction of the disc on m is

$$
\begin{aligned}
F &= km\sigma b \iint_D \frac{dA}{(r^2 + b^2)^{3/2}} \\
&= km\sigma b \int_0^{2\pi} d\theta \int_0^a \frac{r \, dr}{(r^2 + b^2)^{3/2}} \qquad \text{[let } u = r^2 + b^2\text{]} \\
&= \pi km\sigma b \int_{b^2}^{a^2+b^2} u^{-3/2} \, du \\
&= 2\pi km\sigma \left(1 - \frac{b}{\sqrt{a^2 + b^2}} \right).
\end{aligned}
$$

REMARK: If we let a approach infinity in the above formula we obtain the formula

$$F = 2\pi km\sigma$$

for the force of attraction of a plane of area density σ on a mass m located at distance b from the plane. Observe that F does not depend on b. Try to reason on physical grounds why this should be so.

REMARK: The force of attraction on a point mass due to suitably symmetric solid objects (such as spheres, cylinders, and cones) having constant density ρ (units of mass per unit volume) can be found by integrating elements of force contributed by thin, disc-shaped slices of the solid. See Exercises 2–5 at the end of this section.

Moments and Centres of Mass

The centre of mass of a rigid body is that point (fixed in the body) at which the body can be supported so that in the presence of a constant gravitational field it will not experience any unbalanced torques causing it to rotate. The torques experienced by a mass element dm in the body can be expressed in terms of the **moments** of dm about the three coordinate planes. If the body occupies a region R in 3-space and has continuous volume density $\rho(x, y, z)$, then the mass element $dm = \rho(x, y, z) \, dV$ which occupies the volume element dV is said to have **moments** $(x - x_0) \, dm$, $(y - y_0) \, dm$ and $(z - z_0) \, dm$ about the planes $x = x_0$, $y = y_0$ and $z = z_0$ respectively. Thus the total moments of the body about these three planes are

$$M_{x=x_0} = \iiint_R (x - x_0)\rho(x, y, z) \, dV = M_{x=0} - x_0 m$$

$$M_{y=y_0} = \iiint_R (y - y_0)\rho(x, y, z) \, dV = M_{y=0} - y_0 m$$

$$M_{z=z_0} = \iiint_R (z - z_0)\rho(x, y, z) \, dV = M_{z=0} - z_0 m$$

where $m = \iiint_R \rho \, dV$ is the mass of the body and $M_{x=0}$, $M_{y=0}$ and $M_{z=0}$ are the moments about the yz-plane, the xz-plane and the xy-plane respectively. The **centre of mass** $\bar{P} = (\bar{x}, \bar{y}, \bar{z})$ of the body is that point such that $M_{x=\bar{x}}$, $M_{y=\bar{y}}$ and $M_{z=\bar{z}}$ are all equal to zero. Thus

4.6.1
Centre of Mass

$$\bar{x} = \frac{M_{x=0}}{m} = \frac{\iiint_R x\rho \, dV}{\iiint_R \rho \, dV}, \quad \bar{y} = \frac{M_{y=0}}{m} = \frac{\iiint_R y\rho \, dV}{\iiint_R \rho \, dV}, \quad \bar{z} = \frac{M_{z=0}}{m} = \frac{\iiint_R z\rho \, dV}{\iiint_R \rho \, dV}.$$

These formulas may be combined into a single vector formula for the position vector $\bar{\mathbf{r}} = \bar{x}\mathbf{i} + \bar{y}\mathbf{j} + \bar{z}\mathbf{k}$ of the centre of mass in terms of the position vector $\mathbf{r} = x\mathbf{i} + y\mathbf{j} + z\mathbf{k}$ of an arbitrary point in R,

4.6.2
Vector Centre of Mass

$$\bar{\mathbf{r}} = \frac{M_{x=0}\mathbf{i} + M_{y=0}\mathbf{j} + M_{z=0}\mathbf{k}}{m} = \frac{\iiint_R \mathbf{r}\rho \, dV}{\iiint_R \rho \, dV},$$

where the integral of the vector function $\mathbf{r}\rho$ is understood to mean the vector whose components are the integrals of the components of $\mathbf{r}\rho$.

REMARK: Similar expressions hold for distributions of mass over regions in the plane, or over intervals on a line. We use the appropriate area or line densities and double or single definite integrals.

REMARK: If the density is constant it cancels out of the expressions for the centre of mass. In this case the centre of mass is a *geometric* property of the region R, and is called the **centroid** or **centre of gravity** of that region.

EXAMPLE 4.6.3   Find the centroid of the tetrahedron T bounded by the coordinate planes and the plane $\dfrac{x}{a} + \dfrac{y}{b} + \dfrac{z}{c} = 1$.

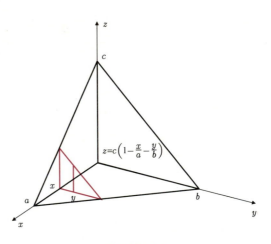

FIGURE 4.6.2

SOLUTION   The density is assumed to be constant, and so we may take it to be unity. The mass of T is thus equal to its volume: $m = V = abc/6$. The moment of T about the yz-plane is (see Fig. 4.6.2)

$$M_{x=0} = \iiint_T x \, dV$$

$$= \int_0^a x \, dx \int_0^{b(1-\frac{x}{a})} dy \int_0^{c(1-\frac{x}{a}-\frac{y}{b})} dz$$

$$= c \int_0^a x \, dx \int_0^{b(1-\frac{x}{a})} \left(1 - \frac{x}{a} - \frac{y}{b}\right) dy$$

$$= c \int_0^a x \left[\left(1 - \frac{x}{a}\right)y - \frac{y^2}{2b}\right]\Big|_0^{b(1-\frac{x}{a})} dx$$

$$= \frac{bc}{2} \int_0^a x \left(1 - \frac{x}{a}\right)^2 dx$$

$$= \frac{bc}{2} \left[\frac{x^2}{2} - \frac{2}{3}\frac{x^3}{a} + \frac{x^4}{4a^2}\right]\Big|_0^a = \frac{a^2 bc}{24}.$$

Since $M_{x=0} = m\bar{x} = abc\bar{x}/6$, we have $\bar{x} = a/4$ and, by symmetry, the centroid of T is $\left(\dfrac{a}{4}, \dfrac{b}{4}, \dfrac{c}{4}\right)$.

EXAMPLE 4.6.4   Find the centre of mass of a solid occupying the region S satisfying $x \geq 0$, $y \geq 0$, $z \geq 0$, $x^2 + y^2 + z^2 \leq a^2$ if the density at distance R from the origin is kR.

SOLUTION   The mass of the solid is distributed symmetrically in the first octant part of the ball $R \leq a$ so that the centre of mass, $(\bar{x}, \bar{y}, \bar{z})$, must satisfy $\bar{x} = \bar{y} = \bar{z}$. The mass of the solid is

$$m = \iiint_S kR\,dV = k \int_0^{\pi/2} d\theta \int_0^{\pi/2} \sin\phi\,d\phi \int_0^a R^3\,dR = \frac{\pi ka^4}{8}.$$

The moment about the xy-plane is

$$M_{z=0} = \iiint_S zkR\,dV = k\iiint_S R^2\cos\phi\,R^2\sin\phi\,dR\,d\phi\,d\theta$$

$$= \frac{k}{2}\int_0^{\pi/2} d\theta \int_0^{\pi/2}\sin(2\phi)\,d\phi\int_0^a R^4\,dR = \frac{k\pi a^5}{20}.$$

Hence $\bar{x} = \dfrac{k\pi a^5}{20}\Big/\dfrac{k\pi a^4}{8} = \dfrac{2a}{5}$ and the centre of mass is $\left(\dfrac{2a}{5}, \dfrac{2a}{5}, \dfrac{2a}{5}\right)$.

Moment of Inertia

The *kinetic energy* of a particle of mass m moving with speed v is

$$E = \frac{1}{2}mv^2.$$

The mass of the particle measures its "inertia"—twice the energy it has when its speed is one unit.

If the particle is moving in a circle of radius D, its motion can be described in terms of its **angular speed**, Ω, measured in radians per unit time. In one revolution the particle travels a distance $2\pi D$ in time $2\pi/\Omega$. Thus its (translational) speed v is related to its angular speed by

$$v = \Omega D.$$

Suppose that a rigid body is rotating with angular speed Ω about an axis L. If (at some instant) the body occupies a region R and has density $\rho = \rho(x, y, z)$ then each mass element $dm = \rho\,dV$ in the body has kinetic energy

$$dE = \frac{1}{2}v^2\,dm = \frac{1}{2}\rho\Omega^2 D^2\,dV,$$

where $D = D(x, y, z)$ is the perpendicular distance from the volume element dV to the axis of rotation L. The total kinetic energy of the rotating body is therefore

$$E = \frac{1}{2}\Omega^2 \iiint_R D^2 \rho \, dV = \frac{1}{2} I \Omega^2,$$

where

**4.6.5
Moment of Inertia**

$$I = \iiint_R D^2 \rho \, dV$$

I is called the **moment of inertia** of the rotating body about the axis L. The moment of inertia plays the same role in the expression for kinetic energy of rotation (in terms of angular speed) that the mass does in the expression for kinetic energy of translation (in terms of linear speed). The moment of inertia is twice the kinetic energy of body rotating with unit angular speed.

If the entire mass of the rotating body were concentrated at a distance D_0 from the axis of rotation then its kinetic energy would be $\frac{1}{2}mD_0^2\Omega^2$. The **radius of gyration** $\bar{D}$ is the value of D_0 for which this energy is equal to the actual kinetic energy $\frac{1}{2}I\Omega^2$ of the rotating body. Thus $m\bar{D}^2 = I$ and

**4.6.6
Radius of Gyration**

$$\bar{D} = \sqrt{I/m} = \left(\frac{\iiint_R D^2 \rho \, dV}{\iiint_R \rho \, dV} \right)^{1/2}.$$

EXAMPLE 4.6.7
a) Find the moment of inertia and radius of gyration of a solid ball of radius a and constant density ρ about a diameter of that ball.

b) With what linear acceleration will the ball roll (without slipping) down a plane inclined at angle α to the horizontal?

SOLUTION
a) We take the z-axis as the diameter and integrate in cylindrical coordinates over the ball B of radius a centred at the origin. Since the density ρ is constant we have

$$I = \rho \iiint_B r^2 \, dV$$

$$= \rho \int_0^{2\pi} d\theta \int_0^a r^3 \, dr \int_{-\sqrt{a^2-r^2}}^{\sqrt{a^2-r^2}} dz$$

$$= 4\pi\rho \int_0^a r^3 \sqrt{a^2 - r^2} \, dr \qquad\qquad [\text{let } u = a^2 - r^2]$$

$$= 2\pi\rho \int_0^{a^2} (a^2 - u)\sqrt{u} \, du$$

$$= 2\pi\rho \left(\frac{2}{3}a^2 u^{3/2} - \frac{2}{5}u^{5/2} \right)\Big|_0^{a^2} = \frac{8}{15}\pi\rho a^5.$$

Since the mass of the ball is $m = \dfrac{4}{3}\pi\rho a^3$, the radius of gyration is

$$\bar{D} = \sqrt{\frac{I}{m}} = \sqrt{\frac{2}{5}}\, a.$$

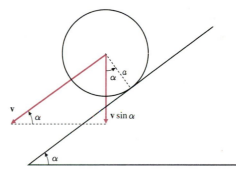

FIGURE 4.6.3

b) We can answer this part by using conservation of total (kinetic plus potential) energy. When the ball is rolling down the plane with speed v its centre is moving with speed v and losing height at a rate $v \sin\alpha$. (See Fig. 4.6.3.) Since the ball is not slipping, it is rotating about a horizontal axis through its centre with angular speed $\Omega = \dfrac{v}{a}$. Hence its kinetic energy (due to translation and rotation) is

$$KE = \frac{1}{2}mv^2 + \frac{1}{2}I\Omega^2$$

$$= \frac{1}{2}mv^2 + \frac{1}{2}\frac{2}{5}ma^2 \frac{v^2}{a^2} = \frac{7}{10}mv^2.$$

When the centre of the ball is at height h (above some reference height) the ball has (gravitational) potential energy

$$PE = mgh.$$

(This is the work that must be done against a constant gravitational force $F = mg$ to raise it to height h.) Since total energy is conserved:

$$\frac{7}{10}\,mv^2 + mgh = \text{constant}.$$

Differentiating with respect to time t we obtain

$$0 = \frac{7}{10}\,m\,2v\frac{dv}{dt} + mg\frac{dh}{dt} = \frac{7}{5}\,mv\frac{dv}{dt} + mgv\sin\alpha.$$

Thus the ball rolls down the incline with acceleration $-\dfrac{dv}{dt} = \dfrac{5}{7}\,g\sin\alpha$.

EXERCISES

1. Find the mass of a spherical planet of radius a whose density at distance R from the centre is $\rho = A/(B+R^2)$.

In Exercises 2–5 find the gravitational attraction that the given object exerts on a mass m located at $(0,0,b)$. Assume the object has constant density ρ. In each case you can obtain the answer by integrating the contributions made by discs of thickness dz, making use of the formula for the attraction exerted by the disc obtained in the text.

2. The ball $x^2 + y^2 + z^2 \le a^2$, where $a < b$.

3. The cylinder $x^2 + y^2 \le a^2$, $0 \le z \le h$, where $h < b$.

4. The cone $0 \le z \le b - (\sqrt{x^2 + y^2})/a$.

5. The half-ball $0 \le z \le \sqrt{a^2 - x^2 - y^2}$, where $a < b$.

6. Find the centre of mass of an object occupying the cube $0 \le x, y, z \le a$ with density given by $\rho = x^2 + y^2 + z^2$.

Find the centroids of the regions in Exercises 7–12.

7. The prism $x \ge 0$, $y \ge 0$, $x + y \le 1$, $0 \le z \le 1$.

8. The unbounded region $0 \le z \le e^{-(x^2+y^2)}$.

9. The first octant part of the ball $x^2 + y^2 + z^2 \le a^2$.

10. The region $\sqrt{x^2 + y^2} \le a^2 z \le a^2$, $y \ge 0$.

11. The region inside the cylinder $x^2 + y^2 = a^2$, above the xy-plane and under the plane $z = a + y$.

12. The region inside the cube $0 \le x, y, z \le 1$ and under the plane $x + y + z = 2$.

13. Explain *in physical terms* why the acceleration of the ball rolling down the incline in Example 4.6.7(b) does not approach g (the acceleration due to gravity) as the angle of incline, α, approaches $90°$.

Find the moments of inertia and radii of gyration of the solid objects in Exercises 14–22. Assume constant density in all cases.

14. A circular cylinder of base radius a and height h about the axis of the cylinder.

15. A circular cylinder of base radius a and height h about a diameter of the base of the cylinder.

16. A right circular cone of base radius a and height h about the axis of the cone.

17. A right circular cone of base radius a and height h about a diameter of the base of the cone.

18. A cube of edge length a about an edge of the cube.

19. A cube of edge length a about a diagonal of a face of the cube.

20. A cube of edge length a about a diagonal of the cube.

21. The rectangular box $-a \le x \le a$, $-b \le y \le b$, $-c \le z \le c$ about the z-axis.

22. The region between the two concentric cylinders $x^2 + y^2 = a^2$ and $x^2 + y^2 = b^2$ (where $0 < a < b$) and between $z = 0$ and $z = c$ about the z-axis.

23. A ball of radius a has constant density ρ. A cylindrical hole of radius $b < a$ is drilled through the centre of the ball. Find the mass of the remaining part of the ball, and its moment of inertia about the axis of the hole.

24. With what acceleration will a solid cylinder of base radius a, height h and constant density ρ roll (without slipping) down a plane inclined at angle α to the horizontal?

25. Repeat the previous exercise for the ball with the cylindrical hole in the second previous exercise. Assume the axis of the hole remains horizontal while the ball rolls.

26.*A rigid pendulum of mass m swings about point A on a horizontal axis. Its moment of inertia about that axis is I. The centre of mass C of the pendulum is at distance a from A. When the pendulum hangs at rest, C is directly under A. (Why?) Suppose the pendulum is swinging. Let $\theta = \theta(t)$ measure the angular displacement of the line AC from the vertical at time t. ($\theta = 0$ when the pendulum is in its rest position.) Use a conservation of energy argument similar to that in Example 4.6.7(b) to show that

$$\frac{1}{2} I \left(\frac{d\theta}{dt} \right)^2 - mga \cos \theta = \text{constant},$$

and hence, differentiating with respect to t, that

$$\frac{d^2\theta}{dt^2} + \frac{mga}{I} \sin \theta = 0.$$

This is a nonlinear differential equation, not easily solved. However, for small oscillations ($|\theta|$ small) we can use the approximation $\sin \theta \approx \theta$. In this case the differential equation is that of simple harmonic motion. What is the period?

27.*Let L_0 be a straight line passing through the centre of mass of a rigid body B of mass m. Let L_k be a straight line parallel to and k units distant from L_0. If I_0 and I_k are the moments of inertia of B about L_0 and L_k

respectively, show that

$$I_k = I_0 + k^2 m.$$

Hence a body always has smallest moment of inertia about an axis through its centre of mass. (Hint: assume that the z-axis coincides with L_0 and L_k passes through the point $(k, 0, 0)$.)

28.*Re-establish the expression for the total kinetic energy of the rolling ball in Example 4.6.7 by regarding the ball at any instant as rotating about a horizontal line through its point of contact with the inclined plane. Use the result of the previous exercise.

29.*A rigid body with density ρ is placed with its centre of mass at the origin and occupies a region R of 3-space. Suppose the six second moments P_{xx}, P_{yy}, P_{zz}, P_{xy}, P_{xz}, and P_{yz} are all known, where

$$P_{xx} = \iiint_R x^2 \rho \, dV, \quad P_{xy} = \iiint_R xy\rho \, dV, \quad \cdots.$$

(There exist tables giving these six moments for bodies of many standard shapes.) Show how to express the moment of inertia of the body about any axis through the origin in term of these six second moments. (If this result is combined with that of Exercise 27, the moment of inertia about *any* axis can be found.)

CHAPTER 5
Curves

This chapter is concerned with functions of a single real variable which have *vector* values. Such functions may be thought of as parametric representations of curves, and we will examine them from both a *kinematic* point of view (involving position, velocity and acceleration of a moving particle) and a *geometric* point of view (involving tangents, normals, curvature and torsion). Finally, we will work through a simple derivation of Kepler's laws of planetary motion.

Most of the material of this chapter does not rely on the content of Chapters 2–4. It reviews, expands upon, and extends to three dimensions the discussion of the vectorial treatment of plane curves in Appendix 1, and makes extensive use of Sections 1.2–1.3. The reason it is placed here is that it sets the stage for the multivariate vector calculus of Chapters 6 and 7.

5.1   VECTOR FUNCTIONS OF ONE VARIABLE

In this section we will examine several aspects of differential and integral calculus as applied to **vector-valued functions** of a single real variable. Such functions can be used to represent curves parametrically. It is natural to interpret a vector-valued function of the real variable t as giving the position, at time t, of a point or "particle" moving around in space. Derivatives of this *position vector* are then other vector functions giving the velocity and acceleration of the particle. To motivate the study of vector functions we will consider such a vectorial description of motion in 3-space.

If a particle moves around in 3-space, its motion can be described by giving the three coordinates of its position as functions of time t:

$$x = x(t), \qquad y = y(t), \qquad z = z(t).$$

It is more convenient, however, to replace these three equations by a single vector equation,

$$\mathbf{r} = \mathbf{r}(t),$$

giving the position vector of the moving particle as a function of t. (Recall that the position vector of a point is the vector from the origin to that point.) In terms of the standard basis vectors, $\mathbf{i}$, $\mathbf{j}$ and $\mathbf{k}$, the position of the particle at time t is

$$\mathbf{r}(t) = x(t)\,\mathbf{i} + y(t)\,\mathbf{j} + z(t)\,\mathbf{k}.$$

As t increases, the particle moves along a *path*, a curve C in 3-space. We assume that C is a *continuous curve*; the particle cannot instantaneously jump from one point to a distant point. This is equivalent to requiring that the component functions $x(t)$, $y(t)$ and $z(t)$ are continuous functions of t, and we therefore say that $\mathbf{r}(t)$ is a continuous vector function of t.

In the time interval from t to $t + \Delta t$ the particle moves from position $\mathbf{r}(t)$ to position $\mathbf{r}(t + \Delta t)$. Therefore its **average velocity** is

$$\frac{\mathbf{r}(t + \Delta t) - \mathbf{r}(t)}{\Delta t},$$

which is a vector parallel to the secant vector from $\mathbf{r}(t)$ to $\mathbf{r}(t + \Delta t)$. If the average velocity has a limit as $\Delta t \to 0$, then we say that $\mathbf{r}$ is **differentiable** at t, and we call the limit the (instantaneous) **velocity** of the particle at time t. We denote the velocity vector by $\mathbf{v}(t)$.

5.1.1
The Velocity Vector

$$\mathbf{v}(t) = \lim_{\Delta t \to 0} \frac{\mathbf{r}(t + \Delta t) - \mathbf{r}(t)}{\Delta t} = \frac{d}{dt}\mathbf{r}(t).$$

This velocity vector has direction tangent to the path C at the point $\mathbf{r}(t)$, (see Fig. 5.1.1), and points in the direction of motion.   The length of the velocity

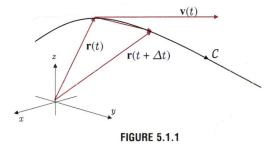

FIGURE 5.1.1

vector, $v(t) = |\mathbf{v}(t)|$, is called the **speed** of the particle. Wherever the velocity vector exists, is continuous, and does not vanish, the path C is a **smooth** curve, that is, it has a continuously turning tangent line. If the velocity vanishes at a point the path may not be smooth. (See Example 5.2.1.)

The rules for addition and scalar multiplication of vectors imply that

$$
\begin{aligned}
\mathbf{v} &= \frac{d\mathbf{r}}{dt} \\
&= \lim_{\Delta t \to 0} \left(\frac{x(t + \Delta t) - x(t)}{\Delta t}\mathbf{i} + \frac{y(t + \Delta t) - y(t)}{\Delta t}\mathbf{j} + \frac{z(t + \Delta t) - z(t)}{\Delta t}\mathbf{k} \right) \\
&= \frac{dx}{dt}\mathbf{i} + \frac{dy}{dt}\mathbf{j} + \frac{dz}{dt}\mathbf{k}.
\end{aligned}
$$

Thus the vector function $\mathbf{r}$ is differentiable at t if and only if its three scalar components, x, y and z are differentiable at t. In general, vector functions can be differentiated (or integrated) by differentiating (or integrating) their component functions, provided that the basis vectors with respect to which the components are taken are fixed in space and not changing with time. As an example of the termwise integration of a vector function, the position vector of the centre of mass of a mass distribution with density $\rho(x, y, z)$ which occupies a region R in 3-space is, as noted in Box 4.6.2, given by the vector integral

$$\bar{\mathbf{r}} = \frac{1}{m} \iiint_R \mathbf{r}\rho \, dV,$$

where $m = \iiint_R \rho \, dV$ is the total mass of the distribution and $\mathbf{r}$ is the vector function $\mathbf{r} = x\mathbf{i} + y\mathbf{j} + z\mathbf{k}$.

Continuing in the same vein, we define the **acceleration** of the moving particle to be the time derivative of the velocity:

5.1.2
Acceleration

$$\mathbf{a}(t) = \frac{d\mathbf{v}}{dt} = \frac{d^2\mathbf{r}}{dt^2}.$$

Newton's second law of motion asserts that this acceleration is proportional to, and *in the same direction as* the force $\mathbf{F}$ causing the motion: if the particle has mass m then the law is expressed by the *vector equation* $\mathbf{F} = m\mathbf{a}$.

EXAMPLE 5.1.3   Find the velocity, speed, and acceleration, and describe the motion of a particle whose position at time t is

$$\mathbf{r} = 3\cos\omega t \, \mathbf{i} + 4\cos\omega t \, \mathbf{j} + 5\sin\omega t \, \mathbf{k}.$$

SOLUTION   The velocity, speed and acceleration are readily calculated:

$$\mathbf{v} = \frac{d\mathbf{r}}{dt} = -3\omega\sin\omega t \, \mathbf{i} - 4\omega\sin\omega t \, \mathbf{j} + 5\omega\cos\omega t \, \mathbf{k}$$
$$v = |\mathbf{v}| = 5\omega$$
$$\mathbf{a} = \frac{d\mathbf{v}}{dt} = -3\omega^2\cos\omega t \, \mathbf{i} - 4\omega^2\cos\omega t \, \mathbf{j} - 5\omega^2\sin\omega t \, \mathbf{k} = -\omega^2\mathbf{r}.$$

Since $|\mathbf{r}| = 5$ the path of the particle lies on the sphere $x^2 + y^2 + z^2 = 25$. Since $x = 3\cos\omega t$ and $y = 4\cos\omega t$, the path lies on the vertical plane $4x = 3y$. Evidently $\mathbf{r}$ is periodic with period $2\pi/\omega$. Hence the particle moves with constant speed around a circle of radius 5 lying in the plane $4x = 3y$, making one revolution in time $2\pi/\omega$. Observe that the acceleration is always in the direction of $-\mathbf{r}$, that is, towards the origin. Such acceleration is called **centripetal acceleration.**

EXAMPLE 5.1.4   *(The Projectile Problem)* Describe the path followed by a particle experiencing a constant downward acceleration, $-g\mathbf{k}$, caused by gravity. Assume that at time $t = 0$ the position of the particle is $\mathbf{r}_0$ and its velocity is $\mathbf{v}_0$.

SOLUTION   If the position of the particle at time t is $\mathbf{r}(t)$ and the z-axis is vertically upward then

$$\frac{d^2\mathbf{r}}{dt^2} = -g\mathbf{k}.$$

We integrate this equation twice. Each integration introduces a *vector* constant of integration which we can determine from the given data by evaluating at $t = 0$:

$$\frac{d\mathbf{r}}{dt} = -gt\mathbf{k} + \mathbf{v}_0$$

$$\mathbf{r} = -\frac{gt^2}{2}\mathbf{k} + \mathbf{v}_0 t + \mathbf{r}_0.$$

The latter equation represents a parabola in the vertical plane passing through the point with position vector $\mathbf{r}_0$ and parallel to the vector $\mathbf{v}_0$. (See Fig. 5.1.2.)   The

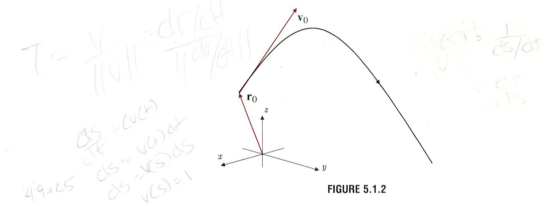

FIGURE 5.1.2

parabola has scalar parametric equations

$$x = u_0 t + x_0$$
$$y = v_0 t + y_0$$
$$z = -\frac{gt^2}{2} + w_0 t + z_0,$$

where $r_0 = x_0\mathbf{i} + y_0\mathbf{j} + z_0\mathbf{k}$ and $\mathbf{v}_0 = u_0\mathbf{i} + v_0\mathbf{j} + w_0\mathbf{k}$.

Differentiating Combinations of Vectors.

Vectors and scalars can be combined in a variety of ways to form other vectors or scalars. Vectors can be added and multiplied by scalars, and can be factors in dot and cross products. Appropriate differentiation rules apply to all such combinations of vector and scalar functions; we summarize them in the following theorem. The proof only involves standard differentiation rules applied to the components of the vectors involved; it is left to the reader.

THEOREM 5.1.5   *Differentiation Rules for Vector Functions* Let $\mathbf{u}(t)$ and $\mathbf{v}(t)$ be differentiable vector-valued functions, and let $\lambda(t)$ and $f(x, y, z)$ be differentiable scalar-valued functions. Then $\mathbf{u}(t) + \mathbf{v}(t)$, $\lambda(t)\mathbf{u}(t)$, $\mathbf{u}(t) \bullet \mathbf{v}(t)$, $\mathbf{u}(t) \times \mathbf{v}(t)$, $\mathbf{u}\big(\lambda(t)\big)$, and $f\big(\mathbf{u}(t)\big)$ are differentiable, and

(a) $$\frac{d}{dt}\Big(\mathbf{u}(t) + \mathbf{v}(t)\Big) = \mathbf{u}'(t) + \mathbf{v}'(t)$$

(b)
$$\frac{d}{dt}\Big(\lambda(t)\mathbf{u}(t)\Big) = \lambda'(t)\mathbf{u}(t) + \lambda(t)\mathbf{u}'(t)$$

(c)
$$\frac{d}{dt}\Big(\mathbf{u}(t) \bullet \mathbf{v}(t)\Big) = \mathbf{u}'(t) \bullet \mathbf{v}(t) + \mathbf{u}(t) \bullet \mathbf{v}'(t)$$

(d)
$$\frac{d}{dt}\Big(\mathbf{u}(t) \times \mathbf{v}(t)\Big) = \mathbf{u}'(t) \times \mathbf{v}(t) + \mathbf{u}(t) \times \mathbf{v}'(t)$$

(e)
$$\frac{d}{dt}\Big(\mathbf{u}\big(\lambda(t)\big)\Big) = \lambda'(t)\mathbf{u}'\big(\lambda(t)\big)$$

(f)
$$\frac{d}{dt}\Big(f\big(\mathbf{u}(t)\big)\Big) = \nabla f\big(\mathbf{u}(t)\big) \bullet \mathbf{u}'(t).$$

REMARK: Formulas (b), (c) and (d) are versions of the Product Rule. Formulas (e) and (f) are versions of the Chain Rule. All have the obvious form. Note that the order of the factors is the same in the terms on both sides of the cross product formula (d). It is essential that the order be preserved because, unlike the dot product or the product of a vector with a scalar, the cross product is *not commutative*.

REMARK: The formula for the derivative of a cross product is a special case of that for the derivative of a 3×3 determinant. Since every term in the expansion of a determinant of any order is a product involving one element from each row (or column), the general product rule implies that the derivative of an $n \times n$ determinant whose elements are functions will be the sum of n such $n \times n$ determinants, each with the elements of one of the rows (or columns) differentiated. For the 3×3 case we have

$$\frac{d}{dt}\begin{vmatrix} a_{11}(t) & a_{12}(t) & a_{13}(t) \\ a_{21}(t) & a_{22}(t) & a_{23}(t) \\ a_{31}(t) & a_{32}(t) & a_{33}(t) \end{vmatrix} = \begin{vmatrix} a'_{11}(t) & a'_{12}(t) & a'_{13}(t) \\ a_{21}(t) & a_{22}(t) & a_{23}(t) \\ a_{31}(t) & a_{32}(t) & a_{33}(t) \end{vmatrix}$$

$$+ \begin{vmatrix} a_{11}(t) & a_{12}(t) & a_{13}(t) \\ a'_{21}(t) & a'_{22}(t) & a'_{23}(t) \\ a_{31}(t) & a_{32}(t) & a_{33}(t) \end{vmatrix} + \begin{vmatrix} a_{11}(t) & a_{12}(t) & a_{13}(t) \\ a_{21}(t) & a_{22}(t) & a_{23}(t) \\ a'_{31}(t) & a'_{32}(t) & a'_{33}(t) \end{vmatrix}.$$

EXAMPLE 5.1.6   Show that the speed of a moving particle remains constant over an interval of time if and only if the acceleration is perpendicular to the velocity throughout that interval.

SOLUTION   Since $\big(v(t)\big)^2 = \mathbf{v}(t) \bullet \mathbf{v}(t)$ we have

$$2v(t)\frac{dv}{dt} = \frac{d}{dt}\Big(v(t)\Big)^2 = \frac{d}{dt}\mathbf{v}(t) \bullet \mathbf{v}(t)$$

$$= \mathbf{a}(t) \bullet \mathbf{v}(t) + \mathbf{v}(t) \bullet \mathbf{a}(t) = 2\mathbf{v}(t) \bullet \mathbf{a}(t).$$

If we assume that $v(t) \neq 0$, it follows that $dv/dt = 0$ if and only if $\mathbf{v} \bullet \mathbf{a} = 0$. The speed is constant if and only if the velocity is perpendicular to the acceleration.

EXAMPLE 5.1.7   If $\mathbf{u}$ is three times differentiable, calculate the triple product derivative

$$\frac{d}{dt}\left(\mathbf{u}\bullet\left(\frac{d\mathbf{u}}{dt}\times\frac{d^2\mathbf{u}}{dt^2}\right)\right).$$

SOLUTION

$$\frac{d}{dt}\left(\mathbf{u}\bullet\left(\frac{d\mathbf{u}}{dt}\times\frac{d^2\mathbf{u}}{dt^2}\right)\right)$$

$$=\frac{d\mathbf{u}}{dt}\bullet\left(\frac{d\mathbf{u}}{dt}\times\frac{d^2\mathbf{u}}{dt^2}\right)+\mathbf{u}\bullet\left(\frac{d^2\mathbf{u}}{dt^2}\times\frac{d^2\mathbf{u}}{dt^2}\right)+\mathbf{u}\bullet\left(\frac{d\mathbf{u}}{dt}\times\frac{d^3\mathbf{u}}{dt^3}\right)$$

$$=\mathbf{u}\bullet\left(\frac{d\mathbf{u}}{dt}\times\frac{d^3\mathbf{u}}{dt^3}\right).$$

The first term vanished because $d\mathbf{u}/dt$ is perpendicular to its cross product with another vector; the second term vanished because of the cross product of identical vectors.

Many interesting problems in mechanics involve the differentiation of vector functions. The remainder of this section is devoted to a brief discussion of two of these.

A Rocket Problem

The **momentum p** of a moving object is the product of its (scalar) mass m and its (vector) velocity $\mathbf{v}$; $\mathbf{p} = m\mathbf{v}$. Newton's second law of motion states that the rate of change of *momentum* is equal to the external force acting on the object:

$$\mathbf{F} = \frac{d\mathbf{p}}{dt} = \frac{d}{dt}(m\mathbf{v}).$$

It is only when the mass of the object remains constant that this law reduces to the more familiar $\mathbf{F} = m\mathbf{a}$.

A rocket moving through space burning its onboard fuel has changing mass $m(t)$ and changing velocity $\mathbf{v}(t)$. If it is not acted on by any external forces (i.e. $\mathbf{F} = \mathbf{0}$), then Newton's law implies that the total momentum of the rocket and exhaust gases will remain constant. Suppose the exhaust gases escape with velocity $\mathbf{v}_e$ *relative to the rocket*. At time t the rocket has mass m and velocity $\mathbf{v}$. At time $t + \Delta t$ the rocket's mass is $m + \Delta m$ (where $\Delta m < 0$), its velocity is $\mathbf{v} + \Delta\mathbf{v}$, and mass $-\Delta m$ of exhaust gases have escaped with velocity $\mathbf{v} + \mathbf{v}_e$ (relative to a coordinate system fixed in space). Equating total momenta at t and $t + \Delta t$ we obtain

$$(m + \Delta m)(\mathbf{v} + \Delta\mathbf{v}) - \Delta m(\mathbf{v} + \mathbf{v}_e) = m\mathbf{v}.$$

Simplifying this equation and dividing by Δt gives

$$(m + \Delta m)\frac{\Delta\mathbf{v}}{\Delta t} - \frac{\Delta m}{\Delta t}\mathbf{v}_e = 0,$$

and, on taking the limit as $\Delta t \to 0$,

$$m\frac{d\mathbf{v}}{dt} - \frac{dm}{dt}\mathbf{v}_e = 0.$$

Suppose that the engine fires from $t = 0$ to $t = T$. Then

$$\mathbf{v}(T) - \mathbf{v}(0) = \int_0^T \frac{d\mathbf{v}}{dt}\,dt = \left(\int_0^T \frac{1}{m}\frac{dm}{dt}\,dt\right)\mathbf{v}_e$$

$$= \left(\ln m(T) - \ln m(0)\right)\mathbf{v}_e = -\ln\left(\frac{m(0)}{m(T)}\right)\mathbf{v}_e.$$

As was to be expected, the change in velocity of the rocket is in the opposite direction to the exhaust velocity $\mathbf{v}_e$. If $p\%$ of the mass of the rocket is ejected during the burn then the velocity of the rocket will change by the amount $-\mathbf{v}_e \ln(100/(100 - p))$.

Circular Motion

It is useful to represent the rate of rotation of a rigid body about an axis in terms of an **angular velocity** vector rather than just the scalar angular speed. The angular velocity vector, Ω, has magnitude equal to the angular speed, Ω, and direction along the axis of rotation such that if the extended right thumb points in the direction of Ω then the fingers surround the axis in the direction of rotation.

If the origin of the coordinate system is on the axis of rotation, and $\mathbf{r}$ is the position vector of a point P in the rotating body then the (linear) velocity of that point is given by

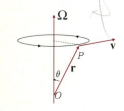

FIGURE 5.1.3

5.1.8
Linear and
Angular Velocity

$$\frac{d\mathbf{r}}{dt} = \mathbf{v} = \Omega \times \mathbf{r}.$$

(See Fig. 5.1.3.) The direction of the angular velocity vector was defined so that this cross product would point in the direction of motion of P. The length of the cross product is

$$|\Omega \times \mathbf{r}| = |\Omega||\mathbf{r}|\sin\theta = \Omega D$$

where θ is the angle between $\mathbf{r}$ and Ω, and D is the perpendicular distance from P to the axis of rotation.

Newton's second law states that $\mathbf{F} = \dfrac{d}{dt}(m\mathbf{v}) = \dfrac{d\mathbf{p}}{dt}$, where $\mathbf{p} = m\mathbf{v}$ is the (linear) momentum of a particle of mass m moving under the influence of a force $\mathbf{F}$. This law may be reformulated in a manner appropriate for describing rotational motion as follows. If $\mathbf{r}(t)$ is the position of the particle at time t, then, since $\mathbf{v} \times \mathbf{v} = \mathbf{0}$,

$$\frac{d}{dt}(\mathbf{r} \times \mathbf{p}) = \frac{d}{dt}\left(\mathbf{r} \times (m\mathbf{v})\right) = \mathbf{v} \times (m\mathbf{v}) + \mathbf{r} \times \frac{d}{dt}(m\mathbf{v}) = \mathbf{r} \times \mathbf{F}.$$

The quantities $\mathbf{H} = \mathbf{r} \times (m\mathbf{v})$ and $\mathbf{T} = \mathbf{r} \times \mathbf{F}$ are respectively the **angular momentum** of the particle about the origin and the **torque** of $\mathbf{F}$ about the origin. We have shown that

$$\mathbf{T} = \frac{d\mathbf{H}}{dt};$$

the torque of the external forces is equal to the rate of change of the angular momentum of the particle. This is the analogue for rotational motion of $\mathbf{F} = \dfrac{d\mathbf{p}}{dt}$.

Rotating Frames and the Coriolis Effect

The procedure of differentiating a vector function by differentiating its components is valid only if the basis vectors themselves do not depend on the variable of differentiation. In some situations in mechanics this is not the case. For instance, in modelling large scale weather phenomena the analysis is affected by the fact that a coordinate system fixed with respect to the earth is, in fact, rotating (along with the earth) relative to directions fixed in space.

In order to understand the effect that the rotation of the coordinate system has on representations of velocity and acceleration, let us consider two Cartesian coordinate frames (that is, systems of axes), sharing a common origin, one "fixed" in space and the other rotating with angular velocity Ω about an axis through that origin. Let $\hat{\mathbf{i}}$, $\hat{\mathbf{j}}$ and $\hat{\mathbf{k}}$ be the standard basis vectors of the fixed coordinate frame, and let $\mathbf{i}$, $\mathbf{j}$ and $\mathbf{k}$ be the basis vectors of the rotating frame. The latter three are constant vectors in their own frame but are functions of time in the fixed frame. We showed above that the velocity of a point with position $\mathbf{r}$ rotating about an axis with angular velocity Ω is $\Omega \times \mathbf{r}$. Therefore

$$\frac{d\mathbf{i}}{dt} = \Omega \times \mathbf{i}, \qquad \frac{d\mathbf{j}}{dt} = \Omega \times \mathbf{j}, \qquad \frac{d\mathbf{k}}{dt} = \Omega \times \mathbf{k}.$$

Any vector function can be expressed in terms of either basis. If $\mathbf{r}(t)$ is the position vector of a moving particle it can be expressed in the fixed frame as

$$\mathbf{r} = \hat{x}(t)\hat{\mathbf{i}} + \hat{y}(t)\hat{\mathbf{j}} + \hat{z}(t)\hat{\mathbf{k}},$$

or in the rotating frame as

$$\mathbf{r} = x(t)\mathbf{i} + y(t)\mathbf{j} + z(t)\mathbf{k}.$$

The velocity of the moving particle can be expressed in the fixed frame as

$$\mathbf{v}_{\mathcal{F}} = \frac{d\hat{x}}{dt}\hat{\mathbf{i}} + \frac{d\hat{y}}{dt}\hat{\mathbf{j}} + \frac{d\hat{z}}{dt}\hat{\mathbf{k}}.$$

Similarly, the velocity of the particle, *measured with respect to the rotating frame* is

$$\mathbf{v}_{\mathcal{R}} = \frac{dx}{dt}\mathbf{i} + \frac{dy}{dt}\mathbf{j} + \frac{dz}{dt}\mathbf{k}.$$

These vectors are, however, not equal. (For instance, a point at rest with respect to the rotating frame would be seen as moving with respect to the fixed frame.) If we want to express the fixed-frame velocity of the particle, $\mathbf{v}_\mathcal{F}$, in terms of the rotating basis, we must also account for the rate of change of the basis vectors in the rotating frame; using three applications of the product rule we have

$$
\begin{aligned}
\mathbf{v}_\mathcal{F} &= \frac{dx}{dt}\mathbf{i} + x\frac{d\mathbf{i}}{dt} + \frac{dy}{dt}\mathbf{j} + y\frac{d\mathbf{j}}{dt} + \frac{dz}{dt}\mathbf{k} + z\frac{d\mathbf{k}}{dt} \\
&= \mathbf{v}_\mathcal{R} + x\Omega \times \mathbf{i} + y\Omega \times \mathbf{j} + z\Omega \times \mathbf{k} \\
&= \mathbf{v}_\mathcal{R} + \Omega \times \mathbf{r}.
\end{aligned}
$$

This formula shows that differentiation with respect to time has different effects in the two coordinate systems. If we denote by $\left(\dfrac{d}{dt}\right)_\mathcal{F}$ and $\left(\dfrac{d}{dt}\right)_\mathcal{R}$ the operators of time differentiation in the two frames then the formula above can be written

$$
\left(\frac{d}{dt}\right)_\mathcal{F} \mathbf{r}(t) = \left(\left(\frac{d}{dt}\right)_\mathcal{R} + \Omega \times \right) \mathbf{r}(t),
$$

or, in terms of operators,

$$
\left(\frac{d}{dt}\right)_\mathcal{F} = \left(\left(\frac{d}{dt}\right)_\mathcal{R} + \Omega \times \right).
$$

These operators may be applied to *any* vector function, and in particular to the function $\mathbf{v}_\mathcal{F} = \mathbf{v}_\mathcal{R} + \Omega \times \mathbf{r}$. Since $(d/dt)_\mathcal{F}\mathbf{v}_\mathcal{F}$ is the acceleration $\mathbf{a}_\mathcal{F}$ of the particle in the fixed frame, and $(d/dt)_\mathcal{R}\mathbf{v}_\mathcal{R}$ is the acceleration $\mathbf{a}_\mathcal{R}$ in the rotating frame, we calculate, assuming that the angular velocity Ω of the rotating frame is constant,

$$
\begin{aligned}
\mathbf{a}_\mathcal{F} &= \left(\frac{d}{dt}\right)_\mathcal{F}(\mathbf{v}_\mathcal{R} + \Omega \times \mathbf{r}) \\
&= \left(\left(\frac{d}{dt}\right)_\mathcal{R} + \Omega \times \right)(\mathbf{v}_\mathcal{R} + \Omega \times \mathbf{r}) \\
&= \mathbf{a}_\mathcal{R} + 2\Omega \times \mathbf{v}_\mathcal{R} + \Omega \times (\Omega \times \mathbf{r}).
\end{aligned}
$$

The term $2\Omega \times \mathbf{v}_\mathcal{R}$ is called the **Coriolis acceleration** and the term $\Omega \times (\Omega \times \mathbf{r})$ is called the **centripetal acceleration**.

In order to interpret these accelerations, suppose that the origin is at the centre of the earth, the fixed frame is fixed with respect to the stars, and the rotating frame is attached to the rotating earth. Suppose that the particle has mass m and is acted upon by an external force $\mathbf{F}$. If we view the moving particle from a vantage point fixed in space (so that we see the fixed frame as unmoving) then, in accordance with Newton's second law, we observe that $\mathbf{F} = m\mathbf{a}_\mathcal{F}$. If, instead, we are sitting on the earth, and regarding the rotating frame as stationary, we would still want to regard $\mathbf{a}_\mathcal{R}$ as the force per unit mass acting on the particle. Thus we would write

$$
\mathbf{a}_\mathcal{R} = \frac{\mathbf{F}}{m} - 2\Omega \times \mathbf{v}_\mathcal{R} - \Omega \times (\Omega \times \mathbf{r}),
$$

and would interpret the Ω terms as other *forces* per unit mass acting on the particle. The term $-\Omega \times (\Omega \times \mathbf{r})$ is a vector pointing directly away from the axis of rotation of the earth and we would interpret it as a **centrifugal force**. (If the earth were spinning fast enough, we would expect objects on the surface to be flung into space.) The term $-2\Omega \times \mathbf{v}_{\mathcal{R}}$ is at right angles to both the velocity and the polar axis of the earth. We would call this a **Coriolis force**. The centrifugal and Coriolis forces are not "real" forces acting on the particle. They are fictitious forces which compensate for the fact that we are measuring acceleration with respect to a frame which we are regarding as fixed although it is really rotating and hence accelerating.

The circulation of winds around a storm centre is an example of the Coriolis effect. The eye of a storm is an area of low pressure sucking air towards it. The direction of rotation of the earth is such that the angular velocity Ω points north and is parallel to the earth's axis of rotation. At any point P on the surface of the earth we can express Ω as a sum of tangential (to the earth's surface) and normal components (see Fig. 5.1.4),

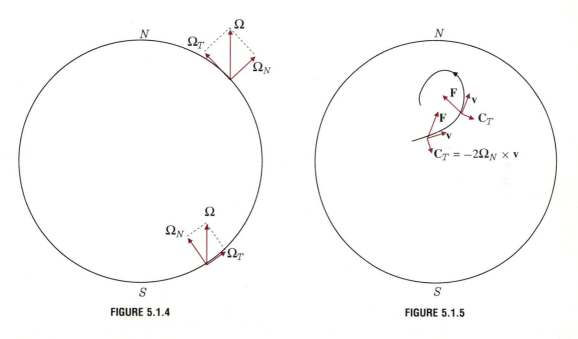

FIGURE 5.1.4   FIGURE 5.1.5

$$\Omega(P) = \Omega_T(P) + \Omega_N(P).$$

If P is in the northern hemisphere $\Omega_N(P)$ points upwards (away from the centre of the earth). At such a point the Coriolis "force" $\mathbf{C} = -2\Omega(P) \times \mathbf{v}$ on a particle of air moving with horizontal velocity $\mathbf{v}$ would itself have horizontal and normal components

$$\mathbf{C} = -2\Omega_T \times \mathbf{v} - 2\Omega_N \times \mathbf{v} = \mathbf{C}_N + \mathbf{C}_T.$$

The tangential component of the Coriolis force, $\mathbf{C}_T = -2\mathbf{\Omega}_N \times \mathbf{v}$ is $90°$ to the right of $\mathbf{v}$, (that is, clockwise from $\mathbf{v}$). Therefore, particles of air which are being sucked towards the eye of the storm experience Coriolis deflection to the right and so actually spiral into the eye in a counterclockwise direction. The opposite is true in the southern hemisphere where the normal component of $\mathbf{\Omega}_N$ is downward. The suction force $\mathbf{F}$, the velocity $\mathbf{v}$ and the component of the Coriolis force tangential to the earth's surface, $\mathbf{C}_T$, are shown at two positions on the path of an air particle spiraling around a low pressure area in the northern hemisphere in Fig. 5.1.5.

EXERCISES

In Exercises 1–8 find the velocity, speed and acceleration at time t of the particle whose position is $\mathbf{r}(t)$. Describe the path of the particle.

1. $\mathbf{r} = t^2\mathbf{i} - t^2\mathbf{j} + \mathbf{k}$

2. $\mathbf{r} = t\mathbf{i} + t^2\mathbf{j} + t^2\mathbf{k}$

3. $\mathbf{r} = a\cos t\,\mathbf{i} + a\sin t\,\mathbf{j} + ct\mathbf{k}$

4. $\mathbf{r} = a\cos\omega t\,\mathbf{i} + b\mathbf{j} + a\sin\omega t\,\mathbf{k}$

5. $\mathbf{r} = ae^t\mathbf{i} + be^t\mathbf{j} + ce^t\mathbf{k}$

6. $\mathbf{r} = at\cos\omega t\,\mathbf{i} + at\sin\omega t\,\mathbf{j} + b\ln t\,\mathbf{k}$

7. $\mathbf{r} = e^{-t}\cos(e^t)\mathbf{i} + e^{-t}\sin(e^t)\mathbf{j} - e^t\mathbf{k}$

8. $\mathbf{r} = a\cos t\sin t\,\mathbf{i} + a\sin^2 t\,\mathbf{j} + a\cos t\,\mathbf{k}$

9. If at all times t the position and velocity vectors of a moving particle satisfy $\mathbf{v}(t) = 2\mathbf{r}(t)$, and if $\mathbf{r}(0) = \mathbf{r}_0$, find $\mathbf{r}(t)$ and the acceleration $\mathbf{a}(t)$. What is the path of motion?

10.*Verify that $\mathbf{r} = \mathbf{r}_0\cos(\omega t) + (\mathbf{v}_0/\omega)\sin(\omega t)$ satisfies the initial-value problem

$$\begin{cases} \dfrac{d^2\mathbf{r}}{dt^2} &=& -\omega^2\mathbf{r} \\ \mathbf{r}'(0) &=& \mathbf{v}_0 \\ \mathbf{r}(0) &=& \mathbf{r}_0. \end{cases}$$

(It is the unique solution.) Describe the path $\mathbf{r}(t)$. What is the path if $\mathbf{r}_0$ is perpendicular to $\mathbf{v}_0$?

11.*Solve the initial-value problem

$$\frac{d\mathbf{r}}{dt} = \mathbf{k} \times \mathbf{r}, \qquad \mathbf{r}(0) = \mathbf{i} + \mathbf{k}.$$

Describe the curve $\mathbf{r} = \mathbf{r}(t)$.

12.*A projectile falling under gravity and slowed by air resistance proportional to its speed has position satisfying

$$\frac{d^2\mathbf{r}}{dt^2} = -g\mathbf{k} - c\frac{d\mathbf{r}}{dt},$$

where c is a positive constant. If $\mathbf{r} = \mathbf{r}_0$ and $d\mathbf{r}/dt = \mathbf{v}_0$ at time $t = 0$ find $\mathbf{r}(t)$. (Hint: let $\mathbf{w} = e^{ct}\dfrac{d\mathbf{r}}{dt}$.) Show that the solution approaches that of the projectile problem given in this section as $c \to 0$.

13. Show that if the dot product of the velocity and acceleration of a moving particle is positive (or negative) then the speed of the particle is increasing (or decreasing).

14. Verify the formula for the derivative of a dot product given in Theorem 5.1.5(c).

15. Verify the formula for the derivative of a 3×3 determinant in the second remark following Theorem 5.1.5. Use this formula to verify the formula for the derivative of the cross product in Theorem 5.1.5(d).

16. If the position and velocity vectors of a moving particle are always perpendicular show that the path of the particle lies on a sphere.

17. Generalize the previous problem to the case where the velocity of the particle is always perpendicular to the line joining the particle to a fixed point P_0.

18. What can be said about the motion of a particle at a time when its position and velocity satisfy $\mathbf{r} \bullet \mathbf{v} > 0$? What can be said when $\mathbf{r} \bullet \mathbf{v} < 0$?

In Exercises 19–24 assume that the vector functions encountered have continuous derivatives of all required orders.

19. Show that $\dfrac{d}{dt}\left(\dfrac{d\mathbf{u}}{dt} \times \dfrac{d^2\mathbf{u}}{dt^2}\right) = \dfrac{d\mathbf{u}}{dt} \times \dfrac{d^3\mathbf{u}}{dt^3}$.

20. Write the product rule for $\dfrac{d}{dt}\left(\mathbf{u} \bullet (\mathbf{v} \times \mathbf{w})\right)$.

21. Write the product rule for $\dfrac{d}{dt}\left(\mathbf{u} \times (\mathbf{v} \times \mathbf{w})\right)$.

22. Expand and simplify: $\dfrac{d}{dt}\left(\mathbf{u} \times \left(\dfrac{d\mathbf{u}}{dt} \times \dfrac{d^2\mathbf{u}}{dt^2}\right)\right)$.

23. Expand and simplify: $\dfrac{d}{dt}\Big((\mathbf{u}+\mathbf{u}'')\bullet(\mathbf{u}\times\mathbf{u}')\Big)$.

24. Expand and simplify: $\dfrac{d}{dt}\Big((\mathbf{u}\times\mathbf{u}')\bullet(\mathbf{u}'\times\mathbf{u}'')\Big)$.

25. What fraction of its total initial mass would the rocket considered in this section have to burn as fuel in order to accelerate in a straight line from rest to the speed of its own exhaust gases? to twice that speed?

26.*When run at maximum power output the motor in a self-propelled tank car can accelerate the full car (mass M kg) along a horizontal track at a m/sec². The tank is full at time zero but the contents pour out of a hole in the bottom at rate k kg/sec thereafter. If the car is at rest at time zero and full forward power is turned on at that time, how fast will it be moving at any time t before the tank is empty?

27.*A satellite is in a low, circular orbit around the earth, passing over the north and south poles. It makes one revolution every two hours. From the point of view of an observer standing on the earth at the equator, what is the approximate value of the Coriolis force acting on the satellite as it crosses over his head heading south? (Assume the radius of the satellite's orbit is approximately the radius of the earth.) In what direction would the satellite seem to the observer to be moving as it crosses over his head?

28.*Describe the tangential and normal components of the Coriolis force on a particle moving with horizontal velocity $\mathbf{v}$ at a) the north pole, b) the south pole, c) the equator. In general, what is the effect of the normal component of the Coriolis force near the eye of a storm?

5.2 CURVES AND PARAMETRIZATIONS

In this section we will consider curves as geometric objects rather than as paths of moving particles. Everyone has an intuitive idea of what a curve is, but it is difficult to give a formal definition of a curve as a geometric object (that is, as a certain kind of set of points) without involving the concept of parametric representation. We will avoid this difficulty by continuing to regard a curve in 3-space as the set of points whose positions are given by the position vector function

$$\mathbf{r}=\mathbf{r}(t)=x(t)\mathbf{i}+y(t)\mathbf{j}+z(t)\mathbf{k}, \qquad a\le t\le b.$$

Of course, the parameter t need no longer represent time, or any other specific physical quantity.

Curves can be very pathological. For instance, there exist continuous curves which pass through every point in a cube. It is difficult to think of such a curve as a one dimensional object. In order to avoid such strange objects we shall assume hereafter that the defining function $\mathbf{r}(t)$ has a *continuous* first derivative, $d\mathbf{r}/dt$, which we will continue to call "velocity" and denote by $\mathbf{v}(t)$ by analogy with the physical case where t is time. (We also continue to call $v(t)=|\mathbf{v}(t)|$ "speed".) As we shall see later, this implies that the curve has an *arc length* between any two points corresponding to parameter values t_1 and t_2; if $t_1<t_2$ this arc length is

$$\int_{t_1}^{t_2} v(t)\,dt = \int_{t_1}^{t_2} |\mathbf{v}(t)|\,dt = \int_{t_1}^{t_2}\left|\frac{d\mathbf{r}}{dt}\right|dt.$$

Frequently we will want $\mathbf{r}(t)$ to have continuous derivatives of higher order. Whenever needed, we will assume that the "acceleration", $\mathbf{a}(t)=d^2\mathbf{r}/dt^2$, and even the third derivative, $d^3\mathbf{r}/dt^3$, are continuous. Of course, most of the curves we encounter in practice have parametrizations with continuous derivatives of all orders.

It should be noted that no assumptions on the continuity of derivatives of the function $\mathbf{r}(t)$ are sufficient to guarantee that the curve $\mathbf{r}=\mathbf{r}(t)$ is a "smooth" curve.

EXAMPLE 5.2.1 Consider the curve

$$\mathbf{r} = t^3\,\mathbf{i} + t^2\,\mathbf{j}, \qquad -\infty < t < \infty.$$

Although t^2 and t^3 are infinitely differentiable, the curve is not smooth at the origin. It has a cusp there. (See Fig. 5.2.1.)

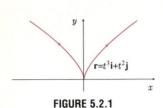

FIGURE 5.2.1

We will show later in this section that if, besides being continuous, the velocity vector $\mathbf{v}(t)$ is never the zero vector, then the curve $\mathbf{r} = \mathbf{r}(t)$ is **smooth** in the sense that it has a continuously turning tangent line. In this context we call a curve, $\mathbf{r} = \mathbf{r}(t)$, $(a \le t \le b)$, **piecewise smooth** if $\mathbf{v}(t)$ is defined, continuous and nonzero for all but finitely many values of t in $[a, b]$. The curve in Example 5.2.1 is piecewise smooth.

Being a set of points in 3-space, any curve C can be represented by more than one vector parametric equation. Generally a curve can have infinitely many such representations.

EXAMPLE 5.2.2 Each of the vector functions

$$\mathbf{r}(t) = \sqrt{2}\cos t\,\mathbf{i} + \sqrt{2}\sin t\,\mathbf{j}, \qquad \frac{\pi}{4} \le t \le \frac{3\pi}{4}$$

$$\mathbf{r}(t) = -t\,\mathbf{i} + \sqrt{2 - t^2}\,\mathbf{j}, \qquad -1 \le t \le 1$$

$$\mathbf{r}(t) = -\sinh t\,\mathbf{i} + \sqrt{3 - \cosh^2 t}\,\mathbf{j}, \qquad \ln(\sqrt{2} - 1) \le t \le \ln(\sqrt{2} + 1),$$

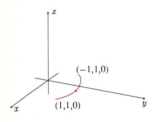

FIGURE 5.2.2

represents the same curve: a circular arc in the half-plane $z = 0$, $y > 0$ having radius $\sqrt{2}$ and centre at the origin, and traversed from $(1,1,0)$ to $(-1, 1, 0)$. (See Fig. 5.2.2.) Of course, all three parametrizations trace out the curve at different speeds.

The curve $\mathbf{r} = \mathbf{r}(t)$, $(a \le t \le b)$ is called a **closed curve** if $\mathbf{r}(a) = \mathbf{r}(b)$ that is, if the curve ends at its starting point. The curve C is **non-self-intersecting** if there exists some parametrization of C such that no points on it other than the endpoints coincide in space; that is, there exists some parametrization $\mathbf{r} = \mathbf{r}(t)$, $(a \le t \le b)$, such that $\mathbf{r}(t_1) \neq \mathbf{r}(t_2)$ if t_1 and t_2 are different numbers in $[a, b]$, and are not both endpoints of that interval. Note that non-self-intersection is a geometric property of the curve, not a property of the parametric equations; other parametrizations of C may not satisfy the condition. Circles and ellipses are examples of non-self-intersecting closed curves.

Every parametrization of a particular curve determines one of two possible **orientations** corresponding to the direction along the curve in which the parameter is increasing. All three parametrizations of the circular arc in the previous example orient the arc counterclockwise as viewed from a point above the xy-plane. This orientation is shown by the arrowhead on the curve in Fig. 5.2.2. The same arc could be given the opposite orientation by, for example, the parametrization

$$\mathbf{r}(t) = t\,\mathbf{i} + \sqrt{2 - t^2}\,\mathbf{j}, \qquad -1 \le t \le 1.$$

Arc Length

We now tackle the problem of defining and calculating the length of a curve. Let C be a bounded, continuous curve specified by

$$\mathbf{r} = \mathbf{r}(t), \qquad a \le t \le b.$$

Subdivide the closed interval $[a, b]$ into n subintervals by points

$$a = t_0 < t_1 < t_2 < \cdots < t_{n-1} < t_n = b.$$

The points $\mathbf{r}_i = \mathbf{r}(t_i)$, $(0 \le i \le n)$, subdivide C into n arcs. If we use the chord length $|\mathbf{r}_i - \mathbf{r}_{i-1}|$ as an approximation to the arc length between $\mathbf{r}_{i-1}$ and $\mathbf{r}_i$ then the sum

$$s_n = \sum_{i=1}^{n} |\mathbf{r}_i - \mathbf{r}_{i-1}|$$

approximates the length of C by the length of a polygonal line. (See Fig. 5.2.3.) Evidently any such approximation is less than or equal to the actual length of C.

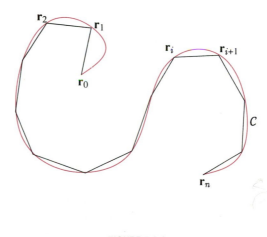

FIGURE 5.2.3

We say that C is **rectifiable** if there exists a constant K such that $s_n \le K$ for every n and every choice of the points t_i. In this case, we call the smallest such K the **length** of C and denote it by s.

Let $\Delta t_i = t_i - t_{i-1}$ and $\Delta \mathbf{r}_i = \mathbf{r}_i - \mathbf{r}_{i-1}$. Then s_n can be written in the form

$$s_n = \sum_{i=1}^{n} \left| \frac{\Delta \mathbf{r}_i}{\Delta t_i} \right| \Delta t_i.$$

If $\mathbf{r}(t)$ has a continuous derivative $\mathbf{v}(t)$ which does not vanish on $[a, b]$ it can be shown that

$$s = \lim_{\max \Delta t_i \to 0} s_n = \int_a^b \left| \frac{d\mathbf{r}}{dt} \right| dt = \int_a^b |\mathbf{v}(t)| \, dt = \int_a^b v(t) \, dt.$$

In kinematic terms, this formula states that the distance travelled by a moving particle is the integral of the speed.

Although the above formula is expressed in terms of the parameter t, the arc length, as defined above, is a strictly geometric property of the curve C. It is independent of the particular parametrization used to represent C. If $s(t)$ denotes the arc length of that part of C corresponding to parameter values in $[a, t]$ then

$$\frac{ds}{dt} = \frac{d}{dt} \int_a^t v(\tau)\, d\tau = v(t)$$

so that

5.2.3
Arc Length Element

$$ds = v(t)\, dt$$

and we define

$$\int_C ds = \text{length of } C = \int_a^b \frac{ds}{dt}\, dt.$$

Several familiar formulas for arc length follow from the above formula by using specific parametrizations of curves. For instance, the length of the Cartesian plane curve $y = f(x)$ on $[a, b]$ is obtained by using x as parameter: here $\mathbf{r} = x\mathbf{i} + f(x)\mathbf{j}$ so $\mathbf{v} = \mathbf{i} + f'(x)\mathbf{j}$ and

$$ds = \sqrt{1 + \left(f'(x)\right)^2}\, dx$$

Similarly, the arc length element ds for a plane polar curve $r = g(\theta)$ can be calculated from the parametrization

$$\mathbf{r}(\theta) = g(\theta)\cos\theta\mathbf{i} + g(\theta)\sin\theta\mathbf{j}.$$

It is

$$ds = \sqrt{\left(g(\theta)\right)^2 + \left(g'(\theta)\right)^2}\, d\theta.$$

EXAMPLE 5.2.4   Find the length s of that part of the **circular helix**

$$\mathbf{r} = a\,\cos t\,\mathbf{i} + a\,\sin t\,\mathbf{j} + bt\,\mathbf{k}$$

between the points $(a, 0, 0)$ and $(a, 0, 2\pi b)$.

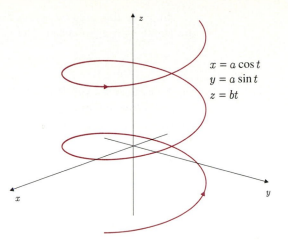

$$x = a \cos t$$
$$y = a \sin t$$
$$z = bt$$

FIGURE 5.2.4

SOLUTION This curve spirals around the z-axis rising as it turns. (See Fig. 5.2.4.) It lies on the cylindrical surface $x^2 + y^2 = a^2$. We have

$$\mathbf{v} = \frac{d\mathbf{r}}{dt} = -a \, \sin t \, \mathbf{i} + a \cos t \, \mathbf{j} + b\mathbf{k}$$
$$v = \sqrt{a^2 + b^2}$$

so that in terms of the parameter t the helix is traced out at constant speed. The required length s corresponds to parameter interval $[0, 2\pi]$. Thus

$$s = \int_0^{2\pi} v(t) \, dt = \int_0^{2\pi} \sqrt{a^2 + b^2} \, dt = 2\pi \sqrt{a^2 + b^2}.$$

The Arc Length Parameter

The selection of a particular parameter in terms of which to specify a given curve will usually depend on the problem in which the curve arises; there is no one "right way" to parametrize a curve. However, there is one parameter which is "natural" in that it arises from the geometry (shape and size) of the curve itself, and not from any particular coordinate system in which the equation of the curve is to be expressed. This parameter is the *arc length* measured from some particular point (the *initial point*) on the curve. The position vector of an arbitrary point P on the curve can be specified as a function of the arc length s along the curve from the initial point P_0 to P,

$$\mathbf{r} = \mathbf{r}(s).$$

This equation is called an **intrinsic parametrization** of the curve. Although it is seldom easy, (and usually not possible), to find $\mathbf{r}(s)$ explicitly when the curve is given in terms of some other parameter, smooth curves always have such parametrizations (see Exercise 19 at the end of this section), and they will prove useful when we develop the fundamentals of *differential geometry* for 3-space curves in the next section.

Suppose that a curve is specified in terms of an arbitrary parameter t. If the arc length over a parameter interval $[t_0, t]$,

$$s = s(t) = \int_{t_0}^{t} \left| \frac{d}{dt} \mathbf{r}(\tau) \right| \, d\tau,$$

can be evaluated explicitly, and if the equation $s = s(t)$ can be explicitly solved for t as a function of s ($t = t(s)$) then the curve can be reparametrized in terms of arc length by substituting for t in the original parametrization:

$$\mathbf{r} = \mathbf{r}(t(s)).$$

EXAMPLE 5.2.5   Parametrize the circular helix

$$\mathbf{r} = a \cos t \mathbf{i} + a \sin t \mathbf{j} + bt \mathbf{k}$$

in terms of the arc length measured from the point $(a, 0, 0)$ in the direction of increasing t.

SOLUTION   The initial point corresponds to $t = 0$. By the previous example we have $\frac{ds}{dt} = \sqrt{a^2 + b^2}$ so

$$s = s(t) = \int_0^t \sqrt{a^2 + b^2} \, d\tau = \sqrt{a^2 + b^2} \, t.$$

Therefore $t = s/\sqrt{a^2 + b^2}$ and the required parametrization is

$$\mathbf{r}(s) = a \cos \left(\frac{s}{\sqrt{a^2 + b^2}} \right) \mathbf{i} + a \sin \left(\frac{s}{\sqrt{a^2 + b^2}} \right) \mathbf{j} + \frac{bs}{\sqrt{a^2 + b^2}} \mathbf{k}.$$

The Unit Tangent Vector

The velocity vector $\mathbf{v}(t) = d\mathbf{r}/dt$ is tangent to the parametric curve $\mathbf{r} = \mathbf{r}(t)$ at the point $\mathbf{r}(t)$, and points in the direction of the orientation of the curve there. Since we are assuming that $\mathbf{v}(t) \neq \mathbf{0}$ we can find a **unit tangent vector**, $\hat{\mathbf{T}}(t)$, at $\mathbf{r}(t)$ by dividing $\mathbf{v}(t)$ by its length:

5.2.6
The Unit
Tangent Vector

$$\hat{\mathbf{T}}(t) = \frac{\mathbf{v}(t)}{v(t)} = \frac{d\mathbf{r}}{dt} \bigg/ \left| \frac{d\mathbf{r}}{dt} \right|.$$

Recall that $ds = v(t) \, dt$ for a parametric curve $\mathbf{r} = \mathbf{r}(t)$. If the curve is parametrized in terms of arc length, $\mathbf{r} = \mathbf{r}(s)$, then $ds = v(s) \, ds$ so $v(s) = 1$; the curve is traced out with unit "speed." Thus the unit tangent vector is

5.2.7
The Unit Tangent
for the Intrinsic
Parametrization

$$\hat{\mathbf{T}}(s) = \frac{d\mathbf{r}}{ds}.$$

EXAMPLE 5.2.8   Find the unit tangent vector, $\hat{\mathbf{T}}$, for the circular helix of Examples 5.2.4 and 5.2.5, both in terms of t and in terms of the arc length parameter s.

SOLUTION   In terms of t we have

$$\mathbf{r} = a \cos t\,\mathbf{i} + a \sin t\,\mathbf{j} + bt\,\mathbf{k}$$

$$\mathbf{v}(t) = -a \sin t\,\mathbf{i} + a \cos t\,\mathbf{j} + b\,\mathbf{k}$$

$$v(t) = \sqrt{a^2 \sin^2 t + a^2 \cos^2 t + b^2} = \sqrt{a^2 + b^2}$$

$$\hat{\mathbf{T}}(t) = -\frac{a}{\sqrt{a^2 + b^2}} \sin t\,\mathbf{i} + \frac{a}{\sqrt{a^2 + b^2}} \cos t\,\mathbf{j} + \frac{b}{\sqrt{a^2 + b^2}}\,\mathbf{k}.$$

In terms of the arc length parameter

$$\mathbf{r}(s) = a \cos\left(\frac{s}{\sqrt{a^2 + b^2}}\right)\mathbf{i} + a \sin\left(\frac{s}{\sqrt{a^2 + b^2}}\right)\mathbf{j} + \frac{bs}{\sqrt{a^2 + b^2}}\mathbf{k}$$

$$\hat{\mathbf{T}}(s) = \frac{d\mathbf{r}}{ds} = -\frac{a}{\sqrt{a^2 + b^2}} \sin\left(\frac{s}{\sqrt{a^2 + b^2}}\right)\mathbf{i} + \frac{a}{\sqrt{a^2 + b^2}} \cos\left(\frac{s}{\sqrt{a^2 + b^2}}\right)\mathbf{j}$$

$$+ \frac{b}{\sqrt{a^2 + b^2}}\mathbf{k}.$$

REMARK: If the curve $\mathbf{r} = \mathbf{r}(t)$ has a continuous, nonvanishing velocity $\mathbf{v}(t)$ then the unit tangent vector $\hat{\mathbf{T}}(t)$ is a continuous function of t. The angle $\theta(t)$ between $\hat{\mathbf{T}}(t)$ and any fixed unit vector $\hat{\mathbf{u}}$ is also continuous in t:

$$\theta(t) = \cos^{-1}(\hat{\mathbf{T}}(t) \bullet \hat{\mathbf{u}}).$$

Thus, as asserted previously, the curve is *smooth* in the sense that it has a continuously turning tangent line.

EXERCISES

In Exercises 1–4 find the required parametrization of the first quadrant part of the circular arc $x^2 + y^2 = a^2$.

1. In terms of the y-coordinate, oriented counterclockwise.

2. In terms of the x-coordinate, oriented clockwise.

3. In terms of the angle between the tangent line and the positive x-axis, oriented counterclockwise.

4. In terms of arc length measured from $(0, a)$, oriented clockwise.

5. Express the length of the curve $\mathbf{r} = at^2\,\mathbf{i} + bt\,\mathbf{j} + c \ln t\,\mathbf{k}$, $(1 \leq t \leq T)$ as a definite integral. Evaluate the integral if $b^2 = 4ac$.

6. Describe the parametric curve C given by

$$x = a \cos t \sin t, \qquad y = a \sin^2 t, \qquad z = bt.$$

What is the length of C between $t = 0$ and $t = T > 0$?

7. Find the length of the conical helix $\mathbf{r} = t \cos t\,\mathbf{i} + t \sin t\,\mathbf{j} + t\,\mathbf{k}$, $(0 \leq t \leq 2\pi)$. Why is the curve called a conical helix?

8. Describe the intersection of the sphere $x^2 + y^2 + z^2 = 1$ and the elliptic cylinder $x^2 + 2z^2 = 1$. Find the total length of this intersection curve.

9. Let C be the curve $x = e^t \cos t$, $y = e^t \sin t$, $z = t$ between $t = 0$ and $t = 2\pi$. Find the length of C.

10.*A cable of length L and circular cross-section of radius a is wound around a cylindrical spool of radius b with no overlapping and so that adjacent windings touch one another. What length of the spool is covered by the cable?

In Exercises 11–14 reparametrize the given curve in the same orientation in terms of arc length measured from the point where $t = 0$.

11. $\mathbf{r} = At\mathbf{i} + Bt\mathbf{j} + Ct\mathbf{k}$, $(A^2 + B^2 + C^2 > 0)$

12. $\mathbf{r} = e^t\mathbf{i} + \sqrt{2}t\mathbf{j} - e^{-t}\mathbf{k}$

13.*$\mathbf{r} = a\cos^3 t\,\mathbf{i} + a\sin^3 t\,\mathbf{j} + b\cos 2t\,\mathbf{k}$, $(0 \le t \le \dfrac{\pi}{2})$

14.*$\mathbf{r} = 3t\cos t\,\mathbf{i} + 3t\sin t\,\mathbf{j} + 2\sqrt{2}t^{3/2}\mathbf{k}$

Find the unit tangent vector $\hat{\mathbf{T}}(t)$ for the curves in Exercises 15–18.

15. $\mathbf{r} = t\mathbf{i} - 2t^2\mathbf{j} + 3t^3\mathbf{k}$

16. $\mathbf{r} = a\sin\omega t\,\mathbf{i} + a\cos\omega t\,\mathbf{k}$

17. $\mathbf{r} = \cos t\sin t\,\mathbf{i} + \sin^2 t\,\mathbf{j} + \cos t\,\mathbf{k}$

18. $\mathbf{r} = a\cos t\,\mathbf{i} + b\sin t\,\mathbf{j} + t\mathbf{k}$

19.*If the curve $\mathbf{r} = \mathbf{r}(t)$ has continuous, nonvanishing velocity $\mathbf{v}(t)$ on the interval $[a, b]$, and if t_0 is some point in $[a, b]$, show that the function

$$g(t) = \int_{t_0}^{t} |\mathbf{v}(u)|\,du$$

is an increasing function on $[a, b]$, and so has an inverse:

$$t = g^{-1}(s) \iff s = g(t).$$

Hence show that the curve can be parametrized in terms of arc length measured from $\mathbf{r}(t_0)$.

5.3   CURVATURE AND TORSION

This section continues the development of the fundamentals of differential geometry of curves in 3-space begun in the last section. We will be introducing several new scalar and vector functions associated with a curve C. At the outset we will assume that C is parametrized in terms of arc length measured from some point on C:

$$\mathbf{r} = \mathbf{r}(s).$$

We also assume that $\mathbf{r}(s)$ has continuous derivatives up to third order on the interval on which it is defined.

Curvature and the Unit Normal

Since it has unit length, the tangent vector $\hat{\mathbf{T}}(s) = d\mathbf{r}/ds$ satisfies $\hat{\mathbf{T}}(s) \bullet \hat{\mathbf{T}}(s) = 1$. Differentiating this equation with respect to s we get

$$2\hat{\mathbf{T}}(s) \bullet \frac{d\hat{\mathbf{T}}}{ds} = 0,$$

so that $d\hat{\mathbf{T}}/ds$ is perpendicular to $\hat{\mathbf{T}}(s)$. Let

5.3.1
Curvature

$$\kappa(s) = \left| \frac{d\hat{\mathbf{T}}}{ds} \right|.$$

The nonnegative number $\kappa(s)$ is called the **curvature** of C at the point $\mathbf{r}(s)$ because, as we shall see below, it measures the rate of turning of the tangent line to the curve. The reciprocal of the curvature,

5.3.2
Radius of
Curvature

$$\rho(s) = \frac{1}{\kappa(s)}$$

is called the **radius of curvature** of C at $\mathbf{r}(s)$. As we shall see, it is the radius of a circle through $\mathbf{r}(s)$ which most closely approximates the turning of C there.

Provided $\kappa(s) \neq 0$ we can divide $d\hat{\mathbf{T}}/ds$ by its length, $\kappa(s)$, and obtain a unit vector $\hat{\mathbf{N}}(s)$ in the same direction:

5.3.3
The Unit
Principal Normal

$$\frac{d\hat{\mathbf{T}}}{ds} = \kappa(s)\hat{\mathbf{N}}(s).$$

The unit vector $\hat{\mathbf{N}}(s)$, which is perpendicular to $\hat{\mathbf{T}}(s)$ and therefore to C at $\mathbf{r}(s)$, is called the **unit principal normal** to C at $\mathbf{r}(s)$, or, more commonly, just the **unit normal**. (See Fig. 5.3.1.)

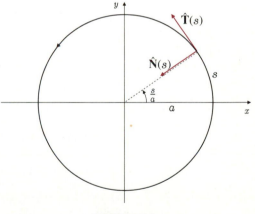

FIGURE 5.3.1   FIGURE 5.3.2

EXAMPLE 5.3.4   Let $a > 0$. The curve

$$\mathbf{r} = a\cos\left(\frac{s}{a}\right)\mathbf{i} + a\sin\left(\frac{s}{a}\right)\mathbf{j}$$

is a circle in the xy-plane having radius a and centre at the origin. Since

$$\left|\frac{d\mathbf{r}}{ds}\right| = \left|-\sin\left(\frac{s}{a}\right)\mathbf{i} + \cos\left(\frac{s}{a}\right)\mathbf{j}\right| = 1,$$

the parameter s must represent arc length, and hence the unit tangent vector is

$$\hat{\mathbf{T}}(s) = -\sin\left(\frac{s}{a}\right)\mathbf{i} + \cos\left(\frac{s}{a}\right)\mathbf{j},$$

and

$$\frac{d\hat{\mathbf{T}}}{ds} = -\frac{1}{a}\cos\left(\frac{s}{a}\right)\mathbf{i} - \frac{1}{a}\sin\left(\frac{s}{a}\right)\mathbf{j}$$
$$= \frac{1}{a}\hat{\mathbf{N}}(s)$$

where

$$\hat{\mathbf{N}}(s) = -\cos\left(\frac{s}{a}\right)\mathbf{i} - \sin\left(\frac{s}{a}\right)\mathbf{j} = -\frac{1}{a}\mathbf{r}(s).$$

The curvature of this circle is constant: $\kappa(s) = 1/a$ and the radius of curvature is $\rho(s) = 1/\kappa(s) = a$, the radius of the circle. The circle and its unit tangent and normal vectors at a typical point are sketched in Fig. 5.3.2. Note that $\hat{\mathbf{N}}$ points towards the centre of the circle.

REMARK: Another observation can be made about the above example. The position vector $\mathbf{r}(s)$ makes angle $\theta = s/a$ with the positive x-axis, and therefore $\hat{\mathbf{T}}(s)$ makes the same angle with the positive y-axis. Therefore the rate of rotation of $\hat{\mathbf{T}}$ with respect to s is

$$\frac{d\theta}{ds} = \frac{1}{a} = \kappa.$$

This generalizes to an arbitrary smooth curve as follows. Suppose $\Delta\theta$ is the angle between $\hat{\mathbf{T}}(s)$ and $\hat{\mathbf{T}}(s + \Delta s) = \hat{\mathbf{T}}(s) + \Delta\hat{\mathbf{T}}$. Because both of these vectors are unit vectors we have

$$\cos(\Delta\theta) = \hat{\mathbf{T}}(s) \bullet \hat{\mathbf{T}}(s + \Delta s) = \hat{\mathbf{T}}(s) \bullet \left(\hat{\mathbf{T}}(s) + \Delta\hat{\mathbf{T}}\right) = 1 + \hat{\mathbf{T}}(s) \bullet \Delta\hat{\mathbf{T}}.$$

Also

$$1 = |\hat{\mathbf{T}}(s + \Delta s)|^2 = |\hat{\mathbf{T}}(s) + \Delta\hat{\mathbf{T}}|^2 = 1 + 2\hat{\mathbf{T}}(s) \bullet \Delta\hat{\mathbf{T}} + |\Delta\hat{\mathbf{T}}|^2.$$

Therefore

$$|\Delta\hat{\mathbf{T}}|^2 = -2\hat{\mathbf{T}}(s) \bullet \Delta\hat{\mathbf{T}} = 2(1 - \cos\Delta\theta) = 4\sin^2\left(\frac{\Delta\theta}{2}\right),$$

and

$$\left|\frac{\Delta\hat{\mathbf{T}}}{\Delta s}\right|^2 = \left(\frac{2\sin(\Delta\theta/2)}{\Delta s}\right)^2 = \left(\frac{\sin(\Delta\theta/2)}{(\Delta\theta/2)}\frac{\Delta\theta}{\Delta s}\right)^2.$$

Taking the limit as $\Delta s \to 0$ and then taking the square root we get

$$\kappa = \lim_{\Delta s \to 0}\left|\frac{\Delta\theta}{\Delta s}\right| = \frac{d\theta}{ds}.$$

The curvature is the *rate of rotation* of the unit tangent vector with respect to the arc length parameter.

The unit tangent $\hat{\mathbf{T}}$ and unit normal $\hat{\mathbf{N}}$ at a point $\mathbf{r}(s)$ on a curve C are typically regarded as having their tails at that point. They are perpendicular, and $\hat{\mathbf{N}}$ points in the direction towards which $\hat{\mathbf{T}}(s)$ turns as s increases. The plane passing through $\mathbf{r}(s)$ and containing the vectors $\hat{\mathbf{T}}(s)$ and $\hat{\mathbf{N}}(s)$ is called the **osculating plane** of C at $\mathbf{r}(s)$ (from the Latin "osculum", meaning "kiss"). For a *plane curve*, such as the circle in the previous example, the osculating plane is just the plane containing the curve. For more general three-dimensional curves the osculating plane varies from point to point; at any point it is that plane which comes closest to containing the part of the curve near that point. The osculating plane is not properly defined at a point where $\kappa(s) = 0$, though if such points are isolated, it can sometimes be defined as a limit of osculating planes for neighbouring points.

Still assuming that $\kappa(s) \neq 0$, let

$$\mathbf{r}_c(s) = \mathbf{r}(s) + \rho(s)\hat{\mathbf{N}}(s).$$

For each s the point with position vector $\mathbf{r}_c(s)$ lies in the osculating plane of C at $\mathbf{r}(s)$, on the concave side of C and at distance $\rho(s)$ from $\mathbf{r}(s)$. It is called the **centre of curvature** of C for the point $\mathbf{r}(s)$. The circle in the osculating plane having centre at the centre of curvature and radius $\rho(s)$ is called the **osculating circle** for C at $\mathbf{r}(s)$. This is the circle which best describes the behavior of C near $\mathbf{r}(s)$; it has the same tangent and normal, and the same curvature. Of course, the osculating circle of a circle at any point is that same circle. A typical example of an osculating circle is shown in Fig. 5.3.3.

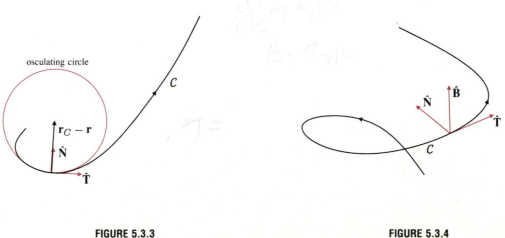

FIGURE 5.3.3   **FIGURE 5.3.4**

Torsion and Binormal, The Frenet-Serret Formulas

At any point $\mathbf{r}(s)$ on the curve C where $\hat{\mathbf{T}}$ and $\hat{\mathbf{N}}$ are defined a third unit vector, the **unit binormal** $\hat{\mathbf{B}}$, is defined by the formula

5.3.5
The Unit
Binormal

$$\hat{\mathbf{B}} = \hat{\mathbf{T}} \times \hat{\mathbf{N}}.$$

Evidently $\hat{\mathbf{B}}(s)$ is normal to the osculating plane of C at $\mathbf{r}(s)$. At each point on C, the three vectors $\{\hat{\mathbf{T}}, \hat{\mathbf{N}}, \hat{\mathbf{B}}\}$ constitute a right-handed basis of mutually perpendicular unit vectors like the standard basis $\{\mathbf{i}, \mathbf{j}, \mathbf{k}\}$. (See Fig. 5.3.4.) This basis is called the **Frenet frame** at the point. Note that $\hat{\mathbf{B}} \times \hat{\mathbf{T}} = \hat{\mathbf{N}}$ and $\hat{\mathbf{N}} \times \hat{\mathbf{B}} = \hat{\mathbf{T}}$.

Since $1 = \hat{\mathbf{B}}(s) \bullet \hat{\mathbf{B}}(s)$, therefore $\hat{\mathbf{B}}(s) \bullet (d\hat{\mathbf{B}}/ds) = 0$, and $d\hat{\mathbf{B}}/ds$ is perpendicular to $\hat{\mathbf{B}}(s)$. Also, differentiating $\hat{\mathbf{B}} = \hat{\mathbf{T}} \times \hat{\mathbf{N}}$ we obtain

$$\frac{d\hat{\mathbf{B}}}{ds} = \frac{d\hat{\mathbf{T}}}{ds} \times \hat{\mathbf{N}} + \hat{\mathbf{T}} \times \frac{d\hat{\mathbf{N}}}{ds} = \kappa\hat{\mathbf{N}} \times \hat{\mathbf{N}} + \hat{\mathbf{T}} \times \frac{d\hat{\mathbf{N}}}{ds} = \hat{\mathbf{T}} \times \frac{d\hat{\mathbf{N}}}{ds}.$$

Therefore $d\hat{\mathbf{B}}/ds$ is also perpendicular to $\hat{\mathbf{T}}$. Therefore $d\hat{\mathbf{B}}/ds$ is parallel to $\hat{\mathbf{N}}$, and there exists a function $\tau(s)$ such that

$$\frac{d\hat{\mathbf{B}}}{ds} = -\tau(s)\hat{\mathbf{N}}(s).$$

The number $\tau(s)$ is called the **torsion** of C at $\mathbf{r}(s)$. The torsion measures the degree of twisting the curve exhibits near a point, that is, the extent to which the curve fails to be planar. It may be positive or negative, depending on the right-handedness or left-handedness of the twisting. We will present an example later in this section.

Making use of the formulas $d\hat{\mathbf{T}}/ds = \kappa\hat{\mathbf{N}}$ and $d\hat{\mathbf{B}}/ds = -\tau\hat{\mathbf{N}}$ we can calculate $d\hat{\mathbf{N}}/ds$ as well:

$$\frac{d\hat{\mathbf{N}}}{ds} = \frac{d}{ds}(\hat{\mathbf{B}} \times \hat{\mathbf{T}}) = \frac{d\hat{\mathbf{B}}}{ds} \times \hat{\mathbf{T}} + \hat{\mathbf{B}} \times \frac{d\hat{\mathbf{T}}}{ds} = -\tau\hat{\mathbf{N}} \times \hat{\mathbf{T}} + \kappa\hat{\mathbf{B}} \times \hat{\mathbf{N}} = -\kappa\hat{\mathbf{T}} + \tau\hat{\mathbf{B}}.$$

Together the three formulas

5.3.6
The Frenet-Serret
Formulas

$$\frac{d\hat{\mathbf{T}}}{ds} = \kappa\hat{\mathbf{N}}$$

$$\frac{d\hat{\mathbf{N}}}{ds} = -\kappa\hat{\mathbf{T}} + \tau\hat{\mathbf{B}}$$

$$\frac{d\hat{\mathbf{B}}}{ds} = -\tau\hat{\mathbf{N}}$$

are known as **The Frenet-Serret Formulas**. They are of fundamental importance in the theory of curves in 3-space. The Frenet-Serret Formulas can be written in matrix form:

$$\frac{d}{ds}\begin{pmatrix}\hat{\mathbf{T}} \\ \hat{\mathbf{N}} \\ \hat{\mathbf{B}}\end{pmatrix} = \begin{pmatrix} 0 & \kappa & 0 \\ -\kappa & 0 & \tau \\ 0 & -\tau & 0 \end{pmatrix}\begin{pmatrix}\hat{\mathbf{T}} \\ \hat{\mathbf{N}} \\ \hat{\mathbf{B}}\end{pmatrix}.$$

Using the Frenet-Serret Formulas we can show that the shape of a curve with non-vanishing curvature is completely determined by the curvature and torsion functions $\kappa(s)$ and $\tau(s)$.

THEOREM 5.3.7   *(The Fundamental Theorem of Space Curves)* Let C_1 and C_2 be two curves both of which have the same non-vanishing curvature function $\kappa(s)$ and the same torsion function $\tau(s)$. Then the curves are congruent. (That is, one can be moved rigidly so as to coincide exactly with the other.)

PROOF   Move C_2 rigidly so that its initial point coincides with the initial point of C_1 and so that the Frenet frames of both curves coincide at that point. Let $\hat{\mathbf{T}}_1$, $\hat{\mathbf{T}}_2$, $\hat{\mathbf{N}}_1$, $\hat{\mathbf{N}}_2$, $\hat{\mathbf{B}}_1$ and $\hat{\mathbf{B}}_2$ be the unit tangents, normals and binormals for the two curves. Let

$$f(s) = \hat{\mathbf{T}}_1(s) \bullet \hat{\mathbf{T}}_2(s) + \hat{\mathbf{N}}_1(s) \bullet \hat{\mathbf{N}}_2(s) + \hat{\mathbf{B}}_1(s) \bullet \hat{\mathbf{B}}_2(s).$$

We calculate the derivative of $f(s)$ using the product rule and the Frenet-Serret Formulas:

$$\begin{aligned} f'(s) &= \hat{\mathbf{T}}_1' \bullet \hat{\mathbf{T}}_2 + \hat{\mathbf{T}}_1 \bullet \hat{\mathbf{T}}_2' + \hat{\mathbf{N}}_1' \bullet \hat{\mathbf{N}}_2 + \hat{\mathbf{N}}_1 \bullet \hat{\mathbf{N}}_2' + \hat{\mathbf{B}}_1' \bullet \hat{\mathbf{B}}_2 + \hat{\mathbf{B}}_1 \bullet \hat{\mathbf{B}}_2' \\ &= \kappa\hat{\mathbf{N}}_1 \bullet \hat{\mathbf{T}}_2 + \kappa\hat{\mathbf{T}}_1 \bullet \hat{\mathbf{N}}_2 - \kappa\hat{\mathbf{T}}_1 \bullet \hat{\mathbf{N}}_2 + \tau\hat{\mathbf{B}}_1 \bullet \hat{\mathbf{N}}_2 - \kappa\hat{\mathbf{N}}_1 \bullet \hat{\mathbf{T}}_2 \\ &\qquad + \tau\hat{\mathbf{N}}_1 \bullet \hat{\mathbf{B}}_2 - \tau\hat{\mathbf{N}}_1 \bullet \hat{\mathbf{B}}_2 - \tau\hat{\mathbf{B}}_1 \bullet \hat{\mathbf{N}}_2 \\ &= 0. \end{aligned}$$

Therefore $f(s)$ is constant. Since the frames coincide at $s = 0$ the constant must be 3:

$$\hat{\mathbf{T}}_1(s) \bullet \hat{\mathbf{T}}_2(s) + \hat{\mathbf{N}}_1(s) \bullet \hat{\mathbf{N}}_2(s) + \hat{\mathbf{B}}_1(s) \bullet \hat{\mathbf{B}}_2(s) = 3.$$

However, each dot product cannot exceed 1 since the factors are unit vectors. Therefore each dot product must be equal to 1. In particular, $\hat{\mathbf{T}}_1(s) \bullet \hat{\mathbf{T}}_2(s) = 1$ for all s, and hence

$$\frac{d\mathbf{r}_1}{ds} = \hat{\mathbf{T}}_1(s) = \hat{\mathbf{T}}_2(s) = \frac{d\mathbf{r}_2}{ds}.$$

Integrating with respect to s and using the fact that both curves start from the same point when $s = 0$ we obtain

$$\mathbf{r}_1(s) = \mathbf{r}_2(s)$$

for all s, which is what we wanted to show. □

Curvature and Torsion for General Parametrizations

The formulas developed above for curvature and torsion as well as for the unit normal and binormal vectors are not very useful if the curve we want to analyse is not expressed in terms of the arc length parameter. We will now consider how to find these quantities in terms of a general parametrization $\mathbf{r} = \mathbf{r}(t)$. We will express them all in terms of the velocity, $\mathbf{v}(t)$, the speed, $v(t) = |\mathbf{v}(t)|$, and the acceleration, $\mathbf{a}(t)$. First observe that

$$\mathbf{v} = \frac{d\mathbf{r}}{dt} = \frac{d\mathbf{r}}{ds}\frac{ds}{dt} = v\hat{\mathbf{T}}$$

$$\mathbf{a} = \frac{d\mathbf{v}}{dt} = \frac{dv}{dt}\hat{\mathbf{T}} + v\frac{d\hat{\mathbf{T}}}{dt}$$

$$= \frac{dv}{dt}\hat{\mathbf{T}} + v\frac{d\hat{\mathbf{T}}}{ds}\frac{ds}{dt} = \frac{dv}{dt}\hat{\mathbf{T}} + v^2\kappa\hat{\mathbf{N}}$$

$$\mathbf{v} \times \mathbf{a} = v\frac{dv}{dt}\hat{\mathbf{T}} \times \hat{\mathbf{T}} + v^3\kappa\hat{\mathbf{T}} \times \hat{\mathbf{N}} = v^3\kappa\hat{\mathbf{B}}$$

Note that $\hat{\mathbf{B}}$ is in the direction of $\mathbf{v} \times \mathbf{a}$. From these formulas we obtain useful formulas for $\hat{\mathbf{T}}$, $\hat{\mathbf{B}}$ and κ:

$$\hat{\mathbf{T}} = \frac{\mathbf{v}}{v}, \qquad \hat{\mathbf{B}} = \frac{\mathbf{v} \times \mathbf{a}}{|\mathbf{v} \times \mathbf{a}|}, \qquad \kappa = \frac{|\mathbf{v} \times \mathbf{a}|}{v^3}.$$

We could calculate $\hat{\mathbf{N}}$ from the formula for $\mathbf{a}$ but it is easier to get it directly from $\hat{\mathbf{T}}$ and $\hat{\mathbf{B}}$:

$$\hat{\mathbf{N}} = \hat{\mathbf{B}} \times \hat{\mathbf{T}}.$$

The torsion remains to be calculated. Observe that

$$\frac{d\mathbf{a}}{dt} = \frac{d}{dt}\left(\frac{dv}{dt}\hat{\mathbf{T}} + v^2\kappa\hat{\mathbf{N}}\right).$$

This differentiation will produce several terms, but only one will involve $\hat{\mathbf{B}}$: the one which comes from evaluating $v^2\kappa(d\hat{\mathbf{N}}/dt) = v^3\kappa(d\hat{\mathbf{N}}/ds) = v^3\kappa(\tau\hat{\mathbf{B}} - \kappa\hat{\mathbf{T}})$. Therefore

$$\frac{d\mathbf{a}}{dt} = \lambda\hat{\mathbf{T}} + \mu\hat{\mathbf{N}} + v^3\kappa\tau\hat{\mathbf{B}},$$

for certain scalars λ and μ. Since $\mathbf{v} \times \mathbf{a} = v^3\kappa\hat{\mathbf{B}}$, it follows that

$$(\mathbf{v} \times \mathbf{a}) \bullet \frac{d\mathbf{a}}{dt} = (v^3\kappa)^2\tau = |\mathbf{v} \times \mathbf{a}|^2\tau.$$

Hence

$$\tau = \frac{(\mathbf{v} \times \mathbf{a}) \bullet (d\mathbf{a}/dt)}{|\mathbf{v} \times \mathbf{a}|^2}.$$

REMARK: In the formula obtained above for the acceleration in terms of the unit tangent and normal,

$$\mathbf{a} = \frac{dv}{dt}\hat{\mathbf{T}} + v^2 \kappa \hat{\mathbf{N}},$$

the term $(dv/dt)\hat{\mathbf{T}}$ is called the **tangential** acceleration and the term $v^2 \kappa \hat{\mathbf{N}}$ is called the **normal** or **centripetal** acceleration. This latter component is directed towards the centre of curvature and its magnitude is $v^2 \kappa = v^2/\rho$. This is consistent with the definition of centripetal acceleration arising in the discussion of rotating frames in Section 5.1. If $\mathbf{r}(t)$ is the position of a moving particle at time t we may regard the motion at any instant as being a rotation about the centre of curvature, so that the angular velocity must be $\mathbf{\Omega} = \Omega \hat{\mathbf{B}}$. The linear velocity is $\mathbf{v} = \mathbf{\Omega} \times (\mathbf{r} - \mathbf{r}_c) = v\hat{\mathbf{T}}$ so the speed is $v = \Omega\rho$, and $\mathbf{\Omega} = (v/\rho)\hat{\mathbf{B}}$. The centripetal acceleration, as arising in the discussion of rotating frames in Section 5.1, is

$$\mathbf{\Omega} \times (\mathbf{\Omega} \times (\mathbf{r} - \mathbf{r}_c)) = \mathbf{\Omega} \times \mathbf{v} = \frac{v^2}{\rho}\hat{\mathbf{B}} \times \hat{\mathbf{T}} = \frac{v^2}{\rho}\hat{\mathbf{N}}.$$

Highway and railway designers attempt to bank curves in such a way that the resultant of the corresponding "centrifugal force," $-m(v^2/\rho)\hat{\mathbf{N}}$, and the weight, $-mg\mathbf{k}$, of the vehicle will be normal to the surface at a desired speed.

EXAMPLE 5.3.8   Find the curvature of the plane curve with equation $y = f(x)$ at an arbitrary point x.

SOLUTION   The graph may be parametrized $\mathbf{r} = x\mathbf{i} + f(x)\mathbf{j}$. Thus

$$\mathbf{v} = \mathbf{i} + f'(x)\mathbf{j},$$
$$\mathbf{a} = f''(x)\mathbf{j}$$
$$\mathbf{v} \times \mathbf{a} = f''(x)\mathbf{k}.$$

Therefore the curvature is

$$\kappa(x) = \frac{|f''(x)|}{\left(1 + (f'(x))^2\right)^{3/2}}.$$

EXAMPLE 5.3.9   Find the unit tangent, normal and binormal, and the curvature and torsion at an arbitrary point on the circular helix

$$\mathbf{r} = a \cos t\, \mathbf{i} + a \sin t\, \mathbf{j} + bt\mathbf{k}.$$

SOLUTION   We have

$$\mathbf{v} = -a \sin t\, \mathbf{i} + a \cos t\, \mathbf{j} + b\mathbf{k}$$

$$v = |\mathbf{v}| = \sqrt{a^2 + b^2}$$

$$\mathbf{a} = -a \cos t\, \mathbf{i} - a \sin t\, \mathbf{j}$$

$$\frac{d\mathbf{a}}{dt} = a \sin t\, \mathbf{i} - a \cos t\, \mathbf{j}$$

$$\mathbf{v} \times \mathbf{a} = \begin{vmatrix} \mathbf{i} & \mathbf{j} & \mathbf{k} \\ -a \sin t & a \cos t & b \\ -a \cos t & -a \sin t & 0 \end{vmatrix} = ab \sin t\, \mathbf{i} - ab \cos t\, \mathbf{j} + a^2\mathbf{k}$$

$$|\mathbf{v} \times \mathbf{a}| = \sqrt{a^2 b^2 + a^4} = a\sqrt{a^2 + b^2}$$

$$(\mathbf{v} \times \mathbf{a}) \bullet \frac{d\mathbf{a}}{dt} = a^2 b \sin^2 t + a^2 b \cos^2 t = a^2 b.$$

Therefore we obtain

$$\hat{\mathbf{T}}(t) = \frac{\mathbf{v}}{v} = -\frac{a}{\sqrt{a^2 + b^2}} \sin t\, \mathbf{i} + \frac{a}{\sqrt{a^2 + b^2}} \cos t\, \mathbf{j} + \frac{b}{\sqrt{a^2 + b^2}}\mathbf{k}$$

$$\hat{\mathbf{B}}(t) = \frac{\mathbf{v} \times \mathbf{a}}{|\mathbf{v} \times \mathbf{a}|} = \frac{b}{\sqrt{a^2 + b^2}} \sin t\, \mathbf{i} - \frac{b}{\sqrt{a^2 + b^2}} \cos t\, \mathbf{j} + \frac{a}{\sqrt{a^2 + b^2}}\mathbf{k}$$

$$\hat{\mathbf{N}}(t) = \hat{\mathbf{B}} \times \hat{\mathbf{T}} = -\cos t\, \mathbf{i} - \sin t\, \mathbf{j}$$

$$\kappa(t) = \frac{|\mathbf{v} \times \mathbf{a}|}{v^3} = \frac{a\sqrt{a^2 + b^2}}{(a^2 + b^2)^{3/2}} = \frac{a}{a^2 + b^2}$$

$$\tau(t) = \frac{(\mathbf{v} \times \mathbf{a}) \bullet (d\mathbf{a}/dt)}{|\mathbf{v} \times \mathbf{a}|^2} = \frac{a^2 b}{a^2(a^2 + b^2)} = \frac{b}{a^2 + b^2}.$$

REMARK: Observe that κ and τ are both constant for a circular helix. In the above example, $\tau > 0$, (assuming that $b > 0$), which corresponds to the fact that the helix is *right-handed*. (See Fig. 5.2.4 in the previous section.) If you grasp the helix with your right hand so your fingers surround it in the direction of increasing t (counterclockwise, looking down from the positive z-axis), then your thumb also points in the axial direction corresponding to increasing t (the upwards direction). Had we started with a left-handed helix, such as

$$\mathbf{r} = a \sin t\, \mathbf{i} + a \cos t\, \mathbf{j} + bt\mathbf{k}, \qquad (b > 0),$$

we would have got $\tau = -b/(a^2 + b^2)$.

REMARK: Any curve with nonzero constant curvature and constant torsion must, in fact, be a circle (if the torsion is zero) or a circular helix (if the torsion is nonzero). This is a consequence of the Fundamental Theorem (Theorem 5.3.7.) See Exercises 14 and 15 at the end of this section.

Evolutes

The centre of curvature $\mathbf{r}_c(t)$ of a given curve can itself trace out another curve as t varies. This curve is called the **evolute** of the given curve $\mathbf{r}(t)$.

EXAMPLE 5.3.10   Find the evolute of the exponential spiral

$$\mathbf{r} = ae^{-t}\cos t\,\mathbf{i} + ae^{-t}\sin t\,\mathbf{j}.$$

SOLUTION   The curve is a plane curve so $\tau = 0$. We will take a shortcut to the curvature and the unit normal without calculating $\mathbf{v} \times \mathbf{a}$. First we calculate

$$\mathbf{v} = ae^{-t}\left(-(\cos t + \sin t)\mathbf{i} - (\sin t - \cos t)\mathbf{j}\right)$$

$$\frac{ds}{dt} = v = \sqrt{2}ae^{-t}$$

$$\hat{\mathbf{T}}(t) = \frac{1}{\sqrt{2}}\left(-(\cos t + \sin t)\mathbf{i} - (\sin t - \cos t)\mathbf{j}\right)$$

$$\frac{d\hat{\mathbf{T}}}{ds} = \frac{1}{(ds/dt)}\frac{d\hat{\mathbf{T}}}{dt} = \frac{1}{2ae^{-t}}\left((\sin t - \cos t)\mathbf{i} - (\cos t + \sin t)\mathbf{j}\right)$$

$$\kappa(t) = \left|\frac{d\hat{\mathbf{T}}}{ds}\right| = \frac{1}{\sqrt{2}ae^{-t}}.$$

It follows that the radius of curvature is $\rho(t) = \sqrt{2}ae^{-t}$. Since $d\hat{\mathbf{T}}/ds = \kappa\hat{\mathbf{N}}$, therefore $\hat{\mathbf{N}} = \rho(d\hat{\mathbf{T}}/ds)$. The centre of curvature is

$$\mathbf{r}_c(t) = \mathbf{r}(t) + \rho(t)\hat{\mathbf{N}}(t)$$

$$= \mathbf{r}(t) + \rho^2\frac{d\hat{\mathbf{T}}}{ds}$$

$$= ae^{-t}\left(\cos t\,\mathbf{i} + \sin t\,\mathbf{j}\right) + 2a^2e^{-2t}\frac{1}{2ae^{-t}}\left((\sin t - \cos t)\mathbf{i} - (\cos t + \sin t)\mathbf{j}\right)$$

$$= ae^{-t}\left(\sin t\,\mathbf{i} - \cos t\,\mathbf{j}\right)$$

$$= ae^{-t}\left(\cos(t - \frac{\pi}{2})\mathbf{i} + \sin(t - \frac{\pi}{2})\mathbf{j}\right).$$

Thus, interestingly, the evolute of the exponential spiral is the same exponential spiral rotated 90° clockwise in the plane. (See Fig. 5.3.5.)

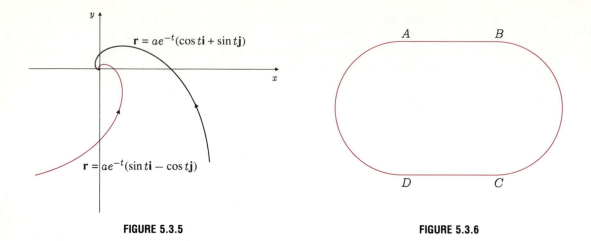

FIGURE 5.3.5   **FIGURE 5.3.6**

An Application to Track Design

Toy model trains frequently come with two kinds of track sections, straight and curved. The curved sections are arcs of a circle of radius R, and the track is intended to be laid out in the shape shown in Fig. 5.3.6; AB and CD are straight, and BC and DA are semicircles. The track looks smooth, but is it smooth enough?

The track is held together by friction and occasionally it can come apart as the train is racing around. It is especially likely to come apart at the points A, B, C and D. To see why, assume that the train is travelling at constant speed v. Then the tangential component of the acceleration, $(dv/dt)\hat{\mathbf{T}}$, is zero and the total acceleration is just the centripetal component, $\mathbf{a} = (v^2/\rho)\hat{\mathbf{N}}$. Evidently, $|\mathbf{a}| = 0$ along the straight sections, and $|\mathbf{a}| = v^2/R$ on the semicircular sections. Hence the acceleration is *discontinuous* at the points A, B, C and D, and the reactive force exerted by the train on the track is also discontinuous at these points. There is a "shock" or "jolt" as the train enters or leaves a curved part of the track. In order to avoid such stress points, tracks should be designed so that the curvature varies continuously from point to point.

EXAMPLE 5.3.11   Existing track along the negative x-axis, and along the ray $x = y$, $x \geq 1$, is to be joined smoothly by track along the curve $y = f(x)$, $0 \leq x \leq 1$, where $f(x)$ is a polynomial of degree as small as possible. Find $f(x)$ so that a train moving along the track will not experience discontinuous acceleration at the joins.

SOLUTION   The situation is shown in Fig. 5.3.7. The polynomial $f(x)$ must be chosen so that the track is continuous, has continuous slope, and has continuous curvature at $x = 0$ and $x = 1$. Since the curvature of $y = f(x)$ is $\kappa = f''(x)\left(1 + (f'(x))^2\right)^{-3/2}$, we need only arrange that f, f' and f'' take the same values at $x = 0$ and $x = 1$ that the straight sections do there:

$$f(0) = 0, \qquad f'(0) = 0, \qquad f''(0) = 0,$$
$$f(1) = 1, \qquad f'(1) = 1, \qquad f''(1) = 0.$$

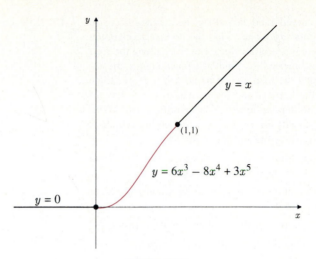

FIGURE 5.3.7

These six independent conditions suggest we should try a polynomial of degree five:

$$f(x) = A + Bx + Cx^2 + Dx^3 + Ex^4 + Fx^5$$
$$f'(x) = B + 2Cx + 3Dx^2 + 4Ex^3 + 5Fx^4$$
$$f''(x) = 2C + 6Dx + 12Ex^2 + 20Fx^3.$$

The three conditions at $x = 0$ imply that $A = B = C = 0$. Those at $x = 1$ imply that

$$D + \quad E + \quad F = f(1) = 1$$
$$3D + \quad 4E + \quad 5F = f'(1) = 1$$
$$6D + 12E + 20F = f''(1) = 0.$$

This system has solution $D = 6$, $E = -8$, $F = 3$, so we should use $f(x) = 6x^3 - 8x^4 + 3x^5$.

EXERCISES

In Exercises 1–4 find the unit tangent, normal and binormal vectors, and the curvature and torsion at a general point on the given curve.

1. $\mathbf{r} = t\mathbf{i} + \dfrac{t^2}{2}\mathbf{j} + \dfrac{t^3}{3}\mathbf{k}$

2. $\mathbf{r} = t\mathbf{i} + 2t\mathbf{j} + \sin t\,\mathbf{k}$

3. $\mathbf{r} = t(\cos t\,\mathbf{i} + \sin t\,\mathbf{j} + \mathbf{k})$

4. $\mathbf{r} = e^t(\cos t\,\mathbf{i} + \sin t\,\mathbf{j} + \mathbf{k})$

5. Find the unit tangent, normal and binormal, and the curvature and torsion for the curve

$$\mathbf{r} = \sin t\,\cos t\,\mathbf{i} + \sin^2 t\,\mathbf{j} + \cos t\,\mathbf{k}$$

at the points i) $t = 0$, and ii) $t = \pi/4$.

6. A particle moves on an elliptical path in the xy-plane so that its position at time t is $\mathbf{r} = a\cos t\mathbf{i} + b\sin t\mathbf{j}$. Find the tangential and normal components of its acceleration at time t. At what points is the tangential acceleration zero?

7. Find the maximum and minimum values for the curvature of the ellipse $x = a\cos t$, $y = b\sin t$, where $a > b > 0$.

8. A level, curved road lies along the curve $y = x^2$ in the horizontal xy-plane. Find the normal acceleration at position (x, x^2) of a vehicle travelling along the road with constant speed v_0. Find, as a function of x, the angle at which the road should be banked (i.e., the angle between the vertical and the normal to the surface of the road) so that the result of the centrifugal and gravitational $(-mg\mathbf{k})$ forces) forces acting on the vehicle is always normal to the surface of the road.

9. Find the curvature of the plane curve $y = e^x$ at x. Find the equation of the evolute of this curve.

10. Find the curvature of the plane polar graph $r = f(\theta)$ at a general point θ.

11. Find the curvature of the cardioid $r = a(1 - \cos\theta)$.

12. Show that if $\kappa(s) = 0$ for all s, then the curve $\mathbf{r} = \mathbf{r}(s)$ is a straight line.

13. Show that if $\tau(s) = 0$ for all s, then the curve $\mathbf{r} = \mathbf{r}(s)$ is a plane curve. (Hint: show that $\mathbf{r}(s)$ lies in the plane through $\mathbf{r}(0)$ with normal $\hat{\mathbf{B}}(0)$.)

14. Show that if $\kappa(s) = C$ is a positive constant, and $\tau(s) = 0$, for all s, then the curve $\mathbf{r} = \mathbf{r}(s)$ is a circle. (Hint: find a circle having the given constant curvature. Then use Theorem 5.3.7.

15. Show that if the curvature $\kappa(s)$ and the torsion $\tau(s)$ are both nonzero constants, then the curve $\mathbf{r} = \mathbf{r}(s)$ is a circular helix. (Hint: find a helix having the given curvature and torsion.)

16. Find the curve $\mathbf{r} = \mathbf{r}(t)$ for which $\kappa(t) = 1$ and $\tau(t) = 1$ for all t, and $\mathbf{r}(0) = \hat{\mathbf{T}}(0) = \mathbf{i}$, $\hat{\mathbf{N}}(0) = \mathbf{j}$, and $\hat{\mathbf{B}}(0) = \mathbf{k}$.

17. If the curve $\mathbf{r} = \mathbf{r}(t)$ satisfies

$$\frac{d\mathbf{r}}{dt} = \mathbf{c} \times \mathbf{r}(t),$$

where $\mathbf{c}$ is a constant vector, show that the curve is the circle in which the plane through $\mathbf{r}(0)$ normal to $\mathbf{c}$ intersects a sphere with radius $|\mathbf{r}(0)|$ centred at the origin.

18. Find the evolute of the circular helix $\mathbf{r} = a\cos t\, \mathbf{i} + a\sin t\, \mathbf{j} + bt\mathbf{k}$.

19. Find the evolute of the parabola $y = x^2$.

20. Find the evolute of the ellipse $x = 2\cos t$, $y = \sin t$.

21. Find the polynomial $f(x)$ of lowest degree so that track along $y = f(x)$ from $x = -1$ to $x = 1$ joins with existing straight tracks $y = -1$, $x \le -1$ and $y = 1$, $x \ge 1$ sufficiently smoothly that a train moving at constant speed will not experience discontinuous acceleration at the joins.

22. *Help out toy train manufacturers. Design a track segment $y = f(x)$, $-1 \le x \le 0$, to provide a jolt-free link between a straight track section $y = 1$, $x \le -1$, and a semicircular arc section $x^2 + y^2 = 1$, $x \ge 0$.

23. *If the position $\mathbf{r}$, velocity $\mathbf{v}$, and acceleration $\mathbf{a}$ of a moving particle satisfy $\mathbf{a}(t) = \lambda(t)\mathbf{r}(t) + \mu(t)\mathbf{v}(t)$, where $\lambda(t)$ and $\mu(t)$ are scalar functions of time t, and if $\mathbf{v} \times \mathbf{a} \neq \mathbf{0}$, show that the path of the particle lies in a plane.

5.4   KEPLER'S LAWS OF PLANETARY MOTION

The German mathematician and astronomer, Johannes Kepler (1571-1630), was a student and colleague of Danish astronomer Tycho Brahe (1546-1601), who, in a lifetime of observing the positions of planets without the aid of a telescope, compiled a vast amount of data, which Kepler analysed. Although Polish astronomer Nicolaus Copernicus (1473-1543) had postulated that the earth and other planets moved around the sun, the religious and philosophical climate in Europe at the end of the sixteenth century still favoured explaining the motion of heavenly bodies in terms of circular orbits around the earth. It was known that planets such as Mars could not move on circular orbits centred at the earth, but models were proposed in which they moved on other circles (epicycles) whose centres moved on circles centred at the earth.

Brahe's observations of Mars were sufficiently detailed that Kepler realized that no simple model based on circles could be made to conform very closely with the actual orbit. He was, however, able to fit a more general ellipse with one focus at the sun, and, based on this success and on Brahe's data on other planets, he formulated the following three laws of planetary motion.

5.4.1
Kepler's Laws

1. The planets move on elliptical orbits with the sun at one focus.
2. The radial line from the sun to a planet sweeps out equal areas in equal times.
3. The squares of the periods of revolution of the planets around the sun are proportional to the cubes of the major axes of their orbits.

The choice of ellipses was reasonable once it became clear that circles would not work. The properties of the conic sections were well understood, having been developed by the Greek mathematician Apollonius of Perga around 200 BC. Nevertheless, based, as it was, on observations rather than theory, Kepler's formulation of his laws without any causal explanation was a truly remarkable feat. The theoretical underpinnings came later when Newton derived the laws mathematically from his universal law of gravitation using his newly created calculus.

Kepler's statement of the third law actually says that the squares of the periods of revolution of the planets are proportional to the cubes of their mean distances from the sun. The mean distance of points on an ellipse from a focus of the ellipse is equal to the semi-major axis. (See Exercise 15 at the end of this section.) Therefore the two statements are equivalent.

Later in this section we will derive Kepler's laws from the gravitational law by an elegant method which exploits vector differentiation to the fullest. First, however, we need to attend to some preliminaries.

Ellipses in Polar Coordinates

The polar coordinates (r, θ) of a point in the plane whose distance from the origin is ε times its distance from the line $x = p$ (see Fig. 5.4.1) satisfy $r = \varepsilon(p - r \cos \theta)$, or

$$r = \frac{\ell}{1 + \varepsilon \cos \theta},$$

where $\ell = \varepsilon p$. For $0 \le \varepsilon < 1$ this equation represents an ellipse. (It is a circle if $\varepsilon = 0$.) Let us transform the equation to Cartesian coordinates:

$$x^2 + y^2 = r^2 = \varepsilon^2(p - r \cos \theta)^2 = \varepsilon^2(p - x)^2 = \varepsilon^2(p^2 - 2px + x^2).$$

With some algebraic manipulation this equation can be juggled into the form

$$\frac{\left(x + \dfrac{\varepsilon \ell}{1 - \varepsilon^2} \right)^2}{\left(\dfrac{\ell}{1 - \varepsilon^2} \right)^2} + \frac{y^2}{\left(\dfrac{\ell}{\sqrt{1 - \varepsilon^2}} \right)^2} = 1,$$

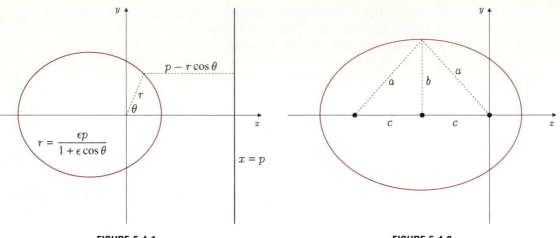

$$r = \frac{\epsilon p}{1 + \epsilon \cos \theta}$$

$p - r \cos \theta$

$x = p$

FIGURE 5.4.1

FIGURE 5.4.2

which should be immediately recognized as an ellipse with **centre** at the point $\left(-\varepsilon\ell/(1 - \varepsilon^2), 0\right)$, and **semi-major axis** a and **semi-minor axis** b given by

5.4.2
Semi-major and
Semi-minor Axes

$$a = \frac{\ell}{1 - \varepsilon^2}, \qquad b = \frac{\ell}{\sqrt{1 - \varepsilon^2}}.$$

Since the sum of the distances of any point on the ellipse from the two **foci** is constant, $2a$, the distance between the foci of the ellipse is $2c$, where

5.4.3
Semi-focal Separation

$$c = \sqrt{a^2 - b^2} = \frac{\ell\varepsilon}{1 - \varepsilon^2} = \varepsilon a.$$

(See Fig. 5.4.2.) Since the centre of the ellipse is at $(-c, 0)$, the foci are at the origin and the point $(-2c, 0)$. The number ε is called the **eccentricity** of the ellipse. (If $\varepsilon = 0$ then $c = 0$ and the ellipse is a circle.) The number ℓ is called the **semi-latus rectum** of the ellipse; the latus rectum is the width measured along the line through a focus, perpendicular to the major axis.

REMARK: The polar equation $r = \ell/(1 + \varepsilon \cos \theta)$ represents a *bounded* curve only if $\varepsilon < 1$: in this case we have $\ell/(1+\varepsilon) \le r \le \ell/(1-\varepsilon)$ for all directions θ. If $\varepsilon = 1$ the equation represents a parabola, and if $\varepsilon > 1$ a hyperbola. It is possible for objects to travel on parabolic or hyperbolic orbits, but they will approach the sun only once, rather than continue to cycle around it. Some comets have hyperbolic orbits.

Polar Components of Velocity and Acceleration

Let $\mathbf{r}(t)$ be the position vector at time t of a particle P moving in the xy-plane. We construct two unit vectors at P, the vector $\hat{\mathbf{r}}$ points in the direction of the position vector $\mathbf{r}$, and the vector $\hat{\boldsymbol{\theta}}$ is rotated 90° counterclockwise from $\hat{\mathbf{r}}$. (See Fig. 5.4.3.) If P has polar coordinates (r, θ) then $\hat{\mathbf{r}}$ points in the direction of increasing r at P, and $\hat{\boldsymbol{\theta}}$ points in the direction of increasing θ. Evidently

5.4.4

Polar Basis Vectors
at (r, θ)

$$\hat{\mathbf{r}} = \cos \theta \, \mathbf{i} + \sin \theta \, \mathbf{j}$$
$$\hat{\boldsymbol{\theta}} = -\sin \theta \, \mathbf{i} + \cos \theta \, \mathbf{j}.$$

Note that $\hat{\mathbf{r}}$ and $\hat{\boldsymbol{\theta}}$ do not depend on r but only on θ:

$$\frac{d\hat{\mathbf{r}}}{d\theta} = \hat{\boldsymbol{\theta}}, \qquad \frac{d\hat{\boldsymbol{\theta}}}{d\theta} = -\hat{\mathbf{r}}.$$

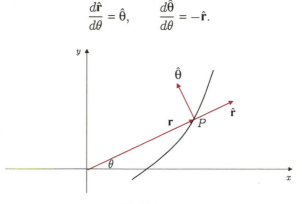

FIGURE 5.4.3

The pair $\{\hat{\mathbf{r}}, \hat{\boldsymbol{\theta}}\}$ form a reference frame (a basis) at P so that vectors in the plane can be expressed in terms of these two unit vectors. The frame varies from point to point, so we must remember that $\hat{\mathbf{r}}$ and $\hat{\boldsymbol{\theta}}$ are both functions of t. In terms of this moving frame, the position $\mathbf{r}(t)$ of P can be expressed very simply:

$$\mathbf{r} = r\hat{\mathbf{r}},$$

where $r = r(t) = |\mathbf{r}(t)|$ is the distance from P to the origin at time t.

We are going to differentiate this equation with respect to t in order to express the velocity and acceleration of P in terms of the moving frame. Along the path of motion, $\mathbf{r}$ can be regarded as a function of either θ or t; θ is itself a function of t. So as to avoid confusion, let us adopt a notation which is used extensively in mechanics and which resembles the notation originally used by Newton in his calculus; we denote the time derivative of a variable by a dot over that variable. Thus $\dot{u}$ means du/dt and $\ddot{u}$ means d^2u/dt^2. First let us record the time derivatives of the vectors $\hat{\mathbf{r}}$ and $\hat{\boldsymbol{\theta}}$:

$$\dot{\hat{\mathbf{r}}} = \frac{d\hat{\mathbf{r}}}{d\theta}\frac{d\theta}{dt} = \dot{\theta}\hat{\boldsymbol{\theta}}$$

$$\dot{\hat{\boldsymbol{\theta}}} = \frac{d\hat{\boldsymbol{\theta}}}{d\theta}\frac{d\theta}{dt} = -\dot{\theta}\hat{\mathbf{r}}.$$

Now the velocity of P is

$$\mathbf{v} = \dot{\mathbf{r}} = \frac{d}{dt}(r\hat{\mathbf{r}}) = \dot{r}\hat{\mathbf{r}} + r\dot{\theta}\hat{\boldsymbol{\theta}}.$$

5.4.5
Polar Components
of Velocity

> The **radial component of velocity** is $\dot{r}$.
> The **transverse component of velocity** is $r\dot{\theta}$.

Since $\hat{\mathbf{r}}$ and $\hat{\boldsymbol{\theta}}$ are perpendicular unit vectors, the speed of P is given by

$$v = |\mathbf{v}| = \sqrt{\dot{r}^2 + r^2\dot{\theta}^2}.$$

Similarly, the acceleration of P may be expressed in terms of radial and transverse components:

$$\begin{aligned}
\mathbf{a} = \dot{\mathbf{v}} = \ddot{\mathbf{r}} &= \frac{d}{dt}(\dot{r}\hat{\mathbf{r}} + r\dot{\theta}\hat{\boldsymbol{\theta}}) \\
&= \ddot{r}\hat{\mathbf{r}} + \dot{r}\dot{\theta}\hat{\boldsymbol{\theta}} + \dot{r}\dot{\theta}\hat{\boldsymbol{\theta}} + r\ddot{\theta}\hat{\boldsymbol{\theta}} - r\dot{\theta}^2\hat{\mathbf{r}} \\
&= (\ddot{r} - r\dot{\theta}^2)\hat{\mathbf{r}} + (r\ddot{\theta} + 2\dot{r}\dot{\theta})\hat{\boldsymbol{\theta}}.
\end{aligned}$$

5.4.6
Polar Components
of Acceleration

> The **radial component of acceleration** is $\ddot{r} - r\dot{\theta}^2$.
> The **transverse component of acceleration** is $r\ddot{\theta} + 2\dot{r}\dot{\theta}$.

Derivation of Kepler's Laws

The planets and the sun move around their common centre of mass. Since the sun is vastly more massive than the planets that centre of mass is quite close to the sun. For example, the joint centre of mass of the sun and the earth lies inside the sun. For the following derivation we will take the sun and a planet as "point masses" and consider the sun to be fixed at the origin.

Suppose that an object of mass m moves through 3-space under the influence of a **central force** directed towards (or away from) a fixed point, and having magnitude $mf(r)$ depending on the distance r from the object to that point. We take the origin at that point, but will not specify the direction of the coordinate axes until later. We are especially interested in the case where the origin is at the sun and the object is a planet, but the model that we are developing applies to other situations as well. If the position of the object at time t is $\mathbf{r}(t)$ then the force on it can be expressed conveniently in terms of the unit vector $\hat{\mathbf{r}} = \mathbf{r}/r$:

$$\mathbf{F} = -mf(r)\hat{\mathbf{r}} = -m\frac{f(r)}{r}\mathbf{r}.$$

(We have included the minus sign so that $\mathbf{F}$ would be an attraction towards the origin when $f(r) > 0$. For a repulsive force use a negative function f.) For gravitational attraction, Newton's law of gravitation requires that

$$f(r) = \frac{k}{r^2},$$

but for the time being we will see what we can learn about the motion without assuming this inverse square behavior for the force.

According to Newton's second law of motion ($\mathbf{F} = m\mathbf{a} = m\dot{\mathbf{v}}$) the acceleration of the object will be given by

$$\dot{\mathbf{v}} = -\frac{f(r)}{r}\mathbf{r}.$$

We are going to show that this equation implies that the path (orbit) of the object lies in a plane. Observe that

$$\frac{d}{dt}(\mathbf{r} \times \mathbf{v}) = \dot{\mathbf{r}} \times \mathbf{v} + \mathbf{r} \times \dot{\mathbf{v}} = \mathbf{v} \times \mathbf{v} - \frac{f(r)}{r}\mathbf{r} \times \mathbf{r} = \mathbf{0}.$$

It follows that $\mathbf{r} \times \mathbf{v} = \mathbf{C}_1$ is a constant vector; it is the angular momentum per unit mass of the object. Angular momentum is therefore conserved for motion under a central force. Let $h = |\mathbf{C}_1|$ and choose the direction of the z-axis so that $\mathbf{C}_1 = h\mathbf{k}$. Thus

$$\mathbf{r} \times \mathbf{v} = h\mathbf{k}.$$

Since the position vector $\mathbf{r}$ is perpendicular to $\mathbf{r} \times \mathbf{v}$, and hence to $\mathbf{k}$, the path of the object lies in the xy-plane. Still without specifying the directions of the x- and y-axes in that plane, let us write the position and velocity of the object in terms of their radial and transverse components:

$$\mathbf{r} = r\hat{\mathbf{r}}$$

$$\mathbf{v} = \dot{r}\hat{\mathbf{r}} + r\dot{\theta}\hat{\boldsymbol{\theta}}.$$

(Although we do not know what θ is without fixing the direction of the x-axis, we do know what r, $\dot{r}$, and $\dot{\theta}$ are since we know where the origin is.) Taking the cross product of these expressions, and noting that $\hat{\mathbf{r}} \times \hat{\boldsymbol{\theta}} = \mathbf{k}$, we get

$$h\mathbf{k} = \mathbf{r} \times \mathbf{v} = r\dot{r}\hat{\mathbf{r}} \times \hat{\mathbf{r}} + r^2\dot{\theta}\hat{\mathbf{r}} \times \hat{\boldsymbol{\theta}} = r^2\dot{\theta}\mathbf{k}.$$

Therefore,

5.4.7
Kepler's Second Law

$$r^2\dot{\theta} = h.$$

This formula is equivalent to Kepler's second law; if $A(t)$ is the area in the plane of motion bounded by the orbit and radial lines $\theta = \theta_0$ and $\theta = \theta(t)$ then

$$A(t) = \frac{1}{2} \int_{\theta_0}^{\theta(t)} r^2 \, d\theta,$$

so that

$$\frac{dA}{dt} = \frac{dA}{d\theta}\frac{d\theta}{dt} = \frac{1}{2}r^2\dot{\theta} = \frac{h}{2}.$$

Thus area is being swept out at the constant rate $h/2$. Note that this law does not depend on the inverse square nature of the gravitational force, nor even on the fact that it is an attraction rather than a repulsion. It depends only on the fact that the force is central.

Now let us specialize to the gravitational case where $f(r) = k/r^2$. Observe that

$$\frac{d\mathbf{v}}{d\theta} = \frac{\dot{\mathbf{v}}}{\dot{\theta}} = \frac{-\dfrac{k}{r^2}\hat{\mathbf{r}}}{\dfrac{h}{r^2}} = -\frac{k}{h}\hat{\mathbf{r}}.$$

Since $d\hat{\theta}/d\theta = -\hat{\mathbf{r}}$, we can integrate the differential equation above to find $\mathbf{v}$:

$$\mathbf{v} = -\frac{k}{h}\int \hat{\mathbf{r}}\, d\theta = \frac{k}{h}\hat{\theta} + \mathbf{C}_2,$$

where $\mathbf{C}_2$ is a vector constant of integration. Therefore,

5.4.8
Hamilton's Theorem

$$|\mathbf{v} - \mathbf{C}_2| = \frac{k}{h}.$$

This result, known as **Hamilton's theorem**, says that as a planet moves around its orbit, its velocity vector (when positioned with its tail at the origin) traces out a *circle*.

Recall that so far we have specified only the position of the origin and the direction of the z-axis. Therefore the xy-plane is determined, but not the directions of the x-axis or the y-axis. Let us choose these axes in the xy-plane so that $\mathbf{C}_2$ is in the direction of the y-axis; say $\mathbf{C}_2 = (\varepsilon k/h)\mathbf{j}$ where ε is a positive constant. We therefore have

$$\mathbf{v} = \frac{k}{h}(\hat{\theta} + \varepsilon\mathbf{j}).$$

The position of the x-axis is now determined by the fact the three vectors $\mathbf{i}$, $\mathbf{j}$, and $\mathbf{k}$ are mutually perpendicular and form a right-handed basis. We calculate $\mathbf{r} \times \mathbf{v}$ again. Remember that $\mathbf{r} = r\cos\theta\mathbf{i} + r\sin\theta\mathbf{j}$, and also $\mathbf{r} = r\hat{\mathbf{r}}$:

$$h\mathbf{k} = \mathbf{r} \times \mathbf{v} = \frac{k}{h}(r\hat{\mathbf{r}} \times \hat{\theta} + r\varepsilon\cos\theta\mathbf{i} \times \mathbf{j} + r\varepsilon\sin\theta\mathbf{j} \times \mathbf{j})$$

$$= \frac{k}{h}r(1 + \varepsilon\cos\theta)\mathbf{k}.$$

Thus $h = \dfrac{kr}{h}(1 + \varepsilon \cos \theta)$, or

5.4.9
Polar Equation
of the Orbit.

$$r = \frac{h^2/k}{1 + \varepsilon \cos \theta}.$$

This is a polar conic, and assuming $\varepsilon < 1$ it is an ellipse with one focus at the origin (the sun) and with parameters

5.4.10
Parameters of
the Orbit

$$\ell = \frac{h^2}{k} \qquad \text{(semi-latus rectum)}$$

$$a = \frac{h^2}{k(1 - \varepsilon^2)} \qquad \text{(semi-major axis)}$$

$$b = \frac{h^2}{k\sqrt{1 - \varepsilon^2}} \qquad \text{(semi-minor axis)}$$

$$c = \sqrt{a^2 - b^2} = \frac{\varepsilon h^2}{k(1 - \varepsilon^2)}. \qquad \text{(semi-focal separation)}$$

We have deduced Kepler's first law. The choices we made for the coordinate axes result in **perihelion** (the point on the orbit which is closest to the sun) being on the positive x-axis ($\theta = 0$).

We can obtain Kepler's third law from the other two as follows. Since the radial line from the sun to a planet sweeps out area at a constant rate $h/2$, the total area A enclosed by the orbit is $A = (h/2)T$ where T is the period of revolution. The area of an ellipse with semiaxes a and b is $A = \pi ab$, so

$$T^2 = \frac{4}{h^2}A^2 = \frac{4}{h^2}\pi^2 a^2 b^2.$$

However, $b^2 = h^4/(k^2(1 - \varepsilon^2)) = h^2 a/k$. Therefore,

5.4.11
Kepler's Third Law

$$T^2 = \frac{4\pi^2}{k}a^3$$

The constant $4\pi^2/k$ does not depend on the particular planet (k depends on the mass of the sun and a universal gravitational constant) so the square of the period is proportional to the length, $2a$, of the major axis of the elliptical orbit. (Modern astronomical data shows that T^2/a^3 varies by only about three tenths of one percent over the nine known planets.)

REMARK: Solving the equation of motion $\mathbf{F} = m\ddot{\mathbf{r}}$ to find the orbit of a planet requires two integrations. In the above derivation we exploited properties of the cross product to make these integrations easy. More traditional derivations of Kepler's laws usually begin with separating the radial and transverse components in the equation of motion:

$$\ddot{r} - r\dot{\theta}^2 = -f(r) = -\frac{k}{r^2}, \qquad r\ddot{\theta} + 2\dot{r}\dot{\theta} = 0.$$

The second of these equations implies that $r^2\dot{\theta} = h$ = constant, which is Kepler's second law. This can be used to eliminate θ from the first equation to give

$$\ddot{r} - \frac{h^2}{r^3} = -\frac{k}{r^2}.$$

Therefore

$$\frac{d}{dt}\left(\frac{\dot{r}^2}{2} + \frac{h^2}{2r^2}\right) = \dot{r}\left(\ddot{r} - \frac{h^2}{r^3}\right) = -\frac{k}{r^2}\dot{r}.$$

If we integrate this equation we obtain

**5.4.12
Conservation
of Energy**

$$\frac{1}{2}\left(\dot{r}^2 + \frac{h^2}{r^2}\right) - \frac{k}{r} = K.$$

This is a **conservation of energy** law. The first term on the left is $v^2/2$, the kinetic energy (per unit mass) of the planet. The term $-k/r$ is the potential energy per unit mass. It is difficult to integrate this equation and to find r as a function of t. In any event, we really want r as a function of θ so that we can recognize that we have an ellipse. A way to obtain this is suggested in Exercise 16 below.

REMARK: The procedure used above to demonstrate Kepler's laws in fact shows that if any object moves under the influence of a force which attracts it towards the origin (or repels it away from the origin) and has magnitude proportional to the reciprocal of the square of distance from the origin, then the object must move in a plane orbit whose shape is a conic section. If the total energy K in the Remark above is negative, then the orbit is *bounded* and must therefore be an ellipse. If $K = 0$, the orbit is a parabola. If $K > 0$, then the orbit is a hyperbola. Hyperbolic orbits are typical for repulsive forces, but may also occur for attractions if the object has high enough velocity (exceeding "escape velocity") See Exercise 20 below for an example.

EXERCISES

1. Fill in the details of the calculation suggested in the text to transform the polar equation of an ellipse, $r = \ell/(1+\varepsilon\cos\theta)$ where $0 < \varepsilon < 1$, to Cartesian coordinates in a form showing the centre and semi-axes explicitly.

2. A particle moves on the circle with polar equation $r = k$. ($k > 0$). What are the radial and transverse components of its velocity and acceleration? Show that the transverse component of the acceleration is equal to the rate of change of the speed of the particle.

3. Find the radial and transverse components of velocity and acceleration of a particle moving at unit speed along the exponential spiral $r = e^\theta$. Express your answers in terms of θ.

4. If a particle moves along the polar curve $r = \theta$ under the influence of a central force attracting it to the origin, find the magnitude of the acceleration as a function of r and the speed of the particle.

5.*A particle moves along the curve $2y = x^2 - 1$ in such a way that its acceleration is always directed towards the origin. Show that its speed is proportional to $1/\sqrt{r}$, and that the magnitude of its acceleration is proportional to $1/r^2$, where r is its distance from the origin.

6. The mean distance from the earth to the sun is approximately 150 million kilometers. Halley's Comet approaches perihelion (comes closest to the sun) in its elliptical orbit approximately every 76 years. Estimate the major axis of the orbit of Halley's Comet.

7. The mean distance from the moon to the earth is about 385,000 km, and its period of revolution around the earth is about 29 days. At approximately what distance from the centre of the earth, and in what plane, should a communications satellite be inserted into circular orbit if it must remain directly above the the same position on the earth at all times?

8. An asteroid is in a circular orbit around the sun. If its period of revolution is T find the radius of the orbit.

9.*If the asteroid in the previous exercise is instantaneously stopped in its orbit it will fall towards the sun. How long will it take to get there? Hint: you can do this question easily if instead you regard the asteroid as *almost* stopped, so that it goes into a highly eccentric elliptical orbit whose major axis is a bit greater than the radius of the original circular orbit.

10.*Suppose that a planet is travelling at speed v_0 at an instant when it is at distance r_0 from the sun. Show that the period of the planet's orbit is

$$T = \frac{2\pi}{\sqrt{k}}\left(\frac{2}{r_0} - \frac{v_0^2}{k}\right)^{-3/2}.$$

Hint: The quantity $\dfrac{k}{r} - \dfrac{1}{2}v^2$ is constant at all points of the orbit as shown in the discussion preceding Box 5.4.12. Find the value of this expression in terms of the semi-major axis, a, at perihelion (the point where the orbit is closest to the sun).

11. Show that the orbital speed of a planet is constant if and only if the orbit is circular. Hint: use the energy identity 5.4.12.

12.*Find the eccentricity of an asteroid's orbit if the asteroid's speed at perihelion is twice its speed at aphelion. (Aphelion is the point on the orbit farthest from the sun.)

13.*As a result of a collision, an asteroid originally in a circular orbit about the sun suddenly has its velocity cut in half, so that it falls into an elliptical orbit with maximum distance from the sun equal to the radius of the original circular orbit. Find the eccentricity of its new orbit.

14.*A planet has an elliptical orbit of eccentricity ε. If its speed at perihelion is v_p find its speed at aphelion (the point where it is farthest from the sun). (Hint: $r^2\dot\theta = h$ is constant over the orbit.)

15.*The sum of the distances from a point P on an ellipse $\mathcal{E}$ to the foci of $\mathcal{E}$ is the constant $2a$, the length of the major axis of the ellipse. Use this fact in a *geometric* argument to show that the mean distance from points P to one focus of $\mathcal{E}$ is a. That is, show that

$$\frac{1}{c(\mathcal{E})}\int_{\mathcal{E}} r\,ds = a,$$

where $c(\mathcal{E})$ is the circumference of $\mathcal{E}$ and r is the distance from a point on $\mathcal{E}$ to one focus.

16.*The result of eliminating θ between the equations for the radial and transverse components of acceleration for a planet is

$$\ddot{r} - \frac{h^2}{r^3} = -\frac{k}{r^2}.$$

Show that the change of dependent and independent variables:

$$r(t) = \frac{1}{u(\theta)}, \qquad \theta = \theta(t),$$

transforms this equation to the simpler equation

$$\frac{d^2u}{d\theta^2} + u = \frac{k}{h^2}.$$

Show that the solution of this equation is $u = (k/h^2)\big(1 + \varepsilon \cos(\theta - \theta_0)\big)$ where ε and θ_0 are constants. Hence show that the orbit is elliptical if $|\varepsilon| < 1$.

17.*Use the technique of the previous exercise to find the trajectory of an object of unit mass attracted to the origin by a force of magnitude $f(r) = k/r^3$. Are there any orbits which do not approach infinity or the origin as $t \to \infty$?

18. Use the Conservation of Energy formula from Box 5.4.12 to show that if $K < 0$, the orbit must be bounded; i.e. it cannot get arbitrarily far away from the origin.

19.*If $\varepsilon > 1$ then the equation $r = \ell/(1 + \varepsilon \cos \theta)$ represents a hyperbola rather than an ellipse. Sketch the hyperbola, find its centre and the directions of its asymptotes, and determine its semi-transverse axis, its semi-conjugate axis, and semi-focal separation in terms of ℓ and ε. (See Appendix I for definitions of terms.)

20.*A meteor travels from infinity on a hyperbolic orbit passing near the sun. At very large distance from the sun it has speed v_∞. The asymptotes of its orbit pass at perpendicular distance D from the sun. Show that the angle δ through which the meteor's path is deflected by the gravitational attraction of the sun is given by

$$\cot\left(\frac{\delta}{2}\right) = \frac{Dv_\infty^2}{k}.$$

(Hint: you will need the result of the previous exercise.) The same analysis, and result, holds for electrostatic attraction or repulsion; $f(r) = \pm k/r^2$ in that case also. The constant k depends on the charges of two particles and r is the distance between them.

CHAPTER 6

Vector Fields

This chapter and the next are concerned mainly with vector-valued functions of a vector variable, typically functions whose domains and ranges lie in the plane or in 3-space. Such functions are frequently called *vector fields*. Applications of vector fields frequently involve integrals taken, not along axes or over regions in the plane or 3-space, but rather over curves and surfaces. We will introduce such line and surface integrals in this chapter. The next chapter will be devoted developing analogues of the Fundamental Theorem of Calculus for integrals of vector fields.

6.1   VECTOR AND SCALAR FIELDS

In Chapters 2–4 we extended the concepts of single-variable calculus to scalar-valued functions of a vector variable (that is, functions of several real variables), and in Chapter 5 we considered vector-valued functions of a single (scalar) variable, that is, curves. It would appear that the time has come to talk about vector-valued functions of a vector variable. In general, this would mean studying functions from $\mathbb{R}^m$ to $\mathbb{R}^n$. However, we do not intend to be this general; we will restrict our attention to cases where m and n are 2 or 3, where the most interesting applications arise.

A function whose domain and range are subsets of Euclidean 3-space, $\mathbb{R}^3$, is called a **vector field.** Thus a vector field, $\mathbf{F}$, associates a vector $\mathbf{F}(x, y, z)$ with each point (x, y, z) in its domain. The three components of $\mathbf{F}$ are scalar-valued (real-valued) functions $F_1(x, y, z)$, $F_2(x, y, z)$, and $F_3(x, y, z)$, and $\mathbf{F}(x, y, z)$ can be expressed in terms of the standard basis in $\mathbb{R}^3$ as

$$\mathbf{F}(x, y, z) = F_1(x, y, z)\mathbf{i} + F_2(x, y, z)\mathbf{j} + F_3(x, y, z)\mathbf{k}.$$

(Note that the subscripts here represent *components* of a vector, *not* partial derivatives.) If $F_3(x, y, z) = 0$ and F_1 and F_2 are independent of z then $\mathbf{F}$ reduces to

$$\mathbf{F}(x, y) = F_1(x, y)\mathbf{i} + F_2(x, y)\mathbf{j}$$

and so is called a **plane vector field** or a vector field in the xy-plane. We will frequently make use of position vectors in the arguments of vector fields. The position vector of (x, y, z) is $\mathbf{r} = x\mathbf{i} + y\mathbf{j} + z\mathbf{k}$, and we can write $\mathbf{F}(\mathbf{r})$ as a shorthand for $\mathbf{F}(x, y, z)$. In the context of discussion of vector fields, a scalar-valued function of a vector variable is frequently called a **scalar field.** Thus the components of a vector field are scalar fields.

Many of the results we prove about vector fields require that the field be smooth in some sense. We will call a vector field **smooth** wherever its component scalar fields have continuous partial derivatives of all orders. (For most purposes, however, second order would be sufficient.)

Vector fields arise in many situations in applied mathematics. Let us list some:

a) The gravitational field $\mathbf{F}(x, y, z)$ due to some object is the force of attraction that object exerts on a unit mass located at position (x, y, z).

b) The electrostatic force field $\mathbf{E}(x, y, z)$ due to an electrically charged object is the force that the object would exert on a unit charge at position (x, y, z). (The force may be either an attraction or a repulsion.)

c) The velocity field $\mathbf{v}(x, y, z)$ in a moving fluid (or solid) is the velocity of motion of the particle at position (x, y, z). If the motion is not "steady state" then the velocity field will also depend on time: $\mathbf{v} = \mathbf{v}(x, y, z, t)$.

d) The gradient $\nabla f(x, y, z)$, of any scalar field f gives the direction and magnitude of the greatest rate of increase of f at (x, y, z). In particular, a *temperature gradient*, $\nabla T(x, y, z)$, is a vector field giving the direction and magnitude of the greatest rate of increase of temperature T at the point (x, y, z) in a heat conducting medium. *Pressure gradients* provide similar information about the variation of pressure in a fluid such as an air mass or an ocean.

e) The unit radial and unit transverse vectors $\hat{\mathbf{r}}$ and $\hat{\boldsymbol{\theta}}$ are examples of vector fields in the xy-plane. Both are defined at all points of the plane except the origin.

EXAMPLE 6.1.1   The gravitational force field due to a point mass m located at point P_0 having position $\mathbf{r}_0$ is

$$\mathbf{F}(x, y, z) = \mathbf{F}(\mathbf{r}) = \frac{-km}{|\mathbf{r} - \mathbf{r}_0|^3}(\mathbf{r} - \mathbf{r}_0)$$

$$= -km \frac{(x - x_0)\mathbf{i} + (y - y_0)\mathbf{j} + (z - z_0)\mathbf{k}}{\left((x - x_0)^2 + (y - y_0)^2 + (z - z_0)^2\right)^{3/2}}.$$

Observe that $\mathbf{F}$ points towards the point $\mathbf{r}_0$ and has magnitude

$$|\mathbf{F}| = km / |\mathbf{r} - \mathbf{r}_0|^2.$$

Some of the vectors in a plane section of the field are shown graphically in Fig. 6.1.1.

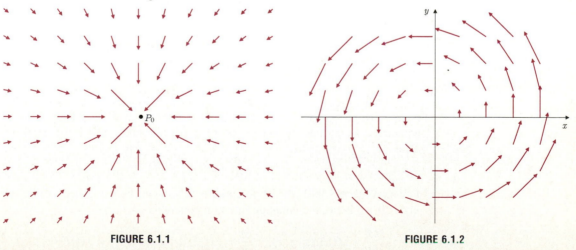

FIGURE 6.1.1   FIGURE 6.1.2

EXAMPLE 6.1.2   The velocity field of a solid rotating about the z-axis with angular velocity $\Omega = \Omega\mathbf{k}$ is (see Box 5.1.8)

$$\mathbf{v}(x, y, z) = \mathbf{v}(\mathbf{r}) = \Omega \times \mathbf{r} = -\Omega y\mathbf{i} + \Omega x\mathbf{j}.$$

Being the same in all planes normal to the z-axis, $\mathbf{v}$ may be regarded as a plane vector field. Some vectors of the field are shown in Fig. 6.1.2.

Field Lines (Integral Curves)

The graphical representation of vector fields such as those shown in Figures 6.1.1 and 6.1.2, and the wind velocity field over a hill shown in Fig. 6.1.3 suggest a pattern of motion through space or in the plane. Whether or not the field is a velocity field, we can interpret it as such and ask what path will be followed by a particle, initially at some point, whose velocity is given by the field. The path will be a curve to which the field is tangent at every point. Such curves are called **field lines** or **integral curves** for the given vector field. In the specific case where the vector field gives the velocity in a fluid flow, the field lines are called **streamlines** of the flow; some of these are shown for the air flow in Fig. 6.1.3. For a force field the field lines are called **lines of force.**

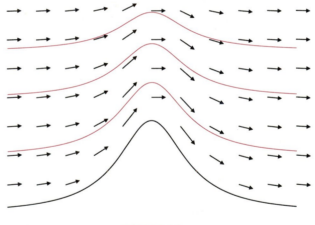

FIGURE 6.1.3

The field lines of $\mathbf{F}$ do not depend on the magnitude of $\mathbf{F}$ at any point, but only on the direction of the field. If the field line through some point has parametric equation $\mathbf{r} = \mathbf{r}(t)$ then its tangent vector $d\mathbf{r}/dt$ must be parallel to $\mathbf{F}(\mathbf{r}(t))$ for all t. Thus

$$\frac{d\mathbf{r}}{dt} = \lambda(t)\mathbf{F}(\mathbf{r}(t)).$$

For *some* vector fields this differential equation can be integrated to find the field lines. If we break the equation into components,

$$\frac{dx}{dt} = \lambda(t)F_1(x, y, z), \quad \frac{dy}{dt} = \lambda(t)F_2(x, y, z), \quad \frac{dz}{dt} = \lambda(t)F_3(x, y, z),$$

we can obtain equivalent differential expressions for $\lambda(t)\,dt$ and hence write the differential equation for the field lines in the form

6.1.3
Differential Equation
for Field Lines

$$\frac{dx}{F_1(x,y,z)} = \frac{dy}{F_2(x,y,z)} = \frac{dz}{F_3(x,y,z)}.$$

If multiplication of these differential equations by some function puts them in the form

$$P(x)\,dx = Q(y)\,dy = R(z)\,dz$$

then we can integrate all three expressions to find the field lines.

EXAMPLE 6.1.4   The field lines for the gravitational force field of Example 6.1.1 are given by

$$\frac{dx}{x - x_0} = \frac{dy}{y - y_0} = \frac{dz}{z - z_0}.$$

Integrating all three expressions leads to

$$\ln|x - x_0| + \ln C_1 = \ln|y - y_0| + \ln C_2 = \ln|z - z_0| + \ln C_3,$$

that is,

$$C_1(x - x_0) = C_2(y - y_0) = C_3(z - z_0).$$

The field lines are all straight lines through the point (x_0, y_0, z_0). (This is a two-parameter family of lines — any one of the constants C_i which is nonzero can be divided out of the equations above.)

EXAMPLE 6.1.5   The field lines of the velocity field $\mathbf{v} = \Omega(-y\mathbf{i} + x\mathbf{j})$ of Example 6.1.2 are given by

$$\frac{dx}{-y} = \frac{dy}{x}.$$

Thus $x\,dx + y\,dy = 0$ and the field lines are $x^2 + y^2 = C$, circles centred at the origin in the xy-plane. If we regard $\mathbf{v}$ as a vector field in 3-space, we find that the field lines are horizontal circles centred on the z-axis

$$\begin{cases} x^2 + y^2 = C_1 \\ z = C_2. \end{cases}$$

EXERCISES

In Exercises 1–8 sketch the given plane vector field and determine its field lines.

1. $F(x, y) = x i + x j$

2. $F(x, y) = x i + y j$

3. $F(x, y) = y i + x j$

4. $F(x, y) = i + \sin x \, j$

5. $F(x, y) = e^x i + e^{-x} j$

6. $F(x, y) = \nabla(x^2 - y)$

7. $F(x, y) = \nabla \ln(x^2 + y^2)$

8. $F(x, y) = \cos y \, i - \cos x \, j$

In Exercises 9–12 describe the streamlines of the given velocity fields.

9. $v(x, y, z) = y i - y j - y k$

10. $v(x, y, z) = x i + y j - x k$

11. $v(x, y, z) = y i - x j + k$

12. $v(x, y, z) = \dfrac{x i + y j}{(1 + z^2)(x^2 + y^2)}$

13. Let $\hat{r}$ and $\hat{\theta}$ be the unit vectors in the direction of increasing r and θ (respectively) at the point with polar coordinates (r, θ). (See Box 5.4.4.) Show that the polar curve $r = e^{\theta}$ is a field line of the vector field $F = \hat{r} + \hat{\theta}$.

14. Show that the polar curve $r = a\theta$ is a field line of the vector field $F = a\hat{r} + a\theta\hat{\theta}$.

6.2   CONSERVATIVE FIELDS

Since the gradient of a scalar field is a vector field it is natural to ask whether all vector fields can be expressed as gradients. Given a vector field $F(x, y, z)$, does there exist a scalar field $\phi(x, y, z)$ such that

$$F(x, y, z) = \nabla\phi(x, y, z) = \frac{\partial \phi}{\partial x} i + \frac{\partial \phi}{\partial y} j + \frac{\partial \phi}{\partial z} k \, ?$$

The answer in general is "no." Only special vector fields can be written in this way. If such a ϕ exists then we call F a **conservative** vector field, and call ϕ a **potential function** for F. Like antiderivatives, potential functions are not determined uniquely; arbitrary constants can be added to them. Note that F is **conservative in a domain** D if and only if $F = \nabla\phi$ at *every* point of D; the potential ϕ cannot have any singular points in D.

Being scalar fields rather than vector fields, potential functions for conservative vector fields are easier to manipulate algebraically than are the vector fields themselves. For instance, a sum of potential functions is the potential function for the sum of the corresponding vector fields. A vector field can always be computed from its potential function by taking the gradient.

EXAMPLE 6.2.1   The gravitational field $F(r) = -km(r - r_0)/|r - r_0|^3$ of Example 6.1.1 is conservative wherever it is defined (that is, everywhere in $\mathbb{R}^3$ except at the origin); a potential function for F is given by

$$\phi(x, y, z) = \frac{km}{|r - r_0|} = \frac{km}{\sqrt{(x - x_0)^2 + (y - y_0)^2 + (z - z_0)^2}}.$$

To see this, observe that

$$\frac{\partial \phi}{\partial x} = \frac{-km(x - x_0)}{\left((x - x_0)^2 + (y - y_0)^2 + (z - z_0)^2\right)^{3/2}} = \frac{-km(x - x_0)}{|r - r_0|^3} = F_1(r),$$

and similar formulas hold for the other partial derivatives of ϕ.

REMARK: Here is a useful formula for the derivative of the length of a vector function $\mathbf{F}$ with respect to a variable x. Expressing $|\mathbf{F}| = \sqrt{\mathbf{F} \bullet \mathbf{F}}$, we calculate

6.2.2
Differentiating the
Length of a Vector

$$\frac{\partial}{\partial x}|\mathbf{F}| = \frac{\partial}{\partial x}\sqrt{\mathbf{F} \bullet \mathbf{F}} = \frac{1}{2\sqrt{\mathbf{F} \bullet \mathbf{F}}} 2\mathbf{F} \bullet \left(\frac{\partial}{\partial x}\mathbf{F}\right) = \frac{\mathbf{F} \bullet \left(\frac{\partial}{\partial x}\mathbf{F}\right)}{|\mathbf{F}|}.$$

Compare this with the derivative of an absolute value of a function of one variable:

$$\frac{d}{dx}|f(x)| = \operatorname{sgn}(f(x))\, f'(x) = \frac{f(x)}{|f(x)|}\, f'(x).$$

In the context of Example 6.2.1 we have

$$\frac{\partial}{\partial x}\frac{km}{|\mathbf{r} - \mathbf{r}_0|} = \frac{-km}{|\mathbf{r} - \mathbf{r}_0|^2}\frac{\partial}{\partial x}|\mathbf{r} - \mathbf{r}_0| = \frac{-km(x - x_0)}{|\mathbf{r} - \mathbf{r}_0|^3},$$

with similar expressions for the other partials of $|\mathbf{r} - \mathbf{r}_0|$.

EXAMPLE 6.2.3   Let us try to find a potential function $\phi(x, y)$ for the vector field $\mathbf{v} = -\Omega y\mathbf{i} + \Omega x\mathbf{j}$ of Example 5.1.2. We have

$$\frac{\partial\phi}{\partial x} = -\Omega y, \qquad \frac{\partial\phi}{\partial y} = \Omega x.$$

The first of these equations implies that $\phi(x, y) = -\Omega xy + C_1(y)$. (We have integrated with respect to x; the constant can still depend on y.) Similarly, the second equation implies that $\phi(x, y) = \Omega xy + C_2(x)$. Therefore, we must have $-\Omega xy + C_1(y) = \Omega xy + C_2(x)$, or $2\Omega xy = C_1(y) - C_2(x)$ for all (x, y). This is not possible for any choice of the single-variable functions $C_1(y)$ and $C_2(x)$. Alternatively, we can form the mixed partial derivatives of ϕ from the two equations and get

$$\frac{\partial^2\phi}{\partial y\partial x} = -\Omega, \qquad \frac{\partial^2\phi}{\partial x\partial y} = \Omega.$$

This is not possible if $\Omega \neq 0$ because the smoothness of $\mathbf{v}$ implies that its potential should be smooth, so the mixed partials should be equal. Thus no such ϕ can exist; $\mathbf{v}$ is not conservative.

Example 6.2.3 suggests a *necessary condition* which must be satisfied by a conservative vector field.

6.2.4
Necessary Condition
for a Conservative
Plane Vector Field

If $\mathbf{F}(x, y) = F_1(x, y)\mathbf{i} + F_2(x, y)\mathbf{j}$ is a conservative vector field in a domain D of the xy-plane, then the condition

$$\frac{\partial}{\partial y} F_1(x, y) = \frac{\partial}{\partial x} F_2(x, y)$$

must be satisfied at all points of D.

To see this, observe that

$$F_1\mathbf{i} + F_2\mathbf{j} = \mathbf{F} = \nabla\phi = \frac{\partial\phi}{\partial x}\mathbf{i} + \frac{\partial\phi}{\partial y}\mathbf{j}$$

implies the two scalar equations

$$F_1 = \frac{\partial\phi}{\partial x}, \qquad F_2 = \frac{\partial\phi}{\partial y},$$

and since the mixed partial derivatives of ϕ should be equal,

$$\frac{\partial F_1}{\partial y} = \frac{\partial^2\phi}{\partial y\partial x} = \frac{\partial^2\phi}{\partial x\partial y} = \frac{\partial F_2}{\partial x}.$$

A similar condition obtains for vector fields in 3-space.

6.2.5
Necessary Conditions
for a Conservative
Vector Field in $I\!R^3$

If $\mathbf{F}(x, y, z) = F_1(x, y, z)\mathbf{i} + F_2(x, y, z)\mathbf{j} + F_3(x, y, z)\mathbf{k}$ is a conservative vector field in a domain D in 3-space, then we must have, everywhere in D,

$$\frac{\partial}{\partial y} F_1 = \frac{\partial}{\partial x} F_2, \qquad \frac{\partial}{\partial z} F_1 = \frac{\partial}{\partial x} F_3, \qquad \frac{\partial}{\partial z} F_2 = \frac{\partial}{\partial y} F_3.$$

Let us make a geometric observation about conservative vector fields. If $\phi(x, y, z)$ is a potential function for the conservative vector field $\mathbf{F}$ then the *level surfaces* $\phi(x, y, z) = C$ of ϕ are called **equipotential surfaces** of $\mathbf{F}$. Since $\mathbf{F} = \nabla\phi$ is normal to these surfaces (wherever it does not vanish), the field lines of $\mathbf{F}$ always intersect the equipotential surfaces at right angles. For instance, the equipotential surfaces of the gravitational force field of a point mass are spheres centred at the point; these spheres are normal to all lines passing through the point. Similarly, for a conservative plane vector field, the *level curves* of the potential function are called **equipotential curves** of the vector field. They are the *orthogonal trajectories* of the field lines; that is, they intersect the field lines at right angles.

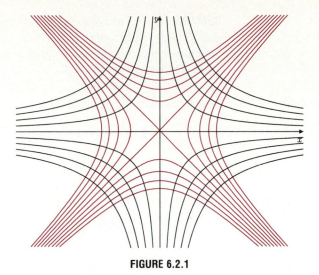

FIGURE 6.2.1

EXAMPLE 6.2.6   Show that the vector field $\mathbf{F}(x, y) = x\mathbf{i} - y\mathbf{j}$ is conservative and find a potential function for it. Describe the field lines and the equipotential curves.

SOLUTION   Since $\partial F_1/\partial y = 0 = \partial F_2/\partial x$ everywhere in $\mathbb{R}^2$, we would expect $\mathbf{F}$ to be conservative. Any potential function ϕ must satisfy

$$\frac{\partial \phi}{\partial x} = F_1 = x, \qquad \frac{\partial \phi}{\partial y} = F_2 = -y.$$

The first of these equations gives

$$\phi(x, y) = \int x\, dx = \frac{1}{2}x^2 + C_1(y).$$

Observe that, since the integral is taken with respect to x, the "constant" of integration is allowed to depend on the other variable. Now we use the second equation to get

$$-y = \frac{\partial \phi}{\partial y} = C_1{}'(y) \quad \Rightarrow \quad C_1(y) = -\frac{1}{2}y^2 + C_2.$$

Thus $\mathbf{F}$ is conservative and, for any constant C_2,

$$\phi(x, y) = \frac{x^2 - y^2}{2} + C_2$$

is a potential function for $\mathbf{F}$. The field lines of $\mathbf{F}$ satisfy

$$\frac{dx}{x} = -\frac{dy}{y} \quad \Rightarrow \quad \ln|x| = -\ln|y| + \ln C_3 \quad \Rightarrow \quad xy = C_3.$$

The field lines of $\mathbf{F}$ are thus rectangular hyperbolas with the coordinate axes as asymptotes. The equipotential curves constitute another family of rectangular hyperbolas, $x^2 - y^2 = C_4$, with the lines $x = \pm y$ as asymptotes. Curves of the two families intersect at right angles. (See Fig. 6.2.1.) Note, however, that $\mathbf{F}$ does not specify a direction at the origin and the orthogonality breaks down there; in fact neither family has a unique curve through that point.

REMARK: In the above example we constructed the potential ϕ by first integrating $\partial\phi/\partial x = F_1$. We could equally well have started by integrating $\partial\phi/\partial y = F_2$, in which case the constant of integration would have depended on x. In the end the same ϕ would have emerged.

EXAMPLE 6.2.7   Decide whether the vector field

$$\mathbf{F} = \left(xy - \sin z\right)\mathbf{i} + \left(\frac{1}{2}x^2 - \frac{e^y}{z}\right)\mathbf{j} + \left(\frac{e^y}{z^2} - x\cos z\right)\mathbf{k}$$

is conservative in $D = \{(x, y, z) : z \neq 0\}$, and find a potential if it is.

SOLUTION   Note that $\mathbf{F}$ is not defined when $z = 0$. However, since

$$\frac{\partial F_1}{\partial y} = x = \frac{\partial F_2}{\partial x}, \qquad \frac{\partial F_1}{\partial z} = -\cos z = \frac{\partial F_3}{\partial x}, \qquad \frac{\partial F_2}{\partial z} = \frac{e^y}{z^2} = \frac{\partial F_3}{\partial y},$$

$\mathbf{F}$ may still be conservative in domains not intersecting the xy-plane $z = 0$. If so, its potential ϕ should satisfy

$$\frac{\partial\phi}{\partial x} = xy - \sin z, \qquad \frac{\partial\phi}{\partial y} = \frac{1}{2}x^2 - \frac{e^y}{z}, \qquad \frac{\partial\phi}{\partial z} = \frac{e^y}{z^2} - x\cos z.$$

From the first of these equations

$$\phi(x, y, z) = \int (xy - \sin z)\, dx = \frac{1}{2}x^2 y - x\sin z + C_1(y, z).$$

(Again note that the constant of integration can be a function of any parameters of the integrand — it is constant only with respect to the variable of integration.) Using the second equation, we obtain

$$\frac{1}{2}x^2 - \frac{e^y}{z} = \frac{\partial\phi}{\partial y} = \frac{1}{2}x^2 + \frac{\partial C_1(y, z)}{\partial y}.$$

Thus

$$C_1(y, z) = -\int \frac{e^y}{z}\, dy = -\frac{e^y}{z} + C_2(z)$$

and

$$\phi(x, y, z) = \frac{1}{2}x^2 y - x\sin z - \frac{e^y}{z} + C_2(z).$$

Finally, using the third equation,

$$\frac{e^y}{z^2} - x\cos z = \frac{\partial\phi}{\partial z} = -x\cos z + \frac{e^y}{z^2} + C_2'(z).$$

Thus $C_2'(z) = 0$ and $C_2(z) = C$ (a constant). Indeed, $\mathbf{F}$ is conservative and, for any constant C,

$$\phi(x, y, z) = \frac{1}{2}x^2 y - x\sin z - \frac{e^y}{z} + C$$

is a potential function for $\mathbf{F}$ in the given domain D. C may have different values in the two regions $z > 0$ and $z < 0$ whose union constitutes D.

REMARK: If, in the above solution, the differential equation for $C_1(y, z)$ had involved x, or if that for $C_2(z)$ had involved either x or y, we would not have been able to find ϕ. This did not happen because of the three conditions on the partials of F_1, F_2 and F_3 verified at the outset.

The existence of a potential for a vector field depends on the "topology" of the domain of the field (that is, whether the domain has "holes" in it, and what kind of holes) as well as on the structure of the components of the field itself. (Even if the necessary conditions in Boxes 6.2.4 or 6.2.5 are satisfied, a vector field may not be conservative in a domain which has "holes.") We will be probing further into the nature of conservative vector fields in Section 6.4 and in the next chapter, and will eventually show that the above *necessary conditions* are also *sufficient* to guarantee that **F** is conservative if the domain of **F** satisfies certain conditions. At this point, however, we give an example in which a plane vector field fails to be conservative on a domain where the necessary condition 6.2.4 is, nevertheless, satisfied.

EXAMPLE 6.2.8   Consider the vector field

$$\mathbf{F}(x, y) = \left(\frac{-y}{x^2 + y^2} \right) \mathbf{i} + \left(\frac{x}{x^2 + y^2} \right) \mathbf{j}, \qquad (x, y) \neq (0, 0).$$

This field satisfies condition 6.2.4, since

$$\frac{\partial}{\partial y} \left(-\frac{y}{x^2 + y^2} \right) = \frac{y^2 - x^2}{(x^2 + y^2)^2} = \frac{\partial}{\partial x} \left(\frac{x}{x^2 + y^2} \right).$$

For every $(x, y) \neq (0, 0)$, let $\theta(x, y)$ be the (unique) polar angle (second polar coordinate) of (x, y), in the range $0 \leq \theta < 2\pi$. Thus

$$x = r \cos\theta, \qquad y = r \sin\theta, \qquad \text{where} \quad r = \sqrt{x^2 + y^2}.$$

If we differentiate these two equations implicitly with respect to x, we obtain

$$1 = \frac{\partial x}{\partial x} = \frac{\partial r}{\partial x} \cos\theta - r \sin\theta \frac{\partial\theta}{\partial x}$$
$$0 = \frac{\partial y}{\partial x} = \frac{\partial r}{\partial x} \sin\theta + r \cos\theta \frac{\partial\theta}{\partial x}.$$

Eliminating $\partial r/\partial x$ from this pair of equations and solving for $\partial\theta/\partial x$ leads to

$$\frac{\partial\theta}{\partial x} = -\frac{r \sin\theta}{r^2} = -\frac{y}{x^2 + y^2}.$$

Similarly, differentiation with respect to y produces

$$\frac{\partial\theta}{\partial y} = \frac{x}{x^2 + y^2}.$$

These formulas hold only if $0 < \theta < 2\pi$; θ is not even continuous on the positive x-axis. Thus $\mathbf{F} = \nabla\theta$ holds everywhere in the plane except at points $(x,0)$ where $x \geq 0$. It follows that $\mathbf{F}$ cannot be conservative on its entire domain (all $(x,y)\neq(0,0)$), for if $\mathbf{F}(x,y) = \nabla\phi(x,y)$ there, then $\nabla(\theta - \phi) = 0$, and $\theta(x,y) = \phi(x,y)+C$, (where C is a constant), for all (x,y) not on the nonnegative x-axis. This would, in turn, imply that θ must be continuous on the positive x-axis, which is not the case. Observe that the origin $(0,0)$ is a "hole" in the domain of $\mathbf{F}$ in the above example. While $\mathbf{F}$ satisfies condition 6.2.4 everywhere except at this "hole," one must remove from the domain of $\mathbf{F}$ a half-line (ray), or, more generally, a curve from the origin to infinity in order to get a potential function for $\mathbf{F}$. $\mathbf{F}$ is *not* conservative on any domain containing a curve which surrounds the origin. Exercises 18–20 in Section 6.4 will shed further light on this situation.

Sources, Sinks and Dipoles

Imagine that 3-space is filled with an incompressible fluid emitted by a point source at the origin at a volume rate $dV/dt = 4\pi m$. (We say that the origin is a **source** of strength m.) By symmetry, the fluid flows outward on radial lines from the origin with equal speed at equal distances from the origin in all directions, and the fluid emitted at the origin at some instant $t = 0$ will at later time t be spread over a sphere of radius $r = r(t)$. All the fluid inside that sphere was emitted in the time interval $[0,t]$, so we have

$$\frac{4}{3}\pi r^3 = 4\pi m t.$$

Differentiating this equation with respect to t we obtain $r^2(dr/dt) = m$, and the outward speed of the fluid at distance r from the origin is $v(r) = m/r^2$. The velocity field of the moving fluid is therefore

$$\mathbf{v}(\mathbf{r}) = v(r)\frac{\mathbf{r}}{|\mathbf{r}|} = \frac{m}{r^3}\mathbf{r}.$$

This velocity field is conservative (except at the origin) and has potential function

$$\phi(\mathbf{r}) = -\frac{m}{r}.$$

A **sink** is a negative source. A sink of strength m at the origin (which annihilates or sucks up fluid at a rate $dV/dt = 4\pi m$) has velocity field and potential given by

$$\mathbf{v}(\mathbf{r}) = -\frac{m}{r^3}\mathbf{r}, \qquad \phi(\mathbf{r}) = \frac{m}{r}.$$

The potentials or velocity fields of sources or sinks located at other points are obtained by simple translation; for instance, the velocity field of a source of strength m at the point with position vector $\mathbf{r}_0$ is

$$\mathbf{v}(\mathbf{r}) = -\nabla\left(\frac{m}{|\mathbf{r} - \mathbf{r}_0|}\right) = \frac{m}{|\mathbf{r} - \mathbf{r}_0|^3}(\mathbf{r} - \mathbf{r}_0).$$

This should be compared with the gravitational force field due to a mass m at the origin. The two are the same except for sign and a constant related to units of measurement. For this reason we regard a point mass as a sink of its own gravitational field. Similarly, the electrostatic field due to a point charge q at $\mathbf{r}_0$ is the field of a source (or sink if $q < 0$) of strength proportional to q; if units of measurement are suitably chosen we have

$$\mathbf{E}(\mathbf{r}) = -\nabla\left(\frac{q}{|\mathbf{r} - \mathbf{r}_0|}\right) = \frac{q}{|\mathbf{r} - \mathbf{r}_0|^3}\,(\mathbf{r} - \mathbf{r}_0).$$

In general, the field lines of a vector field converge at a source or sink of that field.

A **dipole** is a system consisting of a source and sink of equal strength m separated by a short distance ℓ. The product $\mu = m\ell$ is called the **dipole moment** and the line containing the source and sink is called the **axis** of the dipole. Physical dipoles, such as magnets, are frequently modelled by "ideal" dipoles which are the limits of dipoles where $m \to \infty$ and $\ell \to 0$ in such a way that the dipole moment μ remains constant.

EXAMPLE 6.2.9   Calculate the velocity field, $\mathbf{v}(x, y, z)$, associated with a dipole of moment μ located at the origin and having axis along the z-axis.

SOLUTION   We start with a source of strength m at position $(0, 0, \ell/2)$ and a sink of strength m at $(0, 0, -\ell/2)$. The potential ϕ of the dipole will be the limit of the potential of this system as $m \to \infty$ and $\ell \to 0$ in such a way that $m\ell = \mu$:

$$\phi(x, y, z) = \lim_{\substack{\ell \to 0 \\ m\ell = \mu}} \left(-\frac{m}{\sqrt{x^2 + y^2 + \left(z - \frac{\ell}{2}\right)^2}} + \frac{m}{\sqrt{x^2 + y^2 + \left(z + \frac{\ell}{2}\right)^2}} \right)$$

$$= \mu \lim_{\ell \to 0} \frac{\left[x^2 + y^2 + \left(z + \frac{\ell}{2}\right)^2\right]^{-1/2} - \left[x^2 + y^2 + \left(z - \frac{\ell}{2}\right)^2\right]^{-1/2}}{\ell}$$

$$= \mu \lim_{\ell \to 0} \left(-\frac{1}{2}\left[x^2 + y^2 + \left(z + \frac{\ell}{2}\right)^2\right]^{-3/2}\left[2\left(z + \frac{\ell}{2}\right)\frac{1}{2}\right] \right.$$

$$\left. - \left(\frac{-1}{2}\right)\left[x^2 + y^2 + \left(z - \frac{\ell}{2}\right)^2\right]^{-3/2}\left[2\left(z - \frac{\ell}{2}\right)\left(\frac{-1}{2}\right)\right] \right)$$

$$= \frac{-\mu z}{(x^2 + y^2 + z^2)^{3/2}} = -\frac{\mu z}{r^3}.$$

(L'Hôpital's Rule was applied after the second line in the above calculation.)

The required vector field will be the gradient of this potential. We calculate the partial derivatives of ϕ:

$$\frac{\partial \phi}{\partial x} = \frac{3\mu z}{r^4}\frac{x}{r} = \frac{3\mu z x}{r^5}, \quad \frac{\partial \phi}{\partial y} = \frac{3\mu z y}{r^5}, \quad \frac{\partial \phi}{\partial z} = -\frac{\mu}{r^3} + \frac{3\mu z^2}{r^5}.$$

It follows that the velocity field **v** associated with the dipole is

$$\mathbf{v} = \nabla\phi = \frac{\mu}{r^5}\left(3zx\mathbf{i} + 3zy\mathbf{j} + (2z^2 - x^2 - y^2)\mathbf{k}\right),$$

where $r = \sqrt{x^2 + y^2 + z^2}$. Some streamlines are shown in Fig. 6.2.2 for a plane cross-section containing the z-axis.

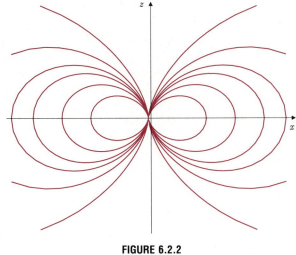

FIGURE 6.2.2

REMARK: Here is an alternative derivation of the potential for the dipole in the above example, done entirely with vectors. If $\mathbf{r} = x\mathbf{i} + y\mathbf{j} + z\mathbf{k}$ then

$$\phi(\mathbf{r}) = \lim_{\substack{\ell\to 0 \\ m\ell=\mu}}\left(\frac{-m}{|\mathbf{r} - \frac{\ell}{2}\mathbf{k}|} + \frac{m}{|\mathbf{r} + \frac{\ell}{2}\mathbf{k}|}\right)$$

$$= \lim_{\ell\to 0} -\mu\frac{|\mathbf{r} + \frac{\ell}{2}\mathbf{k}| - |\mathbf{r} - \frac{\ell}{2}\mathbf{k}|}{\ell} \times \frac{1}{|\mathbf{r} - \frac{\ell}{2}\mathbf{k}||\mathbf{r} + \frac{\ell}{2}\mathbf{k}|}$$

$$= -\mu\left(\frac{\partial}{\partial z}|\mathbf{r}|\right)\left(\frac{1}{|\mathbf{r}|^2}\right) = -\frac{\mu z}{|\mathbf{r}|^3}$$

by the remark following Example 6.2.1 above. If we set $\mathbf{d} = \mu\mathbf{k}$ (the vector dipole moment) then

$$\phi = -\frac{\mathbf{r}\bullet\mathbf{d}}{|\mathbf{r}|^3}.$$

EXERCISES

In Exercises 1–6 determine whether the given vector field is conservative and find a potential if it is conservative.

1. $\mathbf{F}(x, y, z) = x\mathbf{i} - 2y\mathbf{j} + 3z\mathbf{k}$

2. $\mathbf{F}(x, y, z) = y\mathbf{i} + x\mathbf{j} + z^2\mathbf{k}$

3. $\mathbf{F}(x, y) = \dfrac{x\mathbf{i} - y\mathbf{j}}{x^2 + y^2}$ 4. $\mathbf{F}(x, y) = \dfrac{x\mathbf{i} + y\mathbf{j}}{x^2 + y^2}$

5. $\mathbf{F}(x, y, z) = (2xy - z^2)\mathbf{i} + (2yz + x^2)\mathbf{j} - (2zx - y^2)\mathbf{k}$

6. $\mathbf{F}(x, y, z) = e^{x^2+y^2+z^2}(xz\mathbf{i} + yz\mathbf{j} + xy\mathbf{k})$

7. Find the three-dimensional vector field with potential
$$\phi(\mathbf{r}) = \frac{1}{|\mathbf{r}-\mathbf{r}_0|^2}.$$

8. Calculate $\nabla \ln |\mathbf{r}|$, where $\mathbf{r} = x\mathbf{i} + y\mathbf{j} + z\mathbf{k}$.

9. Show that the vector field
$$\mathbf{F}(x, y, z) = \frac{2x}{z}\mathbf{i} + \frac{2y}{z}\mathbf{j} - \frac{x^2 + y^2}{z^2}\mathbf{k}$$

is conservative, and find its potential. Describe the equipotential surfaces. Find the field lines of $\mathbf{F}$.

10. Repeat the previous exercise for the field

$$\mathbf{F}(x, y, z) = \frac{2x}{z}\mathbf{i} + \frac{2y}{z}\mathbf{j} + \left(1 - \frac{x^2 + y^2}{z^2}\right)\mathbf{k}.$$

11. Find the velocity field due to two sources of strength m, one located at $(0, 0, \ell)$ and the other at $(0, 0, -\ell)$. Where is the velocity zero? Find the velocity at any point $(x, y, 0)$ in the xy-plane. Where in the xy-plane is the speed greatest?

12.*Find the velocity field for a system consisting of a source of strength 2 at the origin and a sink of strength 1 at $(0, 0, 1)$. Show that the velocity is vertical at all points of a certain sphere. Sketch the streamlines of the flow.

Exercises 13–18 provide an analysis of two-dimensional sources and dipoles similar to that developed for three dimensions in the text.

13. In 3-space filled with an incompressible fluid we say that the z-axis is a **line source** of strength m if every interval Δz along that axis emits fluid at volume rate $dV/dt = 2\pi m \Delta z$. The fluid then spreads out symmetrically in

all directions perpendicular to the z-axis. Show that the velocity field of the flow is

$$\mathbf{v} = \frac{m}{x^2 + y^2}\,(x\mathbf{i} + y\mathbf{j}).$$

14. The flow in the previous exercise is two-dimensional in that $\mathbf{v}$ depends only on x and y and has no component in the z direction. Regarded as a *plane* vector field, it is the field of a two-dimensional point source of strength m located at the origin. (That is, fluid is emitted at the origin at *area rate* $dA/dt = 2\pi m$.) Show that the vector field is conservative and find a potential function $\phi(x, y)$ for it.

15.*Find the potential, ϕ, and the field, $\mathbf{F} = \nabla\phi$, for a two-dimensional dipole at the origin, with axis in the y direction and dipole moment μ. Such a dipole is the limit of a system consisting of a source of strength m at $(0, \ell/2)$ and a sink of strength m at $(0, -\ell/2)$, as $\ell \to 0$ and $m \to \infty$ such that $m\ell = \mu$.

16.*Show that the equipotential curves of the two-dimensional dipole in the previous exercise are circles tangent to the x-axis at the origin.

17.*Show that the streamlines (field lines) of the two-dimensional dipole in the previous two exercises are circles tangent to the y-axis at the origin. Hint: it is possible to do this geometrically. If you choose to do it by setting up a differential equation you may find the change of dependent variable

$$y = vx, \qquad \frac{dy}{dx} = v + x\frac{dv}{dx}$$

useful for integrating the equation.

18.*Show that the velocity field of a line source of strength $2m$ can be found by integrating the (three-dimensional) velocity field of a point source of strength $m\,dz$ at $(0, 0, z)$ over the whole z-axis. Why does the integral correspond to a line source of strength $2m$ rather than strength m? Can the potential of the line source be obtained by integrating the potentials of the point sources?

6.3   LINE INTEGRALS

If a wire stretched out along the x-axis from $x = a$ to $x = b$ has constant *line density* ρ (units of mass per unit length), then the total mass of the wire will be $m = \rho(b - a)$. If the density of the wire is not constant, but varies continuously from point to point (for example, because the thickness of the wire is not uniform), then we must find the total mass of the wire by "summing" (that is, integrating) differential elements of mass $dm = \rho(x)\,dx$:

$$m = \int_a^b \rho(x)\,dx.$$

In general, the definite integral, $\int_a^b f(x)\,dx$, represents a "sum" or "total amount" of a quantity distributed along the x-axis between a and b in terms of the *line density*, $f(x)$, of that quantity at point x. $f(x)\,dx$ is the amount in an "infinitesimal" interval of length dx at x, and the integral adds up these infinitesimal contributions (or *elements*) to give the total amount of the quantity. Similarly the integrals $\iint_D f(x, y)\,dA$ and $\iiint_R f(x, y, z)\,dV$ represent the total amounts of quantities distributed over regions D in the plane and R in 3-space in terms of *area* or *volume* densities of these quantities.

It may happen that a quantity is distributed with specified line density along a *curve* in the plane or in 3-space, or with specified area density over a *surface* in 3-space. In such cases we require *line integrals* or *surface integrals* to add up the contributing elements and calculate the total quantity. We examine line integrals in these next two sections and surface integrals in the remaining two.

Let C be a bounded, continuous parametric curve in $\mathbb{R}^3$. Recall (from Section 5.1) that C is a *smooth curve* if it has a parametrization of the form

$$\mathbf{r} = \mathbf{r}(t) = x(t)\mathbf{i} + y(t)\mathbf{j} + z(t)\mathbf{k}, \qquad a \le t \le b,$$

with "velocity" vector $\mathbf{v} = d\mathbf{r}/dt$ continuous and nonzero. We will call C a **smooth arc** if it is a smooth curve with *finite* parameter interval $[a, b]$.

In Section 5.2 we saw how to calculate the length of C by subdividing it into short arcs by points corresponding to parameter values

$$a = t_0 < t_1 < t_2 < \cdots < t_{n-1} < t_n = b,$$

adding up the lengths $|\Delta \mathbf{r}_i| = |\mathbf{r}_i - \mathbf{r}_{i-1}|$ of line segments joining these points, and taking the limit as the maximum distance between adjacent points approached zero. The length was denoted

$$\int_C ds$$

and is a special example of a line integral along C having integrand 1.

The line integral of a general function $f(x, y, z)$ can be defined similarly. We choose a point (x_i^*, y_i^*, z_i^*) on the ith subarc and form the Riemann sum

$$S_n = \sum_{i=1}^n f(x_i^*, y_i^*, z_i^*)\,|\Delta \mathbf{r}_i|.$$

If this sum has a limit as max $|\Delta \mathbf{r}_i| \to 0$, independent of the particular choices of the points (x_i^*, y_i^*, z_i^*), then we call this limit the line integral of f along C, and denote it by

$$\int_C f(x, y, z)\, ds.$$

The limit will certainly exist if C is a smooth arc and if f is continuous on C. It will also exist (for continuous f) if C is **piecewise smooth**, consisting of finitely many smooth arcs linked end to end; in this case the line integral of f along C is the sum of the line integrals of f along each of the smooth arcs. Improper line integrals can also be considered, where the length of an arc or curve is not finite.

The length of C was evaluated by expressing the arc length element ds in terms of the given parametrization of the curve: $ds = |d\mathbf{r}/dt|\, dt$ and integrating this from $t = a$ to $t = b$. More general line integrals are evaluated similarly:

6.3.1
Evaluating
Line Integrals

$$\int_C f(x, y, z)\, ds = \int_a^b f(\mathbf{r}(t)) \left| \frac{d\mathbf{r}}{dt} \right| dt.$$

Of course, all the above discussion applies equally well to line integrals of functions $f(x, y)$ along curves C in the xy-plane.

It should be noted that the value of the line integral of a function f along a curve C depends on f and C, but not on the particular way C is parametrized. If $\mathbf{r} = \mathbf{r}^*(u)$, $\alpha \le u \le \beta$, is another parametrization of the same smooth curve C, then any point $\mathbf{r}(t)$ on C can be expressed in terms of the new parametrization as $\mathbf{r}^*(u)$, where u depends on t: $u = u(t)$. If $\mathbf{r}^*(u)$ traces C in the same direction as $\mathbf{r}(t)$ then $u(a) = \alpha$, $u(b) = \beta$, and $du/dt \ge 0$; if $\mathbf{r}^*(u)$ traces C in the opposite direction then $u(a) = \beta$, $u(b) = \alpha$, and $du/dt \le 0$. In either event

$$\int_a^b f(\mathbf{r}(t)) \left| \frac{d\mathbf{r}}{dt} \right| dt = \int_a^b f(\mathbf{r}^*(u(t))) \left| \frac{d\mathbf{r}^*}{du} \frac{du}{dt} \right| dt = \int_\alpha^\beta f(\mathbf{r}^*(u)) \left| \frac{d\mathbf{r}^*}{du} \right| du.$$

Thus the line integral is *independent of parametrization* of the curve C.

Unlike the line integrals of vector fields considered in the next section, the line integrals of scalar fields considered here do not depend on the direction (orientation) of C.

Line integrals frequently lead to definite integrals which are very difficult or impossible to evaluate without using numerical techniques. Only very simple curves and ones which have been contrived to lead to simple expressions for ds are amenable to exact calculation of line integrals.

EXAMPLE 6.3.2   Find $\int_C z\, ds$ along the circular helix C given by

$$\mathbf{r} = a\cos t\, \mathbf{i} + a\sin t\, \mathbf{j} + bt\, \mathbf{k}, \qquad 0 \le t \le 2\pi.$$

SOLUTION   As we observed in Example 5.2.4, $ds = \sqrt{a^2 + b^2}\, dt$ for this helix. On the helix we have $z = bt$, so

$$\int_C z\, ds = b\sqrt{a^2 + b^2} \int_0^{2\pi} t\, dt = 2\pi^2 b\sqrt{a^2 + b^2}.$$

Sometimes a curve, along which a line integral is to be taken, is specified as the intersection of two surfaces with given equations. It is normally necessary to parametrize the curve in order to evaluate a line integral. If one of the surfaces is a cylinder parallel to one of the coordinate axes it is usually easiest to begin by parametrizing that cylinder. (Otherwise, combine the equations to eliminate one variable and thus obtain such a cylinder on which the curve lies.)

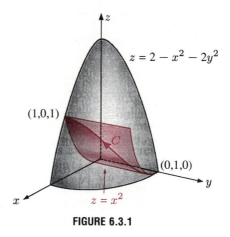

FIGURE 6.3.1

EXAMPLE 6.3.3   Find $\displaystyle\int_C xy\, ds$ where C is the first octant part of the curve of intersection of the elliptic paraboloid $z = 2 - x^2 - 2y^2$ and the parabolic cylinder $z = x^2$ from $(0, 1, 0)$ to $(1, 0, 1)$. (See Fig. 6.3.1.)

SOLUTION   We need a convenient parametrization of C. Since the curve lies on the cylinder $z = x^2$ and is oriented so that x goes from 0 to 1, we can let $x = t$ and $z = t^2$. Then $2y^2 = 2 - x^2 - z = 2 - 2t^2$ so $y^2 = 1 - t^2$. Since C lies in the first octant, it can be parametrized by

$$x = t, \qquad y = \sqrt{1 - t^2}, \qquad z = t^2, \qquad (0 \le t \le 1).$$

Then $dx/dt = 1$, $dy/dt = -t/\sqrt{1 - t^2}$ and $dz/dt = 2t$ so

$$ds = \sqrt{1 + \frac{t^2}{1 - t^2} + 4t^2}\, dt = \frac{\sqrt{1 + 4t^2 - 4t^4}}{\sqrt{1 - t^2}}\, dt.$$

Hence

$$\int_C xy\,ds = \int_0^1 t\sqrt{1-t^2}\,\frac{\sqrt{1+4t^2-4t^4}}{\sqrt{1-t^2}}\,dt$$

$$= \int_0^1 t\sqrt{1+4t^2-4t^4}\,dt \qquad\qquad [\text{let } u=t^2]$$

$$= \frac{1}{2}\int_0^1 \sqrt{1+4u-4u^2}\,du$$

$$= \frac{1}{2}\int_0^1 \sqrt{2-(2u-1)^2}\,du \qquad\qquad [\text{let } v=2u-1]$$

$$= \frac{1}{4}\int_{-1}^1 \sqrt{2-v^2}\,dv = \frac{1}{2}\int_0^1 \sqrt{2-v^2}\,dv$$

$$= \frac{1}{2}\left(\frac{\pi}{4}+\frac{1}{2}\right) = \frac{\pi+2}{8}.$$

(The final integral above was evaluated by interpreting it as the area of part of a circle. You are invited to supply the details. It can also be done by the substitution $v=\sqrt{2}\sin w$.)

REMARK: The curve C in the above example lies on the circular cylinder $2-x^2-2y^2=x^2$, that is, on $x^2+y^2=1$. Therefore, another possible parametrization of C is

$$x=\cos t, \qquad y=\sin t, \qquad z=\cos^2 t, \qquad (0\le t\le \frac{\pi}{2}).$$

You may wish to evaluate the line integral using this parametrization. Of course the result must be the same.

EXERCISES

1. Show that the curve C given by

$$\mathbf{r}=a\cos t\sin t\,\mathbf{i}+a\sin^2 t\,\mathbf{j}+a\cos t\,\mathbf{k},$$

$(0\le t\le \frac{\pi}{2})$, lies on a sphere centred at the origin. Find $\int_C z\,ds$.

2. Let C be the conical helix with parametric equations $x=t\cos t$, $y=t\sin t$, $z=t$, $(0\le t\le 2\pi)$. Find $\int_C z\,ds$.

3. Find the moment of inertia about the z-axis, (that is, the value of $\int_C (x^2+y^2)\,ds$), for a wire of constant density ρ lying along the curve C: $\mathbf{r}=e^t\cos t\,\mathbf{i}+e^t\sin t\,\mathbf{j}+t\mathbf{k}$, from $t=0$ to $t=2\pi$.

4. Evaluate $\int_C e^z\,ds$ where C is the curve in the previous exercise.

5. Find $\int_C x^2\,ds$ along the line of intersection of the two planes $x-y+z=0$, and $x+y+2z=0$, from the origin to the point $(3,1,-2)$.

6. Find $\int_C \sqrt{1+4x^2z^2}\,ds$, where C is the curve of intersection of the surfaces $x^2+z^2=1$ and $y=x^2$.

7.* Find $\int_C x\,ds$ along the first octant part of the curve of intersection of the cylinder $x^2+y^2=a^2$ and the plane $z=x$.

8.* Find $\int_C z\,ds$ along the part of the curve $x^2+y^2+z^2=1$, $x+y=1$, where $z\ge 0$.

9.*Find $\int_C \dfrac{ds}{(2y^2 + 1)^{3/2}}$ where C is the parabola

$z^2 = x^2 + y^2$, $x + z = 1$.

10. Express as a definite integral, but do not try to evaluate, the value of $\int_C xyz \, ds$, where C is the curve $y = x^2$, $z = y^2$ from $(0, 0, 0)$ to $(2, 4, 16)$.

11.*The function

$$E(k, \phi) = \int_0^\phi \sqrt{1 - k^2 \sin^2 t} \, dt$$

is called the **elliptic integral function of the second kind**. The **complete elliptic integral** of the second

kind is the function $E(k) = E(k, \pi/2)$. In terms of these functions express the length of one complete revolution of the elliptic helix

$$x = a \cos t, \qquad y = b \sin t, \qquad z = ct,$$

where $0 < a < b$. What is the length of that part of the helix lying between $t = 0$ and $t = T$ where $0 < T < \pi/2$?

12.*Evaluate $\int_L \dfrac{ds}{x^2 + y^2}$ where L is the entire straight line with equation $Ax + By = C$, $(C \neq 0)$. Hint: use the symmetry of the integrand to replace the line with a line having simpler equation but giving the same value to the integral.

6.4   LINE INTEGRALS OF VECTOR FIELDS

In elementary physics the **work** done by a constant force of magnitude F in moving an object a distance d is defined to be the product of F and d: $W = Fd$. There is, however, a catch to this; it is understood that the force is exerted in the direction of motion of the object. If the object moves in a direction different from that of the force (because of some other forces acting on it) then the work done by the particular force is the product of the distance moved and the component of the force in the direction of motion. For instance, the work done by gravity in causing a 10 kg crate to slide 5 metres down a ramp inclined at 45° to the horizontal is $W = 50g/\sqrt{2}$ N·m, (where $g = 9.8$ m/s^2), since the scalar projection of the $10g$ N gravitational force on the crate in the direction of the ramp is $10g/\sqrt{2}$ N.

The work done by a *variable* force $\mathbf{F}(x, y, z) = \mathbf{F}(\mathbf{r})$, which depends continuously on position, in moving an object along a smooth curve C can be approximated by a Riemann sum of contributions over short arcs of C on each of which $\mathbf{F}$ is essentially constant.

$$W \approx \sum_{i=1}^n \Delta W_i \approx \sum_{i=1}^n \mathbf{F}(\mathbf{r}_i) \bullet \hat{\mathbf{T}}(\mathbf{r}_i) \, |\Delta \mathbf{r}_i|$$

In the limit, as the length of the short arcs approaches zero, the work done is given by the line integral

$$W = \int_C \mathbf{F} \bullet \hat{\mathbf{T}} \, ds = \int_C \mathbf{F} \bullet d\mathbf{r},$$

where we use the vector differential $d\mathbf{r}$ as a convenient shorthand for $\hat{\mathbf{T}} \, ds$. Since

$$\hat{\mathbf{T}} = \frac{d\mathbf{r}}{ds} = \frac{dx}{ds}\mathbf{i} + \frac{dy}{ds}\mathbf{j} + \frac{dz}{ds}\mathbf{k}$$

we have

$$d\mathbf{r} = \hat{\mathbf{T}} \, ds = dx \, \mathbf{i} + dy \, \mathbf{j} + dz \, \mathbf{k}.$$

Thus, the line integral of the tangential component of a continuous vector field $\mathbf{F}$ along C can be expressed in terms of the components of $\mathbf{F}$ ($\mathbf{F} = F_1\mathbf{i} + F_2\mathbf{j} + F_3\mathbf{k}$) in the form

$$\int_C \mathbf{F} \bullet d\mathbf{r} = \int_C F_1(x, y, z)\, dx + F_2(x, y, z)\, dy + F_3(x, y, z)\, dz.$$

Such a line integral is sometimes called, somewhat improperly, the line integral of $\mathbf{F}$ along C. If C is a closed curve it is also called the *circulation* of $\mathbf{F}$ around C. Observe that this line integral has a scalar value, not a vector value.

Like the line integrals studied in the previous section, a line integrals of a continuous vector field is converted into an ordinary definite integral by using a parametrization of the path of integration. For a smooth arc

$$\mathbf{r} = \mathbf{r}(t) = x(t)\mathbf{i} + y(t)\mathbf{j} + z(t)\mathbf{k}, \qquad (a \leq t \leq b),$$

we have

$$\int_C \mathbf{F} \bullet d\mathbf{r} = \int_a^b \mathbf{F} \bullet \frac{d\mathbf{r}}{dt}\, dt$$

$$= \int_a^b \left[F_1\Big(x(t), y(t), z(t) \Big) \frac{dx}{dt} + F_2\Big(x(t), y(t), z(t) \Big) \frac{dy}{dt} \right.$$

$$\left. + F_3\Big(x(t), y(t), z(t) \Big) \frac{dz}{dt} \right] dt.$$

This type of line integral changes sign if the orientation of C is reversed, but otherwise is independent of the particular parametrization used for C. Again, a line integral over a piecewise smooth path is the sum of the line integrals over the individual smooth arcs constituting that path.

EXAMPLE 6.4.1   Let $\mathbf{F}(x, y) = y^2\mathbf{i} + 2xy\mathbf{j}$. Evaluate the line integral

$$\int_C \mathbf{F} \bullet d\mathbf{r}$$

from $(0,0)$ to $(1,1)$ along a) the straight line $y = x$, b) the curve $y = x^2$, and c) the piecewise smooth path consisting of the straight line segments from $(0,0)$ to $(0,1)$ and from there to $(1,1)$.

SOLUTION   The three paths are shown in Fig. 6.4.1. The straight path a) can be parametrized $\mathbf{r} = t\mathbf{i} + t\mathbf{j}$, $0 \leq t \leq 1$. Thus

$$\mathbf{F} \bullet d\mathbf{r} = (t^2\mathbf{i} + 2t^2\mathbf{j}) \bullet (\mathbf{i} + \mathbf{j})dt = 3t^2\, dt$$

and

$$\int_C \mathbf{F} \bullet d\mathbf{r} = \int_0^1 3t^2\, dt = t^3 \Big|_0^1 = 1.$$

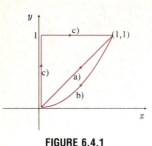

FIGURE 6.4.1

The parabolic path b) can be parametrized $\mathbf{r} = t\mathbf{i} + t^2\mathbf{j}$, $0 \le t \le 1$. Thus

$$\mathbf{F} \bullet d\mathbf{r} = (t^4\mathbf{i} + 2t^3\mathbf{j}) \bullet (\mathbf{i} + 2t\mathbf{j})\, dt = 5t^4\, dt,$$

and

$$\int_C \mathbf{F} \bullet d\mathbf{r} = \int_0^1 5t^4\, dt = t^5\Big|_0^1 = 1.$$

The third path is made up of two segments, and we parametrize each separately. Let us use y as parameter on the vertical segment (where $x = 0$ and $dx = 0$), and x as parameter on the horizontal segment (where $y = 1$ and $dy = 0$):

$$\int_C \mathbf{F} \bullet d\mathbf{r} = \int_C y^2\, dx + 2xy\, dy$$

$$= \int_0^1 (1)\, dx + \int_0^1 (0)\, dy = 1.$$

In this example, the integral appears to be independent of the particular *path* taken to get from (0,0) to (1,1).

EXAMPLE 6.4.2   Let $\mathbf{F} = y\mathbf{i} - x\mathbf{j}$. Find

$$\int_C \mathbf{F} \bullet d\mathbf{r}$$

from (1,0) to $(0, -1)$ along a) the straight line segment joining these points, and b) three quarters of the circle of unit radius centred at the origin and traversed counterclockwise.

SOLUTION   Both paths are shown in Fig. 6.4.2. The straight path can be parametrized

$$\mathbf{r} = (1 - t)\mathbf{i} - t\mathbf{j}, \qquad 0 \le t \le 1.$$

Thus $d\mathbf{r} = -dt\,\mathbf{i} - dt\,\mathbf{j}$, and

$$\int_C \mathbf{F} \bullet d\mathbf{r} = \int_0^1 \Big((-t)(-dt) - (1 - t)(-dt) \Big) = \int_0^1 dt = 1.$$

The circular path can be parametrized

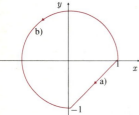

FIGURE 6.4.2

$$\mathbf{r} = \cos t\,\mathbf{i} + \sin t\,\mathbf{j}, \qquad 0 \le t \le \frac{3\pi}{2}.$$

Hence $\mathbf{F} \bullet d\mathbf{r} = -\sin^2 t\, dt - \cos^2 t\, dt = -dt$ and

$$\int_C \mathbf{F} \bullet d\mathbf{r} = -\int_0^{3\pi/2} dt = -\frac{3\pi}{2}.$$

In this case it appears that the line integral does depend on the path to from (1,0) to $(0, -1)$ along which the integral is taken.

Some readers may have noticed that in Example 6.4.1 above the vector field $\mathbf{F}$ is conservative, while in Example 6.4.2 it is not. Theorem 6.4.5 below confirms the link between *independence of path* for a line integral of the tangential component of a vector field and the existence of a scalar potential function for that field. This and subsequent theorems require specific assumptions on the nature of the domain of the vector field $\mathbf{F}$, so we need to formulate some definitions.

Connected and Simply Connected Domains

We shall call a nonempty set in the plane, or in 3-space, a **domain** if it is an *open* set together (possibly) with some or all of its boundary points. Recall that a set S in the plane (or in 3-space) is open if every point in S is the centre of a disc (or a ball) having positive radius and contained in S. A domain may be closed, but it must have interior points near any of its boundary points. (See the early part of Section 3.1 for a discussion of open and closed sets and interior and boundary points.)

6.4.3
Connected Domains

> A domain D in the plane (or in 3-space) is said to be **connected**, if for every pair of points P and Q in D, there exists a piecewise smooth path in D from P to Q.

For instance, the set of points (x, y) in the plane satisfying $x > 0$, $y > 0$ and $x^2 + y^2 \leq 4$ is a connected domain, but the set of points satisfying $|x| > 1$ is not connected. (There is no path from $(-2, 0)$ to $(2,0)$ lying entirely in $|x| > 1$.) The set of points (x, y, z) in 3-space satisfying $0 < z < 1/(x^2 + y^2)$ is a connected domain but the set satisfying $z \neq 0$ is not.

6.4.4
Simply Connected Domains

> A connected domain D is said to be **simply connected** if every *closed curve* in D can be continuously shrunk to a point in D without any part ever passing out of D.

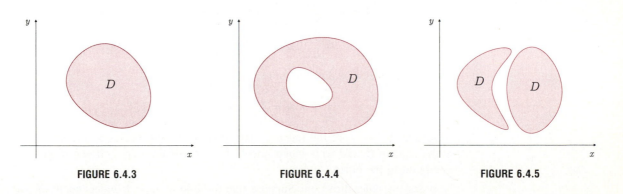

FIGURE 6.4.3   FIGURE 6.4.4   FIGURE 6.4.5

Fig. 6.4.3 shows a simply connected domain in the plane. Fig. 6.4.4 shows a connected but not simply connected domain. (A closed curve surrounding the hole cannot be shrunk to a point without passing out of D.) The domain in Fig. 6.4.5 is not even connected.

In the plane, $\mathbb{R}^2$, a simply connected domain D can have no holes, not even holes consisting of a single point. The interior of every non-self-intersecting closed curve in such a domain D lies in D. For instance, the domain of the function $1/(x^2 + y^2)$ is not simply connected because the origin does not belong to it. (The origin is a "hole" in that domain.) In three dimensions simple connectedness is a little more tricky to characterize. The set of points (x, y, z) satisfying $1 < x^2 + y^2 + z^2 < 4$ (the region between two concentric spheres) is simply connected because any closed curve in that set can be shrunk to a point without having to leave that set. However, the interior of a doughnut (a torus) is not simply connected; a circle in the doughnut surrounding the doughnut hole cannot be shrunk to a point without part of it passing outside the doughnut. The set of all points lying off the z-axis is not simply connected. In general, each of the following conditions characterizes simply connected domains D:

   i) Any closed curve in D is the boundary of a "surface" lying wholly in D.

   ii) If C_1 and C_2 are two curves in D having the same endpoints, then C_1 can be continuously deformed into C_2, remaining in D throughout the deformation process.

Independence of Path

THEOREM 6.4.5   *Independence of Path.* Let $\mathbf{F}$ be a vector field defined on an open connected domain D. The line integral $\int_C \mathbf{F} \bullet d\mathbf{r}$ has the same value for all curves C in D from P_0 to P_1 if and only if $\mathbf{F}$ is conservative in D. If ϕ is a potential function for $\mathbf{F}$ then

$$\int_C \mathbf{F} \bullet d\mathbf{r} = \phi(P_1) - \phi(P_0).$$

PROOF   Let us do the easy direction first. Suppose that $\mathbf{F}$ is conservative in D, so that $\mathbf{F} = \nabla\phi$ for some potential function ϕ defined in D. Then

$$\mathbf{F} \bullet d\mathbf{r} = \left(\frac{\partial\phi}{\partial x}\mathbf{i} + \frac{\partial\phi}{\partial y}\mathbf{j} + \frac{\partial\phi}{\partial z}\mathbf{k}\right) \bullet \left(dx\,\mathbf{i} + dy\,\mathbf{j} + dz\,\mathbf{k}\right)$$
$$= \frac{\partial\phi}{\partial x}\,dx + \frac{\partial\phi}{\partial y}\,dy + \frac{\partial\phi}{\partial y}\,dz = d\phi.$$

If C is any piecewise smooth curve from P_0 to P_1 then

$$\int_C \mathbf{F} \bullet d\mathbf{r} = \int_C d\phi(\mathbf{r}) = \phi(P_1) - \phi(P_0).$$

Note that the value of the integral depends only on the values of the potential ϕ at the ends of C, and so is independent of the particular curve chosen to get from one point to the other.

Now for the other direction. Suppose that the line integral is independent of path. Let $P_0 = (x_0, y_0, z_0)$ be a fixed point in the domain D, and let $P = (x, y, z)$ be an arbitrary point in that domain. Define a function ϕ by

$$\phi(x, y, z) = \int_C \mathbf{F} \bullet d\mathbf{r},$$

where C is some piecewise smooth curve in D from P_0 to P. (Under the hypotheses of the theorem such a curve exists, and by assumption the integral is the same for all such curves, so ϕ is well defined in D.) We will show that $\nabla\phi = \mathbf{F}$ and thus establish that $\mathbf{F}$ is conservative and has potential ϕ.

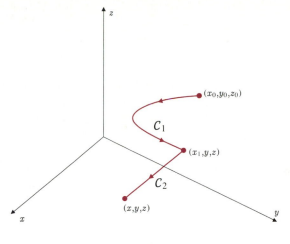

FIGURE 6.4.6

It is sufficient to show that $\partial\phi/\partial x = F_1(x, y, z)$; the other two components are obtained similarly. Since we are free to choose the curve C in the integral defining ϕ, let us choose it to consist of two segments, C_1 which is piecewise smooth and goes from (x_0, y_0, z_0) to (x_1, y, z), and C_2, a straight line segment from (x_1, y, z) to (x, y, z). (See Fig. 6.4.6 for an example.) Then

$$\phi(x, y, z) = \int_{C_1} \mathbf{F} \bullet d\mathbf{r} + \int_{C_2} \mathbf{F} \bullet d\mathbf{r}.$$

Only the second integral depends on x so

$$\frac{\partial\phi}{\partial x} = \frac{\partial}{\partial x} \int_{C_2} \mathbf{F} \bullet d\mathbf{r} = \frac{\partial}{\partial x} \int_{x_1}^{x} F_1(t, y, z)\, dt = F_1(x, y, z),$$

which is what we wanted. □

Recall that a curve C is said to be **closed** if its two endpoints coincide. Circulations of vector fields over closed curves occur frequently in applications of vector calculus, and the closed nature of the curve is often stressed in the notation for the integral:

$$\oint_C \mathbf{F} \bullet d\mathbf{r}.$$

Since closed curves do not have any obvious endpoints it is usually necessary to specify the orientation (direction) of such a curve. Non-self-intersecting closed curves in the plane $\mathbb{R}^2$ are regarded as **positively oriented** if they are traversed counterclockwise. This means that the bounded region which has the curve as boundary is on our left as we trace the curve in the positive direction.

Theorem 6.4.5 has an immediate corollary pertaining to circulations over closed curves.

THEOREM 6.4.6   A vector field defined on an open connected domain D is conservative in D if and only if

$$\oint_C \mathbf{F} \bullet d\mathbf{r} = 0$$

for every piecewise smooth closed curve in D.

PROOF   Let P and Q be two points in D and let C_1 and C_2 be two curves in D from P to Q. Let $-C_2$ be the curve C_2 with the reverse orientation, going from Q to P. Observe that the curve C consisting of C_1 followed by $-C_2$ is a closed curve, and

$$\oint_C \mathbf{F} \bullet d\mathbf{r} = \int_{C_1} \mathbf{F} \bullet d\mathbf{r} + \int_{-C_2} \mathbf{F} \bullet d\mathbf{r} = \int_{C_1} \mathbf{F} \bullet d\mathbf{r} - \int_{C_2} \mathbf{F} \bullet d\mathbf{r}.$$

Thus

$$\int_{C_1} \mathbf{F} \bullet d\mathbf{r} = \int_{C_2} \mathbf{F} \bullet d\mathbf{r} \qquad \Longleftrightarrow \qquad \oint_C \mathbf{F} \bullet d\mathbf{r} = 0.$$

Therefore Theorem 6.4.6 follows at once from Theorem 6.4.5.   □

REMARK: For a vector field defined on an open connected domain we have shown that three conditions are *equivalent:*

(a) $\mathbf{F} = \nabla\phi$ for some scalar potential ϕ,

(b) $\displaystyle\int_C \mathbf{F} \bullet d\mathbf{r}$ is independent of path from P_0 to P_1,

(c) $\displaystyle\oint_C \mathbf{F} \bullet d\mathbf{r} = 0$ for all closed curves C.

In the next chapter we will add another item to this list provided that the domain D is *simply connected.* For such a domain each of the above three conditions is equivalent to

d) $\dfrac{\partial F_1}{\partial y} = \dfrac{\partial F_2}{\partial x},$ $\dfrac{\partial F_1}{\partial z} = \dfrac{\partial F_3}{\partial x},$ $\dfrac{\partial F_2}{\partial z} = \dfrac{\partial F_3}{\partial y}.$

EXAMPLE 6.4.7   Evaluate $I = \oint_C (e^x \sin y + 3y)dx + (e^x \cos y + 2x - 2y)dy$ counterclockwise around the ellipse $4x^2 + y^2 = 4$.

SOLUTION   Observe that the vector field involved is almost, but not quite, conservative. In fact if

$$\phi(x, y) = e^x \sin y + 2xy - y^2$$

then

$$\nabla\phi \bullet d\mathbf{r} = d\phi = (e^x \sin y + 2y)dx + (e^x \cos y + 2x - 2y)dy.$$

Since $\oint_C \nabla\phi \bullet d\mathbf{r} = 0$ we simplify the integral to be evaluated to $\oint_C y\,dx$. Parametrizing C by $x = \cos t$, $y = 2\sin t$, $0 \le t \le 2\pi$, we obtain

$$I = \oint_C y\,dx = -2\int_0^{2\pi} \sin^2 t\,dt = -2\pi.$$

EXERCISES

In Exercises 1–6 evaluate the line integral of the tangential component of the given vector field along the given curve.

1. $\mathbf{F}(x, y) = xy\mathbf{i} - x^2\mathbf{j}$ along $y = x^2$ from (0,0) to (1,1)

2. $\mathbf{F}(x, y) = \cos x\,\mathbf{i} - y\mathbf{j}$ along $y = \sin x$ from (0,0) to $(\pi, 0)$

3. $\mathbf{F}(x, y, z) = y\mathbf{i} + z\mathbf{j} - x\mathbf{k}$ along the straight line from (0,0,0) to (1,1,1)

4. $\mathbf{F}(x, y, z) = z\mathbf{i} - y\mathbf{j} + 2x\mathbf{k}$ along the curve $x = t$, $y = t^2$, $z = t^3$ from (0,0,0) to (1,1,1)

5. $\mathbf{F}(x, y, z) = yz\mathbf{i} + xz\mathbf{j} + xy\mathbf{k}$ from $(-1,0,0)$ to (1,0,0) along either direction of the curve of intersection of the cylinder $x^2 + y^2 = 1$ and the plane $z = y$

6. $\mathbf{F}(x, y, z) = (x - z)\mathbf{i} + (y - z)\mathbf{j} - (x + y)\mathbf{k}$ along the polygonal path from (0,0,0) to (1,0,0) to (1,1,0) to (1,1,1)

7. Find the work done by the force field

$$\mathbf{F} = (x + y)\mathbf{i} + (x - z)\mathbf{j} + (z - y)\mathbf{k}$$

in moving an object from $(1, 0, -1)$ to $(0, -2, 3)$ along any smooth curve.

8. Evaluate $\oint_C x^2 y^2\,dx + x^3 y\,dy$ counterclockwise around the square with vertices (0,0), (1,0), (1,1) and (0,1).

9. Evaluate

$$\int_C e^{x+y} \sin(y + z)\,dx + e^{x+y}\left(\sin(y + z) + \cos(y + z)\right)dy$$
$$+ e^{x+y}\cos(y + z)\,dz$$

along the straight line segment from (0,0,0) to $(1, \frac{\pi}{4}, \frac{\pi}{4})$.

10. Is each of the following sets a domain? a connected domain? a simply connected domain?

a) the set of points (x, y) in the plane such that $x > 0$ and $y \ge 0$.

b) the set of points (x, y) in the plane such that $x = 0$ and $y \ge 0$.

c) the set of points (x, y) in the plane such that $x \ne 0$ and $y > 0$.

d) the set of points (x, y, z) in 3-space such that $x^2 > 1$.

e) the set of points (x, y, z) in 3-space such that $x^2 + y^2 > 1$.

f) the set of points (x, y, z) in 3-space such that $x^2 + y^2 + z^2 > 1$.

In Exercises 11–15 evaluate the closed line integrals

a) $\oint_C x\,dy$,   b) $\oint_C y\,dx$

around the given curves, all oriented counterclockwise.

11. The circle $x^2 + y^2 = a^2$

12. The ellipse $\dfrac{x^2}{a^2} + \dfrac{y^2}{b^2} = 1$

13. The boundary of the half disc $x^2 + y^2 \le a^2$, $y \ge 0$

14. The boundary of the square with vertices $(0,0)$, $(1,0)$, $(1,1)$ and $(0,1)$

15. The triangle with vertices $(0,0)$, $(a, 0)$ and $(0, b)$

16. On the basis of your results for the previous five exercises guess the values of the closed line integrals

$$
\text{a)} \quad \oint_C x\,dy, \qquad\qquad \text{b)} \quad \oint_C y\,dx
$$

for any non-self-intersecting closed curve in the xy-plane. Prove your guess in the case that C bounds a region of the plane which is both x-simple and y-simple. (See Section 4.1.)

17. If f and g are scalar fields with continuous first partial derivatives in a connected domain D, show that

$$
\int_C f \nabla g \bullet d\mathbf{r} + \int_C g \nabla f \bullet d\mathbf{r} = f(Q)g(Q) - f(P)g(P)
$$

for any piecewise smooth curve in D from P to Q.

18. Evaluate

$$
\frac{1}{2\pi} \oint_C \frac{-y\,dx + x\,dy}{x^2 + y^2}
$$

a) counterclockwise around the circle $x^2 + y^2 = a^2$.

b) clockwise around the square with vertices $(-1, -1)$, $(-1, 1)$, $(1, 1)$ and $(1, -1)$.

c) counterclockwise around the boundary of the region $1 \le x^2 + y^2 \le 2$, $y \ge 0$.

19. Review Example 6.2.8, in which it was shown that

$$
\frac{\partial}{\partial y}\left(\frac{-y}{x^2 + y^2}\right) = \frac{\partial}{\partial x}\left(\frac{x}{x^2 + y^2}\right),
$$

for all $(x, y) \ne (0, 0)$. Why does this result, together with that of the previous exercise, not contradict the final assertion in the remark following Theorem 6.4.6?

20.*Let C be a piecewise smooth curve in the xy-plane which does not pass through the origin. Let $\theta = \theta(x, y)$ be the polar angle coordinate of the point $P = (x, y)$ on C, not restricted to an interval of length 2π, but varying continuously as P moves from one end of C to the other. As in Example 6.2.8, it happens that

$$
\nabla\theta = -\frac{y}{x^2 + y^2}\,\mathbf{i} + \frac{x}{x^2 + y^2}\,\mathbf{j}.
$$

If, in addition, C is a closed curve, show that

$$
w(C) = \frac{1}{2\pi} \oint_C \frac{x\,dy - y\,dx}{x^2 + y^2}
$$

has an integer value. w is called the **winding number** of C about the origin.

6.5   SURFACES AND SURFACE INTEGRALS

This section and the next are devoted to integrals of functions defined over surfaces in $\mathbb{R}^3$. Before we can begin, it is necessary to make more precise just what is meant by the term "surface." Until now we have been treating surfaces in an intuitive way, either as the graphs of functions $f(x, y)$, or as the graphs of equations $f(x, y, z) = 0$.

A smooth curve is considered to be a "one-dimensional" object because points on it can be located by giving *one coordinate* (for instance, the distance from an endpoint). Therefore the curve can be defined as the range of a vector-valued function of a single real variable. Similarly, a surface is a "two-dimensional" object; points on it can be located by using *two coordinates*, and the surface can be defined as the range of a vector-valued function of two real variables. We will call certain such functions parametric surfaces.

Parametric Surfaces

6.5.1
Parametric
Surfaces

> A **parametric surface** in $\mathbb{R}^3$ is a one-to-one, continuous 3-vector-valued function $\mathbf{r}$ defined on some rectangle R given by $a \le u \le b$, $c \le v \le d$ in the uv-plane:
>
> $$\mathbf{r}(u, v) = x(u, v)\mathbf{i} + y(u, v)\mathbf{j} + z(u, v)\mathbf{k}, \qquad (u, v) \text{ in } R.$$

Actually, we think of the *range* of the function $\mathbf{r}(u, v)$ as being the parametric surface. It is a set of points (x, y, z) in 3-space whose position vectors are the vectors $\mathbf{r}(u, v)$ for (u, v) in R. The requirement that $\mathbf{r}$ be one-to-one ensures that the surface does not intersect itself. It also ensures that $\mathbf{r}$ maps the boundary of the rectangle R (the four edges) onto a curve in 3-space, which we call the **boundary of the parametric surface**. The requirement that R be a closed rectangle is made only to simplify the discussion. Any connected, closed, bounded set in the uv-plane, having well-defined area, and consisting of an open set together with its boundary points would do as well. Thus, we may from time to time consider parametric surfaces over closed discs, triangles or other such domains in the uv-plane. Being the ranges of continuous functions defined on closed, bounded sets, parametric surfaces are always bounded in 3-space.

EXAMPLE 6.5.2   The graph of $z = f(x, y)$, where f has the rectangle R as its domain, can be represented as the parametric surface

$$\mathbf{r} = u\mathbf{i} + v\mathbf{j} + f(u, v)\mathbf{k}$$

for (u, v) in R. Its scalar parametric equations are

$$x = u, \qquad y = v, \qquad z = f(u, v), \qquad (u, v) \text{ in } D.$$

For such graphs it is sometimes convenient to identify the uv-plane with the xy-plane, and write the equation of the surface in the form

$$\mathbf{r} = x\mathbf{i} + y\mathbf{j} + f(x, y)\mathbf{k}, \qquad (x, y) \text{ in } R.$$

EXAMPLE 6.5.3   The hemisphere $z = \sqrt{a^2 - x^2 - y^2}$ can be represented as a parametric surface

$$\mathbf{r}(u, v) = u\mathbf{i} + v\mathbf{j} + \sqrt{a^2 - u^2 - v^2}\mathbf{k} \qquad \text{for} \quad u^2 + v^2 \le a^2.$$

Here the domain of $\mathbf{r}$ is a closed disc of radius a. The circle $x^2 + y^2 = a^2$ in the plane $z = 0$ is the boundary of the parametric surface.

As a set of points in 3-space, a given parametric surface may be represented by many different functions $\mathbf{r}(u, v)$, not all of which satisfy the restrictions in the definition 6.5.1. When we want to consider a parametric surface as merely a geometric object, apart from any particular parametrization, we will simply call it a **surface**.

EXAMPLE 6.5.4   Describe, geometrically, the surface

$$\mathbf{r} = a\cos u\sin v\mathbf{i} + a\sin u\sin v\mathbf{j} + a\cos v\mathbf{k}, \qquad 0 \le u \le 2\pi, \quad 0 \le v \le \pi/2.$$

What is its boundary?

SOLUTION   Observe that if $x = a\cos u\sin v$, $y = a\sin u\sin v$, and $z = a\cos v$, then $x^2 + y^2 + z^2 = a^2$. Thus the given parametric surface lies on the sphere of radius a centred at the origin. The restrictions on u and v allow (x,y) to be any point in the disc $x^2 + y^2 \le a^2$, but force $z \ge 0$. Thus the surface is the *upper half* of the sphere, that is, it is the same surface as in Example 6.5.3. The parametrization given above is one-to-one on the open rectangle $0 < u < 2\pi$, $0 < v < \pi/2$, but not on the closed rectangle, since the edges $u = 0$ and $u = 2\pi$ get mapped onto the same points, and the entire edge $v = 0$ collapses to a single point. The boundary of the surface is still the circle $x^2 + y^2 = a^2$, $z = 0$, and corresponds to the edge $v = \pi/2$ of the rectangle.

REMARK: Parametrizations of a surface which are one-to-one only in the interior of the domain R are still reasonable representations of the surface. However, the boundary of the surface may be obtained from only part of the boundary of the domain R, or there may be no boundary at all, in which case the surface is called **a closed surface**. For example If the domain of $\mathbf{r}$ in Example 6.5.4 is extended to allow $0 \le v \le \pi$ then the surface becomes the entire sphere of radius a centred at the origin. The sphere is a closed surface, having no boundary curves.

If two parametric surfaces are joined together along part or all of their boundary curves, the result is called a **composite surface**, or, again thinking geometrically, just **a surface**. For example, a sphere can be obtained by joining two hemispheres along their boundary circles. In general, composite surfaces can be obtained by joining a finite number of parametric surfaces pairwise along edges. For example, the surface of a cube consists of the six square faces joined in pairs along the edges of the cube.

Surface Integrals

In order to define integrals of functions defined on a surface as limits of Riemann sums, we need to refer to the *areas* of regions on the surface. It is more difficult to define the area of a curved surface than it is to define the length of a curve. However, the student will have a good idea of what area means for a region lying in a plane. Therefore we will avoid the difficulty by assuming that all the surfaces we will encounter are "smooth enough" that they can be subdivided into small pieces each of which is approximately planar. We can then approximate the surface area of each piece by a plane area and add up the approximations to get a Riemann sum approximation to the area of the whole surface. We will make more precise definitions of "smooth surface" and "surface area" later in this section. For the moment, we assume the reader has an intuitive feel for what they mean.

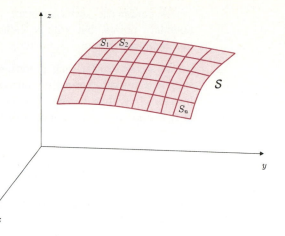

FIGURE 6.5.1

Let S be a "smooth" surface of finite "area" in $\mathbb{R}^3$, and let $f(x, y, z)$ be a bounded function defined at all points of S. If we subdivide S into small, non-overlapping pieces, say S_1, S_2, ..., S_n, where S_i has area ΔS_i, we can form a **Riemann sum** R_n for f on S by choosing arbitrary points (x_i, y_i, z_i) in S_i and letting

$$R_n = \sum_{i=1}^{n} f(x_i, y_i, z_i)\, \Delta S_i.$$

(See Fig. 6.5.1.) If such Riemann sums have a unique limit as the diameters of all the pieces S_i approach zero, independently of how the points (x_i, y_i, z_i) are chosen, then we say that f is **integrable** on S, and denote the limit by

$$\iint_S f(x, y, z)\, dS.$$

Smooth Surfaces

6.5.5
Definition of
Smooth Surface

A set S in 3-space is a **smooth surface** if any point P in S is the centre of a (sufficiently small) ball B which is the domain of a smooth function $g(x, y, z)$ satisfying:

(i) $B \cap S = \{Q \in B : g(Q) = 0\}$, and

(ii) $\nabla g(Q) \neq \mathbf{0}$, if Q is in $B \cap S$.

For example, the cone $x^2 + y^2 = z^2$, with the origin removed, is a smooth surface. Note that $\nabla(x^2 + y^2 - z^2) = \mathbf{0}$ at the origin, and the cone is not smooth there, since it does not have a unique tangent plane.

A parametric surface cannot satisfy the condition of Definition 6.5.5 at its boundary points, but will be called **smooth** if that condition is satisfied at all non-boundary points.

A smooth surface has a nonzero normal vector $\mathbf{n} = \nabla g(P)$ at any point on it. If S is a smooth parametric surface defined on R, and (u_0, v_0) is a point in the interior of R, then $\mathbf{r} = \mathbf{r}(u, v_0)$ and $\mathbf{r} = \mathbf{r}(u_0, v)$ are two curves on S, intersecting at $\mathbf{r}_0 = \mathbf{r}(u_0, v_0)$, and having, at that point, tangent vectors

$$\left.\frac{\partial \mathbf{r}}{\partial u}\right|_{(u_0, v_0)} \quad \text{and} \quad \left.\frac{\partial \mathbf{r}}{\partial v}\right|_{(u_0, v_0)}$$

respectively. Assuming these two tangent vectors are not parallel, their cross product $\mathbf{n}$, which is not zero, is *normal* to S at $\mathbf{r}_0$. Furthermore, the *area element* on S bounded by the four curves $\mathbf{r} = \mathbf{r}(u_0, v)$, $\mathbf{r} = \mathbf{r}(u_0 + du, v)$, $\mathbf{r} = \mathbf{r}(u, v_0)$, and $\mathbf{r} = \mathbf{r}(u, v_0 + dv)$, (see Fig. 6.5.2,) is an infinitesimal parallelogram spanned by the vectors $\dfrac{\partial \mathbf{r}}{\partial u}\, du$, and $\dfrac{\partial \mathbf{r}}{\partial v}\, dv$ (at (u_0, v_0)), and hence has area

$$dS = \left| \frac{\partial \mathbf{r}}{\partial u} \times \frac{\partial \mathbf{r}}{\partial v} \right| du\, dv.$$

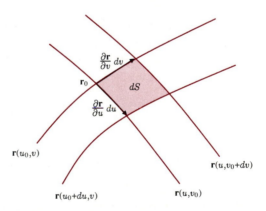

FIGURE 6.5.2

Let us express the normal vector $\mathbf{n}$ and the area element dS in terms of the components of $\mathbf{r}$. Since

$$\frac{\partial \mathbf{r}}{\partial u} = \frac{\partial x}{\partial u}\mathbf{i} + \frac{\partial y}{\partial u}\mathbf{j} + \frac{\partial z}{\partial u}\mathbf{k}, \qquad \text{and} \qquad \frac{\partial \mathbf{r}}{\partial v} = \frac{\partial x}{\partial v}\mathbf{i} + \frac{\partial y}{\partial v}\mathbf{j} + \frac{\partial z}{\partial v}\mathbf{k},$$

we have

6.5.6
Normal Vector
to a Smooth
Parametric Surface

$$\mathbf{n} = \frac{\partial \mathbf{r}}{\partial u} \times \frac{\partial \mathbf{r}}{\partial v} = \begin{vmatrix} \mathbf{i} & \mathbf{j} & \mathbf{k} \\ \dfrac{\partial x}{\partial u} & \dfrac{\partial y}{\partial u} & \dfrac{\partial z}{\partial u} \\ \dfrac{\partial x}{\partial v} & \dfrac{\partial y}{\partial v} & \dfrac{\partial z}{\partial v} \end{vmatrix}$$

$$= \frac{\partial(y, z)}{\partial(u, v)} \mathbf{i} + \frac{\partial(z, x)}{\partial(u, v)} \mathbf{j} + \frac{\partial(x, y)}{\partial(u, v)} \mathbf{k}$$

Also, the area element at a point $\mathbf{r}$ on the surface is given by

6.5.7
Area Element
on a Smooth
Parametric Surface

$$dS = \left| \frac{\partial \mathbf{r}}{\partial u} \times \frac{\partial \mathbf{r}}{\partial v} \right| \, du \, dv$$

$$= \sqrt{\left(\frac{\partial(y, z)}{\partial(u, v)} \right)^2 + \left(\frac{\partial(z, x)}{\partial(u, v)} \right)^2 + \left(\frac{\partial(x, y)}{\partial(u, v)} \right)^2} \, du \, dv.$$

The area of the surface itself is the "sum" of these area elements.

6.5.8
Area of a
Smooth Surface

$$\text{Area of } S = \iint_S dS.$$

EXAMPLE 6.5.9 The graph $z = g(x, y)$ of a function g with continuous first partial derivatives in a domain D of the xy-plane can be regarded as a parametric surface S with parametrization

$$x = u, \qquad y = v, \qquad z = g(u, v), \qquad (u, v) \text{ in } D.$$

In this case

$$\frac{\partial(y, z)}{\partial(u, v)} = -g_1(u, v), \qquad \frac{\partial(z, x)}{\partial(u, v)} = -g_2(u, v), \qquad \frac{\partial(x, y)}{\partial(u, v)} = 1,$$

and, since the parameter region coincides with the domain D of g, the surface integral of $f(x, y, z)$ over S can be expressed as a double integral over D:

6.5.10
Surface Integral
over the Graph
of a Function

$$\iint_D f(x, y, g(x, y)) \sqrt{1 + (g_1(x, y))^2 + (g_2(x, y))^2} \, dx \, dy.$$

This formula can also be justified geometrically. The vector $\mathbf{n} = -g_1(x,y)\mathbf{i} - g_2(x,y)\mathbf{j} + \mathbf{k}$ is normal to $\mathcal{S}$ and makes angle γ with the positive z-axis, where

$$\cos\gamma = \frac{\mathbf{n} \bullet \mathbf{k}}{|\mathbf{n}|} = \frac{1}{\sqrt{1 + \big(g_1(x,y)\big)^2 + \big(g_2(x,y)\big)^2}}.$$

The surface area element dS must have area $1/\cos\gamma$ times the area $dx\,dy$ of its perpendicular projection onto the xy-plane. (See Fig. 6.5.3.)

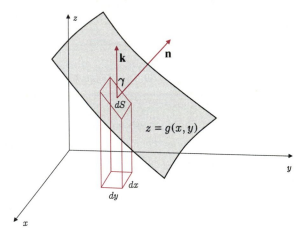

FIGURE 6.5.3

Evaluating Surface Integrals

Formula 6.5.10 is useful for evaluating integrals over the graphs of functions.

EXAMPLE 6.5.11   Evaluate $\iint_{\mathcal{S}} z\,dS$ over the conical surface $z = \sqrt{x^2 + y^2}$ between $z = 0$ and $z = 1$.

SOLUTION   Since $z^2 = x^2 + y^2$ on the surface $\mathcal{S}$, we have $\partial z/\partial x = x/z$ and $\partial z/\partial y = y/z$. Therefore

$$dS = \sqrt{1 + \frac{x^2}{z^2} + \frac{y^2}{z^2}}\,dx\,dy = \sqrt{\frac{z^2 + z^2}{z^2}}\,dx\,dy = \sqrt{2}\,dx\,dy.$$

(Note that we could have anticipated this result since the normal to the cone always makes an angle of $\gamma = 45°$ with the positive z-axis. Therefore $dS = dx\,dy/\cos 45° = \sqrt{2}\,dx\,dy$.) Since $z = \sqrt{x^2 + y^2} = r$ on the conical surface, it is easiest to carry out the integration in polar coordinates:

$$\iint_{\mathcal{S}} z\,dS = \sqrt{2} \iint_{x^2+y^2\leq 1} z\,dx\,dy$$
$$= \sqrt{2} \int_0^{2\pi} d\theta \int_0^1 r^2\,dr = \frac{2\sqrt{2}\pi}{3}.$$

Even though most surfaces we encounter can be easily parametrized, it is usually possible to obtain the surface area element dS geometrically rather than relying on the parametric formula. As we have seen above, if a surface has a one-to-one projection onto a region in the xy-plane, then the area element dS on the surface can be expressed as

6.5.12
Writing dS
in Terms of $dx\,dy$

$$dS = \left| \frac{1}{\cos \gamma} \right| dx\,dy = \frac{|\mathbf{n}|}{|\mathbf{n} \bullet \mathbf{k}|} dx\,dy,$$

where γ is the angle between the normal vector $\mathbf{n}$ to S and the positive z-axis. This formula is useful no matter how we obtain $\mathbf{n}$.

Consider a surface S with equation of the form $F(x, y, z) = 0$. As we observed in Section 2.6, if F has continuous first partial derivatives which do not all vanish at a point (x, y, z) on S, then the nonzero vector

$$\mathbf{n} = \nabla F(x, y, z)$$

is normal to S at that point. Suppose that S has a one-to-one projection onto the domain D in the xy-plane. Then there exists a function $g(x, y)$, defined on D, such that $F(x, y, g(x, y)) = 0$. This implies that S has the equation $z = g(x, y)$. If we know that $\mathbf{n} \bullet \mathbf{k} = F_3(x, y, z) \neq 0$ on S, then

6.5.13
An Area Element
for $F(x, y, z) = 0$.

$$dS = \left| \frac{\nabla F(x, y, z)}{F_3(x, y, z)} \right| dx\,dy.$$

Hence a surface integral of $f(x, y, z)$ over S can be expressed as a double integral over the domain D:

$$\iint_S f(x, y, z)\,dS = \iint_D f(x, y, g(x, y)) \left| \frac{\nabla F(x, y, z)}{F_3(x, y, z)} \right| dx\,dy.$$

Of course, there are analogous formulas for area elements of surfaces (and integrals over surfaces) with one-to-one projections onto the xz-plane or the yz-plane. (F_3 is replaced by F_2 and F_1 respectively.)

EXAMPLE 6.5.14   Find $\iint_S z\,dS$ where S is the hyperbolic bowl $z^2 = 1 + x^2 + y^2$ between the planes $z = 1$ and $z = \sqrt{5}$.

SOLUTION S is given by $F(x, y, z) = 0$, where $F(x, y, z) = x^2 + y^2 - z^2 + 1$. It lies above the disc $x^2 + y^2 \leq 4$ in the xy-plane. We have $\nabla F = 2x\mathbf{i} + 2y\mathbf{j} - 2z\mathbf{k}$, and $F_3 = -2z$. Hence, on S, we have

$$z \, dS = z \, \frac{\sqrt{4x^2 + 4y^2 + 4z^2}}{2z} \, dx \, dy = \sqrt{1 + 2(x^2 + y^2)} \, dx \, dy,$$

and the required integral is

$$\iint_S z \, dS = \iint_{x^2 + y^2 \leq 4} \sqrt{1 + 2(x^2 + y^2)} \, dx \, dy$$

$$= \int_0^{2\pi} d\theta \int_0^2 \sqrt{1 + 2r^2} \, r \, dr = \frac{\pi}{3}(1 + 2r^2)^{3/2} \Big|_0^2 = \frac{26\pi}{3}.$$

The next example illustrates a technique that can often reduce the effort needed to integrate over a cylindrical surface.

EXAMPLE 6.5.15 Find the area of that part of the cylinder $x^2 + y^2 = 2ay$ which lies inside the sphere $x^2 + y^2 + z^2 = 4a^2$.

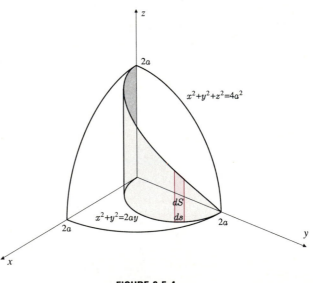

FIGURE 6.5.4

SOLUTION One quarter of the required area lies in the first octant. (See Fig. 6.5.4.) Since the cylinder is generated by vertical lines, we can express an area element dS on it in terms of the length element ds along the curve C in the xy-plane having equation $x^2 + y^2 = 2ay$:

$$dS = z \, ds = \sqrt{4a^2 - x^2 - y^2} \, ds.$$

Again it is convenient to use polar coordinates in the xy-plane. In terms of polar coordinates the arc length element is $ds = \sqrt{r^2 + (dr/d\theta)^2}\, d\theta$ and the curve C has equation $r = 2a \sin\theta$. Thus $dr/d\theta = 2a \cos\theta$ and $ds = 2a\, d\theta$. Therefore the total surface area of that part of the cylinder which lies inside the sphere is given by

$$A = 4 \int_0^{\pi/2} \sqrt{4a^2 - r^2}\, 2a\, d\theta$$

$$= 8a \int_0^{\pi/2} \sqrt{4a^2 - 4a^2 \sin^2\theta}\, d\theta$$

$$= 16a^2 \int_0^{\pi/2} \cos\theta\, d\theta = 16a^2 \text{ units}^2.$$

In spherical coordinates, ϕ and θ can be used as parameters on the spherical surface $R = a$. The area element on that surface can therefore be expressed in terms of these coordinates. (See Chapter 4, Fig. 4.5.4, and Exercise 2 at the end of this section.)

6.5.16
An Area Element
for the Sphere $R = a$

$$dS = a^2 \sin\phi\, d\phi\, d\theta.$$

EXAMPLE 6.5.17   Find $\displaystyle\iint_S z^2\, dS$ over the hemisphere $z = \sqrt{a^2 - x^2 - y^2}$.

SOLUTION   Since $z = a \cos\phi$ and the hemisphere corresponds to $0 \le \theta \le 2\pi$, and $0 \le \phi \le \dfrac{\pi}{2}$, we have

$$\iint_S z^2\, dS = \int_0^{2\pi} d\theta \int_0^{\pi/2} a^2 \cos^2\phi\, a^2 \sin\phi\, d\phi$$

$$= 2\pi a^4 \left(-\frac{1}{3} \cos^3\phi \right)\Bigg|_0^{\pi/2} = \frac{2\pi a^4}{3}.$$

Finally, if a composite surface S is composed of *smooth parametric surfaces* joined pairwise along edges, then we call S a **piecewise smooth surface**. The surface integral of a function f over a piecewise smooth surface S is the sum of the surface integrals of f over the individual smooth surfaces comprising S. We shall encounter an example of this in the next section.

The Attraction of a Spherical Shell

In Section 4.6 we calculated the gravitational attraction of a disc in the xy-plane on a mass m located at position $(0, 0, b)$ on the z-axis. Here we undertake a similar, but somewhat more difficult calculation of the attractive force exerted on m by a spherical shell of radius a and areal density σ (units of mass per unit area). Again symmetry indicates that the net force will be directed towards the centre of the sphere (the origin). Thus the total force will be $-F\mathbf{k}$ where F is the magnitude of the force.

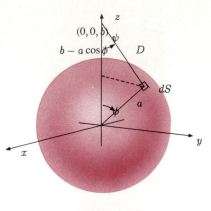

FIGURE 6.5.5

We will calculate F by integrating the vertical component dF of the force of attraction on m due to the mass $\sigma\,dS$ in an area element dS on the sphere. If we use spherical coordinates and denote by ψ the angle between the z-axis and the line joining m to dS (see Fig. 6.5.5) then we have

$$dF = \frac{km\sigma dS}{D^2}\cos\psi = km\sigma\,\frac{(b - a\cos\phi)a^2\sin\phi}{D^3}\,d\phi\,d\theta.$$

D can be written in terms of ϕ using the cosine law:

$$D^2 = a^2 - 2ab\cos\phi + b^2.$$

Hence the magnitude of the total force on m is

$$F = km\sigma a^2 \int_0^{2\pi} d\theta \int_0^\pi \frac{(b - a\cos\phi)\sin\phi\,d\phi}{(a^2 - 2ab\cos\phi + b^2)^{3/2}}$$

$$= 2\pi km\sigma a^2 \int_{-1}^1 \frac{(b - at)dt}{(a^2 - 2abt + b^2)^{3/2}}.$$

We have made the change of variable $t = \cos\phi$ to get the last integral. This integral can be evaluated by using another substitution. Let $u = \sqrt{a^2 - 2abt + b^2}$. Thus

$$t = \frac{a^2 + b^2 - u^2}{2ab}, \qquad dt = -\frac{u\,du}{ab}, \qquad b - at = \frac{u^2 + b^2 - a^2}{2b}.$$

When $t = -1$ and $t = 1$ we have $u = a + b$ and $u = |a - b|$ respectively. Therefore

$$F = 2\pi km\sigma a^2 \int_{a+b}^{|a-b|} \frac{u^2 + b^2 - a^2}{2bu^3}\left(-\frac{u\,du}{ab}\right)$$

$$= \frac{\pi km\sigma a}{b^2} \int_{|a-b|}^{a+b}\left(1 + \frac{b^2 - a^2}{u^2}\right)du$$

$$= \frac{\pi km\sigma a}{b^2}\left(u - \frac{b^2 - a^2}{u}\right)\Bigg|_{|a-b|}^{a+b}.$$

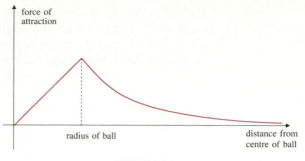

FIGURE 6.5.6

There are now two cases to consider. If the mass m is *outside* the sphere, so that $b > a$ and $|a - b| = b - a$, then

$$F = \frac{\pi k m \sigma a}{b^2} \left((a + b) - (b - a) - (b - a) + (b + a) \right) = 4\pi k m \sigma \frac{a^2}{b^2}.$$

However, if m is *inside* the sphere, so that $b < a$ and $|a - b| = a - b$, then

$$F = \frac{\pi k m \sigma a}{b^2} \left((a + b) + (a - b) - (a - b) - (a + b) \right) = 0.$$

We are led to the somewhat surprising result that if the mass m is anywhere inside the sphere, the net force of attraction of the sphere on it is zero. This is to be expected at the centre of the sphere, but away from the centre it appears that the larger forces due to parts of the sphere close to m are exactly cancelled by smaller forces due to parts further away; these further parts have larger area and therefore larger total mass. If m is outside the sphere the sphere attracts it with a force of magnitude

$$F = \frac{k m M}{b^2}$$

where $M = 4\pi\sigma a^2$ is the total mass of the sphere. This is the same force that would be exerted by a point mass with the same mass as the sphere and located at the centre of the sphere.

REMARK: A solid ball of constant density, or density depending only on the distance from the centre (for instance, a planet), can be regarded as made up of mass elements which are concentric spheres of constant density. Therefore the attraction of such a ball on a mass m located outside the ball will also be the same as if the whole mass of the ball were concentrated at its centre. However, the attraction on a mass m located somewhere inside the ball will be that produced only by that part of the ball which is at least as close to the centre as m is. The maximum force of attraction will occur when m is right at the surface of the ball. If the density is constant, the magnitude of the force increases linearly with the distance from the centre (why?) up to the surface and then decreases with the square of the distance as m recedes from the ball. (See Fig. 6.5.6.)

REMARK: All of the above discussion also holds for electrostatic attraction or repulsion of a point charge by a uniform charge density over a spherical shell, which is also governed by an inverse square law. In particular there is no net electrostatic force on a charge located inside the shell.

EXERCISES

1. Verify that on the curve with polar equation $r = g(\theta)$ the arc length element is given by

$$ds = \sqrt{(g(\theta))^2 + (g'(\theta))^2}\, d\theta.$$

What is the area element on the vertical cylinder given in terms of cylindrical coordinates by $r = g(\theta)$?

2. Verify that on the spherical surface $x^2 + y^2 + z^2 = a^2$ the area element is given in terms of spherical coordinates by $dS = a^2 \sin\phi\, d\phi\, d\theta$.

3. Find the area of that part of the plane $Ax + By + Cz = D$ lying inside the elliptic cylinder

$$\frac{x^2}{a^2} + \frac{y^2}{b^2} = 1.$$

4. Find the area of that part of the sphere $x^2 + y^2 + z^2 = 4a^2$ which lies inside the cylinder $x^2 + y^2 = 2ay$.

5. Find $\displaystyle\iint_S x\, dS$ over that part of the parabolic cylinder $z = x^2/2$ which lies inside the first octant part of the cylinder $x^2 + y^2 = 1$.

6. Find the area of that part of the cone $z^2 = x^2 + y^2$ which lies inside the cylinder $x^2 + y^2 = 2ay$.

7. Find the area of that part of the cylinder $x^2 + y^2 = 2ay$ which lies outside the cone $z^2 = x^2 + y^2$.

8. Find the area of that part of the cylinder $x^2 + z^2 = a^2$ which lies inside the cylinder $y^2 + z^2 = a^2$.

9. A circular cylinder of radius a is circumscribed about a sphere of radius a so the cylinder is tangent to the sphere along the equator. Two planes, each perpendicular to the axis of the cylinder, intersect the sphere and the cylinder in circles. Show that the area of that part of the sphere between the two planes is equal to the area of that part of the cylinder between the two planes. Thus the area of that part of a sphere between two parallel planes which intersect it depends only on the radius of the sphere and the distance between the planes, and not on the particular position of planes.

10. Let $0 < a < b$. In terms of the elliptic integral functions defined in Exercise 11 of Section 6.3, find the area of that part of each of the cylinders $x^2 + z^2 = a^2$ and $y^2 + z^2 = b^2$ which lies inside the other cylinder.

11. Describe the parametric surface

$$x = au\cos v, \qquad y = au\sin v, \qquad z = bv,$$

$(0 \le u \le 1,\ 0 \le v \le 2\pi)$, and find its area.

12. An ellipsoid with two of its semi-axes equal is called a **spheroid**. Find the surface area of the spheroid

$$\frac{x^2}{a^2} + \frac{y^2}{a^2} + \frac{z^2}{c^2} = 1.$$

13.*Evaluate $\displaystyle\iint_{\mathcal{P}} \frac{dS}{(x^2 + y^2 + z^2)^{3/2}}$ where $\mathcal{P}$ is the plane with equation $Ax + By + Cz = D$, $(D \neq 0)$.

14. A spherical shell of radius a is centred at the origin. Find the centroid of that part of the sphere which lies in the first octant.

15. Find the centre of mass of a conical shell of base radius a and height h and constant area density σ.

16.*Find the gravitational attraction of a hemispherical shell of radius a and constant area density σ on a mass m located at the centre of the base of the hemisphere.

17.*Find the gravitational attraction of a circular cylindrical shell of radius a, height h and constant area density σ on a mass m located on the axis of the cylinder b units above the base.

In Exercises 18–20 find the moment of inertia and radius of gyration of the given object about the given axis. Assume constant area density σ in each case.

18. A cylindrical shell of radius a, height h about the axis of the cylinder.

19. A spherical shell of radius a about a diameter.

20. A conical shell of base radius a and height h about the axis of the cone.

21. With what acceleration will the spherical shell of Exercise 19 roll down a plane inclined at angle α to the horizontal. (Compare your result with Example 4.6.7(b).)

6.6   SURFACE INTEGRALS OF VECTOR FIELDS

Surface integrals of normal components of vector fields play a very important role in vector calculus, similar to the role played by line integrals of tangential components of vector fields. Before we consider such surface integrals we need to define the *orientation* of a surface.

Oriented Surfaces

A smooth surface S in 3-space is said to be **orientable** if there exists a unit vector field $\hat{\mathbf{N}}(P)$ defined on S which varies continuously as P ranges over S and which is everywhere normal to S. Any such vector field $\hat{\mathbf{N}}(P)$ determines an **orientation** of S. The surface must have two sides since $\hat{\mathbf{N}}(P)$ can have only one value at each point P. The side out of which $\hat{\mathbf{N}}$ points is called the **positive side**; the other side is the **negative side**. An **oriented surface** is a smooth surface together with a particular choice of orienting unit normal vector field $\hat{\mathbf{N}}(P)$.

For example, if we define $\hat{\mathbf{N}}$ on the smooth surface $z = f(x, y)$ by

$$\hat{\mathbf{N}} = \frac{-f_1(x, y)\mathbf{i} - f_2(x, y)\mathbf{j} + \mathbf{k}}{\sqrt{1 + (f_1(x, y))^2 + (f_2(x, y))^2}}$$

then the top of the surface is the positive side. (See Fig. 6.6.1.)

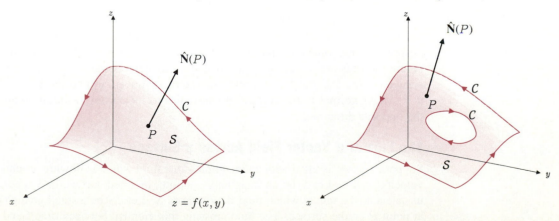

FIGURE 6.6.1   **FIGURE 6.6.2**

A smooth or piecewise smooth surface may be **closed** (that is, it may have no boundary), or it may have one or more boundary curves. (The unit normal vector field $\hat{\mathbf{N}}(P)$ need not be defined at points of the boundary curves.)

An oriented surface S **induces an orientation** on any of its boundary curves C; if we stand on the positive side of the surface S and walk around C in the direction of its orientation then S will be on our left hand side. (See Figures 6.6.1 and 6.6.2.)

A *piecewise smooth* surface is **orientable** if, whenever two smooth component surfaces join along a common boundary curve C, they induce *opposite* orientations along C. This forces the normals $\hat{\mathbf{N}}$ to be on the same side of adjacent components. For instance, the surface of a cube is a piecewise smooth, closed surface, consisting of six smooth surfaces (the square faces) joined along edges. (See Fig. 6.6.3.) If all of the faces are oriented so that their normals $\hat{\mathbf{N}}$ point out of the cube (or if they all point into the cube), then surface of the cube itself is oriented.

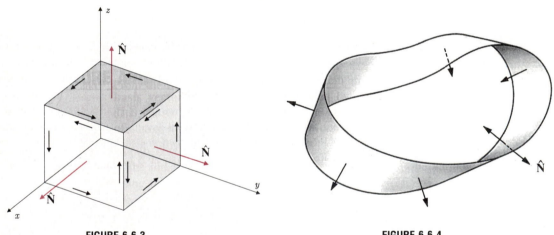

FIGURE 6.6.3   FIGURE 6.6.4

Not every surface can be oriented even if it appears smooth. An orientable surface must have two sides. For example, a Möbius band, consisting of a strip of paper with ends joined together to form a loop, but with one end given a half twist before the ends are joined, has only one side (make one and see), so it cannot be oriented. (See Fig. 6.6.4.) If a nonzero vector is moved around the band so that it is always normal to the surface, it can return to its starting position pointing in the opposite direction.

The Flux of a Vector Field Across a Surface

Suppose 3-space is filled with an incompressible fluid which is flowing around with velocity field $\mathbf{v}$. Let S be an imaginary, smooth, oriented surface in 3-space. Let us calculate the rate at which fluid flows across S. Let dS be a small area element at point P on the surface. The fluid crossing that element between time t and time $t + dt$ occupies a cylinder of base area dS and height $|\mathbf{v}(P)|\, dt \cos\theta$, where θ is the angle between $\mathbf{v}(P)$ and the normal $\hat{\mathbf{N}}(P)$. (See Fig. 6.6.5.) Therefore this cylinder has volume $\mathbf{v}(P) \bullet \hat{\mathbf{N}}(P)\, dS\, dt$. The rate at which fluid is crossing dS is $\mathbf{v}(P) \bullet \hat{\mathbf{N}}(P)\, dS$, and the total rate at which it is crossing S is given by the surface integral

$$\iint_S \mathbf{v} \bullet \hat{\mathbf{N}}\, dS = \iint_S \mathbf{v} \bullet d\mathbf{S},$$

where $d\mathbf{S}$ is the vector surface area element $\hat{\mathbf{N}}\, dS$.

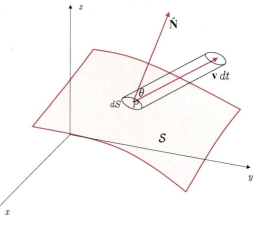

FIGURE 6.6.5

6.6.1
Flux of a
Vector Field
across a Surface

Given any continuous vector field $\mathbf{F}$, the integral of the normal component of $\mathbf{F}$ over S,

$$\iint_S \mathbf{F} \bullet \hat{\mathbf{N}}\, dS = \iint_S \mathbf{F} \bullet d\mathbf{S}$$

is called the **flux** of $\mathbf{F}$ across S.

When the surface is closed, the flux integral can be denoted by

$$\oiint_S \mathbf{F} \bullet \hat{\mathbf{N}}\, dS, \qquad \text{or} \qquad \oiint_S \mathbf{F} \bullet d\mathbf{S}.$$

In this case we refer to the flux of $\mathbf{F}$ *out of* S if $\hat{\mathbf{N}}$ is the unit *exterior* normal, and the flux *into* S if $\hat{\mathbf{N}}$ is the unit *interior* normal.

EXAMPLE 6.6.2   Find the flux of the vector field $\mathbf{F} = m\mathbf{r}/|\mathbf{r}|^3$ out of a sphere S of radius a centred at the origin. (Here $\mathbf{r} = x\mathbf{i} + y\mathbf{j} + z\mathbf{k}$.)

SOLUTION   Since **F** is the field associated with a source of strength m at the origin (which produces, say, $4\pi m$ units of fluid per unit time at the origin), the answer must be $4\pi m$. Let us calculate it anyway. We use spherical coordinates. At any point **r** on the sphere, with spherical coordinates (a, ϕ, θ), the unit outward normal is $\hat{\mathbf{r}} = \mathbf{r}/|\mathbf{r}|$. Since the vector field is $\mathbf{F} = m\hat{\mathbf{r}}/a^2$ on the sphere, and since an area element is $dS = a^2 \sin\phi\, d\phi\, d\theta$, the flux of **F** out of the sphere is

$$\oiint_S \left(\frac{m}{a^2}\hat{\mathbf{r}}\right) \bullet \hat{\mathbf{r}}\, a^2 \sin\phi\, d\phi\, d\theta = m \int_0^{2\pi} d\theta \int_0^{\pi} \sin\phi\, d\phi = 4\pi m.$$

EXAMPLE 6.6.3   Calculate the total flux of $\mathbf{F} = x\mathbf{i} + y\mathbf{j} + z\mathbf{k}$ outward through the surface of the solid cylinder $x^2 + y^2 \le a^2$, $-h \le z \le h$.

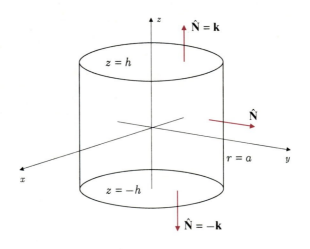

FIGURE 6.6.6

SOLUTION   The cylinder is shown in Fig. 6.6.6. Its surface consists of top and bottom discs and the cylindrical side wall. We calculate the flux of **F** out of each. Naturally, we use cylindrical coordinates.

On the top we have $z = h$, $\hat{\mathbf{N}} = \mathbf{k}$ and $dS = r\, dr\, d\theta$. Hence $\mathbf{F} \bullet \hat{\mathbf{N}}\, dS = hr\, dr\, d\theta$ and

$$\iint_{\text{top}} \mathbf{F} \bullet \hat{\mathbf{N}}\, dS = h \int_0^{2\pi} d\theta \int_0^a r\, dr = \pi a^2 h.$$

On the bottom we have $z = -h$, $\hat{\mathbf{N}} = -\mathbf{k}$ and $dS = r\, dr\, d\theta$. Hence $\mathbf{F} \bullet \hat{\mathbf{N}}\, dS = hr\, dr\, d\theta$ and

$$\iint_{\text{bottom}} \mathbf{F} \bullet \hat{\mathbf{N}}\, dS = \iint_{\text{top}} \mathbf{F} \bullet \hat{\mathbf{N}}\, dS = \pi a^2 h.$$

On the cylindrical wall $\mathbf{F} = a\cos\theta\,\mathbf{i} + a\sin\theta\,\mathbf{j} + z\mathbf{k}$, $\hat{\mathbf{N}} = \cos\theta\,\mathbf{i} + \sin\theta\,\mathbf{j}$ and $dS = a\,d\theta\,dz$. Thus $\mathbf{F}\bullet\hat{\mathbf{N}}\,dS = a^2\,d\theta\,dz$ and

$$\iint_{\text{cylwall}} \mathbf{F}\bullet\hat{\mathbf{N}}\,dS = a^2 \int_0^{2\pi} d\theta \int_{-h}^{h} dz = 4\pi a^2 h.$$

The total flux of $\mathbf{F}$ out of the surface $\mathcal{S}$ of the cylinder is the sum of these three contributions:

$$\oiint_{\mathcal{S}} \mathbf{F}\bullet\hat{\mathbf{N}}\,dS = 6\pi a^2 h.$$

Let $\mathcal{S}$ be a smooth, oriented surface with a one-to-one projection onto a domain D in the xy-plane, and with equation of the form $F(x,y,z) = 0$, where the partial derivative F_3 is never zero on $\mathcal{S}$. In Section 6.5 (see Box 6.5.12) we showed that the surface area element on $\mathcal{S}$ could be written in the form

$$dS = \left| \frac{\nabla F}{F_3} \right| dx\,dy,$$

and hence surface integrals over $\mathcal{S}$ could be reduced to double integrals over the domain D. Flux integrals can be treated likewise. Depending on the orientation of $\mathcal{S}$, the unit normal $\hat{\mathbf{N}}$ can be written as

$$\hat{\mathbf{N}} = \pm \frac{\nabla F}{|\nabla F|}.$$

Thus the vector area element $d\mathbf{S}$ can be written

6.6.4
Vector Area Element
for $F(x, y, z) = 0$

$$d\mathbf{S} = \hat{\mathbf{N}}\,dS = \pm \frac{\nabla F(x, y, z)}{F_3(x, y, z)}\,dx\,dy.$$

The sign must be chosen to give $\mathcal{S}$ the desired orientation. If $F_3 > 0$ and we want the positive side of $\mathcal{S}$ to face upward, we should use the "+" sign. Of course, similar formulas apply for surfaces with one-to-one projections onto the other coordinate planes.

EXAMPLE 6.6.5   Find the flux of $z\mathbf{i} + x^2\mathbf{k}$ upwards through that part of the surface $z = x^2 + y^2$ lying above the square R defined by $-1 \le x \le 1$, $-1 \le y \le 1$.

SOLUTION   For $F(x, y, z) = z - x^2 - y^2$ we have $\nabla F = -2x\mathbf{i} - 2y\mathbf{j} + \mathbf{k}$ and $F_3 = 1$. Thus

$$d\mathbf{S} = (-2x\mathbf{i} - 2y\mathbf{j} + \mathbf{k})\,dx\,dy,$$

and the required flux is

$$\iint_S (z\mathbf{i} + x^2\mathbf{k}) \bullet d\mathbf{S} = \iint_R \left(-2x(x^2 + y^2) + x^2\right) dx\, dy$$

$$= \int_{-1}^{1} dx \int_{-1}^{1} (x^2 - 2x^3 - 2xy^2)\, dx\, dy$$

$$= \int_{-1}^{1} 2x^2\, dx = \frac{4}{3}.$$

(Two of the three terms in the double integral had zero integrals because of symmetry.)

EXERCISES

1. Find the flux of $\mathbf{F} = x\mathbf{i} + z\mathbf{j}$ out of the tetrahedron bounded by the coordinate planes and the plane $x + 2y + 3z = 6$.

2. Find the flux of $\mathbf{F} = x\mathbf{i} + y\mathbf{j} + z\mathbf{k}$ outward across the sphere $x^2 + y^2 + z^2 = a^2$.

3. Find the flux of the vector field of the previous problem out of the surface of the rectangular box $0 \le x \le a$, $0 \le y \le b, 0 \le z \le c$.

4. Find the flux of the vector field $\mathbf{F} = y\mathbf{i} + z\mathbf{k}$ out across the boundary of the solid cone $0 \le z \le 1 - \sqrt{x^2 + y^2}$.

5. Find the flux of $\mathbf{F} = m\mathbf{r}/|\mathbf{r}|^3$ out of the surface of the cube $-a \le x, y, z \le a$.

6.*Find the flux of the vector field of the previous exercise out of the box $1 \le x, y, z \le 2$. Note: This problem can be solved very easily using the Divergence Theorem of Section 7.3; the required flux is, in fact, zero. However, the object here is to do it by direct calculation of the surface integrals involved, and as such it is quite difficult. By symmetry, it is sufficient to evaluate the net flux out of the cube through any one of the three pairs of opposite faces; that is, you must calculate the flux through only two faces, say $z = 1$ and $z = 2$. Be prepared to work very hard to evaluate these integrals! When they are done you may find the identities

$$2\tan^{-1}a = \tan^{-1}\left(\frac{2a}{1 - a^2}\right), \quad \text{and}$$

$$\tan^{-1}a + \tan^{-1}\left(\frac{1}{a}\right) = \frac{\pi}{2}$$

useful for showing that the net flux is zero.

7. Define the flux of a *plane* vector field across a piecewise smooth *curve*. Find the flux of $\mathbf{F} = x\mathbf{i} + y\mathbf{j}$ outward across

a) the circle $x^2 + y^2 = a^2$.

b) the boundary of the square $-1 \le x, y \le 1$.

8. Find the flux of

$$\mathbf{F} = -\frac{x\mathbf{i} + y\mathbf{j}}{x^2 + y^2}$$

inward across each of the two curves in the previous exercise.

9. If S is a smooth, oriented surface in 3-space and $\hat{\mathbf{N}}$ is the unit vector field determining the orientation of S, show that the flux of $\hat{\mathbf{N}}$ across S is the area of S.

10.*The Divergence Theorem presented in Section 7.3 implies that the flux of a constant vector field across any oriented, piecewise smooth, closed surface is zero. Prove this now for (a) a rectangular box, and (b) a sphere.

11.*A smooth surface S is given parametrically by

$$\mathbf{r} = (\cos 2u)(2 + v\cos u)\mathbf{i}$$
$$+ (\sin 2u)(2 + v\cos u)\mathbf{j} + v\sin u\mathbf{k},$$

where $0 \le u \le 2\pi$, $-1 \le v \le 1$. Show that for *every* smooth vector field $\mathbf{F}$ on S,

$$\iint_S \mathbf{F} \bullet \hat{\mathbf{N}}\, dS = 0,$$

where $\hat{\mathbf{N}}$ is a continuous unit normal vector field on S. How do you explain this? (Hint: try to describe what the surface S looks like.)

In this final chapter we develop two- and three-dimensional analogues of the one-dimensional Fundamental Theorem of Calculus. These analogues, Green's Theorem, Gauss's Divergence Theorem and Stokes's Theorem are of great importance both theoretically and in applications. They are phrased in terms of certain differential operators, divergence and curl, related to the gradient operator encountered in Section 2.6. The operators are introduced and their properties are derived in Sections 7.1 and 7.2. Generalizations of the Fundamental Theorem of Calculus and their applications are given in Sections 7.3—7.5. Section 7.6 derives the form of the operators in more general coordinate systems.

7.1   GRADIENT, DIVERGENCE AND CURL

Information about the rate of change of a 3-dimensional scalar field, $f(x, y, z)$, is contained in the three first partial derivatives $\partial f/\partial x$, $\partial f/\partial y$ and $\partial f/\partial z$. The gradient,

$$\mathbf{grad}\ f(x, y, z) = \nabla f(x, y, z) = \frac{\partial f}{\partial x}\mathbf{i} + \frac{\partial f}{\partial y}\mathbf{j} + \frac{\partial f}{\partial z}\mathbf{k},$$

collects this information into a single vector-valued "derivative" of f. We would like to develop similar ways of conveying information about the rate of change of vector fields.

Information about the rate of change of the vector field

$$\mathbf{F}(x, y, z) = F_1(x, y, z)\mathbf{i} + F_2(x, y, z)\mathbf{j} + F_3(x, y, z)\mathbf{k}$$

is contained in nine first partial derivatives, three for each of the three components of $\mathbf{F}$:

$$\begin{array}{ccc} \dfrac{\partial F_1}{\partial x} & \dfrac{\partial F_1}{\partial y} & \dfrac{\partial F_1}{\partial z} \\[2ex] \dfrac{\partial F_2}{\partial x} & \dfrac{\partial F_2}{\partial y} & \dfrac{\partial F_2}{\partial z} \\[2ex] \dfrac{\partial F_3}{\partial x} & \dfrac{\partial F_3}{\partial y} & \dfrac{\partial F_3}{\partial z}. \end{array}$$

Two special combinations of these derivatives organize this information in particularly useful ways, as the gradient does for scalar fields. These are the **divergence** of **F** (**div F**), and the **curl** of **F** (**curl F**), defined as follows:

7.1.1
Divergence
and Curl

$$\mathbf{div}\ \mathbf{F} = \nabla \bullet \mathbf{F} = \frac{\partial F_1}{\partial x} + \frac{\partial F_2}{\partial y} + \frac{\partial F_3}{\partial z},$$

$$\mathbf{curl}\ \mathbf{F} = \nabla \times \mathbf{F} = \left(\frac{\partial F_3}{\partial y} - \frac{\partial F_2}{\partial z}\right)\mathbf{i} + \left(\frac{\partial F_1}{\partial z} - \frac{\partial F_3}{\partial x}\right)\mathbf{j} + \left(\frac{\partial F_2}{\partial x} - \frac{\partial F_1}{\partial y}\right)\mathbf{k}$$

$$= \begin{vmatrix} \mathbf{i} & \mathbf{j} & \mathbf{k} \\ \dfrac{\partial}{\partial x} & \dfrac{\partial}{\partial y} & \dfrac{\partial}{\partial z} \\ F_1 & F_2 & F_3 \end{vmatrix}.$$

Note that the divergence of a vector field is a scalar field while the curl is another vector field. Also observe the notation $\nabla \bullet \mathbf{F}$ and $\nabla \times \mathbf{F}$ which we will sometimes use instead of **div F** and **curl F**. This makes use of the *vector differential operator*,

7.1.2
The Del Operator

$$\nabla = \mathbf{i}\,\frac{\partial}{\partial x} + \mathbf{j}\,\frac{\partial}{\partial y} + \mathbf{k}\,\frac{\partial}{\partial z},$$

frequently called "del" or "nabla". Just as the gradient of the scalar field f can be regarded as *formal scalar multiplication* of ∇ by f, so also can the divergence and curl of $\mathbf{F}$ be regarded as *formal dot* and *cross* products of ∇ with $\mathbf{F}$. When using ∇ the order of "factors" is important; the quantities on which ∇ acts must appear to the right of ∇. For instance, $\nabla \bullet \mathbf{F}$ and $\mathbf{F} \bullet \nabla$ do not mean the same thing; the former is a scalar field, the latter is a scalar differential operator.

EXAMPLE 7.1.3   Find the divergence and curl of the vector field

$$\mathbf{F} = xy\mathbf{i} + (y^2 - z^2)\mathbf{j} + yz\mathbf{k}.$$

SOLUTION   We have

$$\mathbf{div}\,\mathbf{F} = \nabla \bullet \mathbf{F} = \frac{\partial}{\partial x}(xy) + \frac{\partial}{\partial y}(y^2 - z^2) + \frac{\partial}{\partial z}(yz) = y + 2y + y = 4y,$$

$$\mathbf{curl}\,\mathbf{F} = \nabla \times \mathbf{F} = \begin{vmatrix} \mathbf{i} & \mathbf{j} & \mathbf{k} \\ \dfrac{\partial}{\partial x} & \dfrac{\partial}{\partial y} & \dfrac{\partial}{\partial z} \\ xy & y^2 - z^2 & yz \end{vmatrix}$$

$$= \left[\frac{\partial}{\partial y}(yz) - \frac{\partial}{\partial z}(y^2 - z^2)\right]\mathbf{i} + \left[\frac{\partial}{\partial z}(xy) - \frac{\partial}{\partial x}(yz)\right]\mathbf{j}$$

$$+ \left[\frac{\partial}{\partial x}(y^2 - z^2) - \frac{\partial}{\partial y}(xy)\right]\mathbf{k} = 3z\mathbf{i} - x\mathbf{k}.$$

The divergence and curl of a two-dimensional vector field are also defined: if $\mathbf{F}(x, y) = F_1(x, y)\mathbf{i} + F_2(x, y)\mathbf{j}$ then

7.1.4
Div and Curl
in Two Dimensions

$$\mathbf{div}\,\mathbf{F} = \frac{\partial F_1}{\partial x} + \frac{\partial F_2}{\partial y},$$

$$\mathbf{curl}\,\mathbf{F} = \left(\frac{\partial F_2}{\partial x} - \frac{\partial F_1}{\partial y}\right)\mathbf{k}.$$

Note that the curl of a two-dimensional vector field is still a 3-vector and is perpendicular to the plane of the field. While **div** and **grad** are defined in all dimensions, **curl** is defined only in three dimensions and in the plane (provided we allow values in three dimensions).

EXAMPLE 7.1.5   Find the divergence and curl of $\mathbf{F} = xe^y\mathbf{i} - ye^x\mathbf{j}$.

SOLUTION   We have

$$\mathbf{div}\ \mathbf{F} = \nabla\bullet\mathbf{F} = \frac{\partial}{\partial x}(xe^y) + \frac{\partial}{\partial y}(-ye^x) = e^y - e^x,$$

$$\mathbf{curl}\ \mathbf{F} = \nabla\times\mathbf{F} = \left(\frac{\partial}{\partial x}(-ye^x) - \frac{\partial}{\partial y}(xe^y)\right)\mathbf{k}$$

$$= -(ye^x + xe^y)\mathbf{k}.$$

Interpretation of the Divergence

The value of the divergence of a vector field $\mathbf{F}$ at point P is, loosely speaking, a measure of the rate at which the field "spreads away" from P. This spreading away can be measured by the flux out of a small closed surface surrounding P. For instance, **div** $\mathbf{F}(P)$ is the limit of the *flux per unit volume* out of smaller and smaller spheres centred at P.

THEOREM 7.1.6   If $\hat{\mathbf{N}}$ is the unit outward normal on the sphere $\mathcal{S}_\epsilon$ of radius ϵ centred at point P, and if $\mathbf{F}$ is a smooth three-dimensional vector field then

$$\mathbf{div}\ \mathbf{F}(P) = \lim_{\epsilon\to 0^+}\frac{3}{4\pi\epsilon^3}\oiint_{\mathcal{S}_\epsilon}\mathbf{F}\bullet\hat{\mathbf{N}}\,dS.$$

PROOF   Without loss of generality we assume that P is at the origin. We want to expand $\mathbf{F}$ in a Taylor series about the origin (a Maclaurin series). As shown in Section 2.8 for a function of two variables, the Maclaurin series for a scalar-valued function of 3 variables takes the form

$$f(x,y,z) = f(0,0,0) + \frac{\partial f}{\partial x}\bigg|_{(0,0,0)}x + \frac{\partial f}{\partial y}\bigg|_{(0,0,0)}y + \frac{\partial f}{\partial z}\bigg|_{(0,0,0)}z + \cdots,$$

where $\cdots$ represents terms of second and higher degree in x, y, and z. If we apply this formula to the components of $\mathbf{F}$, we obtain

$$\mathbf{F}(x,y,z) = \mathbf{F}_0 + \mathbf{F}_1 x + \mathbf{F}_2 y + \mathbf{F}_3 z + \cdots$$

where

$$\mathbf{F}_0 = \mathbf{F}(0,0,0)$$

$$\mathbf{F}_1 = \frac{\partial \mathbf{F}}{\partial x}\bigg|_{(0,0,0)} = \left(\frac{\partial F_1}{\partial x}\mathbf{i} + \frac{\partial F_2}{\partial x}\mathbf{j} + \frac{\partial F_3}{\partial x}\mathbf{k}\right)\bigg|_{(0,0,0)}$$

$$\mathbf{F}_2 = \frac{\partial \mathbf{F}}{\partial y}\bigg|_{(0,0,0)} = \left(\frac{\partial F_1}{\partial y}\mathbf{i} + \frac{\partial F_2}{\partial y}\mathbf{j} + \frac{\partial F_3}{\partial y}\mathbf{k}\right)\bigg|_{(0,0,0)}$$

$$\mathbf{F}_3 = \frac{\partial \mathbf{F}}{\partial z}\bigg|_{(0,0,0)} = \left(\frac{\partial F_1}{\partial z}\mathbf{i} + \frac{\partial F_2}{\partial z}\mathbf{j} + \frac{\partial F_3}{\partial z}\mathbf{k}\right)\bigg|_{(0,0,0)}$$

and again the "$\cdots$" represents the second and higher degree terms in x, y and z. The unit normal on $\mathcal{S}_\epsilon$ is $\hat{\mathbf{N}} = (x\mathbf{i} + y\mathbf{j} + z\mathbf{k})/\epsilon$, so we have

$$\begin{aligned}
\mathbf{F}\bullet\hat{\mathbf{N}} = \frac{1}{\epsilon}\bigg(&\mathbf{F}_0\bullet\mathbf{i}\,x + \mathbf{F}_0\bullet\mathbf{j}\,y + \mathbf{F}_0\bullet\mathbf{k}\,z \\
&+ \mathbf{F}_1\bullet\mathbf{i}\,x^2 + \mathbf{F}_1\bullet\mathbf{j}\,xy + \mathbf{F}_1\bullet\mathbf{k}\,xz \\
&+ \mathbf{F}_2\bullet\mathbf{i}\,xy + \mathbf{F}_2\bullet\mathbf{j}\,y^2 + \mathbf{F}_2\bullet\mathbf{k}\,yz \\
&+ \mathbf{F}_3\bullet\mathbf{i}\,xz + \mathbf{F}_3\bullet\mathbf{j}\,yz + \mathbf{F}_3\bullet\mathbf{k}\,z^2 + \cdots\bigg).
\end{aligned}$$

We integrate each term within the parentheses over $\mathcal{S}_\epsilon$. By symmetry,

$$\oiint_{\mathcal{S}_\epsilon} x\,dS = \oiint_{\mathcal{S}_\epsilon} y\,dS = \oiint_{\mathcal{S}_\epsilon} z\,dS = 0,$$

$$\oiint_{\mathcal{S}_\epsilon} xy\,dS = \oiint_{\mathcal{S}_\epsilon} xz\,dS = \oiint_{\mathcal{S}_\epsilon} yz\,dS = 0.$$

Also, by symmetry,

$$\oiint_{\mathcal{S}_\epsilon} x^2\,dS = \oiint_{\mathcal{S}_\epsilon} y^2\,dS = \oiint_{\mathcal{S}_\epsilon} z^2\,dS = \epsilon^2\int_0^{2\pi}d\theta\int_0^{\pi}(\epsilon\cos\phi)^2\sin\phi\,d\phi = \frac{4}{3}\pi\epsilon^4$$

and the higher degree terms have surface integrals involving ϵ^5 and higher powers. Thus

$$\frac{3}{4\pi\epsilon^3}\oiint_{\mathcal{S}_\epsilon}\mathbf{F}\bullet\hat{\mathbf{N}}\,dS = \mathbf{F}_1\bullet\mathbf{i} + \mathbf{F}_2\bullet\mathbf{j} + \mathbf{F}_3\bullet\mathbf{k} + \epsilon(\cdots)$$

$$= \nabla\bullet\mathbf{F}(0,0,0) + \epsilon(\cdots)$$

$$\to \nabla\bullet\mathbf{F}(0,0,0) \quad \text{as } \epsilon\to 0^+.$$

This is what we wanted to show. $\square$

REMARK: The spheres $\mathcal{S}_\epsilon$ in the above Theorem can be replaced by other contracting families of piecewise smooth surfaces. For instance, if B is the surface of a rectangular box with dimensions Δx, Δy and Δz containing P then

$$\operatorname{div}\mathbf{F}(P) = \lim_{\Delta x,\Delta y,\Delta z\to 0}\frac{1}{\Delta x\Delta y\Delta z}\oiint_B\mathbf{F}\bullet\hat{\mathbf{N}}\,dS.$$

See Exercise 12 at the end of this section.

REMARK: In two dimensions, the value **div** $\mathbf{F}(P)$ represents the limiting *flux per unit area* outward across small, non-self-intersecting closed curves which enclose P. See Exercise 13 at the end of this section.

Let us return again to the interpretation of a vector field as a velocity field of a moving incompressible fluid. If the total flux of the velocity field outward across the boundary surface of a domain is positive (or negative), then fluid must be produced (or annihilated) within that domain.

The vector field $\mathbf{F} = x\mathbf{i} + y\mathbf{j} + z\mathbf{k}$ of Example 6.6.3 has constant divergence, $\nabla\bullet\mathbf{F} = 3$. In that example we showed that the flux of $\mathbf{F}$ out of a certain cylinder of base radius a and height $2h$ is $6\pi a^2 h$, which is 3 times the volume of the cylinder. Exercises 2 and 3 of Section 6.6 confirm similar results for the flux of $\mathbf{F}$ out of other domains. This leads to another interpretation for the divergence; **div** $\mathbf{F}(P)$ is the *source strength per unit volume* of $\mathbf{F}$ at P. With this interpretation, we would expect, even for a vector field $\mathbf{F}$ with nonconstant divergence, that the total flux of $\mathbf{F}$ out the surface S of a domain D would be equal to the total source strength of $\mathbf{F}$ within D, that is,

$$\oiint_S \mathbf{F}\bullet\hat{\mathbf{N}}\,dS = \iiint_D \nabla\bullet\mathbf{F}\,dV.$$

This is the **Divergence Theorem**, which we will prove in Section 7.3.

EXAMPLE 7.1.7   Verify that the vector field $\mathbf{F} = m\mathbf{r}/|\mathbf{r}|^3$, due to a source of strength m at $(0,0,0)$, has zero divergence at all other points in $\mathbb{R}^3$. What would you expect to be the total flux of $\mathbf{F}$ outward across the boundary surface of a domain D if the origin lies outside D? if the origin is inside D?

SOLUTION

$$\mathbf{F}(x,y,z) = \frac{m}{r^3}\left(x\mathbf{i} + y\mathbf{j} + z\mathbf{k}\right) \quad \text{where} \quad r^2 = x^2 + y^2 + z^2.$$

Since $\partial r/\partial x = x/r$ we have

$$\frac{\partial F_1}{\partial x} = m\frac{\partial}{\partial x}\left(\frac{x}{r^3}\right) = m\frac{r^3 - 3xr^2\left(\frac{x}{r}\right)}{r^6} = m\frac{r^2 - 3x^2}{r^5}.$$

Similarly,

$$\frac{\partial F_2}{\partial y} = m\frac{r^2 - 3y^2}{r^5}, \qquad \frac{\partial F_3}{\partial z} = m\frac{r^2 - 3z^2}{r^5}.$$

Adding these up we get $\nabla\bullet\mathbf{F}(x,y,z) = 0$ if $r > 0$.

If the origin lies outside the domain D then the source density of $\mathbf{F}$ in D is zero so we would expect the total flux of $\mathbf{F}$ out of D to be zero. If the origin lies inside D then D contains a source of strength m (producing $4\pi m$ cubic units of fluid per unit time) and so we would expect the flux out of D to be $4\pi m$. See Example 6.6.2 and Exercises 5 and 6 of Section 6.6 for specific examples.

REMARK: The source *density*, **div F**, in the above example is *infinite* at the origin, and *zero* everywhere else, in such a way that $\iiint_D \text{div } \mathbf{F} \, dV = 4\pi m$ if the origin is inside D. No *function* can have such properties; if a function vanishes everywhere except at a single point then any integral of that function will be zero. It is possible to define "generalized functions" (also called "distributions") which can have such properties. In particular, the **Dirac distribution** $\delta(t)$ is defined so that if $f(t)$ is any smooth function then

$$\int_{-\infty}^{\infty} \delta(t) f(t) \, dt = f(0).$$

In terms of the Dirac distribution, the above source density is

$$\text{div } \mathbf{F}(x, y, z) = 4\pi m \, \delta(x)\delta(y)\delta(z).$$

Interpretation of the Curl

Roughly speaking, **curl F**(P) measures the extent to which the vector field **F** "swirls" around P.

EXAMPLE 7.1.8 Consider the velocity field,
$$\mathbf{v} = -\Omega y \mathbf{i} + \Omega x \mathbf{j},$$

of a solid rotating with angular speed Ω about the z-axis, that is, with angular velocity $\mathbf{\Omega} = \Omega \mathbf{k}$. We have

$$\text{curl } \mathbf{v} = \nabla \times \mathbf{v} = \left(\frac{\partial}{\partial x}(\Omega x) - \frac{\partial}{\partial y}(-\Omega y)\right)\mathbf{k} = 2\Omega\mathbf{k} = 2\mathbf{\Omega}.$$

The curl of this velocity field is *constant*. Now we calculate the circulation of the field **v** around the circle C_ϵ given by

$$\mathbf{r} = (x_0 + \epsilon \cos t)\mathbf{i} + (y_0 + \epsilon \sin t\mathbf{j}), \qquad (0 \le t \le 2\pi),$$

which has radius ϵ and centre the arbitrary point (x_0, y_0).

$$\oint_{C_\epsilon} \mathbf{v} \bullet d\mathbf{r} = \int_0^{2\pi} \left(-\Omega(y_0 + \epsilon \sin t)(-\epsilon \sin t) + \Omega(x_0 + \epsilon \cos t)(\epsilon \cos t)\right) dt$$
$$= \int_0^{2\pi} \left(\Omega\epsilon(y_0 \sin t + x_0 \cos t) + \Omega\epsilon^2\right) dt$$
$$= 2\Omega\pi\epsilon^2$$
$$= (\text{curl } \mathbf{v}) \bullet \mathbf{k} \times (\text{area bounded by } C_\epsilon).$$

Note that this circulation is constant for circles of any fixed radius; it does not depend on the position of the centre.

The calculations in the example above suggest that the curl of a vector field is a measure of the *circulation per unit area* in planes normal to the curl. A more precise version of this conjecture is stated in Theorem 7.1.9 below. We will not prove this theorem now, because a proof at this stage would be quite complicated. (However, see Exercise 14 at the end of this section for a special case.) In Section 7.4 we will be able to give a simple proof.

THEOREM 7.1.9

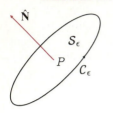

FIGURE 7.1.1

If $\mathbf{F}$ is a smooth vector field and C_ϵ is a circle of radius ϵ centred at point P and bounding a disc S_ϵ with unit normal $\hat{\mathbf{N}}$ (and orientation inherited from C_ϵ—see Fig. 7.1.1), then

$$\lim_{\epsilon \to 0^+} \frac{1}{\pi \epsilon^2} \oint_{C_\epsilon} \mathbf{F} \bullet d\mathbf{r} = \hat{\mathbf{N}} \bullet \mathbf{curl}\ \mathbf{F}(P). \quad \square$$

Example 7.1.8 also suggests the following definition for the *local* angular velocity of a moving fluid.

7.1.10
Local Angular Velocity

The **local angular velocity** at point P in a fluid moving with velocity field $\mathbf{v}(P)$ is given by

$$\Omega(P) = \tfrac{1}{2} \mathbf{curl}\ \mathbf{v}(P).$$

Theorem 7.1.9 states that the local angular velocity $\Omega(P)$ is that vector whose component in the direction of any unit vector $\hat{\mathbf{N}}$ is one half of the limiting circulation per unit area around the (oriented) boundary circles of small discs centred at P and having normal $\hat{\mathbf{N}}$.

Not all vector fields with nonzero curl *appear* to circulate. The velocity field for a rigid body rotation considered in Example 7.1.8 appears to circulate around the axis of rotation, but the circulation around a circle in a plane perpendicular to that axis turned out to be independent of the position of the circle; it depended only on its area. The circle need not even surround the axis of rotation. The following example investigates a fluid velocity field whose streamlines are *straight lines*, but which still has nonzero, constant curl, and therefore constant local angular velocity.

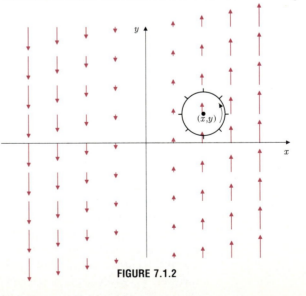

FIGURE 7.1.2

EXAMPLE 7.1.11   Consider the velocity field $\mathbf{v} = x\mathbf{j}$ of a fluid moving in the xy-plane. Evidently, particles of fluid are moving along lines parallel to the y-axis. However, **curl** $\mathbf{v}(x, y) = \mathbf{k}$, and $\Omega(x, y) = \frac{1}{2}\mathbf{k}$. A small "paddle wheel" of radius ϵ placed with its centre at position (x, y) in the fluid, (see Fig. 7.1.2), will be carried along with the fluid at velocity $x\mathbf{i}$, but will also be set rotating with angular velocity $\Omega(x, y)$ which is independent of its position. This angular velocity is due to the fact that the velocity of the fluid along the right side of the wheel exceeds that along the left side.

EXERCISES

In Exercises 1–11 calculate **div F** and **curl F** for the given vector fields.

1. $\mathbf{F} = x\mathbf{i} + y\mathbf{j}$

2. $\mathbf{F} = y\mathbf{i} + x\mathbf{j}$

3. $\mathbf{F} = y\mathbf{i} + z\mathbf{j} + x\mathbf{k}$

4. $\mathbf{F} = yz\mathbf{i} + xz\mathbf{j} + xy\mathbf{k}$

5. $\mathbf{F} = x\mathbf{i} + x\mathbf{k}$

6. $\mathbf{F} = xy^2\mathbf{i} - yz^2\mathbf{j} + zx^2\mathbf{k}$

7. $\mathbf{F} = f(x)\mathbf{i} + g(y)\mathbf{j} + h(z)\mathbf{k}$ **8.** $\mathbf{F} = f(z)\mathbf{i} - f(z)\mathbf{j}$

9. $\mathbf{F}(r, \theta) = r\mathbf{i} + \sin\theta\mathbf{j}$ where (r, θ) are polar coordinates in the plane.

10. $\mathbf{F} = \hat{\mathbf{r}}$ as defined in Box 5.4.4.

11. $\mathbf{F} = \hat{\boldsymbol{\theta}}$ as defined in Box 5.4.4.

12.*Let **F** be a smooth, 3-dimensional vector field. If $B_{a,b,c}$ is the surface of the box $-a \le x \le a$, $-b \le y \le b$, $-c \le z \le c$, with outward normal $\hat{\mathbf{N}}$, show that

$$\lim_{a,b,c\to 0^+} \frac{1}{8abc} \oiint_{B_{a,b,c}} \mathbf{F} \bullet \hat{\mathbf{N}} \, dS = \nabla \bullet \mathbf{F}(0, 0, 0).$$

13.*Let **F** be a smooth 2-dimensional vector field. If C_ϵ is the circle of radius ϵ centred at the origin, and $\hat{\mathbf{N}}$ is the unit outward normal to C_ϵ, show that

$$\lim_{\epsilon\to 0^+} \frac{1}{\pi\epsilon^2} \oint_{C_\epsilon} \mathbf{F} \bullet \hat{\mathbf{N}} \, ds = \mathbf{div} \ \mathbf{F}(0, 0, 0).$$

14.*Prove Theorem 7.1.9 in the special case that C_ϵ is the circle in the xy-plane with parametrization

$$x = \epsilon\cos\theta, \quad y = \epsilon\sin\theta, \quad (0 \le \theta \le 2\pi).$$

In this case $\hat{\mathbf{N}} = \mathbf{k}$. Hint: Expand $\mathbf{F}(x, y, z)$ in a vector Taylor series about the origin as in the proof of Theorem 7.1.6, and calculate the circulation of individual terms around C_ϵ.

7.2   SOME IDENTITIES INVOLVING GRAD, DIV AND CURL

There are numerous identities involving the functions

$$\mathbf{grad} \ f(x, y, z) = \nabla f(x, y, z) = \frac{\partial f}{\partial x}\mathbf{i} + \frac{\partial f}{\partial y}\mathbf{j} + \frac{\partial f}{\partial z}\mathbf{k},$$

$$\mathbf{div} \ \mathbf{F}(x, y, z) = \nabla \bullet \mathbf{F}(x, y, z) = \frac{\partial F_1}{\partial x} + \frac{\partial F_2}{\partial y} + \frac{\partial F_3}{\partial z},$$

$$\mathbf{curl} \ \mathbf{F}(x, y, z) = \nabla \times \mathbf{F}(x, y, z) = \begin{vmatrix} \mathbf{i} & \mathbf{j} & \mathbf{k} \\ \dfrac{\partial}{\partial x} & \dfrac{\partial}{\partial y} & \dfrac{\partial}{\partial z} \\ F_1 & F_2 & F_3 \end{vmatrix},$$

and the **Laplacian operator,** $\nabla^2 = \nabla \bullet \nabla$, defined for a scalar field ϕ by

$$\nabla^2 \phi = \nabla \bullet \nabla \phi = \text{div grad } \phi = \frac{\partial^2 \phi}{\partial x^2} + \frac{\partial^2 \phi}{\partial y^2} + \frac{\partial^2 \phi}{\partial z^2},$$

and for a vector field $\mathbf{F} = F_1 \mathbf{i} + F_2 \mathbf{j} + F_3 \mathbf{k}$ by

$$\nabla^2 \mathbf{F} = (\nabla^2 F_1)\mathbf{i} + (\nabla^2 F_2)\mathbf{j} + (\nabla^2 F_3)\mathbf{k}.$$

(Note: the Laplace operator, $\nabla^2 = (\partial^2/\partial x^2) + (\partial^2/\partial y^2) + (\partial^2/\partial z^2)$, is denoted Δ in some books.) Recall that a function ϕ is called **harmonic** in a domain D if $\nabla^2 \phi = 0$ throughout D. (See Section 2.3.)

We collect the most important identities together in the following theorem. Most of the identities are readily seen to be forms of the Product Rule. We shall prove a few of the identities to illustrate the techniques involved (mostly brute-force calculation) and leave the rest as exercises for the student. Note that two of the identities involve quantities like $(\mathbf{G} \bullet \nabla)\mathbf{F}$ which represents the vector obtained by applying the scalar differential operator $\mathbf{G} \bullet \nabla$ to the vector field $\mathbf{F}$:

$$(\mathbf{G} \bullet \nabla)\mathbf{F} = G_1 \frac{\partial \mathbf{F}}{\partial x} + G_2 \frac{\partial \mathbf{F}}{\partial y} + G_3 \frac{\partial \mathbf{F}}{\partial z}.$$

THEOREM 7.2.1   *(Vector Differential Identities)* Let ϕ and ψ be scalar fields and $\mathbf{F}$ and $\mathbf{G}$ be vector fields, all assumed sufficiently smooth that all the partial derivatives in the identities are continuous. Then the following identities hold:

a) $\nabla(\phi\psi) = \phi\nabla\psi + \psi\nabla\phi$

b) $\nabla \bullet (\phi\mathbf{F}) = (\nabla\phi) \bullet \mathbf{F} + \phi(\nabla \bullet \mathbf{F})$

c) $\nabla \times (\phi\mathbf{F}) = (\nabla\phi) \times \mathbf{F} + \phi(\nabla \times \mathbf{F})$

d) $\nabla \bullet (\mathbf{F} \times \mathbf{G}) = (\nabla \times \mathbf{F}) \bullet \mathbf{G} - \mathbf{F} \bullet (\nabla \times \mathbf{G})$

e) $\nabla \times (\mathbf{F} \times \mathbf{G}) = (\nabla \bullet \mathbf{G})\mathbf{F} + (\mathbf{G} \bullet \nabla)\mathbf{F} - (\nabla \bullet \mathbf{F})\mathbf{G} - (\mathbf{F} \bullet \nabla)\mathbf{G}$

f) $\nabla(\mathbf{F} \bullet \mathbf{G}) = \mathbf{F} \times (\nabla \times \mathbf{G}) + \mathbf{G} \times (\nabla \times \mathbf{F}) + (\mathbf{F} \bullet \nabla)\mathbf{G} + (\mathbf{G} \bullet \nabla)\mathbf{F}$

g) $\nabla \bullet (\nabla \times \mathbf{F}) = 0$ **(div curl** $= 0$**)**

h) $\nabla \times (\nabla\phi) = \mathbf{0}$ **(curl grad** $= \mathbf{0}$**)**

i) $\nabla \times (\nabla \times \mathbf{F}) = \nabla(\nabla \bullet \mathbf{F}) - \nabla^2 \mathbf{F}$

                  (curl curl $=$ **grad div** $-$ Laplacian**)**

REMARK: Identities (a)–(f) are first order identities, involving only one application of ∇. Identities (g)–(i) are second order identities. (There are more of these.) Identities (g) and (h) are especially important for an understanding of **div** and **curl** .

Proof of Parts of Theorem 7.2.1.

c) The first component (**i** component) of $\nabla \times (\phi \mathbf{F})$ is

$$\frac{\partial}{\partial y}(\phi F_3) - \frac{\partial}{\partial z}(\phi F_2) = \frac{\partial \phi}{\partial y} F_3 - \frac{\partial \phi}{\partial z} F_2 + \phi \frac{\partial F_3}{\partial y} - \phi \frac{\partial F_2}{\partial z}.$$

The first two terms on the right constitute the first component of $(\nabla \phi) \times \mathbf{F}$ and the last two terms constitute the first component of $\phi(\nabla \times \mathbf{F})$. Therefore the first components of both sides of identity (c) are equal. The equality of the other components follows similarly.

e) Again, it is sufficient to show that the first components of the vectors on both sides of the identity are equal. To calculate the first component of $\nabla \times (\mathbf{F} \times \mathbf{G})$ we need the second and third components of $\mathbf{F} \times \mathbf{G}$, which are

$$(\mathbf{F} \times \mathbf{G})_2 = F_3 G_1 - F_1 G_3, \qquad (\mathbf{F} \times \mathbf{G})_3 = F_1 G_2 - F_2 G_1.$$

The first component of $\nabla \times (\mathbf{F} \times \mathbf{G})$ is therefore

$$\frac{\partial}{\partial y}(F_1 G_2 - F_2 G_1) - \frac{\partial}{\partial z}(F_3 G_1 - F_1 G_3)$$

$$= \frac{\partial F_1}{\partial y} G_2 + F_1 \frac{\partial G_2}{\partial y} - \frac{\partial F_2}{\partial y} G_1 - F_2 \frac{\partial G_1}{\partial y} - \frac{\partial F_3}{\partial z} G_1$$

$$- F_3 \frac{\partial G_1}{\partial z} + \frac{\partial F_1}{\partial z} G_3 + F_1 \frac{\partial G_3}{\partial z}.$$

The first components of the four terms on the right hand side of identity e) are

$$((\nabla \bullet \mathbf{G})\mathbf{F})_1 = F_1 \frac{\partial G_1}{\partial x} + F_1 \frac{\partial G_2}{\partial y} + F_1 \frac{\partial G_3}{\partial z}$$

$$((\mathbf{G} \bullet \nabla)\mathbf{F})_1 = \frac{\partial F_1}{\partial x} G_1 + \frac{\partial F_1}{\partial y} G_2 + \frac{\partial F_1}{\partial z} G_3$$

$$-((\nabla \bullet \mathbf{F})\mathbf{G})_1 = -\frac{\partial F_1}{\partial x} G_1 - \frac{\partial F_2}{\partial y} G_1 - \frac{\partial F_3}{\partial z} G_1$$

$$-((\mathbf{F} \bullet \nabla)\mathbf{G})_1 = -F_1 \frac{\partial G_1}{\partial x} - F_2 \frac{\partial G_1}{\partial y} - F_3 \frac{\partial G_1}{\partial z}.$$

When we add up all these terms some cancel out and we are left with the same terms as in the first component of $\nabla \times (\mathbf{F} \times \mathbf{G})$.

g) This is a straightforward calculation involving the equality of mixed partial derivatives:

$$\nabla \bullet (\nabla \times \mathbf{F}) = \frac{\partial}{\partial x}\left(\frac{\partial F_3}{\partial y} - \frac{\partial F_2}{\partial z}\right) + \frac{\partial}{\partial y}\left(\frac{\partial F_1}{\partial z} - \frac{\partial F_3}{\partial x}\right)$$

$$+ \frac{\partial}{\partial z}\left(\frac{\partial F_2}{\partial x} - \frac{\partial F_1}{\partial y}\right)$$

$$= \frac{\partial^2 F_3}{\partial x \partial y} - \frac{\partial^2 F_2}{\partial x \partial z} + \frac{\partial^2 F_1}{\partial y \partial z} - \frac{\partial^2 F_3}{\partial y \partial x} + \frac{\partial^2 F_2}{\partial z \partial x} - \frac{\partial^2 F_1}{\partial z \partial y}$$

$$= 0.$$

The remaining identities can be proved in similar ways. □

REMARK: Two "triple product" identities for vectors were previously presented in Exercises 13 and 17 of Section 1.3:

$$\mathbf{a} \bullet (\mathbf{b} \times \mathbf{c}) = \mathbf{b} \bullet (\mathbf{c} \times \mathbf{a}) = \mathbf{c} \bullet (\mathbf{a} \times \mathbf{b}),$$
$$\mathbf{a} \times (\mathbf{b} \times \mathbf{c}) = (\mathbf{a} \bullet \mathbf{c})\mathbf{b} - (\mathbf{a} \bullet \mathbf{b})\mathbf{c}.$$

These can *not* be used to give simpler proofs of the identities in Theorem 7.2.1 by replacing one or other of the vectors with ∇. (Why?)

Scalar and Vector Potentials

A vector field $\mathbf{F}$ for which **curl F = 0** is called an **irrotational** vector field. If $\mathbf{F}$ is a conservative vector field ($\mathbf{F} = \nabla\phi$) then $\mathbf{F}$ is irrotational by identity (h) of Theorem 7.2.1. As we have hinted in Section 6.4, the *converse* of this assertion holds if the domain of $\mathbf{F}$ is simply connected.

THEOREM 7.2.2   If $\mathbf{F}$ is a smooth, irrotational vector field on a simply connected domain D then $\mathbf{F} = \nabla\phi$ for some scalar potential function defined on D, and so $\mathbf{F}$ is conservative.

We cannot prove this result in its full generality, though in Section 7.4 we will be able to give an outline of the proof. At this point we can, however, give a complete proof for a special class of simply connected domains D which are **star-like**, that is, for which there exists a point P_0 such that the line segment from P_0 to any point P in D lies wholly in D. (See Fig. 7.2.1.)

Proof of Theorem 7.2.2 for star-like domains. Without loss of generality we can assume P_0 is the origin. If $P = (x, y, z)$ is any point in D, then the straight line segment

$$\mathbf{r}(t) = tx\mathbf{i} + ty\mathbf{j} + tz\mathbf{k}, \qquad 0 \leq t \leq 1$$

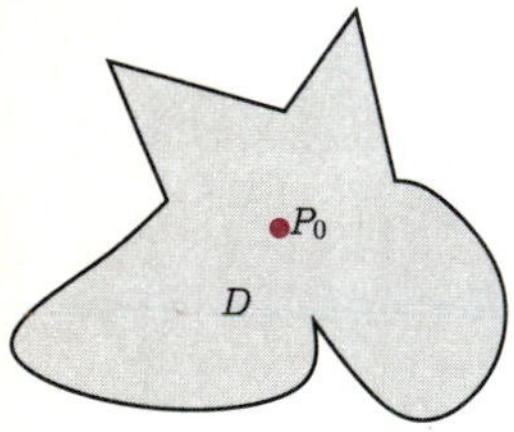

from P_0 to P lies in D. Define the function ϕ on D by

FIGURE 7.2.1

$$\phi(x, y, z) = \int_0^1 \mathbf{F}\big(\mathbf{r}(t)\big) \bullet \frac{d\mathbf{r}}{dt}\, dt$$

$$= \int_0^1 \Big(x F_1(\xi, \eta, \zeta) + y F_2(\xi, \eta, \zeta) + z F_3(\xi, \eta, \zeta) \Big)\, dt,$$

where $\xi = tx$, $\eta = ty$ and $\zeta = tz$. We calculate $\partial\phi/\partial x$, making use of the fact that **curl F = 0** to replace $\partial F_2/\partial\xi$ with $\partial F_1\partial\eta$ and $\partial F_3/\partial\xi$ with $\partial F_1/\partial\zeta$:

$$\frac{\partial\phi}{\partial x} = \int_0^1 \left(F_1(\xi, \eta, \zeta) + tx\frac{\partial F_1}{\partial\xi} + ty\frac{\partial F_2}{\partial\xi} + tz\frac{\partial F_3}{\partial\xi} \right) dt$$

$$= \int_0^1 \left(F_1(\xi, \eta, \zeta) + tx\frac{\partial F_1}{\partial\xi} + ty\frac{\partial F_1}{\partial\eta} + tz\frac{\partial F_1}{\partial\zeta} \right) dt$$

$$= \int_0^1 \frac{d}{dt}\Big(t\, F_1(\xi, \eta, \zeta) \Big)\, dt$$

$$= \Big(t\, F_1(tx, ty, tz) \Big)\Big|_0^1 = F_1(x, y, z).$$

Similarly, $\partial\phi/\partial y = F_2$ and $\partial\phi/\partial z = F_3$. Thus $\nabla\phi = \mathbf{F}$. $\square$

A vector field $\mathbf{F}$ for which **div F** = 0 is called a **solenoidal** vector field. (An example is the velocity field of a rotating rigid body, $\mathbf{F} = -y\mathbf{i} + x\mathbf{j}$.) If $\mathbf{F} = \mathbf{curl\ G}$ for some vector field $\mathbf{G}$, (called a vector potential for $\mathbf{F}$), then $\mathbf{F}$ is solenoidal by identity (g) of Theorem 7.2.1. This result also admits a converse provided the domain of $\mathbf{F}$ has no "holes". We state the converse for a star-like domain.

THEOREM 7.2.3   If $\mathbf{F}$ is a smooth, solenoidal vector field defined on a star-like domain D, then $\mathbf{F} = \mathbf{curl\ G}$ for some vector potential $\mathbf{G}$ defined on D. The details of the proof are similar to those of Theorem 7.2.2, and we relegate the proof to Exercise 18 at the end of this section.

Note that vector potentials, when they exist, are *very* non-unique. Since **curl grad** ϕ is identically zero, an arbitrary conservative field can be added to $\mathbf{G}$ without changing the value of **curl G**. The following example illustrates just how much freedom we have in making simplifying assumptions when trying to find a vector potential.

EXAMPLE 7.2.4   Show that the vector field $\mathbf{F} = (x^2 + yz)\mathbf{i} - 2y(x + z)\mathbf{j} + (xy + z^2)\mathbf{k}$ is solenoidal in $\mathbb{R}^3$ and find a vector potential for it.

SOLUTION   Since **div F** $= 2x - 2(x + z) + 2z = 0$ in $\mathbb{R}^3$, $\mathbf{F}$ is solenoidal. A vector potential $\mathbf{G}$ for $\mathbf{F}$ must satisfy **curl G** = $\mathbf{F}$, that is,

$$\frac{\partial G_3}{\partial y} - \frac{\partial G_2}{\partial z} = x^2 + yz, \quad \frac{\partial G_1}{\partial z} - \frac{\partial G_3}{\partial x} = -2xy - 2yz, \quad \frac{\partial G_2}{\partial x} - \frac{\partial G_1}{\partial y} = xy + z^2.$$

Let us try to find a solution $\mathbf{G}$ with $G_2 = 0$ identically. Then the first equation implies that

$$G_3 = \int (x^2 + yz)\, dy = x^2 y + \frac{1}{2} y^2 z + M(x, z).$$

(Since we were integrating with respect to y, the constant of integration can still depend on x and z.) We make a second simplifying assumption, that $M(x, z) = 0$. From the second equation we have

$$\frac{\partial G_1}{\partial z} = \frac{\partial G_3}{\partial x} - 2xy - 2yz = 2xy - 2xy - 2yz = -2yz,$$

so

$$G_1 = -2 \int yz\, dz = -yz^2 + N(x, y).$$

Now the third equation implies

$$xy + z^2 = -\frac{\partial G_1}{\partial y} = z^2 - \frac{\partial N}{\partial y}$$

Thus, $\dfrac{\partial}{\partial y}N(x,y) = -xy$; observe that the terms involving z have cancelled out. This happened because **div F** = 0. Had **F** not been solenoidal, we could not have determined N as a function of x and z only from the above equation. As it is, however, we have

$$N(x,y) = -\int xy\,dy = -\frac{1}{2}xy^2 + P(x).$$

We will choose $P(x)$ to be identically zero, and hence obtain

$$\mathbf{G} = -\left(yz^2 + \frac{xy^2}{2}\right)\mathbf{i} + \left(x^2y + \frac{y^2z}{2}\right)\mathbf{k}$$

as the required vector potential for **F**. The reader can check that **curl G** = **F**. Of course, other choices of simplifying assumptions would have led to very different functions **G**, which would have been equally correct.

EXERCISES

1. Prove Theorem 7.2.1(a).

2. Prove Theorem 7.2.1(b).

3. Prove Theorem 7.2.1(d).

4. Prove Theorem 7.2.1(f).

5. Prove Theorem 7.2.1(h).

6. Prove Theorem 7.2.1(i).

7.*Given that the field lines of the vector field $\mathbf{F}(x,y,z)$ are parallel straight lines, can you conclude anything about **div F**? about **curl F**?

8. Let $\mathbf{r} = x\mathbf{i}+y\mathbf{j}+z\mathbf{k}$ and let **c** be a constant vector. Show that $\nabla\bullet(\mathbf{c}\times\mathbf{r}) = 0$, $\nabla\times(\mathbf{c}\times\mathbf{r}) = 2\mathbf{c}$, and $\nabla(\mathbf{c}\bullet\mathbf{r}) = \mathbf{c}$.

9. Let $\mathbf{r} = x\mathbf{i}+y\mathbf{j}+z\mathbf{k}$ and let $r = |\mathbf{r}|$. If f is a differentiable function of one variable show that

$$\nabla\bullet(f(r)\mathbf{r}) = rf'(r) + 3f(r).$$

Find $f(r)$ if $f(r)\mathbf{r}$ is solenoidal for $r\neq0$.

10. If the smooth vector field **F** is both irrotational and solenoidal on $\mathbb{R}^3$, show that the three components of **F** and the scalar potential for **F** are all harmonic functions in $\mathbb{R}^3$.

11. If $\mathbf{r} = x\mathbf{i}+y\mathbf{j}+z\mathbf{k}$, $\nabla\bullet\mathbf{F}=0$ and $\nabla\times\mathbf{F}=\mathbf{0}$, show that

$$\nabla\times(\mathbf{r}\times\mathbf{F}) + \nabla(\mathbf{r}\bullet\mathbf{F}) + \mathbf{F} = \mathbf{0}.$$

12. If ϕ and ψ are harmonic functions show that $\phi\nabla\psi - \psi\nabla\phi$ is solenoidal.

13. If ϕ and ψ are smooth scalar fields show that

$$\nabla\times(\phi\nabla\psi) = -\nabla\times(\psi\nabla\phi) = \nabla\phi\times\nabla\psi.$$

14. Verify the identity

$$\nabla\bullet\left(f(\nabla g\times\nabla h)\right) = \nabla f\bullet(\nabla g\times\nabla h),$$

for smooth scalar fields f, g, and h.

15. If the vector fields **F** and **G** are smooth and conservative show that $\mathbf{F}\times\mathbf{G}$ is solenoidal. Find a vector potential for $\mathbf{F}\times\mathbf{G}$.

16. Find a vector potential for $\mathbf{F} = -y\mathbf{i} + x\mathbf{j}$.

17. Show that $\mathbf{F} = xe^{2z}\mathbf{i}+ye^{2z}\mathbf{j}-e^{2z}\mathbf{k}$ is a solenoidal vector field, and find a vector potential for it.

18.*Suppose **div F** = 0 in a domain D any point P of which can by joined to the origin by a straight line segment in D. Let $\mathbf{r} = tx\mathbf{i}+ty\mathbf{j}+tz\mathbf{k}, 0\le t\le1$ be a parametrization of the line segment from the origin to (x,y,z) in D. If

$$\mathbf{G}(x,y,z) = \int_0^1 t\mathbf{F}(\mathbf{r}(t))\times\frac{d\mathbf{r}}{dt}\,dt,$$

show that **curl G** = **F** throughout D. Hint: it is enough to check the first components of **curl G** and **F**. Proceed in a manner similar to the proof of Theorem 7.2.2.

7.3   THE DIVERGENCE THEOREM

The Fundamental Theorem of Calculus,

$$\int_a^b \frac{d}{dx} f(x)\, dx = f(b) - f(a),$$

expresses the integral, taken over the interval $[a, b]$, of the derivative of a single-variable function, f, as a "sum" of values of that function at the *oriented boundary* of the interval $[a, b]$, that is, at the two endpoints a and b, the former providing a "negative" contribution and the later a "positive" one. The line integral of a conservative vector field over a curve C from A to B,

$$\int_C \nabla\phi \bullet d\mathbf{r} = \phi(B) - \phi(A),$$

has a similar interpretation; $\nabla\phi$ is a derivative, and the curve C, though lying in a two- or three-dimensional space, is intrinsically a one-dimensional object, and the points A and B constitute its boundary.

In this section and the next we will extend the Fundamental Theorem to double and triple integrals of certain "derivatives" of vector fields over two and three dimensional structures, and will discover, in each case, that the integral is equal to a "sum" (actually an integral of one lower dimension) over the boundary of the structure. The principal generalizations are three in number: Green's Theorem applies to domains in the plane and their bounding curves, Stokes's Theorem applies to surfaces in 3-space and their bounding curves, and Gauss's Theorem (the Divergence Theorem) applies to domains in 3-space, and their bounding surfaces. We start with the Divergence Theorem.

In the Divergence Theorem, the integral of the "derivative" $\mathbf{div}\ \mathbf{F} = \nabla\bullet\mathbf{F}$ over a domain in 3-space is expressed as the flux of $\mathbf{F}$ out of the surface of that domain. The theorem holds, and we therefore state it, for a general class of domains in $\mathbb{R}^3$ which are bounded by piecewise smooth closed surfaces. However, we shall restrict our proof to domains of a special type. Extending the concept of an x-simple plane domain defined in Section 4.1, we say the three-dimensional domain D is x-**simple** if it is bounded by a piecewise smooth surface S and if every straight line parallel to the x-axis and passing through an interior point of D meets S in exactly two points. Similar definitions hold for y-simple and z-simple, and we call the domain D **regular** if it is a union of finitely many, nonoverlapping subdomains, each of which is x-simple, y-simple and z-simple.

THEOREM 7.3.1   *(Gauss's Divergence Theorem)* Let D be a regular, 3-dimensional domain whose boundary S is an oriented, closed surface with unit normal field $\hat{\mathbf{N}}$ pointing out of D. If $\mathbf{F}$ is a smooth vector field defined on D then

$$\iiint_D \mathbf{div}\ \mathbf{F}\, dV = \oiint_S \mathbf{F} \bullet \hat{\mathbf{N}}\, dS.$$

PROOF We will prove the theorem only for regular domains, and in this case it is sufficient to prove it for subdomains of D which are simultaneously x-simple, y-simple and z-simple. To see this, suppose, for instance, that D and S are each divided into two parts, D_1 and D_2, and S_1 and S_2, by a surface S^* slicing through D. (See Fig. 7.3.1.) S^* is part of the boundary of both D_1 and D_2, but the exterior normals, $\hat{\mathbf{N}}_1$ and $\hat{\mathbf{N}}_2$, of the two subdomains point on opposite sides of S^*. If the formula in the theorem holds for both subdomains,

$$\iiint_{D_1} \operatorname{div} \mathbf{F}\, dV = \oiint_{S_1 \cup S^*} \mathbf{F} \bullet \hat{\mathbf{N}}_1\, dS$$

$$\iiint_{D_2} \operatorname{div} \mathbf{F}\, dV = \oiint_{S_2 \cup S^*} \mathbf{F} \bullet \hat{\mathbf{N}}_2\, dS,$$

then, adding these equations, we get

$$\iiint_{D} \operatorname{div} \mathbf{F}\, dV = \oiint_{S_1 \cup S_2} \mathbf{F} \bullet \hat{\mathbf{N}}\, dS = \oiint_{S} \mathbf{F} \bullet \hat{\mathbf{N}}\, dS;$$

the contributions from S^* cancel out because on that surface $\hat{\mathbf{N}}_2 = -\hat{\mathbf{N}}_1$.

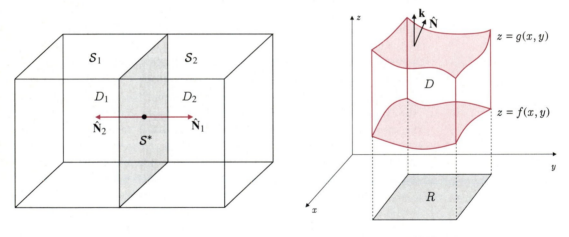

FIGURE 7.3.1   FIGURE 7.3.2

For the rest of this proof we assume, therefore, that D is x-, y- and z-simple. Since D is z-simple, it lies between the graphs of two functions defined on a region R in the xy-plane; if (x, y, z) is in D then (x, y) is in R and $f(x,y) \leq z \leq g(x,y)$. (See Fig. 7.3.2.) We have

$$\iiint_{D} \frac{\partial F_3}{\partial z}\, dV = \iint_{R} dx\, dy \int_{f(x,y)}^{g(x,y)} \frac{\partial F_3}{\partial z}\, dz$$

$$= \iint_{R} \Big(F_3(x, y, g(x,y)) - F_3(x, y, f(x,y)) \Big)\, dx\, dy.$$

Now

$$\oiint_S \mathbf{F} \bullet \hat{\mathbf{N}} \, dS = \oiint_S \left(F_1 \, \mathbf{i} \bullet \hat{\mathbf{N}} + F_2 \, \mathbf{j} \bullet \hat{\mathbf{N}} + F_3 \, \mathbf{k} \bullet \hat{\mathbf{N}} \right) dS.$$

Only the last term involves F_3, and it can be split into three integrals, over the top surface $z = g(x, y)$, the bottom surface $z = f(x, y)$, and vertical side wall lying above the boundary of R:

$$\oiint_S F_3(x, y, z) \, \mathbf{k} \bullet \hat{\mathbf{N}} \, dS = \left(\iint_{\text{top}} + \iint_{\text{bottom}} + \iint_{\text{side}} \right) F_3(x, y, z) \, \mathbf{k} \bullet \hat{\mathbf{N}} \, dS.$$

On the side wall, $\mathbf{k} \bullet \hat{\mathbf{N}} = 0$, so that integral is zero. If γ is that angle between $\mathbf{k}$ and $\hat{\mathbf{N}}$ on the top surface of D then $\mathbf{k} \bullet \hat{\mathbf{N}} = \cos \gamma$. Also, $dS = dx \, dy / \cos \gamma$. (See Box 6.5.12.) Accordingly,

$$\iint_{\text{top}} F_3(x, y, z) \, \mathbf{k} \bullet \hat{\mathbf{N}} \, dS = \iint_R F_3(x, y, g(x, y)) \cos \gamma \, \frac{dx \, dy}{\cos \gamma}$$

$$= \iint_R F_3(x, y, g(x, y)) \, dx \, dy.$$

Similarly,

$$\iint_{\text{bottom}} F_3(x, y, z) \, \mathbf{k} \bullet \hat{\mathbf{N}} \, dS = - \iint_R F_3(x, y, f(x, y)) \, dx \, dy;$$

the negative sign occurs because $\hat{\mathbf{N}}$ points down rather than up on the bottom. Thus we have shown that

$$\iiint_D \frac{\partial F_3}{\partial z} \, dV = \oiint_S F_3 \, \mathbf{k} \bullet \hat{\mathbf{N}} \, dS.$$

Similarly,

$$\iiint_D \frac{\partial F_1}{\partial x} \, dV = \oiint_S F_1 \, \mathbf{i} \bullet \hat{\mathbf{N}} \, dS$$

$$\iiint_D \frac{\partial F_2}{\partial y} \, dV = \oiint_S F_2 \, \mathbf{j} \bullet \hat{\mathbf{N}} \, dS.$$

Adding these three results we get

$$\iiint_D \operatorname{div} \mathbf{F} \, dV = \oiint_S \mathbf{F} \bullet \hat{\mathbf{N}} \, dS,$$

which is the desired result.   □

REMARK: The Divergence Theorem provides an immediate generalization of Theorem 7.1.6. Suppose that, for each $\epsilon > 0$, the point P_0 is an interior point of a domain D_ϵ with boundary $\mathcal{S}_\epsilon$ satisfying the conditions of the Divergence Theorem, and suppose that the maximum distance from P_0 to points P in D_ϵ approaches zero as $\epsilon \to 0^+$. If D_ϵ has volume $\operatorname{vol}(D_\epsilon)$, then

$$\lim_{\epsilon \to 0^+} \frac{1}{\operatorname{vol}(D_\epsilon)} \oiint_{\mathcal{S}_\epsilon} \mathbf{F} \bullet \hat{\mathbf{N}} \, dS = \lim_{\epsilon \to 0^+} \frac{1}{\operatorname{vol}(D_\epsilon)} \iiint_{D_\epsilon} \operatorname{div} \mathbf{F} \, dV = \operatorname{div} \mathbf{F}(P_0).$$

The Divergence Theorem can be used in both directions to simplify explicit calculations of volume or surface integrals. We give an example of each.

EXAMPLE 7.3.2   Let S be the surface of an arbitrary regular domain D in 3-space which contains the origin in its interior. Find

$$\oiint_{S} \mathbf{F} \bullet \hat{\mathbf{N}}\, dS$$

where $\mathbf{F}(\mathbf{r}) = m\mathbf{r}/|\mathbf{r}|^3$ and $\hat{\mathbf{N}}$ is the unit outward normal on S.

SOLUTION   Since $\mathbf{F}$, and therefore $\mathbf{div}\ \mathbf{F}$, is undefined at the origin, we cannot apply the Divergence Theorem directly. To overcome this problem we use a little trick. Let S^{*} be a small sphere centred at the origin bounding a ball contained wholly in D. (See Fig. 7.3.3.) Let $\hat{\mathbf{N}}^{*}$ be the unit normal on S^{*} pointing *into* the sphere, and let D^{*} be that part of D which lies outside S^{*}. As shown in Example 7.1.7, $\mathbf{div}\ \mathbf{F} = 0$ on D^{*}. Also,

$$\oiint_{S^{*}} \mathbf{F} \bullet \hat{\mathbf{N}}^{*}\, dS = -4\pi m,$$

the flux of $\mathbf{F}$ *inward* through the sphere S^{*}. (See Example 6.6.2) Therefore

$$0 = \iiint_{D^{*}} \mathbf{div}\ \mathbf{F}\, dV = \oiint_{S} \mathbf{F} \bullet \hat{\mathbf{N}}\, dS + \oiint_{S^{*}} \mathbf{F} \bullet \hat{\mathbf{N}}^{*}\, dS$$

$$= \oiint_{S} \mathbf{F} \bullet \hat{\mathbf{N}}\, dS - 4\pi m,$$

and it follows that

$$\oiint_{S} \mathbf{F} \bullet \hat{\mathbf{N}}\, dS = 4\pi m.$$

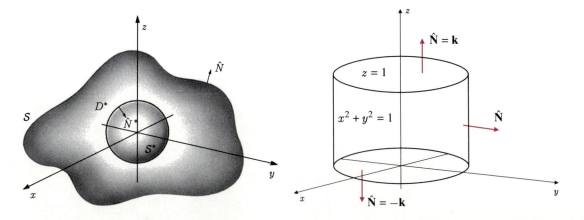

FIGURE 7.3.3   **FIGURE 7.3.4**

EXAMPLE 7.3.3   Find $\iiint_D \mathbf{div}\,\mathbf{F}\,dV$, where D is the cylinder of unit radius with axis along the z-axis between the planes $z = 0$ and $z = 1$, and

$$\mathbf{F} = \left(1 - (x^2 + y^2)^3\right)(\mathbf{i} + 2\mathbf{j}) + x^2 z^2 \mathbf{k}.$$

SOLUTION   The cylinder is shown in Fig. 7.3.4. By the Divergence Theorem, the required triple integral can be determined by integrating $\mathbf{F} \bullet \hat{\mathbf{N}}$ over the surface of the cylinder. ($\hat{\mathbf{N}}$ is the unit outward normal.) On the cylindrical wall we have $\mathbf{F} = x^2 z^2 \mathbf{k}$ and $\hat{\mathbf{N}}$ is horizontal, so $\mathbf{F} \bullet \hat{\mathbf{N}} = 0$ and the surface integral over that part is zero. On the bottom, $\mathbf{F} = (1 - (x^2 + y^2)^3)(\mathbf{i} + 2\mathbf{j})$ and $\hat{\mathbf{N}} = -\mathbf{k}$, so $\mathbf{F} \bullet \hat{\mathbf{N}} = 0$ and that surface gives a zero contribution also. On the top disc, where $\hat{\mathbf{N}} = \mathbf{k}$ and $z = 1$, we have $\mathbf{F} \bullet \hat{\mathbf{N}} = x^2$, and that surface integral is

$$\iint_{x^2+y^2\leq 1} x^2\,dA = \int_0^{2\pi} d\theta \int_0^1 (r\cos\theta)^2\,r\,dr = \frac{1}{4}\int_0^{2\pi} \frac{1+\cos 2\theta}{2}\,d\theta = \frac{\pi}{4}.$$

Thus

$$\iiint_D \mathbf{div}\,\mathbf{F}\,dV = \frac{\pi}{4}.$$

Examples like the one above are, of course, rather contrived. The principal significance of the Divergence Theorem is as a theoretical tool, not a tool for calculation. We will look at some applications in the next section. Here let us note that other versions of the Fundamental Theorem of Calculus can be derived from it. For instance, if D satisfies the conditions of of the Divergence Theorem and has surface S, and if $\mathbf{F}$ is a smooth vector field, and ϕ is a smooth scalar field, then the following two formulas hold:

7.3.4
Versions of the
Fundamental
Theorem

$$\iiint_D \mathbf{curl}\,\mathbf{F}\,dV = -\oiint_S \mathbf{F} \times \hat{\mathbf{N}}\,dS,$$

$$\iiint_D \mathbf{grad}\,\phi\,dV = \oiint_S \phi\hat{\mathbf{N}}\,dS.$$

(Observe that both of these formulas are equations of *vectors*.) They are derived by applying the Divergence Theorem to $\mathbf{F} \times \mathbf{c}$ and $\phi\mathbf{c}$ respectively, where $\mathbf{c}$ is an arbitrary constant vector. We establish the first formula in the following example to show the technique. The second is left as an exercise.

EXAMPLE 7.3.5   Verify the formula $\iiint_D \mathbf{curl}\,\mathbf{F}\,dV = -\oiint_S \mathbf{F} \times \hat{\mathbf{N}}\,dS.$

SOLUTION   Using Theorem 7.2.1(d), we calculate

$$\nabla \bullet (\mathbf{F} \times \mathbf{c}) = (\nabla \times \mathbf{F}) \bullet \mathbf{c} - \mathbf{F} \bullet (\nabla \times \mathbf{c}) = (\nabla \times \mathbf{F}) \bullet \mathbf{c}.$$

Also, (see Exercise 13 of Section 1.3),

$$(\mathbf{F} \times \mathbf{c}) \bullet \hat{\mathbf{N}} = (\hat{\mathbf{N}} \times \mathbf{F}) \bullet \mathbf{c} = -(\mathbf{F} \times \hat{\mathbf{N}}) \bullet \mathbf{c}.$$

Therefore

$$\left(\iiint_D \operatorname{curl} \mathbf{F}\, dV + \oiint_S \mathbf{F} \times \hat{\mathbf{N}}\, dS \right) \bullet \mathbf{c}$$

$$= \iiint_D (\nabla \times \mathbf{F}) \bullet \mathbf{c}\, dV - \oiint_S (\mathbf{F} \times \mathbf{c}) \bullet \hat{\mathbf{N}}\, dS$$

$$= \iiint_D \operatorname{div}\,(\mathbf{F} \times \mathbf{c})\, dV - \oiint_S (\mathbf{F} \times \mathbf{c}) \bullet \hat{\mathbf{N}}\, dS = 0.$$

Since $\mathbf{c}$ is arbitrary, the vector in the large parentheses must be the zero vector. (If $\mathbf{c} \bullet \mathbf{a} = 0$ for every vector $\mathbf{c}$ then $\mathbf{a} = \mathbf{0}$.) This establishes the desired formula.

The following example illustrates how the Divergence Theorem is used to establish a two-dimensional version of itself.

EXAMPLE 7.3.6   Let R be a domain in the xy-plane which lies on one side of its piecewise smooth boundary curve C. If

$$\mathbf{F} = F_1(x, y)\mathbf{i} + F_2(x, y)\mathbf{j}$$

is a smooth vector field show that

7.3.7
The Diver-
gence Theorem
in Two Dimensions

$$\iint_R \operatorname{div} \mathbf{F}\, dA = \oint_C \mathbf{F} \bullet \hat{\mathbf{N}}\, ds,$$

where $\hat{\mathbf{N}}$ is the unit *outward* normal on C.

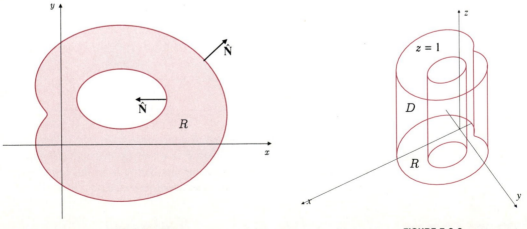

FIGURE 7.3.5   **FIGURE 7.3.6**

SOLUTION R and its boundary normals are shown in Fig. 7.3.5. Let D be the vertical cylinder whose base is the region R and whose top is in the plane $z = 1$. (See Fig. 7.3.6.) We apply the 3-dimensional Divergence Theorem to $\mathbf{F}$ (considered as a 3-dimensional vector field) on D. We have

$$\iiint_D \operatorname{div} \mathbf{F}\, dV = \int_0^1 dz \iint_R \left(\frac{\partial F_1(x,y)}{\partial x} + \frac{\partial F_2(x,y)}{\partial y} \right) dA$$

$$= \iint_R \operatorname{div} \mathbf{F}\, dA.$$

On the top and bottom surfaces of the cylinder D, the normals $\hat{\mathbf{N}}$ are $\mathbf{k}$ and $-\mathbf{k}$ respectively. Since the z-component F_3 is identically zero, $\mathbf{F} \bullet \hat{\mathbf{N}}$ vanishes on these two surfaces. On the vertical cylindrical wall, the outward normal $\hat{\mathbf{N}}(x,y,z) = \hat{\mathbf{N}}(x,y)$, the normal to C, and the area element is $dS = dz\, ds$. Since $\mathbf{F}$ is independent of z we have, denoting the whole surface of D by $\mathcal{S}$,

$$\oiint_{\mathcal{S}} \mathbf{F} \bullet \hat{\mathbf{N}}\, dS = \iint_{\text{cylwall}} \mathbf{F} \bullet \hat{\mathbf{N}}\, dS = \int_0^1 dz \oint_C \mathbf{F} \bullet \hat{\mathbf{N}}\, ds = \oint_C \mathbf{F} \bullet \hat{\mathbf{N}}\, ds.$$

The desired formula now follows at once.

EXERCISES

In Exercises 1–9, D is a three-dimensional domain satisfying the conditions of the Divergence Theorem, and $\mathcal{S}$ is its surface. $\hat{\mathbf{N}}$ is the unit outward (from D) normal field on $\mathcal{S}$. In Exercises 4–9, ϕ and ψ are smooth scalar fields on D. Also, $\partial \phi / \partial n$ denotes the first directional derivative of ϕ in the direction of $\hat{\mathbf{N}}$ at any point on $\mathcal{S}$:

$$\frac{\partial \phi}{\partial n} = \nabla \phi \bullet \hat{\mathbf{N}}.$$

1. Show that $\oiint_{\mathcal{S}} \operatorname{curl} \mathbf{F} \bullet \hat{\mathbf{N}}\, dS = 0$, where $\mathbf{F}$ is an arbitrary smooth vector field.

2. Show that the volume V of D is given by

$$V = \frac{1}{3} \oiint_{\mathcal{S}} (x\mathbf{i} + y\mathbf{j} + z\mathbf{k}) \bullet \hat{\mathbf{N}}\, dS.$$

3. If D has volume V show that

$$\bar{\mathbf{r}} = \frac{1}{2V} \oiint_{\mathcal{S}} (x^2 + y^2 + z^2) \hat{\mathbf{N}}\, dS$$

is the position vector of the centre of gravity of D.

4. Show that $\oiint_{\mathcal{S}} \nabla \phi \times \hat{\mathbf{N}}\, dS = 0$.

5. If $\phi(x,y,z) = 0$ on $\mathcal{S}$, and $\mathbf{F}$ is a smooth vector field on D, show that

$$\iiint_D \phi \operatorname{div} \mathbf{F}\, dV = - \iiint_D \nabla \phi \bullet \mathbf{F}\, dV.$$

(Hint: use Theorem 7.2.1(b).)

6. If ϕ and $\mathbf{F}$ are as in the previous exercise, and ϕ is also harmonic in D, (i.e. $\nabla^2 \phi(x,y,z) = 0$ in D), show that $\phi(x,y,z) = 0$ throughout D. Hence show that if $u(x,y,z)$ and $v(x,y,z)$ are two smooth functions, both harmonic in D, and equal on $\mathcal{S}$, then they are equal throughout D. (This is a **uniqueness theorem** for the **Dirichlet problem** $\nabla^2 u(x,y,z) = f(x,y,z)$ in D, $u(x,y,z) = g(x,y,z)$ on $\mathcal{S}$, an important boundary-value problem in applied mathematics.)

7. By applying the Divergence Theorem to $\mathbf{F} = \phi \mathbf{c}$, where $\mathbf{c}$ is an arbitrary constant vector, show that

$$\iiint_D \nabla \phi\, dV = \oiint_{\mathcal{S}} \phi \hat{\mathbf{N}}\, dS.$$

8. Verify that $\displaystyle\iiint_D \nabla^2\phi \, dV = \oiint_S \frac{\partial\phi}{\partial n} \, dS.$

9. Verify that

$$\iiint_D \left(\phi\nabla^2\psi - \psi\nabla^2\phi\right) dV$$
$$= \oiint_S \left(\phi\frac{\partial\psi}{\partial n} - \psi\frac{\partial\phi}{\partial n}\right) dS.$$

10. Let $\phi(x,y,z) = xy + z^2$. Find the flux of $\nabla\phi$ upwards through the triangular planar surface S with vertices at $(a,0,0)$, $(0,b,0)$ and $(0,0,c)$.

11. A conical domain with vertex $(0,0,b)$ and axis along the z-axis has as base a disk of radius a in the xy-plane. Find the flux of

$$\mathbf{F} = (x+y^2)\mathbf{i} + (3x^2y + y^3 - x^3)\mathbf{j} + (z+1)\mathbf{k}$$

upwards through the conical part of the surface of the domain.

12. Find the flux of $\mathbf{F} = (y+xz)\mathbf{i} + (y+yz)\mathbf{j} - (2x+z^2)\mathbf{k}$ upward through the first octant part of the sphere $x^2 + y^2 + z^2 = a^2$.

13. Let D be the region $x^2 + y^2 + z^2 \le 4a^2$, $x^2 + y^2 \ge a^2$. The surface S of D consists of a cylindrical part, S_1, and a spherical part, S_2. Evaluate the flux of

$$\mathbf{F} = (x+yz)\mathbf{i} + (y-xz)\mathbf{j} + (z - e^x \sin y)\mathbf{k}$$

out of D through a) the whole surface S, b) the surface S_1, and c) the surface S_2.

14. Evaluate $\displaystyle\iint_S (3xz^2\mathbf{i} - x\mathbf{j} - y\mathbf{k})\bullet\hat{\mathbf{N}}\, dS$, where S is that part of the cylinder $y^2 + z^2 = 1$ which lies in the first octant and between the planes $x = 0$ and $x = 1$.

15. A solid region R has volume V and centroid at the point $(\bar{x},\bar{y},\bar{z})$. Find the flux of

$$\mathbf{F} = (x^2 - x - 2y)\mathbf{i} + (2y^2 + 3y - z)\mathbf{j} - (z^2 - 4z + xy)\mathbf{k}$$

out of R through its surface.

16. The plane $x + y + z = 0$ divides the cube $-1 \le x \le 1$, $-1 \le y \le 1$, $-1 \le z \le 1$ into two parts. Let the lower part (with one vertex at $(-1,-1,-1)$) be D. Sketch D. Note that it has seven faces, one hexagonal. Find the flux of $\mathbf{F} = x\mathbf{i} + y\mathbf{j} + z\mathbf{k}$ out of D through each of its faces.

7.4 GREEN'S THEOREM AND STOKES'S THEOREM

Green's Theorem in the Plane

Green's Theorem is a 2-dimensional version of the Fundamental Theorem of Calculus, similar to Example 7.3.6 of the previous section, but rephrased so that the boundary line integral involves the tangential rather than the normal component of **F**. This requires that we specify an orientation for the boundary curves C of the region R. We require this orientation to be *positive*, so that if we move around C in the direction of its orientation, R will be on our left. This corresponds to regarding R as an oriented surface with normal **k**. The region R need not be simply connected; it can have holes, and the boundaries of the holes constitute part of the boundary of the region. (See Fig. 7.4.1.) The "outer" boundary of R is oriented counterclockwise while the boundaries of holes are oriented clockwise.

THEOREM 7.4.1   *(Green's Theorem)* Let R be a region in the xy-plane whose boundary, C, consists of one or more piecewise smooth, non-self-intersecting, closed curves which are

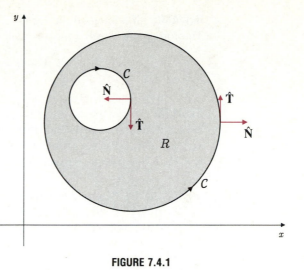

FIGURE 7.4.1

positively oriented. If $\mathbf{F} = F_1(x, y)\mathbf{i} + F_2(x, y)\mathbf{j}$ is a smooth vector field then

$$\oint_C F_1(x, y)\, dx + F_2(x, y)\, dy = \iint_R \left(\frac{\partial F_2}{\partial x} - \frac{\partial F_1}{\partial y} \right) dA.$$

PROOF   Because of the orientation of C, the unit exterior normal $\hat{\mathbf{N}}$ on C (pointing out of R) is $\hat{\mathbf{N}} = \hat{\mathbf{T}} \times \mathbf{k}$, where $\hat{\mathbf{T}}$ is the unit tangent. If C is parametrized in terms of arc length then

$$\hat{\mathbf{T}} = \frac{dx}{ds}\mathbf{i} + \frac{dy}{ds}\mathbf{j}, \qquad \hat{\mathbf{N}} = \frac{dy}{ds}\mathbf{i} - \frac{dx}{ds}\mathbf{j}.$$

Let $\mathbf{G} = F_2(x, y)\mathbf{i} - F_1(x, y)\mathbf{j}$. Then $\mathbf{div}\,\mathbf{G} = (\partial F_2/\partial x) - (\partial F_1/\partial y)$, and therefore $\mathbf{G} \bullet \hat{\mathbf{N}} = \mathbf{F} \bullet \hat{\mathbf{T}}$. Applying the two-dimensional Divergence Theorem from Example 7.3.6, we obtain

$$
\begin{aligned}
\oint_C F_1(x, y)\, dx + F_2(x, y)\, dy &= \oint_C \mathbf{F} \bullet d\mathbf{r} = \oint_C \mathbf{F} \bullet \hat{\mathbf{T}}\, ds \\
&= \oint_C \mathbf{G} \bullet \hat{\mathbf{N}}\, ds \\
&= \iint_R \mathbf{div}\,\mathbf{G}\, dA \\
&= \iint_R \left(\frac{\partial F_2}{\partial x} - \frac{\partial F_1}{\partial y} \right) dA,
\end{aligned}
$$

as required. □

REMARK: If we regard the region R as a surface in 3-space, its normal is $\hat{\mathbf{N}} = \mathbf{k}$. The formula in Green's theorem can therefore be written

$$\oint_C \mathbf{F} \bullet d\mathbf{r} = \iint_R \operatorname{curl} \mathbf{F} \bullet \hat{\mathbf{N}} \, dS.$$

REMARK: The expression $F_1(x,y)\,dx + F_2(x,y)\,dy$ is called a **differential form**. This differential form is said to be **exact** if it is equal to $d\phi$ for some function $\phi(x,y)$. Evidently the differential form is exact if the corresponding vector field $\mathbf{F} = F_1\mathbf{i} + F_2\mathbf{j}$ is conservative, in which case ϕ is the scalar potential of $\mathbf{F}$.

EXAMPLE 7.4.2   For any of the three vector fields

$$\mathbf{F} = x\mathbf{j}, \qquad \mathbf{F} = -y\mathbf{i}, \qquad \mathbf{F} = \frac{1}{2}(-y\mathbf{i} + x\mathbf{j})$$

we have $(\partial F_2/\partial x) - (\partial F_1/\partial y) = 1$. If C is a positively oriented, closed curve bounding a region R in the plane, then by Green's Theorem,

$$\oint_C x\,dy = -\oint_C y\,dx = \frac{1}{2}\oint_C x\,dy - y\,dx = \iint_R 1\,dA = \text{ area of } R.$$

EXAMPLE 7.4.3   Evaluate $I = \oint_C (x - y^3)\,dx + (y^3 + x^3)\,dy$, where C is the positively oriented boundary of the quarter disc $Q: 0 \le x^2 + y^2 \le a^2$, $x \ge 0$, $y \ge 0$.

SOLUTION   We use Green's Theorem to calculate

$$I = \iint_Q \left(\frac{\partial}{\partial x}(y^3 + x^3) - \frac{\partial}{\partial y}(x - y^3) \right) dA$$

$$= 3 \iint_Q (x^2 + y^2)\,dA = 3 \int_0^{\pi/2} d\theta \int_0^a r^3\,dr = \frac{3}{8}\pi a^4.$$

Stokes's Theorem

Stokes's Theorem is a generalization of Green's Theorem which applies to surfaces (not necessarily planar) in 3-space.

THEOREM 7.4.4   *(Stokes's Theorem)* Let S be a piecewise smooth, oriented surface in 3-space, having unit normal field $\hat{\mathbf{N}}$, and having boundary C consisting of one or more piecewise smooth, closed curves with orientation inherited from S. If $\mathbf{F}$ is a smooth vector field defined on an open set containing S, then

$$\oint_C \mathbf{F} \bullet d\mathbf{r} = \iint_S \operatorname{curl} \mathbf{F} \bullet \hat{\mathbf{N}} \, dS.$$

PROOF   An argument similar to that given at the beginning of the proof of the Divergence Theorem shows that if S is decomposed into finitely many nonoverlapping subsurfaces then it is sufficient to prove that the formula in the box holds for each of them. (If subsurfaces S_1 and S_2 meet along the curve C^*, then C^* inherits opposite orientations as part of the boundaries of S_1 and S_2, so the line integrals along C^* cancel out. See Fig. 7.4.2.) We can subdivide S into enough smooth subsurfaces that each one has a one-to-one normal projection onto a coordinate plane. We will establish the formula for one such subsurface, which we will now call S.

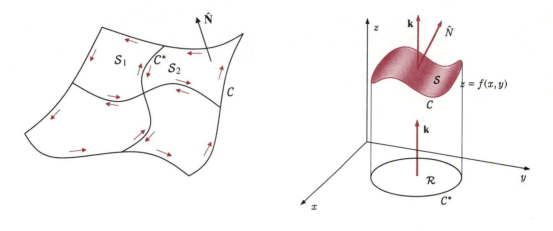

FIGURE 7.4.2   **FIGURE 7.4.3**

Without loss of generality, assume that S has a one-to-one normal projection onto the xy-plane, and that its normal field $\hat{N}$ points upward. Therefore, on S, z is a smooth function of x and y defined for (x, y) in a region R of the xy-plane. The boundaries C of S, and C^* of R, are both oriented counterclockwise as seen from a point high on the z-axis. (See Fig. 7.4.3.) The normal field on S is

$$\hat{N} = \frac{-\dfrac{\partial z}{\partial x}\mathbf{i} - \dfrac{\partial z}{\partial y}\mathbf{j} + \mathbf{k}}{\sqrt{1 + \left(\dfrac{\partial z}{\partial x}\right)^2 + \left(\dfrac{\partial z}{\partial y}\right)^2}},$$

and the surface area element on S is expressed in terms of the area element $dA = dx\,dy$ in the xy-plane as

$$dS = \sqrt{1 + \left(\frac{\partial z}{\partial x}\right)^2 + \left(\frac{\partial z}{\partial y}\right)^2}\,dA.$$

Therefore

$$\iint_S \text{curl } \mathbf{F} \bullet \hat{\mathbf{N}} \, dS = \iint_R \left[\left(\frac{\partial F_3}{\partial y} - \frac{\partial F_2}{\partial z} \right) \left(-\frac{\partial z}{\partial x} \right) + \left(\frac{\partial F_1}{\partial z} - \frac{\partial F_3}{\partial x} \right) \left(-\frac{\partial z}{\partial y} \right) \right.$$
$$\left. + \left(\frac{\partial F_2}{\partial x} - \frac{\partial F_1}{\partial y} \right) \right] dA.$$

Since z is a function of x and y on C, we have $dz = \dfrac{\partial z}{\partial x} \, dx + \dfrac{\partial z}{\partial y} \, dy$. Thus

$$\oint_C \mathbf{F} \bullet d\mathbf{r} = \oint_{C^*} \left[F_1(x, y, z) \, dx + F_2(x, y, z) \, dy \right.$$
$$\left. + F_3(x, y, z) \left(\frac{\partial z}{\partial x} \, dx + \frac{\partial z}{\partial y} \, dy \right) \right]$$
$$= \oint_{C^*} \left(\left[F_1(x, y, z) + F_3(x, y, z) \frac{\partial z}{\partial x} \right] dx \right.$$
$$\left. + \left[F_2(x, y, z) + F_3(x, y, z) \frac{\partial z}{\partial y} \right] dy \right).$$

We now apply Green's Theorem in the xy-plane to obtain

$$\oint_C \mathbf{F} \bullet d\mathbf{r} = \iint_R \left(\frac{\partial}{\partial x} \left[F_2(x, y, z) + F_3(x, y, z) \frac{\partial z}{\partial y} \right] \right.$$
$$\left. - \frac{\partial}{\partial y} \left[F_1(x, y, z) + F_3(x, y, z) \frac{\partial z}{\partial x} \right] \right) dA$$
$$= \iint_R \left(\frac{\partial F_2}{\partial x} + \frac{\partial F_2}{\partial z} \frac{\partial z}{\partial x} + \frac{\partial F_3}{\partial x} \frac{\partial z}{\partial y} + \frac{\partial F_3}{\partial z} \frac{\partial z}{\partial x} \frac{\partial z}{\partial y} + F_3 \frac{\partial^2 z}{\partial x \partial y} \right.$$
$$\left. - \frac{\partial F_1}{\partial y} - \frac{\partial F_1}{\partial z} \frac{\partial z}{\partial y} - \frac{\partial F_3}{\partial y} \frac{\partial z}{\partial x} - \frac{\partial F_3}{\partial z} \frac{\partial z}{\partial y} \frac{\partial z}{\partial x} - F_3 \frac{\partial^2 z}{\partial y \partial x} \right) dA.$$

Observe that four terms in the final integrand cancel out, and the remaining terms are equal to the terms in the expression for $\iint_S \text{curl } \mathbf{F} \bullet \hat{\mathbf{N}} \, dS$ calculated above. We are done. □

REMARK: If **curl F = 0** on a domain D with the property that every piecewise smooth, non-self-intersecting, closed curve in D is the boundary of a piecewise smooth surface in D, then Stokes's Theorem assures us that $\oint_C \mathbf{F} \bullet d\mathbf{r} = 0$ for every such curve C, and therefore **F** must be conservative. A simply connected domain D does have the property specified above. We will not attempt a formal proof of this topological fact here, but it should seem plausible if you recall the definition of simple connectedness (Box 6.4.4). A closed curve C in a simply connected domain D must be able to shrink to a point in D without ever passing out of D. In so shrinking, it traces out a surface in D. This is why Theorem 7.2.2 is valid for simply connected domains.

As with the Divergence Theorem, the principal importance of Stokes's Theorem is as a theoretical tool. However, it is not difficult to imagine vector integrals whose evaluation would be impossibly difficult without the use of one or the other of those theorems. In the following example we use Stokes's Theorem twice, but the result could be obtained just as easily by using the Divergence Theorem.

EXAMPLE 7.4.5   Find $I = \displaystyle\iint_{S} \mathbf{curl\ F} \bullet \hat{\mathbf{N}}\, dS$ where S is that part of the sphere $x^2 + y^2 + (z-2)^2 = 8$ which lies above the xy-plane, $\hat{\mathbf{N}}$ is the unit outward normal field on S, and

$$\mathbf{F} = y^2 \cos xz\, \mathbf{i} + x^3 e^{yz} \mathbf{j} - e^{-xyz} \mathbf{k}.$$

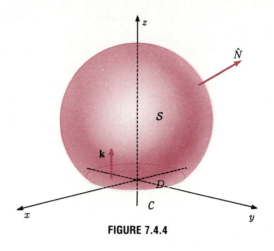

FIGURE 7.4.4

SOLUTION   The boundary, C, of S is the circle $x^2 + y^2 = 4$ in the xy-plane, oriented counterclockwise as seen from the positive z-axis. (See Fig. 7.4.4.) This curve is also the oriented boundary of the plane disc D: $x^2 + y^2 \leq 4$, $z = 0$, with normal field $\hat{\mathbf{N}} = \mathbf{k}$. Thus, two applications of Stokes's Theorem give

$$I = \iint_{S} \mathbf{curl\ F} \bullet \hat{\mathbf{N}}\, dS = \oint_{C} \mathbf{F} \bullet d\mathbf{r} = \iint_{D} \mathbf{curl\ F} \bullet \mathbf{k}\, dA.$$

On D we have

$$\mathbf{curl\ F} \bullet \mathbf{k} = \left(\frac{\partial}{\partial x}\left(x^3 e^{yz} \right) - \frac{\partial}{\partial y}\left(y^2 \cos xz \right) \right)\Bigg|_{z=0}$$

$$= 3x^2 - 2y.$$

By symmetry, $\iint_{D} y\, dA = 0$ so

$$I = 3 \iint_{D} x^2\, dA = 3 \int_{0}^{2\pi} \cos^2 \theta\, d\theta \int_{0}^{2} r^3\, dr = 12\pi.$$

REMARK: A surface S satisfying the conditions of Stokes's Theorem may no longer do so if a single point is removed from it. An isolated boundary point of a surface is not an orientable curve, and Stokes's Theorem may therefore break down for such a surface. Consider, for example, the vector field

$$\mathbf{F} = \frac{\hat{\theta}}{r} = -\frac{y}{x^2 + y^2}\mathbf{i} + \frac{x}{x^2 + y^2}\mathbf{j},$$

which is defined on the *punctured disc* D satisfying $0 < x^2 + y^2 \leq a^2$. (See Exercises 18 and 19 of Section 6.4.) If D is oriented with upward normal $\mathbf{k}$, then its boundary consists of the oriented, smooth, closed curve, C, given by $x = a \cos\theta$, $y = a \sin\theta$, $(0 \leq \theta \leq 2\pi)$, and the isolated point $(0,0)$. We have

$$\oint_C \mathbf{F} \bullet d\mathbf{r} = \int_0^{2\pi} \left(\frac{-\sin\theta}{a}\mathbf{i} + \frac{\cos\theta}{a}\mathbf{j} \right) \bullet (-a\sin\theta\mathbf{i} + a\cos\theta\mathbf{j})\, d\theta$$

$$= \int_0^{2\pi} (\sin^2\theta + \cos^2\theta)\, d\theta = 2\pi.$$

However,

$$\mathbf{curl\ F} = \frac{\partial}{\partial x}\left(\frac{x}{x^2 + y^2} \right) - \frac{\partial}{\partial y}\left(-\frac{y}{x^2 + y^2} \right) = 0$$

identically on D. Thus

$$\iint_D \mathbf{curl\ F} \bullet \hat{\mathbf{N}}\, dS = 0,$$

and Stokes's Theorem fails in this case.

EXERCISES

1. Evaluate $\oint_C (\sin x + 3y^2)\, dx + (2x - e^{-y^2})\, dy$, where C is the boundary of the half-disc $x^2 + y^2 \leq a^2$, $y \geq 0$, oriented counterclockwise.

2. Evaluate $\oint_C (x^2 - xy)\, dx + (xy - y^2)\, dy$ clockwise around the triangle with vertices $(0,0)$, $(1,1)$ and $(2,0)$.

3. Evaluate $\oint_C \left(x\sin(y^2) - y^2 \right)\, dx + \left(x^2 y\cos(y^2) + 3x \right)\, dy$, where C is the counterclockwise boundary of the trapezoid with vertices $(0,-2)$, $(1,-1)$, $(1,1)$ and $(0,2)$.

4. Evaluate $\oint_C \mathbf{F} \bullet d\mathbf{r}$, where $\mathbf{F} = ye^x\mathbf{i} + (x + e^x)\mathbf{j} + z^2\mathbf{k}$ and C is the curve

$$\mathbf{r} = (1 + \cos t)\mathbf{i} + (1 + \sin t)\mathbf{j} + (1 - \sin t - \cos t)\mathbf{k},$$

where $0 \leq t \leq 2\pi$.

5. Sketch the plane curve C: $\mathbf{r} = \sin t\,\mathbf{i} + \sin 2t\,\mathbf{j}$, $(0 \leq t \leq 2\pi)$. Evaluate $\oint_C \mathbf{F} \bullet d\mathbf{r}$ where $\mathbf{F} = ye^{x^2}\mathbf{i} + x^3 e^y\mathbf{j}$.

6. If C is the positively oriented boundary of a plane region R having area A and centroid $(\bar{x}, \bar{y})$, interpret geometrically the line integral $\oint_C \mathbf{F} \bullet d\mathbf{r}$ where:

a) $\mathbf{F} = x^2\mathbf{j}$,   b) $\mathbf{F} = xy\mathbf{i}$,   c) $\mathbf{F} = y^2\mathbf{i} + 3xy\mathbf{j}$.

7. Use a line integral to find the plane area enclosed by the curve $\mathbf{r} = a\cos^3 t\,\mathbf{i} + b\sin^3 t\,\mathbf{j}$, $0 \leq t \leq 2\pi$.

8. Verify the identity

$$\oint_C \phi\nabla\psi \bullet d\mathbf{r} = -\oint_C \psi\nabla\phi \bullet d\mathbf{r}$$

for any smooth scalar fields, ϕ and ψ, where C is the boundary of a piecewise smooth surface.

9. Evaluate $\iint_S \mathbf{curl\ F} \bullet \hat{\mathbf{N}}\, dS$ where S is the hemisphere $x^2 + y^2 + z^2 = a^2$, $z \geq 0$ with outward normal, and $\mathbf{F} = 3y\mathbf{i} - 2xz\mathbf{j} + (x^2 - y^2)\mathbf{k}$.

10. Evaluate $\oint_C y\, dx - x\, dy + z^2\, dz$ around the curve C of intersection of the cylinders $z = y^2$ and $x^2 + y^2 = 4$, oriented counterclockwise as seen from a point high on the z-axis.

11. Evaluate $\oint_C xy\, dx + yz\, dy + zx\, dz$ around the triangle with vertices $(1,0,0)$, $(0,1,0)$ and $(0,0,1)$, oriented clockwise as seen from the point $(1,1,1)$.

12. Evaluate $\iint_S \mathbf{curl\ F} \bullet \hat{\mathbf{N}}\, dS$, where S is the surface $x^2 + y^2 + 2(z - 1)^2 = 6$, $z \geq 0$, $\hat{\mathbf{N}}$ is the unit "outward" (away from the origin) normal on S, and

$$\mathbf{F} = (xz - y^3 \cos z)\mathbf{i} + x^3 e^z \mathbf{j} + xyz\, e^{x^2+y^2+z^2}\mathbf{k}.$$

13. If C is the oriented boundary of surface S and ϕ and ψ are arbitrary smooth scalar fields show that

$$\oint_C \phi\nabla\psi \bullet d\mathbf{r} = -\oint_C \psi\nabla\phi \bullet d\mathbf{r}$$

$$= \iint_S (\nabla\phi \times \nabla\psi) \bullet \hat{\mathbf{N}}\, dS.$$

Is $\nabla\phi \times \nabla\psi$ solenoidal? Find a vector potential for it.

14. Evaluate $\oint_C \mathbf{F} \bullet d\mathbf{r}$ around the curve

$$\mathbf{r} = \cos t\,\mathbf{i} + \sin t\,\mathbf{j} + \sin 2t\,\mathbf{k}, \quad (0 \le t \le 2\pi),$$

where
$$\mathbf{F} = (e^x - y^3)\mathbf{i} + (e^y + x^3)\mathbf{j} + e^z\mathbf{k}.$$

Hint: show that C lies on the surface $z = 2xy$.

15. Use Stokes's Theorem to show that

$$\oint_C y\, dx + z\, dy + x\, dz = \sqrt{3}\,\pi a^2,$$

where C is the suitably oriented intersection of the surfaces $x^2 + y^2 + z^2 = a^2$ and $x + y + z = 0$.

16. Let C be a closed, non-self-intersecting, piecewise smooth plane curve in $\mathbb{R}^3$, which lies in a plane with unit normal $\hat{\mathbf{N}} = a\mathbf{i} + b\mathbf{j} + c\mathbf{k}$, and which has orientation inherited from that of the plane. Show that the plane area enclosed by C is

$$\frac{1}{2}\oint_C (bz - cy)\, dx + (cx - az)\, dy + (ay - bx)\, dz.$$

17. We deduced Green's Theorem from the two-dimensional version of the Divergence Theorem. Reverse the argument and use Green's Theorem to show that

$$\iint_R \mathbf{div}\ \mathbf{F}\, dA = \oint_C \mathbf{F} \bullet \hat{\mathbf{N}}\, ds,$$

where C is the oriented boundary of the plane domain R.

7.5 SOME PHYSICAL APPLICATIONS OF VECTOR CALCULUS

In this final section we will show how the theory developed in this chapter can be used to model concrete applied mathematical problems. We will look at two areas of application, fluid dynamics and electromagnetism, and will develop a few of the fundamental vector equations underlying these disciplines. Our purpose is to illustrate the techniques of vector calculus in applied contexts, rather than to provide any complete or even coherent introductions to the disciplines themselves.

Fluid Dynamics

Suppose that a region of 3-space is filled with a fluid (liquid or gas) in motion. Two approaches may be taken to describe the motion. We could attempt to determine the position, $\mathbf{r} = \mathbf{r}(a, b, c, t)$ at any time t, of a "particle" of fluid which was located at the point (a, b, c) at time $t = 0$. This is the Lagrange approach. Alternately, we could attempt to determine the velocity, $\mathbf{v}(x, y, z, t)$, the density, $\rho(x, y, z, t)$, and other physical variables such as the pressure, $p(x, y, z, t)$, at any time t at any point (x, y, z) in the region occupied by the fluid. This is the Euler approach.

We will examine the latter method, and describe how the Divergence Theorem can be used to translate some fundamental physical "laws" into equivalent mathematical equations. We assume throughout that the velocity, density and pressure vary smoothly in all their variables.

Consider an imaginary closed surface S in the fluid, bounding a domain D. We call S "imaginary" because it is not a barrier impeding the flow of the fluid in any way—it is just a means to concentrate our attention on a particular part of the fluid. Let us assume that the fluid is neither being created nor destroyed anywhere, (in particular there are no sources or sinks), and so the law of **conservation of mass** tells us that the rate of change of the mass of fluid in D equals the rate at which fluid enters D across S.

The mass of fluid in volume element dV at position (x, y, z) at time t is $\rho(x, y, z, t)\, dV$, so the mass in D at time t is $\iiint_D \rho\, dV$. This mass changes at rate

$$\frac{\partial}{\partial t} \iiint_D \rho\, dV = \iiint_D \frac{\partial \rho}{\partial t}\, dV.$$

As we have noted in Section 6.6, the volume of fluid passing *out* of D through area element dS at position (x, y, z) in the interval from time t to $t + dt$ is given by $\mathbf{v}(x, y, z, t) \bullet \hat{\mathbf{N}}\, dS\, dt$, where $\hat{\mathbf{N}}$ is the unit normal at (x, y, z) on S pointing out of D. Hence the mass crossing dS outwards in that time interval is $\rho \mathbf{v} \bullet \hat{\mathbf{N}}\, dS\, dt$, and the *rate* at which mass is flowing out of D across S at time t is

$$\oiint_S \rho \mathbf{v} \bullet \hat{\mathbf{N}}\, dS.$$

The rate at which mass is flowing *into* D is the negative of the above rate. Since mass is conserved, we must have

$$\iiint_D \frac{\partial \rho}{\partial t}\, dV = -\oiint_S \rho \mathbf{v} \bullet \hat{\mathbf{N}}\, dS = -\iiint_D \mathbf{div}\, (\rho \mathbf{v})\, dV,$$

where we have used the Divergence Theorem to replace the surface integral with a volume integral. Thus

$$\iiint_D \left(\frac{\partial \rho}{\partial t} + \mathbf{div}\, (\rho \mathbf{v}) \right) dV = 0.$$

This equation must hold for *any* domain D in the fluid, and since the integrand is assumed to be continuous, we must have

7.5.1
Equation of
Continuity

$$\frac{\partial \rho}{\partial t} + \mathbf{div}\, (\rho \mathbf{v}) = 0$$

throughout the fluid. (If a continuous function f satisfies $\iiint_D f(P)\,dV = 0$ for every domain D, then $f(P) = 0$ at all points P, for if there were a point P_0 such that $f(P_0) \neq 0$, (say $f(P_0) > 0$), then, by continuity, f would be positive at all points in some sufficiently small ball B centered at P_0, and $\iiint_B f(P)\,dV$ would be greater than 0.)

Equation 7.5.1 is called the **equation of continuity** for the moving fluid; it is equivalent to the physical property of conservation of mass. Observe that if the fluid is *incompressible* then ρ is a constant, independent of both time and spatial position. In this case $\partial\rho/\partial t = 0$ and $\mathbf{div}\,(\rho\mathbf{v}) = \rho\,\mathbf{div}\,\mathbf{v}$. Therefore the equation of continuity for an incompressible fluid is simply

$$\mathbf{div}\ \mathbf{v} = 0.$$

The motion of the fluid is governed by Newton's Second Law, which asserts that the rate of change of momentum of any part of the fluid is equal to the sum of the forces applied to that part. Again let us consider the part of the fluid in a domain D. At any time t its momentum is $\iiint_D \rho\mathbf{v}\,dV$, and is changing at rate

$$\iiint_D \frac{\partial}{\partial t}(\rho\mathbf{v})\,dV.$$

This change is due partly to momentum crossing S into or out of D (the momentum of the fluid crossing S), partly to the pressure exerted on the fluid in D by the fluid outside, and partly due to any external "body forces" (such as gravity or electromagnetic forces) acting on the fluid. Let us examine each of these causes in turn.

Momentum is transferred across S into D at rate

$$-\oiint_S \mathbf{v}(\rho\mathbf{v}\bullet\hat{\mathbf{N}})\,dS.$$

The pressure on the fluid in D is exerted across S in the direction of the inward normal $-\hat{\mathbf{N}}$. Thus this part of the force on the fluid in D is

$$-\oiint_S p\hat{\mathbf{N}}\,dS.$$

The body forces are best expressed in terms of the *force density* (force per unit mass), $\mathbf{F}$. The total body force on the fluid in D is therefore

$$\iiint_D \rho\mathbf{F}\,dV.$$

Newton's Second Law now implies that

$$\iiint_D \frac{\partial}{\partial t}(\rho\mathbf{v})\,dV = -\oiint_S \mathbf{v}(\rho\mathbf{v}\bullet\hat{\mathbf{N}})\,dS - \oiint_S p\hat{\mathbf{N}}\,dS + \iiint_D \rho\mathbf{F}\,dV.$$

Again we would like to convert the surface integrals to triple integrals over D. If we use the results of Exercise 7 of Section 7.3 and Exercise 1 of this section, we get

$$\oiint_S p\hat{\mathbf{N}}\,dS = \iiint_D \nabla p\,dV,$$

$$\oiint_S \mathbf{v}(\rho\mathbf{v}\bullet\hat{\mathbf{N}})\,dS = \iiint_D \Big(\rho(\mathbf{v}\bullet\nabla)\mathbf{v} + \mathbf{v}\,\mathbf{div}\,(\rho\mathbf{v})\Big)\,dV.$$

Accordingly we have

$$\iiint_D \left(\rho\frac{\partial\mathbf{v}}{\partial t} + \mathbf{v}\frac{\partial\rho}{\partial t} + \mathbf{v}\,\mathbf{div}\,(\rho\mathbf{v}) + \rho(\mathbf{v}\bullet\nabla)\mathbf{v} + \nabla p - \rho\mathbf{F}\right)dV = 0.$$

The second and third term in the integrand cancel out by virtue of the continuity equation. Since D is arbitrary, we must therefore have

7.5.2
Equation of Motion
for a Fluid

$$\rho\frac{\partial\mathbf{v}}{\partial t} + \rho(\mathbf{v}\bullet\nabla)\mathbf{v} = -\nabla p + \rho\mathbf{F}.$$

This is the **equation of motion** of the fluid. Observe that it is not a *linear* partial differential equation; the second term on the left is not linear in $\mathbf{v}$.

Electrostatics

In 3-space there are defined two vector fields which determine the electric and magnetic forces that would be experienced by a charge at a particular point moving with a particular velocity. (These vector fields are determined by electric charges and currents present in the space.) A charge q_0 at position $\mathbf{r} = x\mathbf{i} + y\mathbf{j} + z\mathbf{k}$ moving with velocity $\mathbf{v}_0$ experiences an electric force $q_0\mathbf{E}(\mathbf{r})$, where $\mathbf{E}$ is the **electric field**, and a magnetic force $\mu q_0\mathbf{v}_0 \times \mathbf{H}(\mathbf{r})$, where $\mathbf{H}$ is the **magnetic field** and μ is a physical constant. We will look briefly at each of these fields, but will restrict ourselves to considering *static* situations, electric fields produced by static charge distributions and magnetic fields produced by constant electric currents. Let us begin with the former.

Experimental evidence shows that the value of the electric field at any point $\mathbf{r}$ is the vector sum of the fields caused by any elements of charge located in 3-space. A "point charge" q at position $\mathbf{s} = \xi\mathbf{i} + \eta\mathbf{j} + \zeta\mathbf{k}$ generates the electric field,

$$\mathbf{E}(\mathbf{r}) = \frac{kq}{4\pi}\frac{\mathbf{r}-\mathbf{s}}{|\mathbf{r}-\mathbf{s}|^3}, \qquad \text{(Coulomb's Law)}$$

where k is a physical constant. This is just the field due to a point source of strength $kq/4\pi$ at **s**. Except at $\mathbf{r} = \mathbf{s}$ the field is conservative, with potential

$$\phi(\mathbf{r}) = -\frac{kq}{4\pi}\frac{1}{|\mathbf{r} - \mathbf{s}|},$$

so for $\mathbf{r} \neq \mathbf{s}$ we have **curl E** = **0**. Also **div E** = 0, except at $\mathbf{r} = \mathbf{s}$ where it is infinite; in terms of the Dirac distribution, **div E** $= kq\delta(x - \xi)\delta(y - \eta)\delta(z - \zeta)$. (See the remark following Example 7.1.7.) The flux of **E** outward across the surface S of any region R containing q is

$$\oiint_S \mathbf{E} \bullet \hat{\mathbf{N}}\, dS = kq$$

by analogy with Example 7.3.2.

Given a *charge distribution* of density $\rho(\xi, \eta, \zeta)$ in 3-space (so that the charge in volume element $dV = d\xi\, d\eta\, d\zeta$ at **s** is $dq = \rho\, dV$), the flux of **E** out of S due to the charge in R is

$$\oiint_S \mathbf{E} \bullet \hat{\mathbf{N}}\, dS = k \iiint_R dq = k \iiint_R \rho\, dV.$$

If we apply the Divergence Theorem to the surface integral, we obtain

$$\iiint_R (\mathbf{div\ E} - k\rho)\, dV = 0,$$

and since R is an arbitrary region,

$$\mathbf{div\ E} = k\rho.$$

This is one of the fundamental equations of electromagnetic theory.

The potential due to a charge distribution of density $\rho(\mathbf{s})$ in the region R is

$$\phi(\mathbf{r}) = -\frac{k}{4\pi} \iiint_R \frac{dq}{|\mathbf{r} - \mathbf{s}|}\, dV = -\frac{k}{4\pi} \iiint_R \frac{\rho(\xi, \eta, \zeta)\, d\xi\, d\eta\, d\zeta}{\sqrt{(x - \xi)^2 + (y - \eta)^2 + (z - \zeta)^2}}.$$

If ρ is continuous and vanishes outside a bounded region, the triple integral is convergent everywhere, so $\mathbf{E} = \nabla\phi$ is conservative throughout 3-space. Thus, at all points,

$$\mathbf{curl\ E} = \mathbf{0}.$$

Since **div E** = div $\nabla\phi = \nabla^2\phi$, the potential ϕ satisfies **Poisson's equation**

$$\nabla^2\phi = k\rho.$$

In particular, ϕ is a harmonic function in regions of space where no charge is distributed.

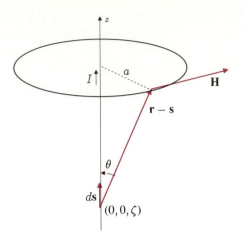

FIGURE 7.5.1

Magnetostatics

Magnetic fields are produced by moving charges, that is, by currents. Suppose that a constant electric current, I, is flowing in a filament along the curve $\mathcal{F}$. It has been determined experimentally that the magnetic field produced at position $\mathbf{r} = x\mathbf{i} + y\mathbf{j} + z\mathbf{k}$ by the elements of current $dI = I\,ds$ along the filament add vectorially, and that the element at position $\mathbf{s} = \xi\mathbf{i} + \eta\mathbf{j} + \zeta\mathbf{k}$ produces the field

$$d\mathbf{H}(\mathbf{r}) = \frac{I}{4\pi}\,\frac{d\mathbf{s} \times (\mathbf{r} - \mathbf{s})}{|\mathbf{r} - \mathbf{s}|^3}, \qquad \text{(the Biot-Savart Law)},$$

where $d\mathbf{s} = \hat{\mathbf{T}}\,ds$, $\hat{\mathbf{T}}$ being the unit tangent to $\mathcal{F}$ in the direction of the current. Under the reasonable assumption that charge is not created or destroyed anywhere, the filament $\mathcal{F}$ must form a closed circuit, and the total magnetic field at $\mathbf{r}$ due to the current flowing in the circuit is

$$\mathbf{H} = \frac{I}{4\pi} \oint_{\mathcal{F}} \frac{d\mathbf{s} \times (\mathbf{r} - \mathbf{s})}{|\mathbf{r} - \mathbf{s}|^3}.$$

Let $\mathbf{A}$ be a vector field be defined by

$$\mathbf{A}(\mathbf{r}) = \frac{I}{4\pi} \oint_{\mathcal{F}} \frac{d\mathbf{s}}{|\mathbf{r} - \mathbf{s}|},$$

for all $\mathbf{r}$ not on the filament $\mathcal{F}$. If we make use of the fact that

$$\nabla\left(\frac{1}{|\mathbf{r} - \mathbf{s}|}\right) = -\frac{\mathbf{r} - \mathbf{s}}{|\mathbf{r} - \mathbf{s}|^3},$$

and the vector identity $\nabla \times (\phi\mathbf{F}) = (\nabla\phi) \times \mathbf{F} + \phi(\nabla \times \mathbf{F})$, (with $\mathbf{F}$ the vector $d\mathbf{s}$, which does not depend on $\mathbf{r}$), we can calculate the curl of $\mathbf{A}$:

$$\nabla \times \mathbf{A} = \frac{I}{4\pi} \oint_{\mathcal{F}} \nabla\left(\frac{1}{|\mathbf{r} - \mathbf{s}|}\right) \times d\mathbf{s} = \frac{I}{4\pi} \oint_{\mathcal{F}} -\frac{\mathbf{r} - \mathbf{s}}{|\mathbf{r} - \mathbf{s}|^3} \times d\mathbf{s} = \mathbf{H}(\mathbf{r}).$$

Thus $\mathbf{A}$ is a vector potential for $\mathbf{H}$, and $\mathbf{div}\,\mathbf{H} = 0$ at points off the filament. We can also verify by calculation that $\mathbf{curl}\,\mathbf{H} = \mathbf{0}$ off the filament. (See Exercises 6–8 at the end of this section.)

Imagine a circuit consisting of a straight filament along the z-axis with return at infinite distance. The field $\mathbf{H}$ at a finite point will then just be due to the current along the z-axis, where the current I is flowing in the direction of $\mathbf{k}$, say. The currents in all elements $d\mathbf{s}$ produce at $\mathbf{r}$ fields in the same direction, normal to the plane containing $\mathbf{r}$ and the z-axis. (See Fig. 7.5.1.) Therefore the field strength $H = |\mathbf{H}|$ at a distance a from the z-axis is obtained by integrating the elements

$$dH = \frac{I}{4\pi} \frac{\sin\theta\, d\zeta}{a^2 + (\zeta - z)^2} = \frac{I}{4\pi} \frac{a\, d\zeta}{\left(a^2 + (\zeta - z)^2\right)^{3/2}}.$$

We have

$$H = \frac{Ia}{4\pi} \int_{-\infty}^{\infty} \frac{d\zeta}{\left(a^2 + (\zeta - z)^2\right)^{3/2}} \qquad [\text{let } \zeta - z = a\tan\phi]$$

$$= \frac{I}{4\pi a} \int_{-\pi/2}^{\pi/2} \cos\phi\, d\phi = \frac{I}{2\pi a}.$$

The field lines of $\mathbf{H}$ are evidently horizontal circles centred on the z-axis. If C_a is such a circle, having radius a, then the circulation of $\mathbf{H}$ around C_a is

$$\oint_{C_a} \mathbf{H} \bullet d\mathbf{r} = \frac{I}{2\pi a}\, 2\pi a = I.$$

Observe that the circulation calculated above is independent of a. In fact, if C is any closed curve which encircles the z-axis once counterclockwise (as seen from above), then C and $-C_a$ comprise the oriented boundary of a washer-like surface S with a hole in it through which the filament passes. Since **curl H** $= \mathbf{0}$ on S, Stokes's Theorem guarantees that

$$\oint_C \mathbf{H} \bullet d\mathbf{r} = \oint_{C_a} \mathbf{H} \bullet d\mathbf{r} = I.$$

Furthermore, when C is very small (and therefore very close to the filament) most of the contribution to the circulation of $\mathbf{H}$ around it comes from that part of the filament which is very close to C. It therefore does not matter that the filament is straight, or infinitely long. For any closed loop filament carrying a current, the circulation of the magnetic field around the oriented boundary of a surface through which the filament passes is equal to the current flowing in the loop. This is **Ampère's Circuital Law**. The surface is oriented with normal on the side out of which the current is flowing.

Now let us replace the filament with a more general current specified by a vector density, $\mathbf{J}$. This means that at any point $\mathbf{s}$ the current is flowing in the direction $\mathbf{J}(\mathbf{s})$, and that the current crossing an area element dS with unit normal $\hat{\mathbf{N}}$ is $\mathbf{J} \bullet \hat{\mathbf{N}}\, dS$. The circulation of $\mathbf{H}$ around the boundary C of surface S is equal to the total current flowing across S, so

$$\oint_C \mathbf{H} \bullet d\mathbf{r} = \iint_S \mathbf{J} \bullet \hat{\mathbf{N}}\, dS.$$

By using Stokes's Theorem, we can replace the line integral with another surface integral, and so obtain

$$\iint_S (\text{curl } \mathbf{H} - \mathbf{J}) \bullet \hat{\mathbf{N}} \, dS = 0.$$

Since S is arbitrary, we must have, at all points,

$$\boxed{\text{curl } \mathbf{H} = \mathbf{J},}$$

which is the pointwise version of Ampère's circuital law. It is readily checked that

$$\mathbf{A}(\mathbf{r}) = \frac{1}{4\pi} \iiint_R \frac{\mathbf{J}(\mathbf{s})}{|\mathbf{r} - \mathbf{s}|} \, dV,$$

where R is the region of 3-space where $\mathbf{J}$ is nonzero, is a vector potential for the magnetic field $\mathbf{H}$. If $\mathbf{J}$ is continuous and vanishes outside a bounded set then the triple integral converges for all $\mathbf{r}$, and $\mathbf{H}$ is everywhere solenoidal:

$$\boxed{\text{div } \mathbf{H} = 0.}$$

REMARK: Even in more general situations we would expect to have **div H** = 0. This corresponds to the fact that the field lines of **H** are always closed curves—there are no *known* magnetic "sources" or "sinks" (magnetic monopoles).

EXERCISES

1. By breaking the vector $\mathbf{F}(\mathbf{G} \bullet \hat{\mathbf{N}})$ into its separate components and applying the Divergence Theorem to each separately, show that

$$\oiint_S \mathbf{F}(\mathbf{G} \bullet \hat{\mathbf{N}})\, dS = \iiint_D \left(\mathbf{F}\,\mathrm{div}\,\mathbf{G} + (\mathbf{G} \bullet \nabla)\mathbf{F} \right) dV,$$

where $\hat{\mathbf{N}}$ is the unit outward normal on the surface S of the domain D.

2. The electric charge density, ρ, in 3-space depends on time as well as position if charge is moving around. The motion is described by the current density, $\mathbf{J}$. Derive the **continuity equation**

$$\frac{\partial \rho}{\partial t} = -\mathrm{div}\,\mathbf{J},$$

from the fact that charge is conserved.

3. If $\mathbf{b}$ is a constant vector show that

$$\nabla \left(\frac{1}{|\mathbf{r} - \mathbf{b}|} \right) = -\frac{\mathbf{r} - \mathbf{b}}{|\mathbf{r} - \mathbf{b}|^3}.$$

4. If $\mathbf{a}$ and $\mathbf{b}$ are constant vectors show that for $\mathbf{r} \neq \mathbf{b}$,

$$\mathrm{div} \left(\mathbf{a} \times \frac{\mathbf{r} - \mathbf{b}}{|\mathbf{r} - \mathbf{b}|^3} \right) = 0.$$

Hint: use identities (d) and (h) from Theorem 7.2.1.

5. Use the result of the previous exercise to give an alternate proof that

$$\mathrm{div} \oint_{\mathcal{F}} \frac{d\mathbf{s} \times (\mathbf{r} - \mathbf{s})}{|\mathbf{r} - \mathbf{s}|^3} = 0.$$

Note that **div** refers to the $\mathbf{r}$ variable.

6. If $\mathbf{a}$ and $\mathbf{b}$ are constant vectors show that for $\mathbf{r} \neq \mathbf{b}$,

$$\mathrm{curl} \left(\mathbf{a} \times \frac{\mathbf{r} - \mathbf{b}}{|\mathbf{r} - \mathbf{b}|^3} \right) = -(\mathbf{a} \bullet \nabla) \frac{\mathbf{r} - \mathbf{b}}{|\mathbf{r} - \mathbf{b}|^3}.$$

Hint: use identity (e) from Theorem 7.2.1.

7. If $\mathbf{F}$ is any smooth vector field show that

$$\oint_{\mathcal{F}} (d\mathbf{s} \bullet \nabla)\mathbf{F}(\mathbf{s}) = \mathbf{0}$$

around any closed loop $\mathcal{F}$. Hint: the gradients of the components of $\mathbf{F}$ are conservative.

8. Verify that if $\mathbf{r}$ does not lie on $\mathcal{F}$ then

$$\mathrm{curl} \oint_{\mathcal{F}} \frac{d\mathbf{s} \times (\mathbf{r} - \mathbf{s})}{|\mathbf{r} - \mathbf{s}|^3} = \mathbf{0}.$$

Here **curl** is taken with respect to the $\mathbf{r}$ variable.

9. Verify the formula $\mathrm{curl}\,\mathbf{A} = \mathbf{H}$, where $\mathbf{A}$ is the magnetic vector potential defined in terms of the steady state current density $\mathbf{J}$.

10. If $\mathbf{A}$ is the vector potential for the magnetic field produced by a steady current in a closed loop filament, show that $\mathrm{div}\,\mathbf{A} = 0$ off the filament.

11. If $\mathbf{A}$ is the vector potential for the magnetic field produced by a steady, continuous current density, show that $\mathrm{div}\,\mathbf{A} = 0$ everywhere. Hence show that $\mathbf{A}$ satisfies the vector Poisson equation: $\nabla^2 \mathbf{A} = -\mathbf{J}$.

12.*A solid occupying region R with surface S is immersed in a liquid of constant density ρ. The pressure at depth h in the liquid is $\rho g h$, so the pressure satisfies $\nabla p = \rho \mathbf{g}$, where $\mathbf{g}$ is the (vector) constant acceleration of gravity. Over each surface element dS on S the pressure of the fluid exerts a force $-p\hat{\mathbf{N}}\, dS$ on the solid. Show that the resultant "buoyancy force" on the solid is

$$\mathbf{B} = -\iiint_R \rho \mathbf{g}\, dV.$$

Thus the buoyancy force has the same magnitude as, and opposite direction to, the weight of the liquid displaced by the solid. This is **Archimedes' Principle.**

13.*Extend the result of the previous exercise to the case where the solid is only partly submerged in the fluid.

14.*The heat content of a volume element dV within a homogeneous solid is $\rho c T\, dV$, where ρ and c are constants (the density and specific heat of the solid material) and $T = T(x, y, z, t)$ is the temperature at time t at position (x, y, z) in the solid. Heat always flows in the direction of the negative temperature gradient, and at a rate proportional to the size of that gradient. Thus the rate of flow of heat energy across a surface element dS with normal $\hat{\mathbf{N}}$ is $-k\nabla T \bullet \hat{\mathbf{N}}\, dS$, where k is also a constant depending on the material of the solid (the coefficient of thermal conductivity). Use "conservation of heat energy" to show that for any region R with surface $\mathcal{S}$ within the solid

$$\rho c \iiint_R \frac{\partial T}{\partial t}\, dV = k \oiint_{\mathcal{S}} \nabla T \bullet \hat{\mathbf{N}}\, dS,$$

where $\hat{\mathbf{N}}$ is the unit outward normal on $\mathcal{S}$. Hence show that heat flow within the solid is governed by the partial differential equation

$$\frac{\partial T}{\partial t} = \frac{k}{\rho c}\nabla^2 T = \frac{k}{\rho c}\left(\frac{\partial^2 T}{\partial x^2} + \frac{\partial^2 T}{\partial y^2} + \frac{\partial^2 T}{\partial z^2}\right).$$

7.6   ORTHOGONAL CURVILINEAR COORDINATES

In this section we will derive formulas for the gradient of a scalar field and the divergence and curl of a vector field in terms of coordinate systems more general than the Cartesian coordinate system used in the earlier sections of this chapter. In particular, we will express these quantities in terms of the cylindrical and spherical coordinate systems introduced in Section 4.5.

We denote by xyz-space, the usual system of Cartesian coordinates (x, y, z) in $\mathbb{R}^3$. A different system of coordinates (u, v, w) in xyz-space can be defined by a continuous transformation of the form

$$x = x(u, v, w), \qquad y = y(u, v, w), \qquad z = z(u, v, w).$$

If the transformation is one-to-one from a region D in uvw-space onto a region R in xyz-space, then a point in R can be represented by a triple (u, v, w), the (Cartesian) coordinates of the unique point Q in uvw-space which the transformation maps to P. In this case we say that the transformation defines a **curvilinear coordinate system** in R, and call (u, v, w) the **curvilinear coordinates** of P with respect to that system. Note that (u, v, w) are Cartesian coordinates in their own space (uvw-space); they are curvilinear coordinates in xyz-space.

Typically, we relax the requirement that the transformation defining a curvilinear coordinate system be one-to-one, that is, that every point P of R should have a unique set of curvilinear coordinates. It is reasonable to require the transformation to be only *locally one-to-one*. Thus there may be more than one point Q which gets mapped to a point P by the transformation, but only one in any suitably small subregion of D. For example, in the plane polar coordinate system

$$x = r \cos \theta, \qquad y = r \sin \theta,$$

the transformation is locally one-to-one from that half D of the $r\theta$-plane where $0 < r < \infty$ to the region R consisting of all points in the xy-plane except the origin. Although, say, $(1, 0)$ and $(1, 2\pi)$ are polar coordinates of the same point in the xy-plane, they are not close together in D. Observe, however, that there is still a problem with the origin, which can be represented by $(0, \theta)$ for *any* θ. Since the transformation is not even locally one-to-one at $r = 0$, we regard the origin of the xy-plane as a **singular point** for the polar coordinate system in the plane.

EXAMPLE 7.6.1 The **cylindrical coordinate system** (r, θ, z) in $\mathbb{R}^3$ is defined by the transformation

$$x = r \cos \theta, \qquad y = r \sin \theta, \qquad z = z,$$

where $r \geq 0$. (See Section 4.5.) This transformation maps the half-space D given by $r > 0$ onto all of xyz-space excluding the z-axis, and is locally one-to-one. We regard (r, θ, z) as cylindrical polar coordinates in all of xyz-space but regard points on the z-axis as singular points of the system since the points $(0, \theta, z)$ are identical for any θ.

EXAMPLE 7.6.2 The **spherical coordinate system** (R, ϕ, θ) is defined by the transformation

$$x = R \sin \phi \cos \theta, \qquad y = R \sin \phi \sin \theta, \qquad z = R \cos \phi,$$

where $R \geq 0$ and $0 \leq \phi \leq \pi$. (See Section 4.5.) The transformation maps the region D in $R\phi\theta$-space given by $R > 0$, $0 < \phi < \pi$ in a locally one-to-one way onto xyz-space excluding the z-axis. The point with Cartesian coordinates $(0, 0, z)$ can be represented by the spherical coordinates $(0, \phi, \theta)$ for arbitrary ϕ and θ if $z = 0$, by $(z, 0, \theta)$ for arbitrary θ if $z > 0$, and by $(|z|, \pi, \theta)$ for arbitrary θ if $z < 0$. Thus all points of the z-axis are singular for the spherical coordinate system.

Coordinate Surfaces and Coordinate Curves

Let (u, v, w) be a curvilinear coordinate system in xyz-space, and let P_0 be a non-singular point for the system. Thus the transformation

$$x = x(u, v, w), \qquad y = y(u, v, w), \qquad z = z(u, v, w)$$

is locally one-to-one near P_0. Let P_0 have curvilinear coordinates (u_0, v_0, w_0). The plane with equation $u = u_0$ in uvw-space gets mapped by the transformation to a surface in xyz-space passing through P_0. We call this surface a u-surface and still refer to it by the equation $u = u_0$; it has parametric equations

$$x = x(u_0, v, w), \qquad y = y(u_0, v, w), \qquad z = z(u_0, v, w)$$

with parameters v and w. Similarly, the v-surface $v = v_0$ and the w-surface $w = w_0$ pass through P_0; they are the images of the planes $v = v_0$ and $w = w_0$ in uvw-space.

7.6.3
Orthogonal Curvilinear
Coordinates

> We say that (u, v, w) is an **orthogonal curvilinear coordinate system** in xyz-space if, for every non-singular point P_0 in xyz-space, the three **coordinate surfaces**, $u = u_0$, $v = v_0$, and $w = w_0$, intersect at P_0 at mutually right angles.

It is tacitly assumed that the coordinate surfaces are smooth at all non-singular points, so we are really assuming that their normal vectors are mutually perpendicular. Figure 7.6.1 shows the coordinate surfaces through P_0 for a typical orthogonal curvilinear coordinate system

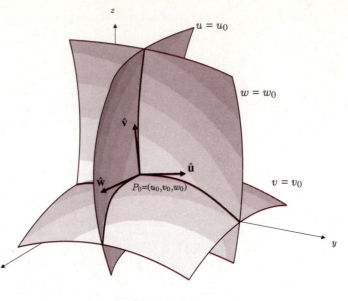

FIGURE 7.6.1

Pairs of coordinate surfaces through a point intersect along a **coordinate curve** through that point. For example, the coordinate surfaces $v = v_0$ and $w = w_0$ intersect along the u-**curve** with parametric equations

$$x = x(u, v_0, w_0), \qquad y = y(u, v_0, w_0), \qquad z = z(u, v_0, w_0),$$

where the parameter is u. A unit vector $\hat{\mathbf{u}}$ tangent to the u-curve through P_0 is normal to the coordinate surface $u = u_0$ there. Similar statements hold for unit vectors $\hat{\mathbf{v}}$ and $\hat{\mathbf{w}}$. For an orthogonal curvilinear coordinate system, the three vectors $\hat{\mathbf{u}}$, $\hat{\mathbf{v}}$, and $\hat{\mathbf{w}}$, form a basis mutually perpendicular unit vectors at any non-singular point P. (See Figure 7.6.1.) We call this basis the **local basis** at P.

EXAMPLE 7.6.4   For the cylindrical coordinate system, (see Figure 7.6.2.), the coordinate surfaces are:

circular cylinders with axis along the z-axis	(r-surfaces),
vertical half-planes radiating from the z-axis	(θ-surfaces),
horizontal planes	(z-surfaces).

The coordinate curves are:

horizontal straight half-lines radiating from the z-axis	(r-curves),
horizontal circles with centres on the z-axis	(θ-curves),
vertical straight lines	(z-curves).

EXAMPLE 7.6.5   For the spherical coordinate system, (see Figure 7.6.3), the coordinate surfaces are:

spheres centred at the origin	(R-surfaces),
vertical circular cones with vertices at the origin	(ϕ-surfaces),
vertical half-planes radiating from the z-axis	(θ-surfaces).

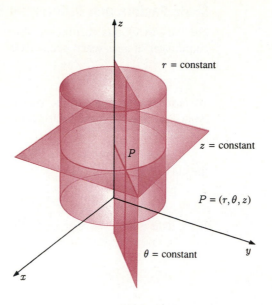

FIGURE 7.6.2

The coordinate curves are:
half-lines radiating from the origin   (R-curves),
vertical semi-circles with centres at the origin   (ϕ-curves),
horizontal circles with centres on the z-axis   (θ-curves).

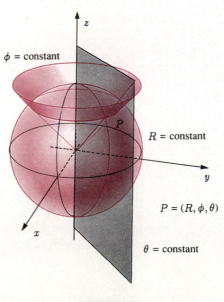

FIGURE 7.6.3

Scale Factors and Differential Elements

For the rest of this section we assume that (u, v, w) are **orthogonal** curvilinear coordinates in xyz-space defined via the transformation

$$x = x(u, v, w), \qquad y = y(u, v, w), \qquad z = z(u, v, w).$$

We also assume that the the coordinate surfaces are smooth at any nonsingular point, and that the local basis vectors $\hat{\mathbf{u}}$, $\hat{\mathbf{v}}$, and $\hat{\mathbf{w}}$ at any such point form a right-handed triad.

The **position vector** of a point P in xyz-space can be expressed in terms of the curvilinear coordinates:

$$\mathbf{r} = x(u, v, w)\mathbf{i} + y(u, v, w)\mathbf{j} + z(u, v, w)\mathbf{k}.$$

If we hold $v = v_0$ and $w = w_0$ fixed and let u vary, then $\mathbf{r} = \mathbf{r}(u, v_0, w_0)$ defines a u-curve in xyz-space. At any point P on this curve, the vector

$$\frac{\partial \mathbf{r}}{\partial u} = \frac{\partial x}{\partial u}\mathbf{i} + \frac{\partial y}{\partial u}\mathbf{j} + \frac{\partial z}{\partial u}\mathbf{k}$$

is tangent to the u-curve at P. In general, the three vectors

$$\frac{\partial \mathbf{r}}{\partial u}, \qquad \frac{\partial \mathbf{r}}{\partial v}, \qquad \frac{\partial \mathbf{r}}{\partial w}$$

are tangent, respectively, to the the u-curve, the v-curve, and the w-curve through P. They are also normal, respectively, to the u-surface, the v-surface, and the w-surface through P, so they are mutually perpendicular. (See Figure 7.6.1.) The lengths of these tangent vectors are called the **scale factors** of the coordinate system.

7.6.6

Scale Factors

> The **scale factors** of the orthogonal curvilinear coordinate system (u, v, w) are the three functions
>
> $$h_u = \left| \frac{\partial \mathbf{r}}{\partial u} \right|, \qquad h_v = \left| \frac{\partial \mathbf{r}}{\partial v} \right|, \qquad h_w = \left| \frac{\partial \mathbf{r}}{\partial w} \right|.$$

The scale factors are nonzero at a nonsingular point P of the coordinate system, so the local basis at P can be obtained by dividing the tangent vectors to the coordinate curves by their lengths. As noted previously, we denote the local basis vectors by $\hat{\mathbf{u}}$, $\hat{\mathbf{v}}$, and $\hat{\mathbf{w}}$. Thus

$$\frac{\partial \mathbf{r}}{\partial u} = h_u \hat{\mathbf{u}}, \qquad \frac{\partial \mathbf{r}}{\partial v} = h_v \hat{\mathbf{v}}, \qquad \frac{\partial \mathbf{r}}{\partial w} = h_w \hat{\mathbf{w}}.$$

The basis vectors $\hat{\mathbf{u}}$, $\hat{\mathbf{v}}$, and $\hat{\mathbf{w}}$ will form a right-handed triad provided we have chosen a suitable order for the coordinates u, v, and w.

EXAMPLE 7.6.7 For cylindrical coordinates we have $\mathbf{r} = r\cos\theta\mathbf{i} + r\sin\theta\mathbf{j} + z\mathbf{k}$, so

$$\frac{\partial \mathbf{r}}{\partial r} = \cos\theta\mathbf{i} + \sin\theta\mathbf{j}, \qquad \frac{\partial \mathbf{r}}{\partial \theta} = -r\sin\theta\mathbf{i} + r\cos\theta\mathbf{j}, \qquad \frac{\partial \mathbf{r}}{\partial z} = \mathbf{k}.$$

Thus the scale factors for the cylindrical coordinate system are given by

$$h_r = \left|\frac{\partial \mathbf{r}}{\partial r}\right| = 1, \qquad h_\theta = \left|\frac{\partial \mathbf{r}}{\partial \theta}\right| = r, \qquad h_z = \left|\frac{\partial \mathbf{r}}{\partial z}\right| = 1,$$

and the local basis consists of the vectors

$$\hat{\mathbf{r}} = \cos\theta\mathbf{i} + \sin\theta\mathbf{j}, \qquad \hat{\boldsymbol{\theta}} = -\sin\theta\mathbf{i} + \cos\theta\mathbf{j}, \qquad \hat{\mathbf{z}} = \mathbf{k}.$$

See Figure 7.6.4. The local basis is right-handed.

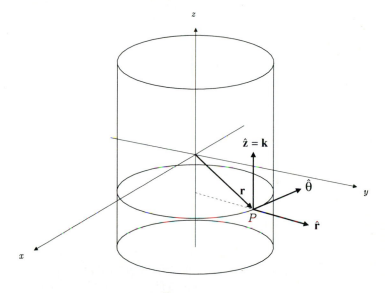

FIGURE 7.6.4

EXAMPLE 7.6.8 For spherical coordinates we have

$$\mathbf{r} = R\sin\phi\cos\theta\mathbf{i} + R\sin\phi\sin\theta\mathbf{j} + R\cos\phi\mathbf{k}.$$

Thus the tangent vectors to the coordinate curves are

$$\frac{\partial \mathbf{r}}{\partial R} = \sin\phi\cos\theta\mathbf{i} + \sin\phi\sin\theta\mathbf{j} + \cos\phi\mathbf{k}$$

$$\frac{\partial \mathbf{r}}{\partial \phi} = R\cos\phi\cos\theta\mathbf{i} + R\cos\phi\sin\theta\mathbf{j} - R\sin\phi\mathbf{k}$$

$$\frac{\partial \mathbf{r}}{\partial \theta} = -R\sin\phi\sin\theta\mathbf{i} + R\sin\phi\cos\theta\mathbf{j},$$

and the scale factors are given by

$$h_R = \left|\frac{\partial \mathbf{r}}{\partial R}\right| = 1, \qquad h_\phi = \left|\frac{\partial \mathbf{r}}{\partial \phi}\right| = R, \qquad h_\theta = \left|\frac{\partial \mathbf{r}}{\partial \theta}\right| = R \sin\phi.$$

The local basis consists of the vectors

$$\hat{\mathbf{R}} = \sin\phi \cos\theta \mathbf{i} + \sin\phi \sin\theta \mathbf{j} + \cos\phi \mathbf{k}$$
$$\hat{\phi} = \cos\phi \cos\theta \mathbf{i} + \cos\phi \sin\theta \mathbf{j} - \sin\phi \mathbf{k}$$
$$\hat{\theta} = - \sin\theta \mathbf{i} + \cos\theta \mathbf{j}.$$

See Figure 7.6.5. The local basis is right-handed.

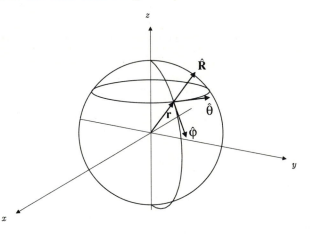

FIGURE 7.6.5

The volume element in an orthogonal curvilinear coordinate system is the volume of an infinitesimal *coordinate box* bounded by pairs of u-, v-, and w-surfaces corresponding to values u and u + du, v and v + dv, and w and w + dw respectively. See Figure 7.6.6. Since these coordinate surfaces are assumed smooth, and since they intersect at right angles, the coordinate box is rectangular, and is spanned by the vectors

$$\frac{\partial \mathbf{r}}{\partial u} \, du = h_u \, du \, \hat{\mathbf{u}}, \qquad \frac{\partial \mathbf{r}}{\partial v} \, dv = h_v \, dv \, \hat{\mathbf{v}}, \qquad \frac{\partial \mathbf{r}}{\partial w} \, dw = h_w \, dw \, \hat{\mathbf{w}}.$$

Therefore the volume element is given by

7.6.9
Volume Element in Orthogonal Curvilinear Coordinates

$$dV = h_u h_v h_w \, du \, dv \, dw.$$

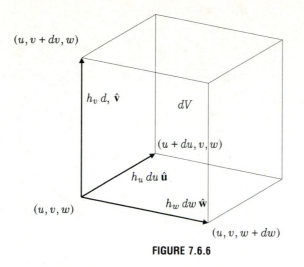

FIGURE 7.6.6

Furthermore, the surface area elements on the u-, v-, and w-surfaces are the areas of the appropriate faces of the coordinate box:

7.6.10
Area Elements on
Coordinate Surfaces

$$dS_u = h_v h_w \, dv \, dw, \qquad dS_v = h_u h_w \, du \, dw, \qquad dS_w = h_u h_v \, du \, dv.$$

The are arc length elements along the u-, v-, and w-coordinate curves are the edges of the coordinate box:

7.6.11
Arc Length Elements
on Coordinate Curves

$$ds_u = h_u \, du, \qquad ds_v = h_v \, dv, \qquad ds_w = h_w \, dw.$$

EXAMPLE 7.6.12   For cylindrical coordinates, the volume element, as shown in Section 4.5, is

$$dV = h_r h_\theta h_z \, dr \, d\theta \, dz = r \, dr \, d\theta \, dz.$$

The surface are elements on the cylinder r = constant, the half-plane θ = constant, and the plane z = constant are, respectively,

$$dS_r = r \, d\theta \, dz, \qquad dS_\theta = dr \, dz, \qquad dS_z = r \, dr \, d\theta.$$

EXAMPLE 7.6.13   For spherical coordinates, the volume element, as shown in Section 4.5, is

$$dV = h_R h_\phi h_\theta \, dR \, d\phi \, d\theta = R^2 \sin\phi \, dR \, d\phi \, d\theta.$$

The area element on the sphere $R =$ constant is

$$dS_R = h_\phi h_\theta \, d\phi \, d\theta = R^2 \sin\phi \, d\phi \, d\theta.$$

The area element on the cone $\phi =$ constant is

$$dS_\phi = h_R h_\theta \, dR \, d\theta = R \sin\phi \, dR \, d\theta.$$

The area element on the half-plane $\theta =$ constant is

$$dV = h_R h_\phi \, dR \, d\phi = R \, dR \, d\phi.$$

Gradient, Divergence and Curl in Orthogonal Curvilinear Coordinates

The gradient ∇f of a scalar field f can be expressed in terms of the local basis at any point P with curvilinear coordinates (u, v, w) in the form

$$\nabla f = F_u \hat{\mathbf{u}} + F_v \hat{\mathbf{v}} + F_w \hat{\mathbf{w}}.$$

In order to determine the coefficients F_u, F_v, and F_w in this formula, we will compare two expressions for the directional derivative of f along an arbitrary curve in xyz-space.

If the curve C has parametrization $\mathbf{r} = \mathbf{r}(s)$ in terms of arc length, then the directional derivative of f along C is given by

$$\frac{df}{ds} = \frac{\partial f}{\partial u}\frac{du}{ds} + \frac{\partial f}{\partial v}\frac{dv}{ds} + \frac{\partial f}{\partial w}\frac{dw}{ds}.$$

On the other hand, this directional derivative is also given by $\dfrac{df}{ds} = \nabla f \bullet \hat{\mathbf{T}}$, where $\hat{\mathbf{T}}$ is the unit tangent vector to C. We have

$$\hat{\mathbf{T}} = \frac{d\mathbf{r}}{ds} = \frac{\partial \mathbf{r}}{\partial u}\frac{du}{ds} + \frac{\partial \mathbf{r}}{\partial v}\frac{dv}{ds} + \frac{\partial \mathbf{r}}{\partial w}\frac{dw}{ds}$$

$$= h_u \frac{du}{ds} \hat{\mathbf{u}} + h_v \frac{dv}{ds} \hat{\mathbf{v}} + h_w \frac{dw}{ds} \hat{\mathbf{w}}.$$

Thus

$$\frac{df}{ds} = \nabla f \bullet \hat{\mathbf{T}} = F_u h_u \frac{du}{ds} + F_v h_v \frac{dv}{ds} + F_w h_w \frac{dw}{ds}.$$

Comparing these two expressions for df/ds along C, we see that

$$F_u h_u = \frac{\partial f}{\partial u}, \qquad F_v h_v = \frac{\partial f}{\partial v}, \qquad F_w h_w = \frac{\partial f}{\partial w}.$$

Therefore, we have shown that

7.6.14
The Gradient in
Orthogonal Curvilinear
Coordinates

$$\nabla f = \frac{1}{h_u} \frac{\partial f}{\partial u} \, \hat{\mathbf{u}} + \frac{1}{h_v} \frac{\partial f}{\partial v} \, \hat{\mathbf{v}} + \frac{1}{h_w} \frac{\partial f}{\partial w} \, \hat{\mathbf{w}}.$$

EXAMPLE 7.6.15   In terms of cylindrical coordinates, the gradient of the scalar field $f(r, \theta, z)$ is

$$\nabla f(r, \theta, z) = \frac{\partial f}{\partial r} \, \hat{\mathbf{r}} + \frac{1}{r} \frac{\partial f}{\partial \theta} \, \hat{\boldsymbol{\theta}} + \frac{\partial f}{\partial z} \, \mathbf{k}.$$

EXAMPLE 7.6.16   In terms of spherical coordinates, the gradient of the scalar field $f(R, \phi, \theta)$ is

$$\nabla f(R, \phi, \theta) = \frac{\partial f}{\partial R} \, \hat{\mathbf{R}} + \frac{1}{R} \frac{\partial f}{\partial \phi} \, \hat{\boldsymbol{\phi}} + \frac{1}{R \sin \phi} \frac{\partial f}{\partial \theta} \, \hat{\boldsymbol{\theta}}.$$

Now consider a vector field $\mathbf{F}$ expressed in terms of the curvilinear coordinates:

$$\mathbf{F}(u, v, w) = F_u(u, v, w)\hat{\mathbf{u}} + F_v(u, v, w)\hat{\mathbf{v}} + F_w(u, v, w)\hat{\mathbf{w}}.$$

The flux of $\mathbf{F}$ out of the infinitesimal coordinate box of Figure 7.6.6 is the sum of the fluxes of $\mathbf{F}$ out of the three pairs of opposite surfaces of the box. The flux out of the u-surfaces corresponding to u and $u + du$ is

$$\mathbf{F}(u + du, v, w) \bullet \hat{\mathbf{u}} \, dS_u - \mathbf{F}(u, v, w) \bullet \hat{\mathbf{u}} \, dS_u$$
$$= \big(F_u(u + du, v, w)h_v(u + du, v, w)h_w(u + du, v, w)$$
$$- F_u(u, v, w)h_v(u, v, w)h_w(u, v, w) \big) \, dv \, dw$$
$$= \frac{\partial}{\partial u} \big(h_v h_w F_u \big) \, du \, dv \, dw.$$

Similar expressions hold for the fluxes out of the other pairs of coordinate surfaces.

The divergence at P of $\mathbf{F}$ is the flux *per unit volume* out of the infinitesimal coordinate box at P. Thus it is given by

7.6.17
The Divergence in
Orthogonal
Curvilinear
Coordinates

$$\mathbf{div}\ \mathbf{F}(u, v, w) = \frac{1}{h_u h_v h_w} \left[\frac{\partial}{\partial u} \left(h_v h_w F_u(u, v, w) \right) + \frac{\partial}{\partial v} \left(h_u h_w F_v(u, v, w) \right) \right.$$
$$\left. + \frac{\partial}{\partial w} \left(h_u h_v F_w(u, v, w) \right) \right].$$

EXAMPLE 7.6.18   For cylindrical coordinates, $h_r = h_z = 1$, and $h_\theta = r$. Thus the divergence of $\mathbf{F} = F_r \hat{\mathbf{r}} + F_\theta \hat{\boldsymbol{\theta}} + F_z \mathbf{k}$ is

$$\mathbf{div}\ \mathbf{F} = \frac{1}{r} \left[\frac{\partial}{\partial r} \left(r F_r \right) + \frac{\partial}{\partial \theta} F_\theta + \frac{\partial}{\partial z} \left(r F_z \right) \right]$$
$$= \frac{\partial F_r}{\partial r} + \frac{1}{r} F_r + \frac{1}{r} \frac{\partial F_\theta}{\partial \theta} + \frac{\partial F_z}{\partial z}.$$

EXAMPLE 7.6.19   For spherical coordinates, $h_R = 1$, $h_\phi = R$, and $h_\theta = R \sin \phi$. The divergence of the vector field $\mathbf{F} = F_R \hat{\mathbf{R}} + F_\phi \hat{\boldsymbol{\phi}} + F_\theta \hat{\boldsymbol{\theta}}$ is

$$\mathbf{div}\ \mathbf{F} = \frac{1}{R^2 \sin \phi} \left[\frac{\partial}{\partial R} \left(R^2 \sin \phi\, F_R \right) + \frac{\partial}{\partial \phi} \left(R \sin \phi\, F_\phi \right) + \frac{\partial}{\partial \theta} \left(R F_\theta \right) \right]$$
$$= \frac{\partial}{\partial R} \left(R^2 F_R \right) + \frac{1}{R \sin \phi} \frac{\partial}{\partial \phi} \left(\sin \phi\, F_\phi \right) + \frac{1}{R \sin \phi} \frac{\partial F_\theta}{\partial \theta}$$
$$= \frac{\partial F_R}{\partial R} + \frac{2}{R} F_R + \frac{1}{R} \frac{\partial F_\phi}{\partial \phi} + \frac{\cot \phi}{R} F_\phi + \frac{1}{R \sin \phi} \frac{\partial F_\theta}{\partial \theta}.$$

To calculate the curl of a function expressed in terms of orthogonal curvilinear coordinates we can make use of some previously obtained vector identities. First, observe that the gradient of the scalar field $f(u, v, w) = u$ is $\hat{\mathbf{u}}/h_u$, so that $\hat{\mathbf{u}} = h_u \nabla u$. Similarly, $\hat{\mathbf{v}} = h_v \nabla v$ and $\hat{\mathbf{w}} = h_w \nabla w$. Therefore, the vector field

$$\mathbf{F} = F_u \hat{\mathbf{u}} + F_v \hat{\mathbf{v}} + F_w \hat{\mathbf{w}}$$

can be written in the form

$$\mathbf{F} = F_u h_u \nabla u + F_v h_v \nabla v + F_w h_w \nabla w.$$

Using the identity **curl** $(f \nabla g) = \nabla f \times \nabla g$ (see Exercise 13 of Section 7.2) we can calculate the curl of each term in the expression above. We have

$$\mathbf{curl}\,\left(F_u h_u \nabla u\right) = \nabla(F_u h_u) \times \nabla u$$

$$= \left[\frac{1}{h_u} \frac{\partial}{\partial u}(F_u h_u)\hat{\mathbf{u}} + \frac{1}{h_v} \frac{\partial}{\partial v}(F_u h_u)\hat{\mathbf{v}} + \frac{1}{h_w} \frac{\partial}{\partial w}(F_u h_u)\hat{\mathbf{w}} \right] \times \frac{\hat{\mathbf{u}}}{h_u}$$

$$= \frac{1}{h_u h_w} \frac{\partial}{\partial w}(F_u h_u)\hat{\mathbf{v}} - \frac{1}{h_u h_v} \frac{\partial}{\partial v}(F_u h_u)\hat{\mathbf{w}}$$

$$= \frac{1}{h_u h_v h_w} \left[\frac{\partial}{\partial w}(F_u h_u)(h_v \hat{\mathbf{v}}) - \frac{\partial}{\partial v}(F_u h_u)(h_w \hat{\mathbf{w}}) \right].$$

We have used the facts that $\hat{\mathbf{u}} \times \hat{\mathbf{u}} = \mathbf{0}$, $\hat{\mathbf{v}} \times \hat{\mathbf{u}} = -\hat{\mathbf{w}}$, and $\hat{\mathbf{w}} \times \hat{\mathbf{u}} = \hat{\mathbf{v}}$ to obtain the result above. This is why we assumed that the curvilinear coordinate system was right-handed.

Corresponding expressions can be calculated for the other two terms in the formula for **curl F**. Combining the three terms, we conclude that the curl of

$$\mathbf{F} = F_u \hat{\mathbf{u}} + F_v \hat{\mathbf{v}} + F_w \hat{\mathbf{w}}$$

is given by

**7.6.20
The Curl in
Orthogonal
Curvilinear
Coordinates**

$$\mathbf{curl}\ \mathbf{F}(u, v, w) = \frac{1}{h_u h_v h_w} \begin{vmatrix} h_u \hat{\mathbf{u}} & h_v \hat{\mathbf{v}} & h_w \hat{\mathbf{w}} \\ \dfrac{\partial}{\partial u} & \dfrac{\partial}{\partial v} & \dfrac{\partial}{\partial w} \\ F_u h_u & F_v h_v & F_w h_w \end{vmatrix}.$$

EXAMPLE 7.6.21   For cylindrical coordinates, the curl of

$$\mathbf{F} = F_r \hat{\mathbf{r}} + F_\theta \hat{\boldsymbol{\theta}} + F_z \mathbf{k}$$

is given by

$$\mathbf{curl}\ \mathbf{F} = \frac{1}{r} \begin{vmatrix} \hat{\mathbf{r}} & r\hat{\boldsymbol{\theta}} & \mathbf{k} \\ \dfrac{\partial}{\partial r} & \dfrac{\partial}{\partial \theta} & \dfrac{\partial}{\partial z} \\ F_r & rF_\theta & F_z \end{vmatrix}$$

$$= \left(\frac{1}{r} \frac{\partial F_z}{\partial \theta} - \frac{\partial F_\theta}{\partial z} \right) \hat{\mathbf{r}} + \left(\frac{\partial F_r}{\partial z} - \frac{\partial F_z}{\partial r} \right) \hat{\boldsymbol{\theta}} + \left(\frac{\partial F_\theta}{\partial r} + \frac{F_\theta}{r} - \frac{1}{r} \frac{\partial F_r}{\partial \theta} \right) \mathbf{k}.$$

EXAMPLE 7.6.22   For spherical coordinates, the divergence of

$$\mathbf{F} = F_R\hat{\mathbf{R}} + F_\phi\hat{\boldsymbol{\phi}} + F_\theta\hat{\boldsymbol{\theta}}$$

is given by

$$
\mathbf{curl\ F} = \frac{1}{R^2\sin\phi}
\begin{vmatrix}
\hat{\mathbf{R}} & R\hat{\boldsymbol{\phi}} & R\sin\phi\,\hat{\boldsymbol{\theta}} \\
\dfrac{\partial}{\partial R} & \dfrac{\partial}{\partial\phi} & \dfrac{\partial}{\partial\theta} \\
F_R & RF_\phi & R\sin\phi\,F_\theta
\end{vmatrix}
$$

$$
= \frac{1}{R\sin\phi}\left[\frac{\partial}{\partial\phi}(\sin\phi\,F_\theta) - \frac{\partial F_\phi}{\partial\theta}\right]\hat{\mathbf{R}}
$$

$$
+ \frac{1}{R\sin\phi}\left[\frac{\partial F_R}{\partial\theta} - \sin\phi\frac{\partial}{\partial R}(RF_\theta)\right]\hat{\boldsymbol{\phi}}
$$

$$
+ \frac{1}{R}\left[\frac{\partial}{\partial R}(RF_\phi - \frac{\partial F_R}{\partial\phi}\right]\hat{\boldsymbol{\theta}}
$$

$$
= \frac{1}{R\sin\phi}\left[(\cos\phi)F_\theta + (\sin\phi)\frac{\partial F_\theta}{\partial\phi} - \frac{\partial F_\phi}{\partial\theta}\right]\hat{\mathbf{R}}
$$

$$
+ \frac{1}{R\sin\phi}\left[\frac{\partial F_R}{\partial\theta} - (\sin\phi)F_\theta - (R\sin\phi)\frac{\partial F_\theta}{\partial R}\right]\hat{\boldsymbol{\phi}}
$$

$$
+ \frac{1}{R}\left[F_\phi + R\frac{\partial F_\phi}{\partial R} - \frac{\partial F_R}{\partial\phi}\right]\hat{\boldsymbol{\theta}}.
$$

EXERCISES

In Exercises 1–2 calculate the gradients of the given scalar fields expressed in terms of cylindrical or spherical coordinates.

1. $f(r,\theta,z) = r\theta z$ **2.** $f(R,\phi,\theta) = R\phi\theta$

In Exercises 3–8 calculate **div F** and **curl F** for the given vector fields expressed in terms of cylindrical coordinates or spherical coordinates.

3. $\mathbf{F}(r,\theta,z) = r\hat{\mathbf{r}}$ **4.** $\mathbf{F}(r,\theta,z) = r\hat{\boldsymbol{\theta}}$

5. $\mathbf{F}(R,\phi,\theta) = \sin\phi\,\hat{\mathbf{R}}$ **6.** $\mathbf{F}(R,\phi,\theta) = R\hat{\boldsymbol{\phi}}$

7. $\mathbf{F}(R,\phi,\theta) = R\hat{\boldsymbol{\theta}}$ **8.** $\mathbf{F}(R,\phi,\theta) = R^2\hat{\mathbf{R}}$

9. Let $x = x(u,v)$, $y = y(u,v)$ define orthogonal curvilinear coordinates (u,v) in the xy-plane. Find the scale factors, local basis vectors, and area element for the system of coordinates (u,v).

10. Continuing the previous exercise, express the gradient of a scalar field $f(u,v)$, and the divergence and curl of a vector field $\mathbf{F}(u,v)$ in terms of the curvilinear coordinates.

11. Express the gradient of the scalar field $f(r,\theta)$, and the divergence and curl of a vector field $\mathbf{F}(r,\theta)$ in terms of plane polar coordinates (r,θ).

12. The transformation

$$x = a\cosh u\cos v$$
$$y = a\sinh u\sin v$$

defines **elliptical coordinates** in the xy-plane. This coordinate system has singular points at $x = \pm a$, $y = 0$.

a) Show that the v-curves, $u = $ constant, are ellipses with foci at the singular points.

b) Show that the u-curves, $v = $ constant, are hyperbolas with foci at the singular points.

c) Show that the u-curve and the v-curve through a nonsingular point intersect at right angles.

d) Find the scale factors h_u and h_v, and the area element dA for the elliptical coordinate system.

13. Describe the coordinate surfaces and coordinate curves of the system of elliptical cylindrical coordinates in xyz-space defined by

$$x = a \cosh u \cos v$$
$$y = a \sinh u \sin v$$
$$z = z.$$

14. The Laplacian $\nabla^2 f$ of a scalar field f can be calculated as **div** ∇f. Use this method to calculate the Laplacian of the function $f(r, \theta, z)$ expressed in terms of cylindrical coordinates. (This repeats Exercise 22 of Section 4.5.)

15. Calculate the Laplacian $\nabla^2 f = $ **div** ∇f for the function $f(R, \phi, \theta)$, expressed in terms of spherical coordinates. (This repeats Exercise 23 of Section 4.5, but is now much easier.)

16. Calculate the Laplacian $\nabla^2 f = $ **div** ∇f for a function $f(u, v, w)$ expressed in terms of arbitrary orthogonal curvilinear coordinates (u, v, w).

Appendices

In studying the calculus of functions of a single variable one examines the role of derivatives in describing motion in one dimension; velocity and acceleration are seen to be derivatives of position. Parametric equations provide a framework for extending these ideas to the study of motion in more than one dimension. In this Appendix we consider motion in the xy-plane.

Suppose that $P = (x, y)$ is the position at time t of a point moving in the plane. The parametric equations of the path of the point,

$$x = f(t), \qquad y = g(t),$$

represent independent motions of the point in directions parallel to the x-axis and y-axis respectively; each equation determines a *component* of the overall motion. Similarly, the velocity and acceleration of the moving point have, at time t, two components. The x and y components of velocity are

$$v_x = \frac{dx}{dt} = f'(t), \qquad v_y = \frac{dy}{dt} = g'(t).$$

The x and y components of acceleration are

$$a_x = \frac{d^2x}{dt^2} = f''(t), \qquad a_y = \frac{d^2y}{dt^2} = g''(t).$$

In spite of the fact that we have used two quantities (v_x and v_y) to represent the velocity, we clearly think of this velocity as being a single quantity possessing two attributes, size and direction. (At a specific time the point is moving in a specific direction with a specific speed.) In order to deal effectively with velocity and acceleration as single quantities, we need to develop the notion of a vector.

Plane Vectors

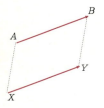

FIGURE A1.1

A **vector** is a quantity that involves both **magnitude** (size or length) and **direction**. Such quantities are conveniently represented geometrically by arrows (directed line segments) and are often actually identified with these arrows. For instance, the vector $\overrightarrow{AB}$ is an arrow with tail at the point A and head at the point B. We often denote such a vector by a single boldface letter,

$$\mathbf{v} = \overrightarrow{AB},$$

(see Fig. A1.1), though you may prefer to use an arrow over a letter ($\vec{v} = \overrightarrow{AB}$) when you are writing vectors. The magnitude of $\mathbf{v}$ is the length of the arrow and is denoted $|\mathbf{v}|$ or $|\overrightarrow{AB}|$.

FIGURE A1.2

While vectors have magnitude and direction, they do not generally have *position*, that is, they are not regarded as being in a particular place. We consider as equal two vectors $\mathbf{u}$ and $\mathbf{v}$ that have *the same length and the same direction*, even if their representative arrows do not coincide. The arrows must be parallel, have the same length, and point in the same direction. In Fig. A1.2, for example, if $ABYX$ is a parallelogram, then $\overrightarrow{AB} = \overrightarrow{XY}$.

In this appendix we consider only plane vectors, that is, vectors whose representative arrows lie in a plane. If we introduce a Cartesian coordinate system into the plane, we can talk about the x and y components of any vector. If $A = (a, b)$ and $P = (p, q)$, as shown in Fig. A1.3, then the x and y components of $\overrightarrow{AP}$ are, respectively, $p - a$ and $q - b$. Note that if O is the origin and X is the point $(p - a, q - b)$, then

$$|\overrightarrow{AP}| = \sqrt{(p-a)^2 + (q-b)^2} = |\overrightarrow{OX}|$$

$$\text{slope of } \overrightarrow{AP} = \frac{q-b}{p-a} = \text{slope of } \overrightarrow{OX}.$$

Hence $\overrightarrow{AP} = \overrightarrow{OX}$. In general, two vectors are equal if and only if they have the same x components and y components.

There are two important algebraic operations defined for vectors: addition and scalar multiplication.

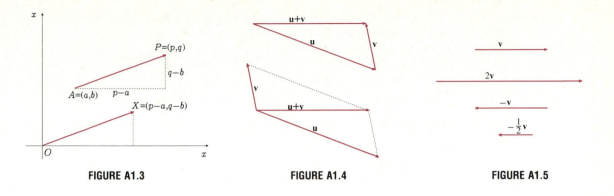

FIGURE A1.3   **FIGURE A1.4**   **FIGURE A1.5**

A1.1
Vector Addition

Given two vectors **u** and **v**, their **sum u+v** is defined as follows. If an arrow representing **v** is placed with its tail at the head of an arrow representing **u**, then an arrow from the tail of **u** to the head of **v** represents **u+v**. Equivalently, if **u** and **v** have tails at the same point, then **u** + **v** is represented by an arrow with its tail at that point and its head at the opposite vertex of the parallelogram spanned by **u** and **v**. This is shown in Fig. A1.4.

A1.2
Scalar
Multiplication

If **v** is a vector and t is a real number (also called a **scalar**), then the **scalar multiple** $t\mathbf{v}$ is a vector with magnitude $|t|$ times that of **v** and direction the same as **v** if $t > 0$, or opposite to that of **v** if $t < 0$. See Fig. A1.5. If $t = 0$, then $t\mathbf{v}$ has zero length and therefore no particular direction. It is the **zero vector**, denoted **0**.

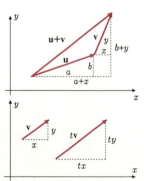

Suppose that **u** has components a and b and that **v** has components x and y. Then the components of **u** + **v** are $a + x$ and $b + y$, and those of $t\mathbf{v}$ are tx and ty. See Fig. A1.6.

In the Cartesian plane we single out two particular vectors for special attention. They are

i) the vector **i** from the origin to the point $(1, 0)$, and

ii) the vector **j** from the origin to the point $(0, 1)$.

Thus **i** has components 1 and 0, and **j** has components 0 and 1. These vectors are called the **standard basis vectors** in the plane. If **v** is a vector with components x and y, then **v** can be expressed in the form

$$\mathbf{v} = x\mathbf{i} + y\mathbf{j}.$$

FIGURE A1.6

We say that we have written **v** as a **linear combination of the standard basis vectors**. (See Fig. A1.7.) The length of **v** is $|\mathbf{v}| = \sqrt{x^2 + y^2}$.

EXAMPLE A1.3   If $A = (2, -1)$, $B = (-1, 4)$, and $C = (0, 2)$, express each of the following vectors as a linear combination of the standard basis vectors.

a) $\overrightarrow{AB}$ b) $\overrightarrow{BC}$ c) $\overrightarrow{AC}$ d) $\overrightarrow{AB} + \overrightarrow{BC}$ e) $2\overrightarrow{AC} - 3\overrightarrow{CB}$

SOLUTION

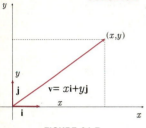

FIGURE A1.7

a) $\overrightarrow{AB} = (-1 - 2)\mathbf{i} + (4 - (-1))\mathbf{j} = -3\mathbf{i} + 5\mathbf{j}$

b) $\overrightarrow{BC} = (0 - (-1))\mathbf{i} + (2 - 4)\mathbf{j} = \mathbf{i} - 2\mathbf{j}$

c) $\overrightarrow{AC} = (0 - 2)\mathbf{i} + (2 - (-1))\mathbf{j} = -2\mathbf{i} + 3\mathbf{j}$

d) $\overrightarrow{AB} + \overrightarrow{BC} = \overrightarrow{AC} = -2\mathbf{i} + 3\mathbf{j}$

e) $2\overrightarrow{AC} - 3\overrightarrow{CB} = 2(-2\mathbf{i} + 3\mathbf{j}) - 3(-\mathbf{i} + 2\mathbf{j}) = -\mathbf{i}$

Implicit in the above example is the fact that the operations of addition and scalar multiplication obey appropriate algebraic rules, such as

$$\mathbf{u} + \mathbf{v} = \mathbf{v} + \mathbf{u}$$
$$(\mathbf{u} + \mathbf{v}) + \mathbf{w} = \mathbf{u} + (\mathbf{v} + \mathbf{w})$$
$$\mathbf{u} - \mathbf{v} = \mathbf{u} + (-1)\mathbf{v}$$
$$t(\mathbf{u} + \mathbf{v}) = t\mathbf{u} + t\mathbf{v}$$

We require one additional operation on vectors, the dot product.

A1.4
The Dot Product
of Two Vectors

Given two vectors, $\mathbf{u} = a\mathbf{i} + b\mathbf{j}$ and $\mathbf{v} = x\mathbf{i} + y\mathbf{j}$, we define their **dot product** as the *number*

$$\mathbf{u} \bullet \mathbf{v} = ax + by.$$

Note that the dot product of two vectors is not a vector but a number (a scalar). Moreover, the arrows representing the vectors $\mathbf{u}$ and $\mathbf{v}$ are perpendicular if and only if $\mathbf{u} \bullet \mathbf{v} = 0$. To see this, observe that the slopes of the arrows $\mathbf{u}$ and $\mathbf{v}$ are b/a and y/x, respectively (assuming a and x are not 0), and the product of these slopes is -1 if and only if $ax + by = 0$.

The dot product has the following algebraic properties

$$\mathbf{u} \bullet \mathbf{v} = \mathbf{v} \bullet \mathbf{u}$$
$$\mathbf{u} \bullet (\mathbf{v} + \mathbf{w}) = \mathbf{u} \bullet \mathbf{v} + \mathbf{u} \bullet \mathbf{w}$$
$$\mathbf{v} \bullet \mathbf{v} = |\mathbf{v}|^2$$
$$(t\mathbf{u}) \bullet \mathbf{v} = \mathbf{u} \bullet (t\mathbf{v}) = t(\mathbf{u} \bullet \mathbf{v}),$$

all of which are easily verified using the definition of dot product.

Finally we show that

$$\mathbf{u} \bullet \mathbf{v} = |\mathbf{u}||\mathbf{v}| \cos \theta,$$

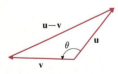

FIGURE A1.8

where θ is the angle between the directions of $\mathbf{u}$ and $\mathbf{v}$ ($0 \le \theta \le \pi$). To see this, refer to Fig. A1.8 and apply the Cosine Law (Theorem 3.1.12) to the triangle with the arrows $\mathbf{u}$, $\mathbf{v}$, and $\mathbf{u} - \mathbf{v}$ as sides.

$$\begin{aligned} |\mathbf{u}|^2 + |\mathbf{v}|^2 - 2|\mathbf{u}|\,|\mathbf{v}|\cos\theta &= |\mathbf{u} - \mathbf{v}|^2 = (\mathbf{u} - \mathbf{v}) \bullet (\mathbf{u} - \mathbf{v}) \\ &= \mathbf{u} \bullet (\mathbf{u} - \mathbf{v}) - \mathbf{v} \bullet (\mathbf{u} - \mathbf{v}) \\ &= \mathbf{u} \bullet \mathbf{u} - \mathbf{u} \bullet \mathbf{v} - \mathbf{v} \bullet \mathbf{u} + \mathbf{v} \bullet \mathbf{v} \\ &= |\mathbf{u}|^2 + |\mathbf{v}|^2 - 2\mathbf{u} \bullet \mathbf{v} \end{aligned}$$

Hence $|\mathbf{u}||\mathbf{v}|\cos\theta = \mathbf{u} \bullet \mathbf{v}$ as claimed.

EXAMPLE A1.5   The angle θ between the vectors $\mathbf{i} + \mathbf{j}$ and $\mathbf{i} - 3\mathbf{j}$ satisfies

$$\cos\theta = \frac{(\mathbf{i} + \mathbf{j}) \bullet (\mathbf{i} - 3\mathbf{j})}{|\mathbf{i} + \mathbf{j}|\,|\mathbf{i} - 3\mathbf{j}|} = \frac{1 - 3}{\sqrt{2}\sqrt{10}} = -\frac{2}{\sqrt{2}\sqrt{10}} = -\frac{1}{\sqrt{5}}.$$

Thus $\theta = \cos^{-1}(-1/\sqrt{5}) \approx 116.565°$.

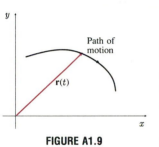

FIGURE A1.9

Position, Velocity, and Acceleration as Vectors

A **position vector** is an arrow that has its tail at the origin; the head of the arrow indicates the position of some point in the plane, and the components of the vector are the coordinates of that point.

If a particle moves in the plane so that its position at time t is given by the parametric equations $x = f(t)$, $y = g(t)$, we can use these functions as components of a **position vector function** $\mathbf{r} = \mathbf{r}(t)$ defined by (see Fig. A1.9)

$$\mathbf{r} = x\mathbf{i} + y\mathbf{j} = f(t)\mathbf{i} + g(t)\mathbf{j}.$$

The velocity of the particle at time t is also a vector since it embodies the direction as well as the speed of motion. The velocity is the rate of change of the position vector with respect to time:

$$\begin{aligned} \mathbf{v}(t) = \frac{d\mathbf{r}}{dt} &= \lim_{h \to 0} \frac{\mathbf{r}(t+h) - \mathbf{r}(t)}{h} \\ &= \lim_{h \to 0} \left(\frac{f(t+h) - f(t)}{h}\mathbf{i} + \frac{g(t+h) - g(t)}{h}\mathbf{j} \right) \\ &= f'(t)\mathbf{i} + g'(t)\mathbf{j}. \end{aligned}$$

As we might have anticipated, the components of the velocity vector are just the horizontal and verical components of velocity, as considered earlier. The *speed* $s(t)$ of the particle at time t is the length of the velocity vector:

$$s(t) = |\mathbf{v}(t)| = \left|\frac{d\mathbf{r}}{dt}\right| = \sqrt{(f'(t))^2 + (g'(t))^2}.$$

Note that the length of the path traced by the moving point in the time interval $[a, b]$ is just the integral of the speed over that interval.

The Newton quotient $\dfrac{\mathbf{r}(t+h) - \mathbf{r}(t)}{h}$ is a vector along a secant line to the path of motion. Hence its limit, the velocity vector $\mathbf{v}(t)$, is tangent to the path of motion at the position $\mathbf{r}(t)$, as shown in Fig. A1.10. Evidently $\mathbf{v}(t)$ points in the direction in which the particle is moving at time t.

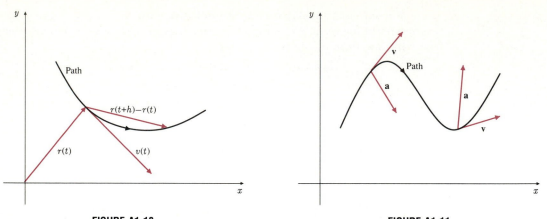

FIGURE A1.10   FIGURE A1.11

Similarly, the acceleration vector $\mathbf{a}(t)$ is the derivative of the velocity vector:

$$\mathbf{a}(t) = \frac{d\mathbf{v}}{dt} = \frac{d^2\mathbf{r}}{dt^2} = f''(t)\,\mathbf{i} + g''(t)\,\mathbf{j}.$$

The acceleration is also represented by an arrow with tail at $\mathbf{r}(t)$. The position of this arrow with respect to the velocity arrow indicates whether the speed is increasing or decreasing and which way the curve of motion is bending. If the angle between $\mathbf{v}$ and $\mathbf{a}$ at a point is less than $\pi/2$, then the speed is increasing; if it is greater than $\pi/2$, the speed is decreasing. (See Fig. A1.11 and Exercise 22 at the end of this appendix.)

The algebraic rules governing dot product ensure that the product rule for differentiation also holds for a dot product of vector functions: If $\mathbf{u}(t) = a(t)\mathbf{i} + b(t)\mathbf{j}$ and $\mathbf{w}(t) = x(t)\mathbf{i} + y(t)\mathbf{j}$, then

$$\begin{aligned}
\frac{d}{dt}\big[\mathbf{u}(t) \bullet \mathbf{w}(t)\big] &= \frac{d}{dt}\,(a(t)x(t) + b(t)y(t)) \\
&= a'(t)x(t) + a(t)x'(t) + b'(t)y(t) + b(t)y'(t) \\
&= \frac{d\mathbf{u}}{dt} \bullet \mathbf{w}(t) + \mathbf{u}(t) \bullet \frac{d\mathbf{w}}{dt}.
\end{aligned}$$

If the speed of a moving particle is constant over an interval of time, then

$$0 = \frac{d}{dt}|\mathbf{v}(t)|^2 = \frac{d}{dt}\big(\mathbf{v}(t) \bullet \mathbf{v}(t)\big) = \frac{d\mathbf{v}}{dt} \bullet \mathbf{v}(t) + \mathbf{v}(t) \bullet \frac{d\mathbf{v}}{dt} = 2\mathbf{a}(t) \bullet \mathbf{v}(t).$$

Thus $\mathbf{a}(t)$ is perpendicular to $\mathbf{v}(t)$. Conversely, if $\mathbf{a}$ is perpendicular to $\mathbf{v}$ over a time interval, then the speed is constant over that interval. Note that constant speed does *not* imply constant velocity; $\mathbf{a}$ need not be $\mathbf{0}$.

EXAMPLE A1.6   An object is moving in the plane so that its position at time t is given by

$$\mathbf{r} = t^3\,\mathbf{i} - (4t^2 - 8t + 1)\,\mathbf{j}.$$

Find the velocity, speed, and acceleration of the object at any time t. Where is the object at time $t = 1$, in what direction and how fast is it moving at that time? Is it speeding up or slowing down?

SOLUTION   The velocity, speed, and acceleration at time t are given by

$$\mathbf{v} = \frac{d\mathbf{r}}{dt} = 3t^2\,\mathbf{i} - 8(t-1)\,\mathbf{j}$$
$$s = |\mathbf{v}| = \sqrt{9t^4 + 64(t-1)^2}$$
$$\mathbf{a} = \frac{d\mathbf{v}}{dt} = 6t\,\mathbf{i} - 8\mathbf{j}$$

At time $t = 1$ we have $\mathbf{r} = \mathbf{i} + 3\mathbf{j}$, $\mathbf{v} = 3\mathbf{i}$, and $\mathbf{a} = 6\mathbf{i} - 8\mathbf{j}$. At that time the object is at the point $(1, 3)$, and is moving in the direction of the positive x-axis with speed 3. Since $\mathbf{v} \bullet \mathbf{a} = 18 > 0$ at $t = 1$, the angle between the velocity and the acceleration is less than $90°$, so the object is speeding up.

EXAMPLE A1.7   Find the position at time t of an object moving in the plane if its acceleration is proportional in magnitude to its position vector and is directed in the opposite direction. Assume that the position $\mathbf{r}_0$ and the velocity $\mathbf{v}_0$ at time $t = 0$ are given.

SOLUTION   The relation between acceleration and position can be expressed by the differential equation

$$\frac{d^2\mathbf{r}}{dt^2} = -k^2\mathbf{r}$$

where k^2 is a positive constant. This is simply the vector form of the equation of Simple Harmonic Motion. As for the scalar case, we can verify by differentiation that

$$\mathbf{r} = \mathbf{A}\cos kt + \mathbf{B}\sin kt$$

is a solution for any constant vectors $\mathbf{A} = a_1\mathbf{i} + a_2\mathbf{j}$ and $\mathbf{B} = b_1\mathbf{i} + b_2\mathbf{j}$. Since

$$\mathbf{r}_0 = \mathbf{r}(0) = \mathbf{A} \quad\text{and}\quad \mathbf{v}_0 = \mathbf{v}(0) = (-k\mathbf{A}\sin kt + k\mathbf{B}\cos kt)\big|_{t=0} = k\mathbf{B},$$

we have

$$\mathbf{r} = \mathbf{r}(t) = \mathbf{r}_0\cos kt + \frac{1}{k}\mathbf{v}_0\sin kt.$$

For typical constant vectors $\mathbf{r}_0$ and $\mathbf{v}_0$, the path of the object is an ellipse. (See Exercise 19.)

The Projectile Problem

Suppose that an object is thrown or fired at time $t = 0$ with an initial speed s_0 in a direction making an angle α above the horizontal. The object will follow an arched path until it strikes the ground some distance away from its firing point (which we assume also to be at ground level). (See Fig. A1.12.)

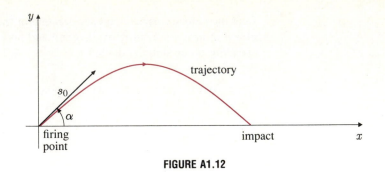

FIGURE A1.12

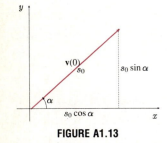

FIGURE A1.13

Assuming level ground, no air resistance, and s_0 small enough that during its flight the object may be regarded as subject only to constant downward acceleration due to gravity, we can find the equation of the trajectory (that is, path) of the object. Choosing the firing point as origin, the y-axis vertical, and the x-axis horizontal in the plane of motion, let $\mathbf{r}(t)$ denote the position of the object at time $t > 0$. We have

$$\mathbf{r}(0) = \mathbf{0} = 0\mathbf{i} + 0\mathbf{j}.$$

The initial velocity has horizontal component $s_0 \cos \alpha$ and vertical component $s_0 \sin \alpha$ as shown in Fig. A1.13. Thus

$$\mathbf{v}(0) = s_0 \cos \alpha\,\mathbf{i} + s_0 \sin \alpha\,\mathbf{j}.$$

Since the acceleration of object has constant magnitude (g say), and is in the downward direction, $\mathbf{r}(t)$ must satisfy the differential equation

$$\frac{d^2\mathbf{r}}{dt^2} = \mathbf{a}(t) = -g\,\mathbf{j}.$$

Integrating this vector equation once, we obtain

$$\frac{d\mathbf{r}}{dt} = \mathbf{v}(t) = -gt\,\mathbf{j} + \mathbf{C}_1.$$

Note that the constant of integration is a constant vector. Using the value for $\mathbf{v}(0)$ given above, we determine that

$$\mathbf{C}_1 = \mathbf{v}(0) = s_0 \cos \alpha\,\mathbf{i} + s_0 \sin \alpha\,\mathbf{j},$$

and hence that

$$\frac{d\mathbf{r}}{dt} = \mathbf{v}(t) = s_0 \cos \alpha\,\mathbf{i} + (s_0 \sin \alpha - gt)\,\mathbf{j}.$$

Now integrate again to get

$$\mathbf{r}(t) = (s_0 \cos \alpha)t\,\mathbf{i} + \left((s_0 \sin \alpha)t - \frac{gt^2}{2}\right)\mathbf{j} + \mathbf{C}_2.$$

Since $\mathbf{r}(0) = \mathbf{0}$ we have $C_2 = \mathbf{0}$. Thus the position of the object at any time during its flight is given by

$$\mathbf{r}(t) = (s_0 \cos \alpha)t\, \mathbf{i} + \left((s_0 \sin \alpha)t - \frac{gt^2}{2} \right) \mathbf{j}.$$

The parametric equations of the trajectory are

$$x = (s_0 \cos \alpha)t, \qquad \text{and} \qquad y = -\frac{1}{2}gt^2 + (s_0 \sin \alpha)t.$$

The ordinary Cartesian equation of the trajectory can be found by eliminating the parameter between this pair of equations. Solving the first equation for $t = x/(s_0 \cos \alpha)$ and substituting into the second equation, we obtain

$$y = - \left(\frac{g}{2s_0^2 \cos^2 \alpha} \right) x^2 + (\tan \alpha)x.$$

Evidently the trajectory is a parabola.

We can use the parametric equations to calculate the *maximum height*, the *time of flight*, and the *range* of the projectile. (The range is the horizontal distance traveled by the projectile before impact.)

Clearly the maximum height is attained when the vertical component of the velocity is 0, that is, at time $t = (s_0 \sin \alpha)/g$. The maximum height is

$$y_{max} = -\frac{g}{2} \left(\frac{s_0 \sin \alpha}{g} \right)^2 + (s_0 \sin \alpha)\frac{s_0 \sin \alpha}{g} = \frac{s_0^2}{2g}\sin^2 \alpha.$$

Since the projectile leaves ground level at time $t = 0$, the time of flight (the elapsed time until impact with the ground) is the positive time t for which $y = 0$:

$$-\frac{1}{2}gt^2 + (s_0 \sin \alpha)t = 0$$

$$t \left(s_0 \sin \alpha - \frac{gt}{2} \right) = 0.$$

Thus the time of flight is $t_{max} = (2s_0 \sin \alpha)/g$. (Why do we ignore the root $t = 0$?) The range is the value of x at $t = t_{max}$. Thus the range is

$$x_{max} = (s_0 \cos \alpha)\frac{2s_0 \sin \alpha}{g} = \frac{s_0^2}{g}\sin 2\alpha.$$

For given initial speed s_0, the range x_{max} will be maximum if $\sin 2\alpha = 1$, that is, if $\alpha = \dfrac{\pi}{4} = 45°$. If the projectile is a shell being fired from a gun, this maximum range, s_0^2/g, increases as the square of the muzzle speed s_0.

EXERCISES

1. Let $A = (-1, 2)$, $B = (2, 0)$, $C = (1, -3)$, $D = (0, 4)$. Express each of the following vectors as a linear combination of the standard basis vectors.

a) $\overrightarrow{AB}$, b) $\overrightarrow{BA}$, c) $\overrightarrow{AC}$, d) $\overrightarrow{BD}$, e) $\overrightarrow{DA}$,

f) $\overrightarrow{AB} - \overrightarrow{BC}$, g) $\overrightarrow{AC} - 2\overrightarrow{AB} + 3\overrightarrow{CD}$,

h) $\dfrac{\overrightarrow{AB} + \overrightarrow{AC} + \overrightarrow{AD}}{3}$.

In Exercises 2–7, find $\mathbf{u} + \mathbf{v}$, $\mathbf{u} - \mathbf{v}$, $|\mathbf{u}|$, $|\mathbf{v}|$, $\mathbf{u} \bullet \mathbf{v}$, and the angle between $\mathbf{u}$ and $\mathbf{v}$. Sketch arrows for $\mathbf{u}$, $\mathbf{v}$, $\mathbf{u} + \mathbf{v}$, and $\mathbf{u} - \mathbf{v}$.

2. $\mathbf{u} = \mathbf{i}$, $\mathbf{v} = \mathbf{j}$ **3.** $\mathbf{u} = \mathbf{i} + \mathbf{j}$, $\mathbf{v} = \mathbf{i} - \mathbf{j}$

4. $\mathbf{u} = 3\mathbf{i}$, $\mathbf{v} = 4\mathbf{i} - 3\mathbf{j}$ **5.** $\mathbf{u} = \mathbf{i} - 2\mathbf{j}$, $\mathbf{v} = -\mathbf{i} + 3\mathbf{j}$

6. $\mathbf{u} = \mathbf{j}$, $\mathbf{v} = -\mathbf{i} - \mathbf{j}$ **7.** $\mathbf{u} = \mathbf{i} + 2\mathbf{j}$, $\mathbf{v} = 2\mathbf{i} - \mathbf{j}$

8. Use vectors to show that the triangle with vertices $(-1, 1)$, $(2, 5)$, and $(10, -1)$ is right-angled.

In Exercises 9–12 $\mathbf{r}$ is the position of a point moving in the plane. Sketch the path of motion, and show on the sketch the velocity and acceleration vectors at time $t = 1$ and $t = 2$.

9. $\mathbf{r} = t\mathbf{i} - \dfrac{1}{2}t^2\mathbf{j}$ **10.** $\mathbf{r} = \sin\dfrac{\pi t}{2}\mathbf{i} + \cos\dfrac{\pi t}{2}\mathbf{j}$

11. $\mathbf{r} = t\mathbf{i} + (4t - t^3)\mathbf{j}$ **12.** $\mathbf{r} = \dfrac{1}{t}\mathbf{i} - t\mathbf{j}$

13. Describe the motion of an object whose position vector is $\mathbf{r}(t) = \mathbf{r}_0 + t\mathbf{u}$, where $\mathbf{u}$ is a nonzero constant vector. What are the parametric equations of the path?

In Exercises 14–17 find the position vector at time t of a point that moves with given acceleration $\mathbf{a}(t)$ and has given position and velocity at the time indicated.

14. $\mathbf{a}(t) = 2\mathbf{i} - \mathbf{j}$, $\mathbf{v}(0) = \mathbf{i} + \mathbf{j}$, $\mathbf{r}(0) = -3\mathbf{j}$

15. $\mathbf{a}(t) = t\mathbf{i}$, $\mathbf{v}(1) = \mathbf{0}$, $\mathbf{r}(1) = -\mathbf{i} + \mathbf{j}$

16. $\mathbf{a}(t) = 6t\mathbf{i} - 6t^2\mathbf{j}$, $\mathbf{v}(0) = 2\mathbf{i}$, $\mathbf{r}(0) = \mathbf{0}$

17. $\mathbf{a}(t) = \sin t\mathbf{i} + e^{-t}\mathbf{j}$, $\mathbf{v}(0) = \mathbf{i}$, $\mathbf{r}(0) = \mathbf{0}$

18. The acceleration due to gravity, g, is approximately 9.8 m/s². Find the muzzle speed s_0 of a shell fired at an angle $30°$ above the horizontal if the shell strikes the ground at a point 2 km horizontally away from its firing point.

19. *Verify that the path of the object in Example A1.7 is an ellipse if $\mathbf{r}_0$ is not parallel to $\mathbf{v}_0$. Hint: eliminate t from the parametric equations of the path. Under what conditions is the ellipse a circle?

20. Find the acceleration at time t of a point whose position is given by $\mathbf{r} = a(t - \sin t)\mathbf{i} + a(1 - \cos t)\mathbf{j}$. (The point is moving on a cycloid.) Show that the acceleration has constant magnitude. What is the direction of motion at the cusps of the cycloid? At the peaks?

21. *A point moves on the curve $y = e^x$ in the direction of increasing x. If the speed is constant (say k), find the velocity and acceleration vectors as functions of x.

22. *Let $\mathbf{v}(t)$ and $\mathbf{a}(t)$ be the velocity and acceleration, respectively, of an object moving in the plane. Show that the following three conditions are equivalent:

i) the speed of the object is increasing at time t,

ii) $\mathbf{v}(t) \bullet \mathbf{a}(t) > 0$,

iii) the angle between $\mathbf{v}(t)$ and $\mathbf{a}(t)$ is less than $\pi/2$.

State an analogous result for decreasing speed.

In Exercises 23–26 prove the stated geometric result using vectors.

23. The line segment joining the midpoints of two sides of a triangle is parallel to and half as long as the third side.

24. If P, Q, R, S are midpoints of sides AB, BC, CD, and DA, respectively, of quadrilateral $ABCD$, then $PQRS$ is a parallelogram.

25. *The diagonals of any parallelogram bisect each other.

26. *The medians of any triangle meet in a common point. (A median is a line joining one vertex to the midpoint of the opposite side. The common point is the *centroid* of the triangle.)

APPENDIX II   CONICS

Circles, ellipses, parabolas and hyperbolas are called **conic sections**, (or, more simply, just **conics**), because they are curves in which planes intersect right-circular cones.

To be specific, suppose that a line A is fixed in space, and V is a point fixed on A. The right-circular cone having axis A, vertex V, and **semi-vertical angle** α is the surface consisting of all points on straight lines through V which make angle α with the line A. (See Figure A2.1.)   The cone has two halves (called **nappes**) lying on opposite sides of the vertex V. Any plane P which does not pass through V will intersect the cone (one or both nappes) in a curve C. (See Figure A2.2.) If a line normal (that is, perpendicular) to P makes angle θ with the axis A of the cone, where $0 \leq \theta \leq \pi/2$, then

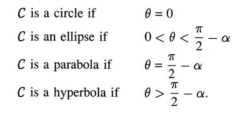

$$
\begin{aligned}
&C \text{ is a circle if} && \theta = 0 \\
&C \text{ is an ellipse if} && 0 < \theta < \frac{\pi}{2} - \alpha \\
&C \text{ is a parabola if} && \theta = \frac{\pi}{2} - \alpha \\
&C \text{ is a hyperbola if} && \theta > \frac{\pi}{2} - \alpha.
\end{aligned}
$$

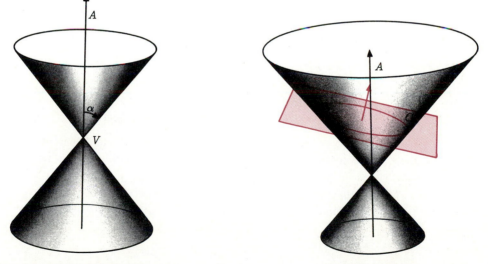

FIGURE A2.1   FIGURE A2.2

Since planes are represented by first degree equations and cones by second degree equations, all conics can be represented analytically (in terms of Cartesian coordinates x and y in the plane of the conic) by a second degree equation of the general form

$$Ax^2 + Bxy + Cy^2 + Dx + Ey + F = 0,$$

where A, B, ..., F are constants. However, any such an equation can represent a conic, the empty set, a single point, or, if the left-hand side factors into linear factors,

$$(A_1 x + B_1 y + C_1)(A_2 x + B_2 y + C_2) = 0,$$

one or two straight lines.

After straight lines the conic sections are the simplest of plane curves. They have many important properties, most of which were discovered by the Greek geometer, Apollonius of Perga, about 200 BC. It is remarkable that he was able to obtain these properties using only the techniques of classical Euclidean geometry; today most of these properties are expressed more conveniently using analytic geometry and specific coordinate systems.

The rest of this appendix is devoted to giving alternative definitions of the conics and developing some of their more useful properties. We will not attempt to prove every assertion, but, in the spirit of Apollonius, we will present proofs of the focal properties of the conics by elementary geometry.

Circles

A2.1
Circles

> A **circle** consists of all points in a plane which are at constant distance (the **radius**) from a fixed point (the **centre**).

EXAMPLE A2.2

The circle with centre at the point (a, b) and radius r has equation

$$(x - a)^2 + (y - b)^2 = r^2,$$

or, equivalently,

$$x^2 + y^2 - 2ax - 2by + c = 0,$$

where $c = a^2 + b^2 - r^2$. (See Figure A2.3.)   Note that in the equation of a circle, the coefficients of x^2 and y^2 are equal and there is no xy term.

Circles have many useful geometrical properties. Of particular importance is the fact that a *radial line* drawn from the centre to a point on the circle is perpendicular to the line tangent to the circle at that point.

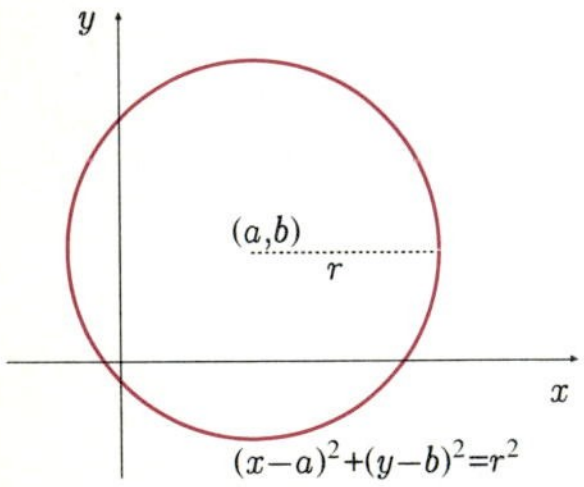

(a,b)

r

$(x-a)^2 + (y-b)^2 = r^2$

FIGURE A2.3

Parabolas

A2.3
Parabolas

> A **parabola** consists of points in the plane which are equidistant from a given point (the **focus**) and a given straight line (the **directrix**). The line through the focus perpendicular to the directrix is called the **principal axis** (or simply the **axis**) of the parabola. The **vertex** of the parabola is the point where the parabola crosses its principal axis. It is on the axis halfway between the focus and the directrix.

EXAMPLE A2.4 The parabola with focus at the point $F = (a, 0)$ and directrix the line L with equation $x = -a$ has axis along the x-axis and vertex at the origin (see Fig. A2.4). If $P = (x, y)$ is any point on the parabola, then the distance from P to F is equal to the perpendicular distance from P to L. Thus

$$\sqrt{(x-a)^2 + y^2} = x + a$$
$$\text{or } x^2 - 2ax + a^2 + y^2 = x^2 + 2ax + a^2,$$

or, upon simplification,

$$y^2 = 4ax.$$

Similarly we can obtain standard equations for parabolas with vertices at the origin and foci at $(-a, 0)$, $(0, a)$ and $(0, -a)$:

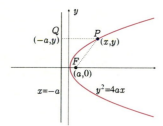

FIGURE A2.4

Focus	Directrix	Equation
$(a, 0)$	$x = -a$	$y^2 = 4ax$
$(-a, 0)$	$x = a$	$y^2 = -4ax$
$(0, a)$	$y = -a$	$x^2 = 4ay$
$(0, -a)$	$y = a$	$x^2 = -4ay$

Parabolas (and other conics), whose axes of symmetry are not parallel to one of the coordinate axes, may have a *cross term* xy in their equations.

EXAMPLE A2.5 Show that the equation $x^2 + y^2 + 2xy - x + y = 0$ represents a parabola with vertex at the origin and axis along the line $x + y = 0$. Find its focus and directrix.

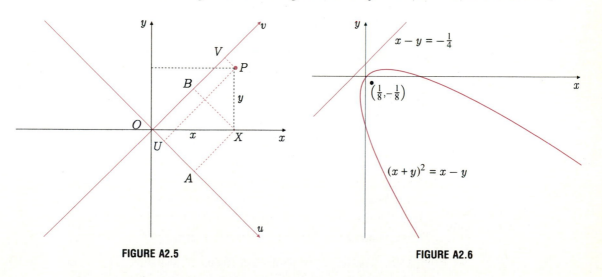

FIGURE A2.5   **FIGURE A2.6**

SOLUTION The equation can be rewritten with completed square in the form

$$(x + y)^2 = x - y.$$

Let (u, v) be the Cartesian coordinates of a point P with respect to axes u and v rotated $-45°$ from the x- and y-axes. (See Figure A2.5.) (The u- and v-axes lie along the perpendicular lines $x + y = 0$ and $x - y = 0$ respectively.) As can be observed in the figure,

$$u = OU = OA - UA = \frac{x}{\sqrt{2}} - \frac{y}{\sqrt{2}}, \qquad v = OV = OB + BV = \frac{x}{\sqrt{2}} + \frac{y}{\sqrt{2}}.$$

With respect to these new coordinates, the given curve has equation

$$v^2 = \frac{u}{\sqrt{2}},$$

which is evidently a parabola with vertex at the origin, focus at the point $(u, v) = (\frac{1}{4\sqrt{2}}, 0)$ and directrix $u = -\frac{1}{4\sqrt{2}}$. In terms of the original coordinates (x, y) the focus is $(\frac{1}{8}, -\frac{1}{8})$ and the directrix is $x - y = -\frac{1}{4}$. (See Figure A2.6.)

The Focal Property of a Parabola

All of the conic sections have interesting and useful focal properties relating to the way they would reflect light if they were used to generate surfaces of revolution which were mirrors. For instance, a circle will clearly reflect back along the same path any ray of light incident along a line passing through its centre. The focal properties of parabolas, ellipses and hyperbolas can be derived from the reflecting property of a straight line (that is, a plane mirror) by elementary geometrical arguments.

It is well-known that in a medium of constant optical density, (one where light travels with constant speed), light travels in straight lines. This is a consequence of the physical Principle of Least Action which asserts that in travelling between two points, light takes the path requiring the minimum travel time. Given a straight line L in a plane and two points A and B in the plane on the same side of L, the point P on L for which the sum of the distances $AP + PB$ is minimum is such that AP and PB make equal angles with L, or equivalently, with the normal to L at P. (See Figure A2.7.) If B' is the point such that L is the right bisector of the line segment BB', then P is the intersection of L and AB'. Since one side of a triangle cannot exceed the sum of the other two sides,

$$AP + PB = AP + PB' \leq AQ + QB' = AQ + QB.$$

A2.6
Reflection in a Straight Line

> The point P on L at which a ray from A would reflect so as to pass through B is just the point which minimizes the sum of the distances $AP + PB$.

Now consider a parabola with focus F and directrix D. Let P be on the parabola and let T be the line tangent to the parabola at P. (See Figure A2.8.) Let Q be any point on T. Then FQ meets the parabola at a point X between F and Q. Let M and N be points on D such that MX and NP are perpendicular to D, and let A be a point on the line through N and P which lies on the same side of the parabola as F. We have

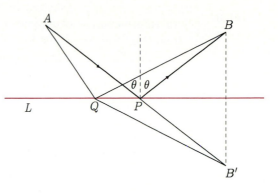

FIGURE A2.7

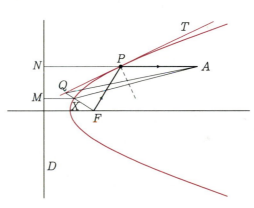

FIGURE A2.8

$$FP + PA = NP + PA = NA \le MX + XA = FX + XA$$
$$\le FX + XQ + QA = FQ + QA.$$

Thus, among all points Q on the line T, $Q = P$ is the one which minimizes the sum of distances $FQ + QA$. By the observation made for straight lines above, FP and PA make equal angles with T and so also with the normal to the parabola at P. (The parabola and the tangent line have the same normal at P.)

A2.7
Reflection by
a Parabola

Any ray from the focus will be reflected parallel to the axis of the parabola. Equivalently, any ray incident parallel to the axis of the parabola will be reflected through the focus.

Ellipses

> An **ellipse** consists of all points in the plane, the sum of whose distances from two fixed points (the **foci**) is constant.

EXAMPLE A2.9   If the foci of an ellipse are at the points $(-c, 0)$ and $(c, 0)$ and the sum of the distances from any point $P = (x, y)$ on the ellipse to these two foci is the constant $2a$ (where $0 < c < a$) then the ellipse clearly passes through the four points $(a, 0)$, $(-a, 0)$, $(0, b)$ and $(0, -b)$, where $b^2 = a^2 - c^2$. (See Figure A2.9.)   Also,

$$\sqrt{(x - c)^2 + y^2} + \sqrt{(x + c)^2 + y^2} = 2a.$$

Transposing one term from the left side to the right side, squaring, cancelling terms, transposing and squaring again leads to (the reader should verify this!)

$$\frac{x^2}{a^2} + \frac{y^2}{b^2} = 1.$$

The following quantities describe this ellipse:

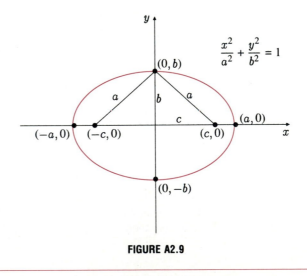

FIGURE A2.9

> a is the **semi-major axis**
> b is the **semi-minor axis**
> $c = \sqrt{a^2 - b^2}$ is the **semi-focal separation**.

The point halfway between the foci is called the **centre** of the ellipse. In the Example above it is the origin. Note that $a > b$ in this Example. If $a < b$ then the ellipse has semi-major axis along the y-axis instead of the x-axis and its foci are at $(0, c)$ and $(0, -c)$, where $c = \sqrt{b^2 - a^2}$. In general, the line containing the foci (the **major axis**), and the line through the centre perpendicular to that line (the **minor axis**) are called the **principal axes** of the ellipse.

The **eccentricity** of an ellipse is the ratio of the semi-focal separation to the semi-major axis. We denote the eccentricity ε. For the ellipse $\dfrac{x^2}{a^2} + \dfrac{y^2}{b^2} = 1$ with $a > b$

$$\varepsilon = \frac{c}{a} = \frac{\sqrt{a^2 - b^2}}{a}.$$

Evidently $\varepsilon < 1$ for any ellipse; the greater the value of ε the more elongated (less circular) is the ellipse. If $\varepsilon = 0$ so that $a = b$ and $c = 0$, the two foci coincide and the ellipse is a circle.

EXAMPLE A2.10 The equation

$$\frac{(x - 2)^2}{4} + \frac{(y + 3)^2}{9} = 1$$

represents an ellipse with centre at the point $(2, -3)$, semi-major axis 3, semi-minor axis 2, and semi-focal separation $\sqrt{9 - 4} = \sqrt{5}$. The foci are at the points $(2, -3 \pm \sqrt{5})$. The eccentricity is $\varepsilon = \sqrt{5}/3$.

The Focal Property of an Ellipse

Let P be any point on an ellipse having foci F_1 and F_2. The normal to the ellipse at P bisects the angle between the lines F_1P and F_2P.

A2.11 Reflection by an Ellipse

Any ray coming from one focus of an ellipse will be reflected through the other focus.

To see this, observe that if Q is any point on the line T tangent to the ellipse at P then F_1Q meets the ellipse at a point X between F_1 and Q (see Figure A2.10), and so

$$F_1P + PF_2 = F_1X + XF_2 \leq F_1X + XQ + QF_2 = F_1Q + QF_2.$$

Among all points on T, P is the one which minimizes the sum of the distances to F_1 and F_2. This implies that the normal to the ellipse at P bisects the angle F_1PF_2.

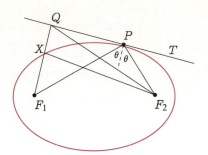

FIGURE A2.10

Directrices

If $a > b > 0$, each of the lines $x = a/\varepsilon$ and $x = -a/\varepsilon$ is called a **directrix** of the ellipse $\dfrac{x^2}{a^2} + \dfrac{y^2}{b^2} = 1$. If P is on the ellipse then the ratio of the distance from P to a focus to its distance from the corresponding directrix is equal to the eccentricity ε. If $P = (x, y)$, F is the focus $(c, 0)$, Q is on the corresponding directrix $x = a/\varepsilon$ and PQ is perpendicular to the directrix, then (see Figure A2.11),

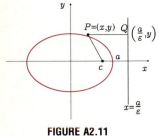

FIGURE A2.11

$$\begin{aligned}
PF^2 &= (x - c)^2 + y^2 \\
&= x^2 - 2cx + c^2 + b^2 \left(1 - \frac{x^2}{a^2}\right) \\
&= x^2 \left(\frac{a^2 - b^2}{a^2}\right) - 2cx + a^2 - b^2 + b^2 \\
&= \varepsilon^2 x^2 - 2\varepsilon a x + a^2 \qquad \text{(because } c = \varepsilon a\text{)} \\
&= (a - \varepsilon x)^2.
\end{aligned}$$

Thus $PF = a - \varepsilon x$. Also, $QP = (a/\varepsilon) - x = (a - \varepsilon x)/\varepsilon$. Therefore $PF/QP = \varepsilon$ as asserted.

A parabola may be considered as the limiting case of an ellipse whose eccentricity has increased to 1. The distance between the foci is infinite, so the centre, one focus and its corresponding directrix have moved off to infinity leaving only one focus and its directrix in the finite plane.

Hyperbolas

A2.12
Hyperbolas

A **hyperbola** consists of all points in the plane, the difference of whose distances from two fixed points (the **foci**) is constant.

EXAMPLE A2.13 If the foci are $F_1 = (c, 0)$ and $F_2 = (-c, 0)$, and the difference of the distances from $P = (x, y)$ to these foci is $2a$ (where $a < c$) then

$$PF_2 - PF_1 = \sqrt{(x+c)^2 + y^2} - \sqrt{(x-c)^2 + y^2} = \begin{cases} 2a & \text{(right branch)} \\ -2a & \text{(left branch)}. \end{cases}$$

Simplifying this equation by squaring and transposing as was suggested for the ellipse (do it!), we are led to the standard equation for the hyperbola:

$$\frac{x^2}{a^2} - \frac{y^2}{b^2} = 1,$$

where $b^2 = c^2 - a^2$. The points $(a, 0)$ and $(-a, 0)$ (called **vertices**) lie on the hyperbola, one on each branch. (The two branches correspond to the intersections of the plane of the hyperbola with the two nappes of a cone.) Parameters used to describe the hyperbola are

$$
\begin{aligned}
a \quad & \text{the \textbf{semi-transverse axis}} \\
b \quad & \text{the \textbf{semi-conjugate axis}} \\
c = \sqrt{a^2 + b^2} \quad & \text{the \textbf{semi-focal separation}}.
\end{aligned}
$$

The midpoint of the line segment F_1F_2 (in this case the origin) is again called the centre of the hyperbola. If a rectangle with sides $2a$ and $2b$ is drawn centred at the centre of the hyperbola and with two sides parallel to the transverse axis (the line containing the foci and the vertices), the two straight lines which are diagonals of the box are called **asymptotes** of the hyperbola. They have equations $(x/a) \pm (y/b) = 0$; that is, they are solutions of the degenerate equation

$$\frac{x^2}{a^2} - \frac{y^2}{b^2} = 0.$$

The hyperbola approaches arbitrarily close to these lines as it recedes from the origin. (See Figure A2.12.) A **rectangular** hyperbola is one whose asymptotes are perpendicular lines.

The equation

$$\frac{x^2}{a^2} - \frac{y^2}{b^2} = -1$$

represents a hyperbola with the same asymptotes as the hyperbola in the above example, but with transverse axis along the y-axis, vertices at $(0, b)$ and $(0, -b)$ and foci at $(0, c)$ and $(0, -c)$. The two hyperbolas are said to be **conjugate** to one another. (See Figure A2.12.) The **conjugate axis** of a hyperbola is the transverse axis of the conjugate hyperbola. Together, the transverse and conjugate axes of a hyperbola are called its **principal axes**.

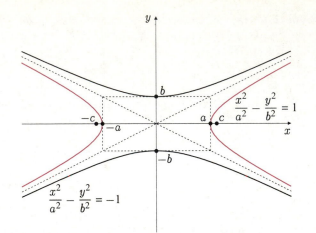

FIGURE A2.12

The eccentricity of the hyperbola is

$$\varepsilon = \frac{c}{a} = \frac{\sqrt{a^2 + b^2}}{a}.$$

Evidently $\varepsilon > 1$. The lines $x = \pm(a/\varepsilon)$ are called **directrices** of the hyperbola $(x^2/a^2) - (y^2/b^2) = 1$. In a manner similar to that used for the ellipse one can show that if P is on the hyperbola then

$$\frac{\text{distance from } P \text{ to a focus}}{\text{distance from } P \text{ to the corresponding directrix}} = \varepsilon.$$

The eccentricity of a rectangular hyperbola is $\sqrt{2}$.

The Focal Property of the Hyperbola

Let P be any point on a hyperbola with foci F_1 and F_2. Then the tangent line to the hyperbola at P bisects the angle between the lines $F_1 P$ and $F_2 P$.

A2.14
Reflection by
a Hyperbola

A ray from one focus of a hyperbola is reflected by the hyperbola so that it appears to have come from the other focus.

To see this, let P be on the right branch, let T be the line tangent to the hyperbola at P, and let C be a circle of large radius centred at F_2 (see Fig. A2.13). Let $F_2 P$ intersect this circle at D. Let Q be any point on T. Then QF_1 meets the hyperbola at X between Q and F_1, and $F_2 X$ meets C at E. Since X is on the radial line $F_2 E$, it is closer to E than it is to other points on C. That is, $XE \le XD$. Thus

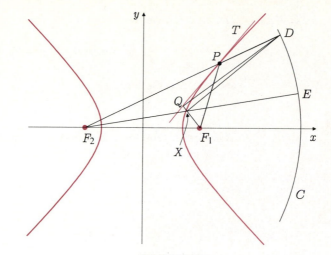

FIGURE A2.13

$$F_1P + PD = F_1P + F_2D - F_2P = F_2D - (F_2P - F_1P)$$
$$= F_2E - (F_2X - F_1X)$$
$$= F_1X + F_2E - F_2X$$
$$= F_1X + XE$$
$$\leq F_1X + XD$$
$$\leq F_1X + XQ + QD = F_1Q + QD.$$

P is the point on T which minimizes the sum of distances to F_1 and D, and therefore the normal to the hyperbola at P bisects the angle F_1PD. Therefore T bisects the angle F_1PF_2.

Classifying General Conics

A second degree equation in two variables,

$$Ax^2 + Bxy + Cy^2 + Dx + Ey + F = 0, \qquad (A^2 + B^2 + C^2 > 0)$$

generally represents a conic curve, but in certain degenerate cases may represent two straight lines (e.g. $x^2 - y^2 = 0$ represents the lines $x = y$ and $x = -y$), one straight line (e.g. $x^2 = 0$ represents the line $x = 0$), a single point (e.g. $x^2 + y^2 = 0$ represents the origin), or no points at all (e.g. $x^2 + y^2 = -1$ is not satisfied by any points in the plane).

The nature of the set of points represented by a given second degree equation can be determined by rewriting the equation in a standard form which can be recognized as one of the standard types. If $B = 0$ this rewriting can be accomplished by completing the squares in x and y.

EXAMPLE A2.15   Describe the curve with equation $x^2 + 2y^2 + 6x - 4y + 7 = 0$.

SOLUTION   The equation can be written in the form

$$x^2 + 6x + 9 + 2(y^2 - 2y + 1) = 9 + 2 - 7 = 4,$$

and hence in the form

$$\frac{(x+3)^2}{4} + \frac{(y-1)^2}{2} = 1.$$

Therefore it represents an ellipse with centre at $(-3, 1)$, semi-major axis 2, semi-minor axis $\sqrt{2}$, and foci at $(-3 \pm \sqrt{2}, 1)$.

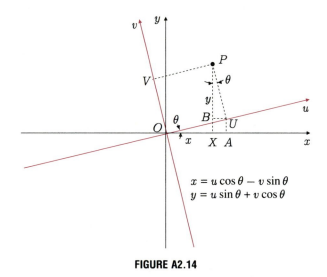

FIGURE A2.14

If $B \neq 0$, the equation has an xy term, and it cannot represent a circle. To see what it does represent, we can rotate the coordinate axes to produce an equation with no xy term. Let new coordinate axes (a u-axis and an v-axis) have the same origin but be rotated an angle θ from the x- and y-axes respectively. (See Figure A2.14.)   If point P has coordinates (x, y) with respect to the old axes and coordinates (u, v) with respect to the new axes, then an analysis of triangles in the figure shows that

$$x = OA - XA = OU \cos \theta - OV \sin \theta = u \cos \theta - v \sin \theta$$
$$y = XB + BP = OU \sin \theta + OV \cos \theta = u \sin \theta + v \cos \theta.$$

Substituting these expressions into the equation

!!DANGER!!

Long calculations are needed here.

$$Ax^2 + Bxy + Cy^2 + Dx + Ey + F = 0, \qquad (A^2 + B^2 + C^2 > 0)$$

leads to a new equation

$$A'u^2 + B'uv + C'v^2 + D'u + E'v + F = 0$$

where

$$A' = A\cos^2\theta + B\cos\theta\sin\theta + C\sin^2\theta$$
$$B' = (2C - 2A)\cos\theta\sin\theta + B(\cos^2\theta - \sin^2\theta)$$
$$C' = A\sin^2\theta - B\cos\theta\sin\theta + C\cos^2\theta$$
$$D' = D\cos\theta + E\sin\theta$$
$$E' = -D\sin\theta + E\cos\theta.$$

Note that F remains unchanged. If we choose θ so that

$$\tan 2\theta = \frac{B}{A - C}, \qquad (\theta = \frac{\pi}{4} \text{ if } A = C, \ B \neq 0),$$

then $B' = 0$, and the new equation can then be analysed as described previously.

EXAMPLE A2.16 What curve is represented by the equation $xy = 1$?

SOLUTION The reader is likely well aware that the given equation represents a rectangular hyperbola with the coordinate axes as asymptotes. Since the given equation involves $A = C = D = E = 0$ and $B = 1$, it is appropriate to rotate the axes through angle $\pi/4$ so that

$$x = \frac{1}{\sqrt{2}}(u - v)$$
$$y = \frac{1}{\sqrt{2}}(u + v).$$

The transformed equation is

$$\frac{u^2}{2} - \frac{v^2}{2} = 1$$

which is, as suspected, a rectangular hyperbola with vertices at $u = \pm\sqrt{2}$, $v = 0$, foci at $u = \pm 2$, $v = 0$, and asymptotes $u = \pm v$. Hence $xy = 1$ represents a rectangular hyperbola with coordinate axes as asymptotes, vertices at $(1, 1)$ and $(-1, -1)$, and foci at $(\sqrt{2}, \sqrt{2})$ and $(-\sqrt{2}, -\sqrt{2})$.

EXAMPLE A2.17 Show that $x^2 + 2\sqrt{3}xy - y^2 + 2\sqrt{3}x + 2y = 6$ represents a hyperbola. What are its principal axes? its vertices? its foci? its asymptotes?

SOLUTION Here $A = 1$, $B = 2\sqrt{3}$, $C = -1$, $D = 2\sqrt{3}$, $E = 2$ and $F = -6$. We rotate the axes through angle θ satisfying $\tan 2\theta = B/(A - C) = \sqrt{3}$, that is, $\theta = \pi/6$, and obtain $A' = 2$, $B' = 0$, $C' = -2$, $D' = 4$, and $E' = 0$. The transformed equation is

$$2u^2 - 2v^2 + 4u = 6,$$

or, with completed square,

$$(u + 1)^2 - v^2 = 4.$$

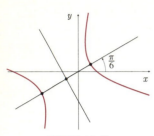

FIGURE A2.15

This is a rectangular hyperbola with centre at $u = -1$, $v = 0$, vertices at $u = -1 \pm 2$, $v = 0$, foci at $u = -1 \pm 2\sqrt{2}$, $v = 0$, and asymptotes $u + 1 \pm v = 0$. Since the rotation of axes is specified by

$$x = \frac{\sqrt{3}}{2}u - \frac{1}{2}v, \qquad y = \frac{u}{2} + \frac{\sqrt{3}}{2}v,$$

the given equation represents a rectangular hyperbola with centre $\left(-\frac{\sqrt{3}}{2}, -\frac{1}{2}\right)$ and transverse and conjugate axes through that point inclined at angle $\frac{\pi}{6}$ to the x- and y-axes respectively. (See Figure A2.15.)   Its vertices are at the points $\left(\frac{\sqrt{3}}{2}, \frac{1}{2}\right)$ and $\left(-\frac{3\sqrt{3}}{2}, -\frac{3}{2}\right)$, its foci at the points $\left(-\frac{\sqrt{3}(1+2\sqrt{2})}{2}, -\frac{1+2\sqrt{2}}{2}\right)$ and $\left(\frac{\sqrt{3}(-1+2\sqrt{2})}{2}, \frac{-1+2\sqrt{2}}{2}\right)$, and its asymptotes are $\sqrt{3}x + y + 2 \pm (\sqrt{3}y - x) = 0$.

EXERCISES

In Exercises 1–9 identify and sketch the set of points in the plane satisfying the given equation. Specify the asymptotes of any hyperbolas.

1. $x^2 + y^2 + 2x = -1$

2. $x^2 + 4y^2 - 4y = 0$

3. $4x^2 + y^2 - 4y = 0$

4. $4x^2 - y^2 - 4y = 0$

5. $x^2 + 2x - y = 3$

6. $x + 2y + 2y^2 = 1$

7. $x^2 - 2y^2 + 3x + 4y = 2$

8. $9x^2 + 4y^2 - 18x + 8y = -13$

9. $9x^2 + 4y^2 - 18x + 8y = 23$

10. Identify and sketch the curve which is the graph of the equation $(x - y)^2 - (x + y)^2 = 1$.

In Exercises 11–16 identify the conic and find its centre, principal axes, foci and eccentricity. Specify the asymptotes of any hyperbolas.

11. $xy + x - y = 2$

12.* $x^2 + 4xy + y^2 - 2\sqrt{2}(x - y) = 2$

13.* $x^2 + xy = \frac{1}{2\sqrt{2}}$

14.* $x^2 + 2xy + y^2 = 4x - 4y + 4$

15.* $8x^2 + 12xy + 17y^2 = 20$

16.* $x^2 - 4xy + 4y^2 + 2x + y = 0$

17. The *focus-directrix definition of a conic* defines a conic as a set of points P in the plane which satisfy the condition

$$\frac{\text{distance from } P \text{ to } F}{\text{distance from } P \text{ to } D} = \varepsilon$$

where F is a fixed point, D a fixed straight line, and ε a fixed positive number. The conic is an ellipse, a parabola or a hyperbola according to whether $\varepsilon < 1$, $\varepsilon = 1$ or $\varepsilon > 1$. Find the equation of the conic if F is the origin and D is the line $x = -p$.

Another parameter associated with conics is the **semi-latus rectum**, usually denoted ℓ.   For a circle it is equal to the radius.   For other conics it is half the length of the chord through a focus and perpendicular to the axis (for a parabola), the major axis (for an ellipse), or the transverse axis (for a hyperbola). That chord is called the **latus rectum** of the conic.

18. Show that the semi-latus rectum of the parabola is twice the distance from the vertex to the focus.

19. Show that the semi-latus rectum for an ellipse with semi-major axis a and semi-minor axis b is $\ell = b^2/a$.

20. Show that the formula in the above exercise also gives the semi-latus rectum of a hyperbola with semi-transverse axis a and semi-conjugate axis b.

21.*Suppose a plane intersects a right-circular cone in an ellipse, and that two spheres (one on each side of the plane) are inscribed between the cone and the plane so that each is tangent to the cone around a circle and is also tangent to the plane at a point. Show that the points where these two spheres touch the plane are the foci of the ellipse. Hints: All tangent lines drawn to a sphere from a given point outside the sphere are equal in length. The distance between the two circles in which the spheres intersect the cone, measured along generators of the cone (i.e. straight lines lying on the cone), is the same for all generators.

22.*State and prove a result analogous to that in the above exercise but pertaining to a hyperbola.

23.*Suppose a plane intersects a right-circular cone in a parabola with vertex at V. Suppose that a sphere is inscribed between the cone and the plane as in the previous exercises, and is tangent to the plane of the parabola at point F. Show that the chord to the parabola through F which is perpendicular to FV has length equal to that of the latus rectum of the parabola. Therefore F is the focus of the parabola.

APPENDIX III   FIRST ORDER DIFFERENTIAL EQUATIONS

A **differential equation** is an equation which involves one or more derivatives of an unknown function. Solving the differential equation means finding a function (or every function) that satisfies the differential equation.

Many physical laws and relationships which hold between quantities studied in various scientific disciplines are expressed mathematically as differential equations. For example, Newton's second law of motion ($F = ma$) states that the position $x(t)$ at time t of an object of constant mass m subjected to a force $F(t)$ must satisfy the differential equation (equation of motion):

$$m \frac{d^2 x}{dt^2} = F(t).$$

Similarly, the biomass $m(t)$ at time t of a bacterial culture growing in a uniformly supporting medium is proportional to that biomass:

$$\frac{dm}{dt} = km(t),$$

which is the differential equation of exponential growth (or, if $k < 0$, exponential decay). Because differential equations arise so extensively in the abstract modelling of concrete phenomena, such equations and techniques for solving them are at the heart of applied mathematics. Indeed, most of the existing mathematical literature is either directly involved with differential equations, or is motivated by problems arising in the study of such equations. This Appendix and the one following it provide a brief introduction to the study of ordinary differential equations. They are necessarily short. Students of mathematics and its applications usually take one or more full courses on differential equations, and even then hardly scratch the surface of the subject.

Differential equations are classified in several ways. The most significant classification is based on the number of variables with respect to which derivatives appear in the equation. An **ordinary differential equation** is one which involves derivatives with respect to only one variable. Both of the examples given above are ordinary differential equations. A **partial differential equation** is one which involves partial derivatives of the unknown function with respect to more than one variable. For example, the **one-dimensional wave equation**

$$\frac{\partial^2 u}{\partial t^2} = c^2 \frac{\partial^2 u}{\partial x^2}$$

models the lateral displacement $u(x, t)$ at position x at time t of a stretched vibrating string. (See Section 2.3.) We will not discuss partial differential equations in these Appendices.

Differential equations are also classified with respect to **order**. The order of a differential equation is the order of the highest order derivative present in the equation.

$$\frac{d^2 y}{dx^2} + y = \sin x \qquad \text{has order 2,}$$

$$\frac{d^3 y}{dx^3} + 4x \left(\frac{dy}{dx} \right)^2 = y \frac{d^2 y}{dx^2} \qquad \text{has order 3.}$$

This Appendix is concerned with differential equations having order 1. Appendix 4 deals with differential equations of order 2.

A differential equation is **linear** if no term has more than one factor which is either the unknown function or one of its derivatives. The first example immediately above is linear; the second is not. The equation

$$(1 + x^2) \frac{d^3 y}{dx^3} + \sin x \frac{d^2 y}{dx^2} - 4 \frac{dy}{dx} + y = e^x \cos x$$

is a linear equation of order 3.

Among first order ordinary differential equations, the easiest to solve are those which are either *separable*, *linear*, *homogeneous*, or *exact*. We examine each of these types.

First Order Separable

Consider the **logistic equation**:

$$\frac{dy}{dt} = ky \left(1 - \frac{y}{L} \right),$$

which models the growth of an animal population with limited food supply. Here $y(t)$ is the size of the population at time t, k is a positive constant related to the fertility of the population, and L is the steady-state population size that can be sustained by the available food supply. This equation is an example of a class of first-order differential equations called **separable equations** because when they are written in terms of differentials they can be separated with only the dependent variable on one side of the equation and only the independent variable on the other. The logistic equation can be written in the form

$$\frac{L \, dy}{y(L - y)} = k \, dt,$$

and solved by integrating both sides. Expanding the left side in partial fractions and integrating, we get

$$\int \left(\frac{1}{y} + \frac{1}{L - y} \right) dy = kt + C.$$

Assuming that $0 < y < L$, we therefore obtain

$$\ln\left(\frac{y}{L-y}\right) = \ln y - \ln(L-y) = kt + C,$$

and this equation can be solved for y to give

$$y = \frac{C_1 L e^{kt}}{1 + C_1 e^{kt}}, \qquad \text{where } C_1 = e^C.$$

Generally, separable equations are of the form

$$\frac{dy}{dx} = f(x)g(y).$$

We solve them by rewriting them in the form

$$\frac{dy}{g(y)} = f(x)\,dx$$

and integrating both sides. We provide several examples.

EXAMPLE A3.1 Solve the equation $\dfrac{dy}{dx} = \dfrac{x}{y}$.

SOLUTION We have $y\,dy = x\,dx$, so, on integrating both sides, we get $\frac{1}{2}y^2 = \frac{1}{2}x^2 + C$ or $y^2 - x^2 = C_1$ where $C_1 = 2C$ is an arbitrary constant. The solution curves are rectangular hyperbolas with asymptotes $y = x$ and $y = -x$.

EXAMPLE A3.2 Find the function $y(x)$ that satisfies $\dfrac{dy}{dx} = x^2 y^3$ and the initial condition $y(1) = 3$.

SOLUTION We have $\dfrac{dy}{y^3} = x^2\,dx$, so $\displaystyle\int \frac{dy}{y^3} = \int x^2\,dx$ and

$$\frac{-1}{2y^2} = \frac{x^3}{3} + C.$$

Since $y = 3$ when $x = 1$, we have $-\frac{1}{18} = \frac{1}{3} + C$ and $C = -\frac{7}{18}$. Substituting this value into the above solution and solving for y, we obtain

$$y(x) = \frac{3}{\sqrt{7 - 6x^3}}.$$

This solution is valid for $x \le \left(\frac{7}{6}\right)^{1/3}$.

EXAMPLE A3.3   (**A Solution Concentration Problem**) Initially a tank contains 1000 L of brine with 50 kg of dissolved salt. If brine containing 10 g of salt per litre is flowing into the tank at a constant rate of 10 L/min, if the contents of the tank are kept thoroughly mixed at all times, and if the solution also flows out at 10 L/min, how much salt remains in the tank at the end of 40 min?

SOLUTION   Let $x(t)$ be the number of kg of salt in solution in the tank after t minutes. Thus $x(0) = 50$. Salt is coming into the tank at a rate of 10 g/L $\times$ 10 L/min $= 100$ g/min $= 1/10$ kg/min. At all times the tank contains 1000 L of liquid, so the concentration of salt in the tank at time t is $x/1000$ kg/L. Since the contents flow out at 10 L/min, salt is being removed at a rate of $10x/1000 = x/100$ kg/min. Therefore,

$$\frac{dx}{dt} = \text{rate in} - \text{rate out} = \frac{1}{10} - \frac{x}{100} = \frac{10 - x}{100}$$

or

$$\frac{dx}{10 - x} = \frac{dt}{100}.$$

Integrating both sides of this equation, we obtain

$$-\ln|10 - x| = \frac{t}{100} + C.$$

Observe that $x(t) \neq 10$ for any finite time t (since $\ln 0$ is not defined). Since $x(0) = 50 > 10$, it follows that $x(t) > 10$ for all $t > 0$. ($x(t)$ is necessarily continuous so it cannot take any value less than 10 without somewhere taking the value 10 by the Intermediate-Value Theorem.) Hence

$$\ln(x - 10) = -\frac{t}{100} - C.$$

Since $x(0) = 50$, we have $-C = \ln 40$ and

$$x = x(t) = 10 + 40e^{-t/100}.$$

After 40 min there will be $10 + 40e^{-0.4} \approx 36.8$ kg of salt in the tank.

EXAMPLE A3.4   (**A Rate of Reaction Problem**) In a chemical reaction that goes to completion in solution, one molecule of each of two reactants, A and B, combines to form each molecule of the product C. According to the law of mass action, the reaction proceeds at a rate proportional to the product of the concentrations of A and B in the solution. Thus if there were initially present a molecules/cm^3 of A and b molecules/cm^3 of B, then the number $x(t)$ of molecules/cm^3 of C present at time t thereafter is determined by the differential equation

$$\frac{dx}{dt} = k(a - x)(b - x).$$

We solve this equation by the technique of partial fraction decomposition under the assumption that $b \neq a$.

$$\int \frac{dx}{(a-x)(b-x)} = k \int dt = kt + C.$$

Since $\dfrac{1}{(a-x)(b-x)} = \dfrac{1}{b-a} \left(\dfrac{1}{a-x} - \dfrac{1}{b-x} \right)$, and since necessarily $x \leq a$ and $x \leq b$, we have

$$\frac{1}{b-a}\left(-\ln(a-x) + \ln(b-x) \right) = kt + C,$$

or

$$\ln\left(\frac{b-x}{a-x}\right) = (b-a)\,kt + C_1 \qquad (C_1 = (b-a)C).$$

By assumption, $x(0) = 0$, so $C_1 = \ln(b/a)$ and

$$\ln \frac{a}{b}\left(\frac{b-x}{a-x}\right) = (b-a)\,kt.$$

This equation can be solved for x to yield

$$x = x(t) = \frac{ab(e^{(b-a)kt} - 1)}{be^{(b-a)kt} - a}.$$

EXAMPLE A3.5   Find a family of curves, each of which intersects each parabola with equation of the form $y = Cx^2$ at right angles.

SOLUTION   The family of parabolas $y = Cx^2$ satisfies the differential equation

$$\frac{d}{dx}\left(\frac{y}{x^2}\right) = \frac{d}{dx} C = 0,$$

that is,

$$x^2 \frac{dy}{dx} - 2xy = 0 \qquad \text{or} \qquad \frac{dy}{dx} = \frac{2y}{x}.$$

Any curve that meets the parabolas $y = Cx^2$ at right angles must, at any point (x, y) on it, have slope equal to the negative reciprocal of the slope of the particular parabola passing through that point. Thus such a curve must satisfy

$$\frac{dy}{dx} = -\frac{x}{2y}.$$

Separation of the variables leads to $2y\,dy = -x\,dx$, and integration of both sides then yields $y^2 = -\frac{1}{2}x^2 + C_1$ or $x^2 + 2y^2 = C_2$, $(C_2 = 2C_1)$. This equation represents a family of ellipses centred at the origin. Each ellipse meets each parabola at right angles, as shown in the Fig. A3.1.

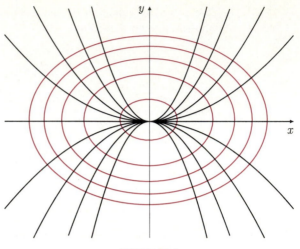

FIGURE A3.1

First-Order Linear Equations

A first-order **linear** differential equation is one of the type

$$\frac{dy}{dx} + p(x)y = q(x),$$

where $p(x)$ and $q(x)$ are given functions, which we assume to be continuous. We can solve such equations (that is, find y as a function of x) by the following procedure.

Let $\mu(x)$ be any antiderivative of $p(x)$; thus $d\mu/dx = p(x)$. If $y = y(x)$ satisfies the given equation, then we calculate, using the product rule,

$$\frac{d}{dx}\left(e^{\mu(x)}y(x)\right) = e^{\mu(x)}\frac{dy}{dx} + e^{\mu(x)}\frac{d\mu}{dx}y(x)$$

$$= e^{\mu(x)}\left(\frac{dy}{dx} + p(x)y\right) = e^{\mu(x)}q(x).$$

Therefore,

$$e^{\mu(x)}y(x) = \int e^{\mu(x)}q(x)\,dx$$

or

$$y(x) = e^{-\mu(x)}\int e^{\mu(x)}q(x)\,dx.$$

We reuse this method, rather than the final formula, in the examples below. $\mu(x)$ is called an **integrating factor**.

EXAMPLE A3.6   Solve $\dfrac{dy}{dx} + \dfrac{y}{x} = 1$ for $x > 0$.

SOLUTION   Here we want $d\mu/dx = 1/x$, so $\mu(x) = \ln x$ (for $x > 0$). Thus $e^{\mu(x)} = x$ and we calculate

$$\frac{d}{dx}(xy) = x\frac{dy}{dx} + y = x\left(\frac{dy}{dx} + \frac{y}{x}\right) = x,$$

and

$$xy = \int x\,dx = \frac{1}{2}x^2 + C.$$

Finally,

$$y = \frac{1}{x}\left(\frac{1}{2}x^2 + C\right) = \frac{x}{2} + \frac{C}{x}.$$

This function is a solution of the given equation for any value of the constant C.

EXAMPLE A3.7   Solve $\dfrac{dy}{dx} + xy = x^3$.

SOLUTION   Here $p(x) = x$ so $\mu(x) = x^2/2$. We calculate

$$\frac{d}{dx}\left(e^{x^2/2}y\right) = e^{x^2/2}\frac{dy}{dx} + e^{x^2/2}xy = x^3 e^{x^2/2}.$$

Thus,

$$e^{x^2/2}y = \int x^3 e^{x^2/2}\,dx \qquad \text{Let} \quad U = x^2 \qquad dV = x\,e^{x^2/2}\,dx$$
$$\text{Then} \quad dU = 2x\,dx \qquad V = e^{x^2/2}$$
$$= x^2 e^{x^2/2} - 2\int x e^{x^2/2}\,dx$$
$$= x^2 e^{x^2/2} - 2e^{x^2/2} + C,$$

and, finally,

$$y = x^2 - 2 + Ce^{-x^2/2}.$$

EXAMPLE A3.8   A savings account is opened with a deposit of A dollars. At any time t years thereafter, money is being continually deposited into the account at a rate of $(C+Dt)$ dollars per year. If interest is also being paid into the account at a nominal rate of $100R\%$ per year, compounded continuously, find the balance $B(t)$ dollars in the account after t years. Illustrate the solution for the data $A = 5000$, $C = 1000$, $D = 200$, $R = 0.13$, and $t = 5$.

SOLUTION   As noted in Section 3.7, continuous compounding of interest at a nominal rate of $100R\%$ causes $\$1.00$ to grow to $\$e^{Rt}$ in t years. Without subsequent deposits, the balance in the account would grow according to the differential equation of exponential growth:

$$\frac{dB}{dt} = RB.$$

Allowing for additional growth due to the continual deposits, we obtain that B must satisfy the differential equation

$$\frac{dB}{dt} = RB + (C + Dt)$$

or, equivalently, $dB/dt - RB = C + Dt$. This is a linear equation for B having $p(t) = -R$. Hence we may take $\mu(t) = -Rt$ and $e^{\mu(t)} = e^{-Rt}$. We now calculate

$$\frac{d}{dt}\left(e^{-Rt} B(t)\right) = e^{-Rt}\frac{dB}{dt} - Re^{-Rt} B(t) = (C + Dt) e^{-Rt},$$

and

$$e^{-Rt} B(t) = \int (C + Dt)e^{-Rt}\, dt \qquad \text{Let} \quad U = C + Dt \quad dV = e^{-Rt}\, dt$$
$$\text{Then} \ \ dU = D\, dt \qquad V = -e^{-Rt}/R$$
$$= -\frac{C + Dt}{R} e^{-Rt} + \frac{D}{R}\int e^{-Rt}\, dt$$
$$= -\frac{C + Dt}{R} e^{-Rt} - \frac{D}{R^2} e^{-Rt} + K \qquad (K = \text{constant}).$$

Hence

$$B(t) = -\frac{C + Dt}{R} - \frac{D}{R^2} + Ke^{Rt}.$$

Since $A = B(0) = -\dfrac{C}{R} - \dfrac{D}{R^2} + K$, we have $K = A + \dfrac{C}{R} + \dfrac{D}{R^2}$ and

$$B(t) = \left(A + \frac{C}{R} + \frac{D}{R^2}\right) e^{Rt} - \frac{C + Dt}{R} - \frac{D}{R^2}.$$

For the illustration $A = 5000$, $C = 1000$, $D = 200$, $R = 0.13$, and $t = 5$, we calculate, using a scientific calculator, $B(5) = 19,762.82$. Thus the account will contain \$19,762.82, after 5 years, under these circumstances.

First Order Homogeneous Equations

A differential equation which can be written in the form

$$\frac{dy}{dx} = f\left(\frac{y}{x}\right)$$

is said to be **homogeneous**. Such an equation can be transformed into a separable equation (and therefore solved) by means of a change of dependent variable. If we set

$$v = \frac{y}{x}, \qquad \text{or equivalently} \qquad y = vx,$$

then we have

$$\frac{dy}{dx} = v + x\frac{dv}{dx}$$

and the original differential equation transforms into

$$\frac{dv}{dx} = \frac{f(v) - v}{x},$$

which is separable.

EXAMPLE A3.9 Solve the equation

$$\frac{dy}{dx} = \frac{x^2 + xy}{xy + y^2}.$$

SOLUTION The equation is homogeneous. (Divide the numerator and denominator of the right-hand side by x^2 to see this.) If $y = vx$ the equation becomes

$$v + x\frac{dv}{dx} = \frac{1+v}{v+v^2} = \frac{1}{v},$$

or

$$x\frac{dv}{dx} = \frac{1-v^2}{v}.$$

Separating variables and integrating, we calculate

$$\int \frac{v\,dv}{1-v^2} = \int \frac{dx}{x} \qquad\qquad \text{let } u = 1 - v^2$$

$$-\frac{1}{2}\int \frac{du}{u} = \int \frac{dx}{x}$$

$$-\ln|u| = 2\ln|x| + C_1 = \ln C_2 x^2 \qquad (C_1 = \ln C_2)$$

$$\frac{1}{|u|} = C_2 x^2$$

$$|1 - v^2| = \frac{C_3}{x^2} \qquad\qquad (C_3 = 1/C_2)$$

$$\left|1 - \frac{y^2}{x^2}\right| = \frac{C_3}{x^2}.$$

The solution is best expressed in the form $x^2 - y^2 = C_4$, though near points where $y \neq 0$ it can be solved for y as a function of x. Separation of variables frequently leads to solutions defining the unknown function only implicitly; it is not always possible to give an explicit solution for the dependent variable.

Exact Equations and Integrating Factors

A first order differential equation expressed in differential form as

$$M(x,y)\,dx + N(x,y)\,dy = 0,$$

(which is equivalent to $\dfrac{dy}{dx} = -\dfrac{M(x,y)}{N(x,y)}$), is said to be **exact** if the left-hand side is the differential of a function $\phi(x,y)$:

$$d\phi(x,y) = M(x,y)\,dx + N(x,y)\,dy.$$

ϕ is called an **integral function** of the differential equation. Evidently the level curves $\phi(x,y) = C$ of the function ϕ provide the solutions of the differential equation. For example, the differential equation

$$x\,dx + y\,dy = 0$$

has solutions given by

$$x^2 + y^2 = C$$

since $d(x^2 + y^2) = 2(x\,dx + y\,dy) = 0$.

(The condition that the differential equation $M\,dx + N\,dy = 0$ should be exact is exactly the condition that the vector field

$$\mathbf{F} = M(x,y)\,\mathbf{i} + N(x,y)\,\mathbf{j}$$

should be *conservative*; the integral function of the differential equation is then the potential function of the vector field. See Section 6.2.)

A *necessary condition* for the exactness of the differential equation $M\,dx + N\,dy = 0$ is that

$$\frac{\partial M}{\partial y} = \frac{\partial N}{\partial x},$$

and this condition will also guarantee that the differential equation is exact in any simply connected domain.

Any ordinary differential equation of order 1 and degree 1 can be expressed in differential form: $M\,dx + N\,dy = 0$. However, this latter equation will not usually be exact. It *may* be possible to multiply the equation by an **integrating factor** $\mu(x,y)$ so that the resulting equation

$$\mu(x,y)\,M(x,y)\,dx + \mu(x,y)\,N(x,y)\,dy = 0$$

is exact. In general such integrating factors are difficult to find; they must satisfy the partial differential equation

$$M(x,y)\,\frac{\partial \mu}{\partial y} - N(x,y)\,\frac{\partial \mu}{\partial x} = \mu(x,y)\left(\frac{\partial N}{\partial x} - \frac{\partial M}{\partial y}\right),$$

which follows from the necessary condition for exactness stated above.

Sometimes it happens that a differential equation has an integrating factor depending on only one of the two variables. Suppose, for instance, that $\mu(x)$ is an integrating factor for $M\,dx + N\,dy = 0$. Then $\mu(x)$ must satisfy the differential equation

$$N(x,y)\,\frac{d\mu}{dx} = \mu(x)\left(\frac{\partial M}{\partial y} - \frac{\partial N}{\partial x}\right),$$

or,

$$\frac{1}{\mu(x)}\frac{d\mu}{dx} = \frac{\dfrac{\partial M}{\partial y} - \dfrac{\partial N}{\partial x}}{N(x,y)}.$$

This equation can be solved (by integration) for μ as a function of x alone provided the right-hand side is independent of y.

EXAMPLE A3.10   Solve $(x + y^2)\, dx + xy\, dy = 0$.

SOLUTION   Here $M = x + y^2$ and $N = xy$. Since

$$\frac{\dfrac{\partial M}{\partial y} - \dfrac{\partial N}{\partial x}}{N(x, y)} = \frac{2y - y}{xy} = \frac{1}{x},$$

the equation has an integrating factor depending only on x. This factor is given by $d\mu/\mu = dx/x$. Evidently $\mu = x$ is a suitable integrating factor; if we multiply the given differential equation by x, we obtain

$$0 = (x^2 + xy^2)\, dx + x^2 y\, dy = d\left(\frac{x^3}{3} + \frac{x^2 y^2}{2}\right).$$

The solution is therefore $2x^3 + 3x^2 y^2 = C$.

EXERCISES

Solve the differential equations in Exercises 1–24

1. $\dfrac{dy}{dx} = \dfrac{y}{2x}$

2. $\dfrac{dy}{dx} = \dfrac{3y - 1}{x}$

3. $\dfrac{dy}{dx} = \dfrac{x^2}{y^2}$

4. $\dfrac{dy}{dx} = x^2 y^2$

5. $\dfrac{dY}{dt} = tY$

6. $\dfrac{dx}{dt} = e^x \sin t$

7. $\dfrac{dy}{dx} = 1 - y^2$

8. $\dfrac{dy}{dx} = 1 + y^2$

9. $\dfrac{dy}{dt} = 2 + e^y$

10. $\dfrac{dy}{dx} = y^2(1 - y)$

11. $\dfrac{dy}{dx} - \dfrac{2y}{x} = x^2$

12. $\dfrac{dy}{dx} + \dfrac{2y}{x} = \dfrac{1}{x^2}$

13. $\dfrac{dy}{dx} + 2y = 3$

14. $\dfrac{dy}{dx} + y = e^x$

15. $\dfrac{dy}{dx} + y = x$

16. $\dfrac{dy}{dx} + 2e^x y = e^x$

17. $\dfrac{dy}{dx} = \dfrac{x + y}{x - y}$

18. $\dfrac{dy}{dx} = \dfrac{xy}{x^2 + 2y^2}$

19. $\dfrac{dy}{dx} = \dfrac{x^2 + xy + y^2}{x^2}$

20. $\dfrac{dy}{dx} = \dfrac{x^3 + 3xy^2}{3x^2 y + y^3}$

21. $(xy^2 + y)\, dx + (x^2 y + x)\, dy = 0$

22. $(e^x \sin y + 2x)\, dx + (e^x \cos y + 2y)\, dy = 0$

23. $(x^2 + 2y)\, dx - x\, dy = 0$

24. $(xe^x + x \ln y + y)\, dx + \left(\dfrac{x^2}{y} + x \ln x + x \sin y\right) dy = 0$

25. Find an equation of the curve in the xy-plane which passes through the point $(2,3)$, and has, at every point (x, y) on it, slope equal to $2x/(1 + y^2)$.

26. Repeat the previous problem for the point $(1,3)$ and slope $1 + (2y/x)$.

27. Show that the change of variables $\xi = x - x_0$, $\eta = y - y_0$ transforms the equation

$$\frac{dy}{dx} = \frac{ax + by + c}{ex + fy + g}$$

into the homogeneous equation

$$\frac{d\eta}{d\xi} = \frac{a\xi + b\eta}{e\xi + f\eta}$$

provided (x_0, y_0) is the solution of the system

$$ax + by + c = 0$$
$$ex + fy + g = 0.$$

Hence solve the equation $\dfrac{dy}{dx} = \dfrac{x + 2y - 4}{2x - y - 3}$.

28. What condition must the coefficients $M(x, y)$ and $N(x, y)$ satisfy if the equation $M\, dx + N\, dy = 0$ is to have an integrating factor of the form $\mu(y)$? Find an integrating factor of this form for the equation $y\, dx - (2x + y^3 e^y)\, dy = 0$, and hence solve the equation.

29. What condition must the coefficients $M(x,y)$ and $N(x,y)$ satisfy if the equation $M\,dx + N\,dy = 0$ is to have an integrating factor of the form $\mu(xy)$? Find such an integrating factor for the equation

$$\left(x\cos x + \frac{y^2}{x} \right) dx - \left(\frac{x\sin x}{y} + y \right) dy = 0,$$

and hence solve the equation.

30. A first order, linear, differential equation of the form

$$\frac{dy}{dx} + p(x)y = 0$$

which contains no term independent of y is said to be **homogeneous**. (This is a different but more common use of the word "homogeneous" than that applied to more general first order equations in this appendix.) If $y_1(x)$ and $y_2(x)$ are two solutions of the above linear, homogeneous equation show that $y(x) = C_1y_1(x)+C_2y_2(x)$ is also a solution. This property (often described by saying that the solutions form a "vector space") always holds for linear, homogeneous, differential equations, ordinary or partial, of any order.

31. If $y_1(x)$ and $y_2(x)$ are two solutions of the linear, non-homogeneous equation

$$\frac{dy}{dx} + p(x)y = q(x),$$

show that $y = y_1(x) - y_2(x)$ satisfies the corresponding homogeneous equation in which $q(x) = 0$. This is a property of linear equations in general.

32. Show that $u(x,y) = f(bx - ay)$ is a solution of the partial differential equation

$$a\frac{\partial u}{\partial x} + b\frac{\partial u}{\partial y} = 0,$$

where f is any differentiable function of one variable. While solutions of first order, ordinary differential equations generally involve an arbitrary constant, solutions of first order, partial differential equations generally involve an arbitrary function.

33. Why is the solution given for the chemical reaction rate problem in Example A3.4 not valid for $a = b$? Find the solution for the case $a = b$.

34. An object of mass m falling near the surface of the earth is retarded by air resistance proportional to its velocity so that, according to Newton's second law of motion,

$$m\frac{dv}{dt} = mg - kv,$$

where $v = v(t)$ is the velocity of the object at time t, and g is the acceleration of gravity near the surface of the earth. Assuming that the object falls from rest at time $t = 0$, that is, $v(0) = 0$, find the velocity $v(t)$ for any $t > 0$ (up until the object strikes the ground). Show $v(t)$ approaches a limit as $t \to \infty$. Do you need the explicit formula for $v(t)$ to determine this limiting velocity?

35. Repeat Exercise 34 except assuming that the air resistance is proportional to the square of the velocity so that the equation of motion is

$$m\frac{dv}{dt} = mg - kv^2.$$

36. Find the amount in a savings account after 1 year if the initial balance in the account was $1000, if the interest is paid continuously into the account at a nominal rate of 10% per annum, compounded continuously, and if the account is being continuously depleted (by taxes, say) at a rate of $y^2/1,000,000$ dollars per year, where $y = y(t)$ is the balance in the account after t years. How large can the account grow? How long will it take the account to grow to half this balance?

37. Find the family of curves each of which intersects all of the hyperbolas $xy = C$ at right angles.

38. Repeat the solution concentration problem in Example A3.3, changing the rate of inflow of brine into the tank to 12 L/min but leaving all the other data as they were in that example. Note that the volume of liquid in the tank is no longer constant as time increases.

39. A system of n first order, linear, differential equations in n unknown functions $y_1, y_2, \cdots, y_n$ is written

$$y_1' = a_{11}(x)y_1 + a_{12}(x)y_2 + \cdots + a_{1n}(x)y_n + f_1(x)$$
$$y_2' = a_{21}(x)y_1 + a_{22}(x)y_2 + \cdots + a_{2n}(x)y_n + f_2(x)$$
$$\vdots$$
$$y_n' = a_{n1}(x)y_1 + a_{n2}(x)y_2 + \cdots + a_{nn}(x)y_n + f_n(x).$$

Such a system is called an $n \times n$ **first order linear system** and can be rewritten in vector-matrix form as $\mathbf{y}' = \mathcal{A}(x)\mathbf{y} + \mathbf{f}(x)$ where

$$\mathbf{y}(x) = \begin{pmatrix} y_1(x) \\ \vdots \\ y_n(x) \end{pmatrix}, \quad \mathbf{f}(x) = \begin{pmatrix} f_1(x) \\ \vdots \\ f_n(x) \end{pmatrix},$$

$$\mathcal{A}(x) = \begin{pmatrix} a_{11}(x) & \cdots & a_{1n}(x) \\ \vdots & \ddots & \vdots \\ a_{n1}(x) & \cdots & a_{nn}(x) \end{pmatrix}.$$

Show that the second order, linear equation $y'' + a_1(x)y' + a_0(x)y = f(x)$ can be transformed into a 2×2 first order system with $y_1 = y$ and $y_2 = y'$ having

$$\mathcal{A}(x) = \begin{pmatrix} 0 & 1 \\ -a_0(x) & -a_1(x) \end{pmatrix}, \quad \mathbf{f}(x) = \begin{pmatrix} 0 \\ f(x) \end{pmatrix}.$$

40. Generalize the previous exercise to transform an n'th order, linear equation

$$y^{(n)} + a_{n-1}(x)y^{(n-1)} + a_{n-2}(x)y^{(n-2)} + \cdots + a_0(x)y = f(x)$$

into an $n \times n$ first order system.

41. If $\mathcal{A}$ is an $n \times n$ constant matrix, and if there exists a scalar λ and a nonzero constant vector $\mathbf{v}$ for which $\mathcal{A}\mathbf{v} = \lambda\mathbf{v}$ show that $\mathbf{y} = C_1 e^{\lambda x}\mathbf{v}$ is a solution of the homogeneous system $\mathbf{y}' = \mathcal{A}\mathbf{y}$.

42. Show that the determinant $\begin{vmatrix} 2 - \lambda & 1 \\ 2 & 3 - \lambda \end{vmatrix}$ is zero for two distinct values of λ. For each of these values find a nonzero vector $\mathbf{v}$ which satisfies the condition $\begin{pmatrix} 2 & 1 \\ 2 & 3 \end{pmatrix}\mathbf{v} = \lambda\mathbf{v}$. Hence solve the system

$$y_1' = 2y_1 + y_2, \qquad y_2' = 2y_1 + 3y_3.$$

APPENDIX IV   DIFFERENTIAL EQUATIONS OF SECOND ORDER

The general second order ordinary differential equation is of the form

$$F\left(\frac{d^2y}{dx^2}, \frac{dy}{dx}, y, x\right) = 0$$

for some function F of four variables. When such an equation can be solved explicitly for y, the solution typically involves two integrations and therefore two arbitrary constants. A unique solution usually results from prescribing the values of the solution y and its first derivative $y' = dy/dx$ at a particular point. Such a prescription constitutes an **initial-value problem** for the second order equation.

Equations Reducible to First Order

A second order equation of the form

$$F\left(\frac{d^2y}{dx^2}, \frac{dy}{dx}, x\right) = 0$$

which does not involve the unknown function y explicitly (except through its derivatives) can be reduced to a first order equation by a change of dependent variable; if $v = dy/dx$ then the equation can be written

$$F\left(\frac{dv}{dx}, v, x\right) = 0.$$

This equation may be amenable to the techniques described in Appendix 3. If an explicit solution $v = v(x)$ can be found, then the function

$$y = \int v(x)\, dx$$

is an explicit solution of the given equation.

EXAMPLE A4.1 Solve the initial-value problem

$$\frac{d^2y}{dx^2} = x\left(\frac{dy}{dx}\right)^2, \qquad y(0) = 1, \qquad y'(0) = -2.$$

SOLUTION If we set $v = y'(x)$ in the differential equation we obtain $(dv/dx) = xv^2$, which is a separable first order equation. Thus

$$\frac{dv}{v^2} = x\,dx$$
$$-\frac{1}{v} = \frac{x^2}{2} + \frac{C_1}{2}$$
$$v = -\frac{2}{x^2 + C_1}.$$

The initial condition $y'(0) = -2$ implies $v(0) = -2$ and so $C_1 = 1$. Therefore

$$y = -2\int \frac{dx}{x^2 + 1} = -2\tan^{-1}x + C_2.$$

The initial condition $y(0) = 1$ implies that $C_2 = 1$ so the solution is

$$y = 1 - 2\tan^{-1}x.$$

A second order equation of the form

$$F\left(\frac{d^2y}{dx^2}, \frac{dy}{dx}, y\right) = 0$$

which does not involve the independent variable x explicitly can be reduced to a first order equation by a change of both dependent and independent variables. Again let $v = dy/dx$, but regard v as a function of y rather than x; $v = v(y)$. Then

$$\frac{d^2y}{dx^2} = \frac{dv}{dx} = \frac{dv}{dy}\frac{dy}{dx} = v\frac{dv}{dy}$$

by the Chain Rule. Hence the given differential equation becomes

$$F\left(v\frac{dv}{dy}, v, y\right) = 0$$

which is a first order equation for v as a function of y. If this equation can be solved for $v = v(y)$ there still remains the problem of solving $(dy/dx) = v(y)$ for y as a function of x.

EXAMPLE A4.2   Solve the equation $y\dfrac{d^2y}{dx^2} = \left(\dfrac{dy}{dx}\right)^2$.

SOLUTION   The change of variable suggested above leads to the equation

$$yv\frac{dv}{dy} = v^2,$$

which is separable, $dv/v = dy/y$, and has solution $v = C_1 y$. The equation

$$\frac{dy}{dx} = C_1 y$$

is again separable, and leads to

$$\frac{dy}{y} = C_1\,dx$$
$$\ln|y| = C_1 x + C_2$$
$$y = \pm e^{C_1 x + C_2} = C_3 e^{C_1 x}.$$

Second Order Linear Equations

The most frequently encountered ordinary differential equations arising in applications are second order linear equations. The general second order linear equation is of the form

$$a_2(x)\frac{d^2y}{dx^2} + a_1(x)\frac{dy}{dx} + a_0(x)y = f(x).$$

If $f(x) = 0$ identically, we say that the equation is **homogeneous**. If the coefficients $a_2(x)$, $a_1(x)$ and $a_0(x)$ are continuous on an interval and $a_2(x)\neq 0$ there, then the homogeneous equation

$$a_2(x)\frac{d^2y}{dx^2} + a_1(x)\frac{dy}{dx} + a_0(x)y = 0$$

has a general solution of the form

$$y_h = C_1 y_1(x) + C_2 y_2(x)$$

where $y_1(x)$ and $y_2(x)$ are two **independent** solutions, that is, two solutions with the property that $C_1 y_1(x) + C_2 y_2(x) = 0$ for all x in the interval only if $C_1 = C_2 = 0$.

Whenever one solution, $y_1(x)$, of a homogeneous linear second order equation is known, another independent solution (and therefore the general solution) can be found by substituting $y = v(x)y_1(x)$ into the differential equation. This leads to a first order, linear, separable equation for v'. We will see examples of this below.

The general solution of the second order, linear, non-homogeneous equation (with $f(x)\neq 0$) is of the form

$$y = y_p(x) + y_h(x)$$

where $y_p(x)$ is any particular solution of the non-homogeneous equation and $y_h(x)$ is the general solution (as described above) of the corresponding homogeneous equation. Later in this appendix we will discuss the solution of non-homogeneous linear equations. First, however, we concentrate on some special classes of homogeneous, linear equations.

Homogeneous Linear Equations with Constant Coefficients

If a, b and c are constants and $a \neq 0$ the equation

A4.3
Second Order Linear
Equation with
Constant Coefficients

$$a\frac{d^2y}{dt^2} + b\frac{dy}{dt} + cy = 0$$

is a second order, linear, homogeneous, ordinary differential equation with constant coefficients. Such equations arise frequently in the analysis of mechanical systems and electrical circuits; a represents the "inertia" (mass, inductance) of the system, b measures the "resistance" (or damping), and c is related to the "springiness" (or capacitance) of the system. Note that we are calling the independent variable t here, instead of x. That's because in most applications the independent variable represents time.

The best-known example of a second order linear equation with constant coefficients is the equation of **simple harmonic motion**,

$$\frac{d^2y}{dt^2} + \omega^2 y = 0,$$

which has general solution in either of the two forms

$$y = A\cos\omega t + B\sin\omega t = R\cos\omega(t - t_0),$$

where A and B, or alternatively R and t_0, are arbitrary constants.

Let us try to find a solution of equation A4.3 having the form $y = e^{rt}$. Substituting this expression into the equation, we obtain

$$ar^2 e^{rt} + bre^{rt} + ce^{rt} = 0.$$

Since e^{rt} does not vanish, $y = e^{rt}$ will be a solution of the differential equation A4.3 if and only if r satisfies the quadratic **auxiliary equation**

A4.4
The Auxiliary
Equation

$$ar^2 + br + c = 0,$$

which has roots given by the *quadratic formula*:

$$r = \frac{-b \pm \sqrt{b^2 - 4ac}}{2a} = -\frac{b}{2a} \pm \frac{\sqrt{D}}{2a},$$

where $D = b^2 - 4ac$ is the **discriminant** of the auxiliary equation A4.4.

There are three cases to consider, depending on whether D is positive, zero or negative.

CASE I. Suppose $D = b^2 - 4ac > 0$. Then the auxiliary equation has two different real roots, r_1 and r_2 given by

$$r_1 = \frac{-b - \sqrt{D}}{2a}, \qquad r_2 = \frac{-b + \sqrt{D}}{2a}.$$

(Often these roots can be found easily by factoring the left side of the auxiliary equation.) In this case both $y = y_1(t) = e^{r_1 t}$ and $y = y_2(t) = e^{r_2 t}$ are solutions of the differential equation, and so is

$$y = A e^{r_1 t} + B e^{r_2 t},$$

for any choice of the constants A and B. Since the differential equation is of second order and this solution involves two arbitrary constants we suspect it is the **general solution**, that is, that every solution of the differential equation can be written in this form. Exercise 27 at the end of this section outlines a way to prove this.

EXAMPLE A4.5   Find the general solution of $y'' + y' - 2y = 0$.

SOLUTION   The auxiliary equation is $r^2 + r - 2 = 0$, or $(r + 2)(r - 1) = 0$. The auxiliary roots are $r_1 = -2$ and $r_2 = 1$. Hence the general solution of the differential equation is

$$y = A e^{-2t} + B e^t.$$

In order to facilitate discussion of the other two cases, $D = 0$, and $D < 0$, let us make a change of dependent variable in the differential equation A4.3; let $k = -\dfrac{b}{2a}$ and let $y(t) = e^{kt} u(t)$. Hence

$$y'(t) = e^{kt}[u'(t) + ku(t)]$$
$$y''(t) = e^{kt}[u''(t) + 2ku'(t) + k^2 u(t)].$$

Substituting these expressions into the differential equation A4.3, we obtain

$$e^{kt}\left(au'' + (2ak + b)u' + (ak^2 + bk + c)u\right) = 0.$$

Since $2ak = -b$, the coefficient of u' in this equation is 0 and that of u is

$$ak^2 + bk + c = \frac{ab^2}{4a^2} - \frac{b^2}{2a} + c = \frac{4ac - b^2}{4a} = \frac{-D}{4a}.$$

Dividing by a and e^{kt}, we are left with the **reduced equation**

A4.6
The Reduced
Equation

$$u'' - \left(\frac{D}{4a^2}\right) u = 0.$$

CASE II. Suppose $D = b^2 - 4ac = 0$. Then the auxiliary equation has two equal roots $r_1 = r_2 = -b/(2a) = k$. Moreover, the reduced equation is $u'' = 0$, which has general solution $u = A + Bt$. Here A and B are any constants. Thus, the general solution to the differential equation A4.3 for the case $D = 0$ is

$$y = A e^{-(b/2a)t} + Bt\, e^{-(b/2a)t}.$$

EXAMPLE A4.7   Find the general solution of $y'' + 6y' + 9y = 0$.

SOLUTION   The auxiliary equation is $r^2 + 6r + 9 = 0$, or $(r + 3)^2 = 0$, which has identical roots $r = -3$. According to the discussion above, the general solution of the differential equation is

$$y = A e^{-3t} + Bt\, e^{-3t}.$$

CASE III. Suppose $D = b^2 - 4ac < 0$. Then the auxiliary equation has complex roots, and the reduced equation for u is

$$u'' + \omega^2 u = 0, \qquad \text{where} \quad \omega = \frac{\sqrt{-D}}{2a}.$$

We recognize this as the equation of Simple Harmonic Motion. It has general solution

$$u = A\, \cos(\omega t) + B\, \sin(\omega t),$$

where A and B are arbitrary constants. Therefore the given differential equation has general solution

$$y = A e^{-(b/2a)t} \cos(\omega t) + B e^{-(b/2a)t} \sin(\omega t), \qquad \text{where} \quad \omega = \frac{\sqrt{4ac - b^2}}{2a}.$$

EXAMPLE A4.8   Find the general solution of $y'' + 4y' + 13y = 0$.

SOLUTION   The auxiliary equation is $r^2 + 4r + 13 = 0$. Since $a = 1$, $b = 4$, and $c = 13$, the discriminant is $D = b^2 - 4ac = 16 - 52 = -36 < 0$ and Case III applies. We have $-(b/2a) = -2$ and $\omega = \sqrt{36}/2 = 3$ so the general solution of the given differential equation is

$$y = A e^{-2t} \cos(3t) + B e^{-2t} \sin(3t).$$

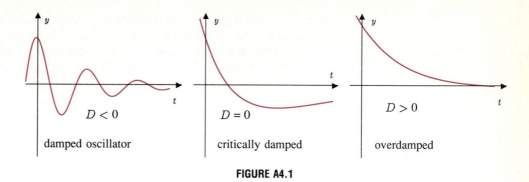

FIGURE A4.1

REMARK: If a and c are positive, but $b = 0$, then A4.3 is the differential equation of Simple Harmonic Motion and has oscillatory solutions of fixed amplitude. If $b > 0$ but $b^2 < 4ac$ (Case III) the solutions still oscillate, but the amplitude diminishes exponentially as $t \to \infty$ because of the factor $e^{-(b/2a)t}$. A system whose behavior is modelled by such an equation is said to exhibit **damped harmonic motion.** If $b > 0$ and $b^2 = 4ac$ (Case II) the system is **critically damped**, and if $b^2 > 4ac$ (Case I) it is **overdamped**. In these latter cases the behavior is no longer oscillatory. (See Fig. A4.1. Imagine a spring-suspended mass in a jar of molasses.)

Here is a typical initial-value problem for a differential equation of type A4.3.

EXAMPLE A4.9   Solve the initial-value problem $\begin{cases} y'' + 2y' + 2y = 0 \\ y(0) = 2 \\ y'(0) = -3. \end{cases}$

SOLUTION   We have $a = 1$, $b = 2$, and $c = 2$, so $b^2 - 4ac = 4 - 8 = -4 < 0$ and Case III applies. We have $-(b/2a) = -1$ and $\omega = \sqrt{4}/2 = 1$. Thus the differential equation has general solution

$$y = A e^{-t} \cos t + B e^{-t} \sin t.$$

Also

$$y' = e^{-t}(-A \cos t - B \sin t - A \sin t + B \cos t) = (B - A) e^{-t} \cos t - (A + B) e^{-t} \sin t.$$

Applying the initial conditions $y(0) = 2$ and $y'(0) = -3$, we obtain $A = 2$ and $B - A = -3$. Hence $B = -1$ and the initial-value problem has solution

$$y = 2 e^{-t} \cos t - e^{-t} \sin t.$$

Euler (Equidimensional) Equations

A homogeneous, linear equation of the form

$$ax^2 \frac{d^2 y}{dx^2} + bx \frac{dy}{dx} + cy = 0$$

is called an **Euler equation** or an **equidimensional equation**, the latter term being appropriate since all the terms in the equation have the same dimension, (that is, they are measured in the same units), provided that the constants a, b and c all have the same dimension. As in the case of constant coefficient equations, we assume that these constants are real numbers, and that $a \neq 0$. Even so, the leading coefficient, ax^2, does vanish at $x = 0$, (which is called a **singular point** of the equation) and this can cause solutions to fail to be defined at $x = 0$. We will solve the equation in the interval $x > 0$; the same solution will also hold for $x < 0$ provided we replace x by $|x|$ in the solution.

Let us search for solutions in $x > 0$ given by powers of x; if

$$y = x^r, \qquad \frac{dy}{dx} = rx^{r-1}, \qquad \frac{d^2y}{dx^2} = r(r-1)x^{r-2},$$

then the Euler equation becomes

$$\left(ar(r-1) + br + c \right) x^r = 0.$$

This will be satisfied for all $x > 0$ provided that r satisfies the **auxiliary equation**

$$ar^2 + (b-a)r + c = 0.$$

As for constant coefficient equations, there are three possibilities.

If $(b-a)^2 \geq 4ac$ then the auxiliary equation has two real roots

$$r_1 = \frac{a - b + \sqrt{(b-a)^2 - 4ac}}{2a}, \qquad r_2 = \frac{a - b - \sqrt{(b-a)^2 - 4ac}}{2a}.$$

In this case, the Euler equation has general solution

$$y = C_1 x^{r_1} + C_2 x^{r_2}, \qquad (x > 0).$$

The general solution is usually quoted in the form

$$y = C_1 |x|^{r_1} + C_2 |x|^{r_2}$$

which is valid in any interval not containing $x = 0$, and may even be valid on intervals containing the origin if, for example, r_1 and r_2 are nonnegative integers.

EXAMPLE A4.10   Solve the initial-value problem

$$2x^2 y'' - y' - 2y = 0, \qquad y(1) = 5, \qquad y'(1) = 0.$$

SOLUTION   The auxiliary equation is $2r(r-1) - r - 2 = 0$, that is, $2r^2 - 3r - 2 = 0$, and has roots $r = 2$ and $r = -(1/2)$. Thus, the general solution of the differential equation (valid for $x > 0$) is

$$y = C_1 x^2 + C_2 x^{-1/2}.$$

The initial conditions imply that

$$5 = y(1) = C_1 + C_2, \qquad 0 = y'(1) = 2C_1 - \frac{1}{2}C_2,$$

and hence that $C_1 = 1$ and $C_2 = 4$. The initial-value problem has solution

$$y = x^2 + \frac{4}{\sqrt{x}}, \qquad (x > 0).$$

If $(b - a)^2 = 4ac$ then the auxiliary equation has one double root, namely $r = (a - b)/2a$. It is left to the reader to verify that in this case the transformation $y = x^r v(x)$ leads to the general solution

$$y = C_1 x^r + C_2 x^r \ln x, \qquad (x > 0),$$

or, more generally,

$$y = C_1 |x|^r + C_2 |x|^r \ln |x|, \qquad (x \neq 0).$$

If $(b - a)^2 < 4ac$ then the auxiliary equation has complex conjugate roots

$$r = a \pm ib, \qquad \text{where} \quad a = \frac{a - b}{2a}, \quad b = \frac{\sqrt{4ac - (b - a)^2}}{2a}.$$

The corresponding powers x^r can be expressed in real form in a manner similar to that used for constant coefficient equations; we have

$$x^{a \pm ib} = e^{(a \pm ib) \ln x} = e^{a \ln x} \left[\cos(b \ln x) \pm i \sin(b \ln x) \right]$$
$$= x^a \cos(b \ln x) \pm i x^a \sin(b \ln x).$$

Accordingly, the Euler equation has general solution

$$y = C_1 |x|^a \cos(b \ln |x|) + C_2 |x|^a \sin(b \ln |x|).$$

EXAMPLE A4.11   The differential equation $x^2 y'' - 3xy' + 13y = 0$ has auxiliary equation of the form, $r(r - 1) - 3r + 13 = 0$, that is, $r^2 - 4r + 13 = 0$, which has roots $r = 2 \pm 3i$. The differential equation, therefore, has general solution

$$y = C_1 x^2 \cos(3 \ln |x|) + C_2 x^2 \sin(3 \ln |x|).$$

Non-homogeneous Equations

We now consider the problem of solving the non-homogeneous second order differential equation

$$a_2(x)\frac{d^2y}{dx^2} + a_1(x)\frac{dy}{dx} + a_0(x)y = f(x).$$

We assume that two independent solutions, $y_1(x)$ and $y_2(x)$, of the corresponding homogeneous equation

$$a_2(x)\frac{d^2y}{dx^2} + a_1(x)\frac{dy}{dx} + a_0(x)y = 0$$

are known. The function $y_h(x) = C_1y_1(x) + C_2y_2(x)$, which is the general solution of the homogeneous equation, is called the **complementary function** for the non-homogeneous equation. If we can find any one solution $y_p(x)$ (a **particular solution**) of the non-homogeneous equation, the general solution of the non-homogeneous equation is

$$y = y_p(x) + y_h(x) = y_p(x) + C_1y_1(x) + C_2y_2(x).$$

To see this, observe that the difference between any two solutions of the non-homogeneous equation satisfies the homogeneous equation.

One method for finding a particular solution $y_p(x)$ of the non-homogeneous equation when we know two independent solutions, $y_1(x)$ and $y_2(x)$, of the homogeneous equation is to replace the constants in the complementary function by functions, that is, search for y_p in the form

$$y_p = u_1(x)y_1(x) + u_2(x)y_2(x).$$

If we calculate the first and second derivatives of y_p and substitute them into the non-homogeneous differential equation and use the fact that y_1 and y_2 satisfy the homogeneous equation, we find that u_1 and u_2 must satisfy the equation

$$u_1'(x)y_1'(x) + u_2'(x)y_2'(x) = f(x).$$

This is only one condition on the two unknown functions u_1 and u_2, and we are free to add another condition to force a unique solution. It is convenient to choose as the second condition

$$u_1'(x)y_1(x) + u_2'(x)y_2(x) = 0.$$

We can solve these two equations for u_1' and u_2' by Cramer's Rule (Theorem 1.5.10), or otherwise, to obtain

$$u_1' = -\frac{y_2(x)f(x)}{W(x)}, \qquad u_2' = \frac{y_1(x)f(x)}{W(x)},$$

where $W(x)$, called the **Wronskian** of y_1 and y_2, is the determinant

$$W(x) = \begin{vmatrix} y_1(x) & y_2(x) \\ y_1'(x) & y_2'(x) \end{vmatrix}.$$

Then u_1 and u_2 can be found by integration.

The above method for finding a particular solution of a non-homogeneous linear differential equation is called the **Method of Variation of Parameters.** It is completely general and extends to higher order equations in a reasonable way, but it is computationally somewhat difficult. Another method frequently used for constant coefficient equations is to guess the form of a particular solution (a sum of suitable functions with unknown constant coefficients) and substitute into the differential equation to get a condition enabling determination of the coefficients.

EXAMPLE A4.12   Find the general solution of $y'' - 3y' + 2y = 4x$.

SOLUTION   First we solve the homogeneous equation $y'' - 3y' + 2y = 0$ which has auxiliary equation $r^2 - 3r + 2 = 0$ with roots $r = 1$ and $r = 2$. Therefore two independent solutions of the homogeneous equation are $y_1 = e^x$ and $y_2 = e^{2x}$, and the complementary function is

$$y_h = C_1 e^x + C_2 e^{2x}.$$

A particular solution $y_p(x)$ of the non-homogeneous equation can be found in the form

$$y_p = u_1(x)e^x + u_2(x)e^{2x}$$

where u_1 and u_2 satisfy

$$u_1' e^x + 2u_2' e^{2x} = 4x$$
$$u_1' e^x + u_2' e^{2x} = 0.$$

We solve these linear equations for u_1' and u_2' and then integrate to obtain

$$u_1' = -4xe^{-x} \qquad\qquad u_2' = 4xe^{-2x}$$
$$u_1 = 4(x+1)e^{-x} \qquad u_2 = -(2x+1)e^{-2x}.$$

Hence $y_p = 4x + 4 - (2x+1) = 2x + 3$ is a particular solution of the non-homogeneous equation, and the general solution is

$$y = 2x + 3 + C_1 e^x + C_2 e^{2x}.$$

REMARK: We could have found y_p more easily had we "guessed" that it would be of the form $y_p = Ax + B$ and substituted this into the differential equation to get

$$-3A + 2(Ax + B) = 4x$$
$$\text{or} \quad 2Ax + (2B - 3A) = 4x.$$

The only way this latter equation can be satisfied for all x is to have $2A = 4$ and $2B - 3A = 0$, that is, $A = 2$ and $B = 3$. For constant coefficient equations it is frequently easy to guess the correct form of a particular solution given the nature of the non-homogeneous term $f(x)$.

Series Solutions

Many of the second order, linear, differential equations which arise in applications do not have constant coefficients and are not Euler equations. If the coefficient functions of such an equation are sufficiently well behaved we can often find solutions in the form of power series (Taylor series). Such series solutions are frequently used to define new functions, whose properties are deduced partly from the fact that they solve particular differential equations. For example, Bessel functions of order ν are defined to be certain series solutions of Bessel's differential equation

$$x^2 y'' + xy' + (x^2 - \nu^2)y = 0.$$

Series solutions for second order homogeneous linear differential equations are most easily found near an **ordinary point** of the equation. This is a point $x = a$ such that the equation can be expressed in the form

$$y'' + p(x)y' + q(x)y = 0$$

where the functions $p(x)$ and $q(x)$ are **analytic** at $x = a$. (A function f is analytic at $x = a$ if $f(x)$ can be expressed as the sum of its Taylor series in powers of $x - a$ in an interval of positive radius centred at $x = a$.) Thus we assume

$$p(x) = \sum_{n=0}^{\infty} p_n(x - a)^n, \qquad q(x) = \sum_{n=0}^{\infty} q_n(x - a)^n$$

with both series converging in some interval of the form $a - R < x < a + R$. Frequently $p(x)$ and $q(x)$ are polynomials and so are analytic everywhere. A change of independent variable $\xi = x - a$ will put the point $x = a$ at the origin $\xi = 0$, so we may assume that $a = 0$.

The following example illustrates the technique of series solution around an ordinary point.

EXAMPLE A4.13   Find two independent solutions in powers of x for the Hermite equation

$$y'' - 2xy' + \nu y = 0.$$

For what values of ν does the equation have a polynomial solution?

SOLUTION   We try

$$y = \sum_{n=0}^{\infty} a_n x^n = a_0 + a_1 x + a_2 x^2 + a_3 x^3 + \cdots$$

$$y' = \sum_{n=1}^{\infty} n a_n x^{n-1}$$

$$y'' = \sum_{n=2}^{\infty} n(n-1)a_n x^{n-2} = \sum_{n=0}^{\infty} (n+2)(n+1)a_{n+2} x^n.$$

(We have replaced n by $n + 2$ in order to get x^n in the sum for y''.) We substitute these expressions into the differential equation to get

$$\sum_{n=0}^{\infty}(n+2)(n+1)a_{n+2}x^n - 2\sum_{n=1}^{\infty} n a_n x^n + \nu \sum_{n=0}^{\infty} a_n x^n = 0$$

or $2a_2 + \nu a_0 + \sum_{n=1}^{\infty} \Big[(n+2)(n+1)a_{n+2} - (2n - \nu)a_n \Big] x^n = 0.$

This identity holds for all x provided that the coefficient of every power of x vanishes; that is

$$a_2 = -\frac{\nu a_0}{2}, \qquad a_{n+2} = \frac{(2n - \nu)a_n}{(n+2)(n+1)}, \qquad (n = 1, 2, \cdots).$$

The latter of these formulas is called a **recurrence relation**.

We may choose a_0 and a_1 to have any values; then the above conditions determine all the remaining coefficients a_n, $(n \geq 2)$. We can get one solution by choosing, for instance, $a_0 = 1$ and $a_1 = 0$. Then

$$a_3 = 0, \quad a_5 = 0, \quad a_7 = 0, \quad \cdots, \qquad \text{and}$$

$$a_2 = -\frac{\nu}{2}$$

$$a_4 = \frac{(4 - \nu)a_2}{4 \times 3} = -\frac{\nu(4 - \nu)}{2 \times 3 \times 4} = -\frac{\nu(4 - \nu)}{4!}$$

$$a_6 = \frac{(8 - \nu)a_4}{6 \times 5} = -\frac{\nu(4 - \nu)(8 - \nu)}{6!}$$

$$\cdots$$

The pattern is obvious here:

$$a_{2n} = -\frac{\nu(4 - \nu)(8 - \nu) \cdots (4n - 4 - \nu)}{(2n)!}, \qquad (n = 1, 2, \cdots).$$

One solution to the Hermite equation is

$$y_1 = 1 + \sum_{n=1}^{\infty} -\frac{\nu(4 - \nu)(8 - \nu) \cdots (4n - 4 - \nu)}{(2n)!} x^{2n}.$$

We observe that if $\nu = 4n$ for some nonnegative integer n then y_1 is an even polynomial of degree $2n$, for $a_{2n+2} = 0$ and all subsequent even coefficients therefore also vanish.

The second solution, y_2, can be found in the same way, by choosing $a_0 = 0$ and $a_1 = 1$. It is

$$y_2 = x + \sum_{n=1}^{\infty} \frac{(2 - \nu)(6 - \nu) \cdots (4n - 2 - \nu)}{(2n + 1)!} x^{2n+1},$$

and is an odd polynomial of degree $2n + 1$ if $\nu = 4n + 2$.

If $x = a$ is not an ordinary point of the equation

$$y'' + p(x)y' + q(x)y = 0$$

then it is called a **singular point** of that equation. This means that at least one of the functions $p(x)$ and $q(x)$ is not analytic at $x = a$. If, however, $(x - a)p(x)$ and $(x - a)^2 q(x)$ are analytic at $x = a$ then the singular point is said to be a **regular singular point**. For example, the origin $x = 0$ is a regular singular point of any Euler equation, and also of Bessel's equation,

$$x^2 y'' + xy' + (x^2 - \nu^2)y = 0,$$

since $p(x) = 1/x$ and $q(x) = (x^2 - \nu^2)/x^2$ are such that $xp(x) = 1$ and $x^2q(x) = x^2 - \nu^2$ are both polynomials, and therefore analytic.

The solutions of differential equations are usually not analytic at singular points. However, it is still possible to find at least one series solution about such a point. The method involves searching for a series solution of the form x^μ times a power series, that is,

$$y = \sum_{n=0}^{\infty} a_n (x - a)^{n+\mu}, \qquad \text{where } a_0 \neq 0.$$

Substitution into the differential equation produces a quadratic **indicial equation**, which determines one or two values of μ for which such solutions can be found, and a **recurrence relation** enabling the coefficients a_n to be calculated for $n \geq 1$. If the indicial roots are not equal, and do not differ by an integer, two independent solutions can be calculated. If the indicial roots are equal, or differ by an integer, one such solution can be calculated (corresponding to the larger indicial root), and a second solution can be found by using the technique suggested early in this appendix. These calculations can be quite difficult. The reader is referred to standard texts on differential equations for more discussion and examples. We content ourselves with one final example.

EXAMPLE A4.14   Find one solution, in powers of x, of Bessel's equation with $\nu = 1$,

$$x^2 y'' + xy' + (x^2 - 1)y = 0.$$

SOLUTION   We try

$$y = \sum_{n=0}^{\infty} a_n x^{\mu+n}$$

$$y' = \sum_{n=0}^{\infty} (\mu + n) a_n x^{\mu+n-1}$$

$$y'' = \sum_{n=0}^{\infty} (\mu + n)(\mu + n - 1) a_n x^{\mu+n-2}.$$

Substituting these expressions into the Bessel equation, we get

$$\sum_{n=0}^{\infty} \left[\big((\mu + n)(\mu + n - 1) + (\mu + n) - 1 \big) a_n x^n + a_n x^{n+2} \right] = 0$$

$$\sum_{n=0}^{\infty} \left[(\mu + n)^2 - 1 \right] a_n x^n + \sum_{n=2}^{\infty} a_{n-2} x^n = 0$$

$$(\mu^2 - 1) a_0 + \big((\mu + 1)^2 - 1 \big) a_1 x + \sum_{n=2}^{\infty} \left[\big((\mu + n)^2 - 1 \big) a_n + a_{n-2} \right] x^n = 0.$$

All of the terms must vanish. Since $a_0 \neq 0$ (we may take $a_0 = 1$) we obtain

$$\mu^2 - 1 = 0, \qquad \text{the indicial equation}$$
$$[(\mu + 1)^2 - 1]a_1 = 0,$$
$$a_n = -\frac{a_{n-2}}{(\mu + n)^2 - 1}, \quad (n \geq 2). \qquad \text{the recurrence relation}$$

Evidently $\mu = \pm 1$, and therefore $a_1 = 0$. If we take $\mu = 1$, then the recurrence relation is $a_n = -a_{n-2}/(n)(n + 2)$. Thus

$$a_3 = 0, \quad a_5 = 0, \quad a_7 = 0, \quad \cdots$$

$$a_2 = \frac{-1}{2 \times 4}, \quad a_4 = \frac{1}{2 \times 4 \times 4 \times 6}, \quad a_6 = \frac{-1}{2 \times 4 \times 4 \times 6 \times 6 \times 8}, \quad \cdots.$$

Again the pattern is obvious:

$$a_{2n} = \frac{(-1)^n}{2^{2n}n!(n+1)!}$$

and one solution of the Bessel equation of order 1 is

$$y = \sum_{n=0}^{\infty} \frac{(-1)^n}{2^{2n}n!(n+1)!} x^{2n+1}.$$

REMARK: Observe that if we tried to calculate a second solution using $\mu = -1$ we would get the recurrence relation

$$a_n = -\frac{a_{n-2}}{n(n-2)},$$

and we would be unable to calculate a_2. This shows what can happen if the indicial roots differ by an integer.

EXERCISES

In Exercises 1–16 solve the given first order differential equations.

In Exercises 1–22 find general solutions of the given second order differential equations.

1. $y'' + (y')^2 = 0$

2. $xy'' = (1 - 2x^2)y'$

3. $(x + 1)y'' = y'$

4. $yy'' + 2(y')^2 = 0$

5. $yy'' = (y')^2 \ln y'$

6. $y'' = (y')^2 \tan y$

7. $y'' + 7y' + 10y = 0$

8. $y'' - 2y' - 3y = 0$

9. $y'' + 2y' = 0$

10. $4y'' - 4y' - 3y = 0$

11. $y'' + 8y' + 16y = 0$

12. $y'' - 2y' + y = 0$

13. $y'' - 6y' + 10y = 0$

14. $9y'' + 6y' + y = 0$

15. $y'' + 2y' + 5y = 0$

16. $y'' - 4y' + 5y = 0$

17. $y'' + 2y' + 3y = 0$

18. $y'' + y' + y = 0$

19. $x^2y'' - 4xy' + 6y = 0$

20. $xy'' + y' = 0$

21. $4x^2y'' + y = 0$

22. $x^2y'' + 4xy' + 9y = 0$

Solve the initial-value problems in Exercises 23–26.

23. $y'' + \omega^2 y = 0, \qquad y(0) = 3, \qquad y'(0) = -2$

24. $y'' + 2y' + 10y = 0, \qquad y(0) = 1, \qquad y'(0) = 0$

25. $xy'' + y' = 0, \qquad y(-1) = 1, \qquad y'(-1) = 2$

26. $y^2 y'' = y', \qquad y(2) = 1, \qquad y'(2) = -1$

27. *Prove that the solution given in the discussion of Case I, namely $y = A e^{r_1 t} + B e^{r_2 t}$, is the general solution for that case as follows: first let $y = e^{r_1 t} u$ and show that u satisfies the equation

$$u'' - (r_2 - r_1)u' = 0.$$

Then let $v = u'$, so that v must satisfy $v' = (r_2 - r_1)v$. The general solution of this equation is $v = C e^{(r_2 - r_1)t}$. Hence find u and y.

28. Show that $y = x$ is a solution of the differential equation $x^2 y'' - x(x+2)y' + (x+2)y = 0$ and find the general solution of that equation.

29. Show that $y = x^{-1/2} \cos x$ is a solution of the Bessel equation with $\nu = 1/2$:

$$x^2 y'' + xy' + \left(x^2 - \frac{1}{4}\right) y = 0.$$

Find the general solution of this equation.

Find general solutions for the non-homogeneous equations in Exercises 30–33 by the method of variation of parameters.

30. $y'' + y' - 2y = 1$

31. $y'' + y' - 2y = x$

32. $y'' + y' - 2y = e^{-x}$

33. $y'' + y' - 2y = e^x$

34. Show that $y'' - 2y' + y = e^{2x}$ has a solution of the form $y = Ce^{2x}$, and find the value of C.

35. Show that $y'' - 2y' + y = e^x$ has a solution of the form $y = Cx^2 e^x$ and find C. Does the equation have a solution of the form $y = Ae^x$? of the form $y = Bxe^x$? Why?

In Exercises 36–41 try to find a particular solution of the given equation by guessing its form as a sum of one or more terms with coefficients to be determined by substitution into the equation.

36. $y'' + 4y = x^2$

37. $y'' + 2y' + 5y = x^2 + e^x$

38. $y'' + 4y = \sin x$

39. $y'' + 4y = \sin 2x$

40. $y'' + 2y' + 5y = \sin 2x$

41. $y'' + 2y' + 5y = e^{-x} \sin 2x$

42. Find the general solution of $y'' = xy$ in the form of a power series $y = \sum_{n=0}^{\infty} a_n x^n$ with a_0 and a_1 arbitrary.

43. Find the general solution of $y'' = (x-1)^2 y$ in the form of a power series $y = \sum_{n=0}^{\infty} a_n (x-1)^n$.

44. Find the solution, in powers of x, for the initial-value problem

$$(1 - x^2)y'' - xy' + 9y = 0, \quad y(0) = 0, \quad y'(0) = 1.$$

45. Find the first three nonzero terms in a power series solution in powers of x for the initial-value problem $y'' + (\sin x)y = 0, y(0) = 1, y'(0) = 0$.

46. Find one power series solution for the Bessel equation with $\nu = 0$, that is, the equation $xy'' + y' + xy = 0$.

47. Find two power series solutions in powers of x for $3xy'' + 2y' + y = 0$.

ANSWERS TO ODD-NUMBERED EXERCISES

CHAPTER 1. COORDINATE GEOMETRY AND VECTORS IN 3-SPACE

Section 1.1   (page 5)

1. 3 units

3. $\sqrt{6}$ units

5. $|z|$ units; $\sqrt{y^2 + z^2}$ units

7. $\sqrt{3}/2$ sq. units

9. $\sqrt{n-1}$ units

11. the half-space containing the origin and bounded by the plane passing through $(0, -1, 0)$ perpendicular to the y-axis.

13. the vertical plane (parallel to the z-axis) passing through $(1, 0, 0)$ and $(0, 1, 0)$.

15. the sphere of radius 2 centred at $(1, -2, 3)$.

17. the solid circular cylinder of radius 2 with axis along the z-axis.

19. the parabolic cylinder generated by translating the parabola $z = y^2$ in the yz-plane in the direction of the x-axis .

21. the plane through the points $(1, 0, 0)$, $(0, 1, 0)$ and $(0, 0, 1)$.

23. the straight line through $(1, 0, 0)$ and $(1, 1, 1)$.

25. the circle in which the sphere of radius 2 centred at the origin intersects the sphere of radius 2 with centre $(2, 0, 0)$.

27. the ellipse in which the plane $z = x$ intersects the circular cylinder of radius 1 and axis along the z-axis.

29. the part of the solid circular cylinder of radius 1 and axis along the z-axis lying above or on the plane $z = y$.

31. the part of the solid ball of radius 1 centred at the origin which lies above or on the parabolic cylinder $z = x^2$.

Section 1.2   (page 11)

1. a) $6\mathbf{i} - 10\mathbf{k}$, $8\mathbf{j}$, $-3\mathbf{i} + 20\mathbf{j} + 5\mathbf{k}$
   b) $5\sqrt{2}$, $5\sqrt{2}$
   c) $\frac{3}{5\sqrt{2}}\mathbf{i} \pm \frac{4}{5\sqrt{2}}\mathbf{j} - \frac{1}{\sqrt{2}}\mathbf{k}$ d) 18
   e) $\cos^{-1}(9/25) \approx 68.9°$ f) $18/5\sqrt{2}$
   g) $(27/25)\mathbf{i} + (36/25)\mathbf{j} - (9/5)\mathbf{k}$

3. a) $3\mathbf{i} - 3\mathbf{k}$, $-\mathbf{i} - 4\mathbf{j} + 3\mathbf{k}$, $-4\mathbf{i} - 10\mathbf{j} + 9\mathbf{k}$
   b) $\sqrt{5}$, $\sqrt{17}$
   c) $\frac{1}{\sqrt{5}}\mathbf{i} - \frac{2}{\sqrt{5}}\mathbf{j}$, $\frac{2}{\sqrt{17}}\mathbf{i} + \frac{2}{\sqrt{17}}\mathbf{j} - \frac{3}{\sqrt{17}}\mathbf{k}$ d) -2
   e) $\cos^{-1}(-2/\sqrt{85}) \approx 102.5°$ f) $-2/\sqrt{17}$
   g) $-(2/5)\mathbf{i} + (4/5)\mathbf{j}$

5. head at angle θ to the east of AC, where $\theta = \sin^{-1}\dfrac{3}{2\sqrt{1 + 4k^2}}$.
   The trip not possible if $k < \frac{1}{4}\sqrt{5}$. If $k > \frac{1}{4}\sqrt{5}$ there is a second possible heading, $\pi - \theta$, but the trip will take longer.

7. from southwest at $50\sqrt{2}$ km/h.

9. $\cos^{-1}(2/\sqrt{6}) \approx 35.26°$, $90°$

11. $(\mathbf{i} + \mathbf{j} + \mathbf{k})/\sqrt{3}$

15. $(|\mathbf{u}|\mathbf{v} + |\mathbf{v}|\mathbf{u})/\big||\mathbf{u}|\mathbf{v} + |\mathbf{v}|\mathbf{u}\big|$

Section 1.3 (page 17)

1. $5\mathbf{i} + 13\mathbf{j} + 7\mathbf{k}$ **3.** $\sqrt{6}$ sq. units

5. $\pm\frac{1}{3}(2\mathbf{i} - 2\mathbf{j} + \mathbf{k})$ **9.** $4/3$ cubic units

11. They are coplanar.

15. $\mathbf{u} \times (\mathbf{v} \times \mathbf{w}) = -2\mathbf{i} + 7\mathbf{j} - 4\mathbf{k}$, $(\mathbf{u} \times \mathbf{v}) \times \mathbf{w} = \mathbf{i} + 9\mathbf{j} + 9\mathbf{k}$;
the first is in the plane of $\mathbf{v}$ and $\mathbf{w}$, the second is in the plane of $\mathbf{u}$ and $\mathbf{v}$.

Section 1.4 (page 29)

1. a) $x^2 + y^2 + z^2 = z^2$;   b) $x + y + z = x + y + z$;
c) $x^2 + y^2 + z^2 = -1$

3. $x - y + 2z = 0$ **5.** $7x + 5y - z = 12$

7. $x - 5y - 3z = -7$ **9.** $x + 6y - 5z = 17$

11. $(\mathbf{r}_1 - \mathbf{r}_2) \bullet [(\mathbf{r}_1 - \mathbf{r}_3) \times (\mathbf{r}_1 - \mathbf{r}_4)] = 0$

13. planes passing through the line $x = 0$, $y + z = 1$ (except the plane $y + z = 1$ itself)

15. $\mathbf{r} = (1 + 2t)\mathbf{i} + (2 - 3t)\mathbf{j} + (3 - 4t)\mathbf{k}$, $(-\infty < t < \infty)$
$x = 1 + 2t$, $y = 2 - 3t$, $z = 3 - 4t$, $(-\infty < t < \infty)$
$\dfrac{x - 1}{2} = \dfrac{y - 2}{-3} = \dfrac{z - 3}{-4}$

17. $\mathbf{r} = t(7\mathbf{i} - 6\mathbf{j} - 5\mathbf{k})$; $x = 7t$, $y = -6t$, $z = -5t$; $x/7 = -y/6 = -z/5$

19. $\mathbf{r} = \mathbf{i} + 2\mathbf{j} - \mathbf{k} + t(\mathbf{i} + \mathbf{j} + \mathbf{k})$;
$x = 1 + t$, $y = 2 + t$, $z = -1 + t$;
$x - 1 = y - 2 = z + 1$

21. $\dfrac{x - 4}{-5} = \dfrac{y}{3}$, $z = 7$

23. $\mathbf{r}_i \neq \mathbf{r}_j$, $(i, j = 1, \cdots, 4,\ i \neq j)$,
$\mathbf{v} = (\mathbf{r}_1 - \mathbf{r}_2) \times (\mathbf{r}_3 - \mathbf{r}_4) \neq 0$, $(\mathbf{r}_1 - \mathbf{r}_3) \bullet \mathbf{v} = 0$.

25. $7\sqrt{2}/10$ units   **27.** $18/\sqrt{69}$ units

29. all lines parallel to the xy-plane and passing through (x_0, y_0, z_0).

31. (x, y, z) satisfies the quadratic if either $A_1 x + B_1 y + C_1 z = D_1$ or $A_2 x + B_2 y + C_2 z = D_2$.

33. ellipsoid centred at the origin with semiaxes 6, 3 and 2 along the x-, y- and z-axes respectively.

35. elliptic paraboloid with vertex at the origin, axis along the z-axis, and cross-section $x^2 + 2y^2 = 1$ in the plane $z = 1$.

37. hyperboloid of two sheets with vertices $(\pm 2, 0, 0)$ and circular cross-sections in planes $x = c$, $(c^2 > 4)$.

39. hyperbolic paraboloid — same as $z = x^2 - y^2$ but rotated $45°$ about the z-axis (counterclockwise as seen from above).

41. hyperbolic cylinder parallel to the y-axis, intersecting the xz-plane in the hyperbola $(x^2/4) - z^2 = 1$.

43. parabolic cylinder parallel to the y-axis.

45. circular cone with vertex $(2, 3, 1)$, vertical axis, and semi-vertical angle $45°$.

47. circle in the plane $x + y + z = 1$ having centre $(1/3, 1/3, 1/3)$ and radius $\sqrt{11/3}$.

49. a parabola in the plane $z = 1 + x$ having vertex at $(-1/2, 0, 1/2)$ and axis along the line $z = 1 + x$, $y = 0$.

51. $\dfrac{y}{b} - \dfrac{z}{c} = \lambda\left(1 - \dfrac{x}{a}\right)$, $\dfrac{y}{b} + \dfrac{z}{c} = \dfrac{1}{\lambda}\left(1 + \dfrac{x}{a}\right)$;
$\dfrac{y}{b} - \dfrac{z}{c} = \mu\left(1 + \dfrac{x}{a}\right)$, $\dfrac{y}{b} + \dfrac{z}{c} = \dfrac{1}{\mu}\left(1 - \dfrac{x}{a}\right)$

Section 1.5 (page 38)

1. $\begin{pmatrix} 6 & 7 \\ 5 & -3 \\ 1 & 1 \end{pmatrix}$ **3.** $\begin{pmatrix} aw + by & ax + bz \\ cw + dy & cx + dz \end{pmatrix}$

5. $\mathcal{A}\mathcal{A}^T = \begin{pmatrix} 4 & 3 & 2 & 1 \\ 3 & 3 & 2 & 1 \\ 2 & 2 & 2 & 1 \\ 1 & 1 & 1 & 1 \end{pmatrix}$ $\mathcal{A}^2 = \begin{pmatrix} 1 & 2 & 3 & 4 \\ 0 & 1 & 2 & 3 \\ 0 & 0 & 1 & 2 \\ 0 & 0 & 0 & 1 \end{pmatrix}$

7. 36   **15.** $\begin{pmatrix} 1 & -1 & 0 \\ 0 & 1 & -1 \\ 0 & 0 & 1 \end{pmatrix}$

17. $x = 1$, $y = 2$, $z = 3$

19. $x_1 = 1$, $x_2 = 2$, $x_3 = -1$, $x_4 = -2$

CHAPTER 2. PARTIAL DIFFERENTIATION

Section 2.1 (page 48)

1. all (x, y) with $x \neq y$ **3.** all (x, y) except $(0, 0)$

5. all (x, y) satisfying $4x^2 + 9y^2 \geq 36$

7. all (x, y) with $xy > -1$ **9.** all (x, y, z) except $(0, 0, 0)$

11. $z = f(x, y) = x$ **13.** $z = f(x, y) = y^2$

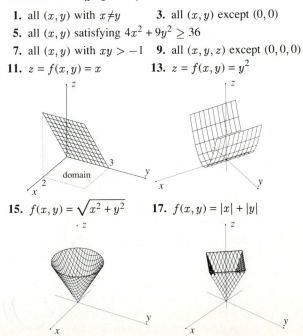

15. $f(x, y) = \sqrt{x^2 + y^2}$ **17.** $f(x, y) = |x| + |y|$

19. $f(x, y) = x - y = C$ **21.** $f(x, y) = xy = C$

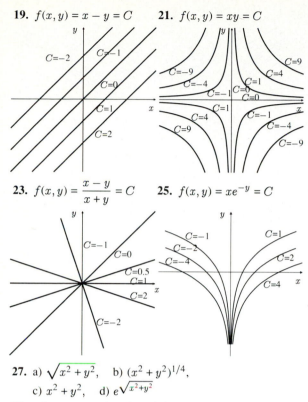

23. $f(x, y) = \dfrac{x - y}{x + y} = C$ **25.** $f(x, y) = xe^{-y} = C$

27. a) $\sqrt{x^2 + y^2}$,   b) $(x^2 + y^2)^{1/4}$,
     c) $x^2 + y^2$,   d) $e^{\sqrt{x^2 + y^2}}$

29. spheres centred at the origin

31. circular cylinders with axis along the z-axis

33. regular octahedra with vertices on the coordinate axes

35. 2   **37.** 0

39. does not exist   **41.** 0

43. $f(0, 0) = 1$

45. all (x, y) such that $x^2 \neq y^2$; no; yes; yes $f(x, x) = \dfrac{1}{2x}$; no.

Section 2.2   (page 56)

1. $f_1(x, y) = f_1(3, 2) = 1$, $f_2(x, y) = f_2(3, 2) = -1$

3. $f_1 = 3x^2y^4z^5$, $f_2 = 4x^3y^3z^5$, $f_3 = 5x^3y^4z^4$
    All three vanish at $(0, -1, -1)$.

5. $\dfrac{\partial z}{\partial x} = \dfrac{-y}{x^2 + y^2}$, $\dfrac{\partial z}{\partial y} = \dfrac{x}{x^2 + y^2}$,
    At $(-1, 1)$: $\dfrac{\partial z}{\partial x} = -\dfrac{1}{2}$, $\dfrac{\partial z}{\partial y} = -\dfrac{1}{2}$

7. $f_1 = \sqrt{y}\cos(x\sqrt{y})$, $f_2 = \dfrac{x\cos(x\sqrt{y})}{2\sqrt{y}}$,
    At $(\pi/3, 4)$: $f_1 = -1$, $f_2 = -\pi/24$

9. $\dfrac{\partial w}{\partial x} = y\ln z\, x^{(y\ln z - 1)}$, $\dfrac{\partial w}{\partial y} = \ln x\ln z\, x^{y\ln z}$,
    $\dfrac{\partial w}{\partial z} = \dfrac{y\ln x}{z}x^{y\ln z}$ At $(e, 2, e)$: $\dfrac{\partial w}{\partial x} = \dfrac{\partial w}{\partial z} =$
    $2e$, $\dfrac{\partial w}{\partial y} = e^2$.

11. $z = -4x - 2y - 3$; $\dfrac{x + 2}{-4} = \dfrac{y - 1}{-2} = \dfrac{z - 3}{-1}$

13. $z = \dfrac{1}{\sqrt{2}}\left(1 - \dfrac{x - \pi}{4} + \dfrac{\pi}{16}(y - 4)\right)$;
    $\dfrac{x - \pi}{-1/4\sqrt{2}} = \dfrac{y - 4}{\pi/16\sqrt{2}} = \dfrac{z - 1/\sqrt{2}}{-1}$

15. $z = \dfrac{2}{5} + \dfrac{3x}{25} - \dfrac{4y}{25}$; $\dfrac{x - 1}{3} = \dfrac{y - 2}{-4} = \dfrac{z - 1/5}{-25}$

17. $z = \ln 5 + \frac{2}{5}(x - 1) - \frac{4}{5}(y + 2)$;
    $\dfrac{x - 1}{2/5} = \dfrac{y + 2}{-4/5} = \dfrac{z - \ln 5}{-1}$

19. $z = \dfrac{x + y}{2} - \dfrac{\pi}{4}$; $2(x - 1) = 2(y + 1) = -z - \dfrac{\pi}{4}$

21. $(0, 0)$, $(1, 1)$, $(-1, -1)$

31. $\sqrt{7}/4$ units

Section 2.3   (page 61)

1. $\dfrac{\partial^2 z}{\partial x^2} = 2(1 + y^2)$, $\dfrac{\partial^2 z}{\partial x\partial y} = 4xy$, $\dfrac{\partial^2 z}{\partial y^2} = 2x^2$

3. $\dfrac{\partial^2 w}{\partial x^2} = 6xy^3z^3$, $\dfrac{\partial^2 w}{\partial y^2} = 6x^3yz^3$,
    $\dfrac{\partial^2 w}{\partial z^2} = 6x^3y^3z$, $\dfrac{\partial^2 w}{\partial x\partial y} = 9x^2y^2z^3$,
    $\dfrac{\partial^2 w}{\partial x\partial z} = 9x^2y^3z^2$, $\dfrac{\partial^2 w}{\partial y\partial z} = 9x^3y^2z^2$

5. $\dfrac{\partial^2 z}{\partial x^2} = -ye^x$, $\dfrac{\partial^2 z}{\partial x\partial y} = e^y - e^x$, $\dfrac{\partial^2 z}{\partial y^2} = xe^y$

7. 24, 7, $x^2e^{xy}\left(xz\sin xz - (3 + xy)\cos xz\right)$

17. $u(x, y, z, t) = t^{-3/2}e^{-(x^2 + y^2 + z^2)/4t}$

Section 2.4   (page 71)

1. $\dfrac{\partial w}{\partial t} = f_1g_2 + f_2h_2 + f_3k_2$

3. $\dfrac{\partial z}{\partial u} = g_1h_1 + g_2f'h_1$

5. $\dfrac{\partial w}{\partial x}\Big|_z = f_1 + f_2g_1$

7. $\dfrac{dw}{dz} = f_1g_1h' + f_1g_2 + f_2h' + f_3$,
    $\dfrac{\partial w}{\partial z}\Big|_x = f_2h' + f_3$,
    $\dfrac{\partial w}{\partial z}\Big|_{x,y} = f_3$

9. $\dfrac{\partial z}{\partial x} = \dfrac{-5y}{13x^2 - 2xy + 2y^2}$

11. $2f_1(2x, 3y)$ **13.** $2x\, f_2(y^2, x^2)$

15. $f_1(x, y)\Big(f_1\big(f(x, y), f(x, y)\big) + f_2\big(f(x, y), f(x, y)\big)\Big)$

17. $dT/dt = e^{-t}\big(f'(t) - f(t)\big)$; $dT/dt = 0$ if $f(t) = e^t$: in this case the decrease in T with time (at fixed depth) is exactly balanced by the increase in T with depth.

19. $4f_{11} + 12f_{12} + 9f_{22}$, $6f_{11} + 5f_{12} - 6f_{22}$, $9f_{11} - 12f_{12} + 4f_{22}$

23. $f_1 \cos s - f_2 \sin s + f_{11}\, t \cos s \sin s + f_{12}\, t(\cos^2 s - \sin^2 s) - f_{22}\, t \sin s \cos s$

25. $f_2 + 2y^2 f_{12} + xy f_{22} - 4xy f_{31} - 2x^2 f_{32}$; all derivatives at $(y^2, xy, -x^2)$

29. $\displaystyle\sum_{i,j=1}^{n} x_i\, x_j\, f_{ij}(x_1, \cdots, x_n) = k(k-1)\, f(x_1, \cdots, x_n)$

31. $u(x, y) = f(x + ct)$

Section 2.5   (page 78)

1. 6.9   **3.** 0.0814

5. 2.967   **7.** decreases by approx 4%

Section 2.6   (page 87)

1. $4\mathbf{i} + 2\mathbf{j}$; $z = 4x + 2y - 3$; $2x + y = 3$

3. $(-\mathbf{i} + (\pi/4)\mathbf{j})/4\sqrt{2}$; $4x - \pi y + 16\sqrt{2}z = 16$; $4x - \pi y = 0$

5. $(3\mathbf{i} - 4\mathbf{j})/25$; $3x - 4y - 25z + 10 = 0$; $3x - 4y + 5 = 0$

7. $(2\mathbf{i} - 4\mathbf{j})/5$; $2x - 4y - 5z = 10 - 5\ln 5$; $x - 2y = 5$

9. $x + y - 3z = -3$ **11.** $\sqrt{3}y + z = \sqrt{3} + \pi/3$

13. $\dfrac{4}{\sqrt{5}}$ **15.** $1 - 2\sqrt{3}$

17. $\dfrac{-61}{144\sqrt{3}}$

21. in directions making angles $-30°$ or $-150°$ with positive x-axis; no; $-\mathbf{j}$.

23. $7\mathbf{i} - \mathbf{j}$

25. a)

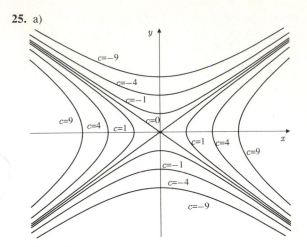

25. b) in direction $-\mathbf{i} - \mathbf{j}$
     c) $4\sqrt{2}k$ deg/unit time
     d) $12k/\sqrt{5}$ deg/unit time
     e) $x^2 y = -4$

27. $3x^2 - 2y^2 = 10$ **29.** $-4/3$

31. $\mathbf{i} - 2\mathbf{j} + \mathbf{k}$

37. $D_{\mathbf{v}}(D_{\mathbf{v}}f) = v_1^2 f_{11} + v_2^2 f_{22} + v_3^2 f_{33} + 2v_1 v_2 f_{12} + 2v_1 v_3 f_{13} + 2v_2 v_3 f_{23}$. This is the second derivative of f as measured by an observer moving with velocity $\mathbf{v}$.

39. $\dfrac{\partial^2 T}{\partial t^2} + 2D_{\mathbf{v}(t)}\left(\dfrac{\partial T}{\partial t}\right) + D_{\mathbf{a}(t)}T + D_{\mathbf{v}(t)}(D_{\mathbf{v}(t)}T)$

Section 2.7   (page 98)

1. $-\dfrac{x^4 + 3xy^2}{y^3 + 4x^3 y}$, $y \neq 0$, $y^2 \neq -4x^3$

3. $\dfrac{3xy^4 + xz}{xy - 2y^2 z}$, $y \neq 0$, $x \neq 2yz$

5. $\dfrac{x - 2t^2 w}{2xy^2 - w}$, $w \neq 2xy^2$

7. $-\dfrac{\partial G/\partial x}{\partial G/\partial u}$, $\dfrac{\partial G}{\partial u} \neq 0$

9. $-\dfrac{v^2 H_2 + w H_3}{u^2 H_1 + t H_3}$, $u^2 H_1 + t H_3 \neq 0$, all derivatives at $(u^2 w, v^2 t, wt)$

11. $\dfrac{2w - 4y}{4x - w}$, $4x \neq w$

13. $\dfrac{1}{6}, \dfrac{1}{2}, \dfrac{1}{6}, -\dfrac{1}{2}, -\dfrac{1}{6}$

15. r; all points except the origin

17. $-\dfrac{\partial(F, G, H)}{\partial(y, z, w)} \Big/ \dfrac{\partial(F, G, H)}{\partial(x, z, w)}$

19. $15;$ $-\dfrac{\partial(F,G,H)}{\partial(x_2,x_3,x_5)} \Big/ \dfrac{\partial(F,G,H)}{\partial(x_1,x_3,x_5)}$

21. $2(u+v),$ $-2,$ 0

Section 2.8   (page 104)

1. $\displaystyle\sum_{n=0}^{\infty}(-1)^n \frac{x^n y^{2n}}{2^{n+1}}$

3. $\displaystyle\sum_{n=0}^{\infty}(-1)^n \frac{x^{2n+1}(y+1)^{2n+1}}{2n+1}$

5. $\displaystyle\sum_{n=0}^{\infty}\sum_{k=0}^{n}\frac{1}{k!(n-k)!}\,x^{2k}y^{2n-2k}$

7. $\frac{1}{2}-\frac{1}{4}(x-2)+\frac{1}{2}(y-1)+\frac{1}{8}(x-2)^2$
$-\frac{1}{2}(x-2)(y-1)+\frac{1}{2}(y-1)^2-\frac{1}{16}(x-2)^3$
$+\frac{3}{8}(x-2)^2(y-1)-\frac{3}{4}(x-2)(y-1)^2+\frac{1}{2}(y-1)^3$

9. $x+y^2-\dfrac{x^3}{3}$

11. $1-(y-1)+(y-1)^2-\dfrac{1}{2}\left(x-\dfrac{\pi}{2}\right)^2$

13. $-x-x^2-(5/6)x^3$

15. $1-x^2-\dfrac{1}{2}x^4$

17. $-\dfrac{x}{3}-\dfrac{2y}{3}-\dfrac{2x^2}{27}-\dfrac{8xy}{27}-\dfrac{8y^2}{27}$

19. $\dfrac{[(2n)!]^3}{(n!)^2}$

CHAPTER 3. APPLICATIONS OF PARTIAL DERIVATIVES

Section 3.1   (page 117)

1. bdry $(0,0)$ and $x^2+y^2=1$; interior$=S$; S open and bounded

3. bdry of S is S; interior empty; S is closed and unbounded

5. $(2,-1)$, loc. (abs) min.

7. $(0,0)$, saddle pt; $(1,1)$, loc. min.

9. $(-4,2)$, loc. max.

11. $(0,n\pi)$, $n=0,\pm1,\pm2,\cdots$, all saddle points

13. $(0,a)$, $(a>0)$, loc min; $(0,a)$, $(a<0)$, loc max; $(0,0)$ saddle point; $(\pm1,1/\sqrt{2})$, loc. (abs) max; $(\pm1,-1/\sqrt{2})$, loc. (abs) min.

15. $(3^{-1/3},0)$, saddle pt.

17. $(-1,-1)$, $(1,-1)$, $(-1,1)$, saddle pts; $(-3,-3)$, loc. min.

19. $(1,1,\frac{1}{2})$, saddle pt.

21. $(0,0)$, saddle pt; $(\frac{1}{\sqrt2},\frac{1}{\sqrt2})$, $(-\frac{1}{\sqrt2},-\frac{1}{\sqrt2})$, loc. (abs) max; $(\frac{1}{\sqrt2},-\frac{1}{\sqrt2})$, $(-\frac{1}{\sqrt2},\frac{1}{\sqrt2})$, loc. (abs) min.

23. max $e^{-3/2}/2\sqrt2$, min $-e^{-3/2}/2\sqrt2$; f is continuous everywhere, and $f(x,y,z)\to 0$ as $x^2+y^2+z^2\to\infty$.

25. CPs are $(\sqrt{\ln 3},-\sqrt{\ln 3})$ and $(-\sqrt{\ln 3},\sqrt{\ln 3})$.

27. f does not have a local minimum at $(0,0)$; the Second Derivative Test is inconclusive $(B^2=AC)$.

29. $A>0$, $\begin{vmatrix} A & E \\ E & B \end{vmatrix}>0$, $\begin{vmatrix} A & E & F \\ E & B & H \\ F & H & C \end{vmatrix}>0$,
$\begin{vmatrix} A & E & F & G \\ E & B & H & I \\ F & H & C & J \\ G & I & J & D \end{vmatrix}>0$

Section 3.2   (page 123)

1. max $5/4$, min -2

3. max $(\sqrt2-1)/2$, min $-(\sqrt2+1)/2$.

5. max $2/3\sqrt3$, min 0

7. max 1, min -1 **9.** max $1/\sqrt e$, min $-1/\sqrt e$

11. no limit; yes, max $f=e^{-1}$ (at all points of the curve $xy=1$)

13. $\$625{,}000$, $\$733{,}333$ **15.** max $37/2$ at $(7/4,5)$

17. 6667 kg deluxe, 6667 kg standard

Section 3.3   (page 133)

3. 1 unit   **5.** max 4 units, min 2 units

7. $a=\pm\sqrt3$, $b=\pm2\sqrt3$, $c=\pm\sqrt3$

9. max 2, min -2 **11.** max 7, min -1

13. $\dfrac{2\sqrt6}{3}$ units   **15.** $\pm\sqrt{\dfrac{3n(n+1)}{2(2n+1)}}$

17. $\frac{1}{6}\times\frac{1}{3}\times\frac{2}{3}$

19. width $=\left(\dfrac{2V}{15}\right)^{1/3}$, depth $=3\times$width, height $=\dfrac{5}{2}\times$width

21. max 1, min $-\frac{1}{2}$

25. method will not fail if $\nabla f=\mathbf{0}$ at extreme point; but we will have $\lambda=0$.

Section 3.4   (page 141)

1. at $(\bar{x},\bar{y})$ where $\bar{x}=\left(\sum_{i=1}^{n}x_i\right)/n$, $\bar{y}=\left(\sum_{i=1}^{n}y_i\right)/n$

3. $a=\left(\displaystyle\sum_{i=1}^{n}y_i e^{x_i}\right)\Big/\left(\displaystyle\sum_{i=1}^{n}e^{2x_i}\right)$

5. If $A = \sum x_i{}^2$, $B = \sum x_i y_i$, $C = \sum x_i$, $D = \sum y_i{}^2$, $E = \sum y_i$, $F = \sum x_i z_i$, $G = \sum y_i z_i$, and $H = \sum z_i$, then

$$\Delta = \begin{vmatrix} A & B & C \\ B & D & E \\ C & E & n \end{vmatrix}, \qquad a = \frac{1}{\Delta}\begin{vmatrix} F & B & C \\ G & D & E \\ H & E & n \end{vmatrix},$$

$$b = \frac{1}{\Delta}\begin{vmatrix} A & F & C \\ B & G & E \\ C & H & n \end{vmatrix}, \qquad c = \frac{1}{\Delta}\begin{vmatrix} A & B & F \\ B & D & G \\ C & E & H \end{vmatrix}.$$

7. Use linear regression to fit $\eta = a + bx$ to the data $(x_i, \ln y_i)$. Then $p = e^a$, $q = b$. These are not the same values as would be obtained by minimizing the expression $\sum(y_i - pe^{qx_i})^2$.

9. Use linear regression to fit $\eta = a + b\xi$ to the data $\left(x_i, \dfrac{y_i}{x_i}\right)$. Then $p = a, q = b$. Not the same as minimizing $\sum(y_i - px_i - qx_i{}^2)^2$.

11. Use linear regression to fit $\eta = a + b\xi$ to the data $\left(e^{-2x_i}, \dfrac{y_i}{e^{x_i}}\right)$. Then $p = a, q = b$. Not the same as minimizing $\sum(y_i - pe^{x_i} - qe^{-x_i})^2$. Other answers possible.

13. If $A = \sum x_i{}^4$, $B = \sum x_i{}^3$, $C = \sum x_i{}^2$, $D = \sum x_i$, $H = \sum x_i{}^2 y_i$, $I = \sum x_i y_i$, and $J = \sum y_i$, then

$$\Delta = \begin{vmatrix} A & B & C \\ B & C & D \\ C & D & n \end{vmatrix}, \qquad a = \frac{1}{\Delta}\begin{vmatrix} H & B & C \\ I & C & D \\ J & D & n \end{vmatrix},$$

$$b = \frac{1}{\Delta}\begin{vmatrix} A & H & C \\ B & I & D \\ C & J & n \end{vmatrix}, \qquad c = \frac{1}{\Delta}\begin{vmatrix} A & B & H \\ B & C & I \\ C & D & J \end{vmatrix}.$$

15. $a = \dfrac{20}{\pi^5}(\pi^2 - 16)$, $b = \dfrac{12}{\pi^4}(20 - \pi^2)$

17. $a_k = \dfrac{2}{\pi}\displaystyle\int_0^\pi f(x) \cos kx\, dx$, $(k = 0, 1, 2, \cdots)$

19. $\pi - \dfrac{4}{\pi}\displaystyle\sum_{k=0}^\infty \dfrac{\cos((2k+1)x)}{(2k+1)^2}$; $-x$

Section 3.5 (page 150)

1. $\dfrac{(-1)^n n!}{(x+1)^{n+1}}$

3. $2\sqrt{\pi}(\sqrt{y} - \sqrt{x})$

5. $\dfrac{2x}{(1+x^2)^2}$; $\dfrac{(6x^2 - 2)}{(1+x^2)^3}$

7. $\dfrac{\pi}{2x}$, assume $x > 0$; $\dfrac{\pi}{4x^3}$; $\dfrac{3\pi}{16x^5}$

9. $n!$

11. $f(x) = \displaystyle\int_0^x e^{-t^2/2}\, dt$

13. $y = x^2$

15. $x^2 + y^2 = 1$

17. $y = x - \dfrac{1}{4}$

19. no

21. no; a line of singular points

23. $x^2 + y^2 + z^2 = 1$

25. $y = x - \epsilon \sin(\pi x) + \dfrac{\pi\epsilon^2}{2}\sin(2\pi x) + \cdots$

27. $y = \dfrac{1}{2} - \dfrac{2}{5}\epsilon x - \dfrac{16}{125}\epsilon^2 x^2 + \cdots$

29. $x \approx 1 - \dfrac{1}{100e} - \dfrac{1}{30000e^2}$, $y \approx 1 - \dfrac{1}{30000e^2}$

Section 3.6 (page 155)

1. $(0.797105, 2.219107)$

3. $(\pm 0.2500305, \pm 3.9995115)$, $(\pm 1.9920783, \pm 0.5019883)$

5. $(0.3727730, 0.3641994)$, $(-1.4141606, -0.9877577)$

7. $x = x_0 - \dfrac{\Delta_1}{\Delta}$, $y = y_0 - \dfrac{\Delta_2}{\Delta}$, $z = z_0 - \dfrac{\Delta_3}{\Delta}$, where $\Delta = \left.\dfrac{\partial(f,g,h)}{\partial(x,y,z)}\right|_{(x_0,y_0,z_0)}$
and Δ_i is Δ with the ith column replaced with $\begin{array}{c} f \\ g \\ h \end{array}$

9. 18 iterations near $(0,0)$, 4 iterations near $(1,1)$; the two curves are tangent at $(0,0)$, but not at $(1,1)$.

CHAPTER 4.   MULTIPLE INTEGRATION

Section 4.1 (page 169)

1. 20

3. 0

5. 5π

7. $\dfrac{\pi a^3}{3}$

9. $\dfrac{1}{6}$

11. $\dfrac{ab(a^2 + b^2)}{3}$

13. π

15. $\dfrac{3}{56}$

17. $\dfrac{33}{8}\ln 2 - \dfrac{45}{16}$

19. $\dfrac{e-2}{2}$

21. $\dfrac{1}{2}\left(1 - \dfrac{1}{e}\right)$; region is a triangle with vertices $(0,0)$, $(1,0)$ and $(1,1)$

23. $\dfrac{\pi}{4\lambda}$; region is a triangle with vertices $(0,0)$, $(0,1)$ and $(1,1)$

25. $\dfrac{\pi}{2\sqrt{2}}$ cu. units

27. $\dfrac{16a^3}{3}$ cu. units

Section 4.2 (page 174)

1. converges to 4

3. converges to $1 - \dfrac{1}{e}$

5. diverges to ∞

7. diverges to ∞

9. converges to $2\ln 2$

11. $k > a - 1$

13. $k < -1 - a$

15. $k > -\dfrac{1+a}{1+b}$ (provided $b > -1$)

17. $\dfrac{1}{2}, -\dfrac{1}{2}$ (different answers are possible because the *double integral* does not exist.)

19. $\dfrac{a^2}{3}$

21. $\dfrac{4\sqrt{2}a}{3\pi}$

Section 4.3 (page 185)

1. $\dfrac{(\sqrt{3}+1)a^3}{6}$

3. $\dfrac{1}{3}$

5. $\dfrac{2a}{3}$

7. $k < 1$; $\dfrac{\pi}{1-k}$

9. $\dfrac{a^4}{16}$

11. $\dfrac{2\pi}{3}$ cu. units

13. $\dfrac{4\pi(2\sqrt{2}-1)a^3}{3}$ cu. units

15. $\dfrac{64a^3}{9}$ cu. units

17. $16[1 - (1/\sqrt{2})]\,a^3$ cu. units

19. $1 - \dfrac{4\sqrt{2}}{3\pi}$ units

21. $\dfrac{4}{3}\pi abc$ cu. units

23. $2a\sinh a$

25. $\dfrac{3\ln 2}{2}$ sq. units

27. $\dfrac{1}{4}(e - e^{-1})$

Section 4.4 (page 191)

1. $8abc$

3. $2/3$

5. $1/15$

7. $2/(3\pi)$

9. $\dfrac{3}{16}\ln 2$

11. $\pi\sqrt{\dfrac{\pi}{6}}$

13. $\pi abc \left[\dfrac{2}{3} - \dfrac{b}{(b^2+c^2)^{1/2}} + \dfrac{b^3}{3(b^2+c^2)^{3/2}} \right]$ cu. units

15. $\displaystyle\int_0^1 dx \int_0^1 dy \int_0^{1-y} f(x,y,z)\,dz$

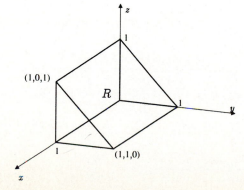

17. $\displaystyle\int_0^1 dx \int_0^x dy \int_0^{x-y} f(x,y,z)\,dz$

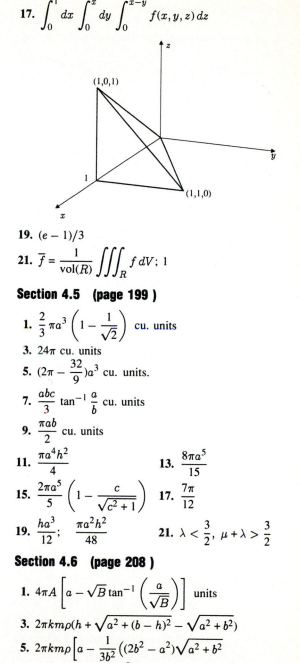

19. $(e-1)/3$

21. $\overline{f} = \dfrac{1}{\text{vol}(R)} \displaystyle\iiint_R f\,dV;\ 1$

Section 4.5 (page 199)

1. $\dfrac{2}{3}\pi a^3 \left(1 - \dfrac{1}{\sqrt{2}}\right)$ cu. units

3. 24π cu. units

5. $(2\pi - \dfrac{32}{9})a^3$ cu. units.

7. $\dfrac{abc}{3}\tan^{-1}\dfrac{a}{b}$ cu. units

9. $\dfrac{\pi ab}{2}$ cu. units

11. $\dfrac{\pi a^4 h^2}{4}$

13. $\dfrac{8\pi a^5}{15}$

15. $\dfrac{2\pi a^5}{5}\left(1 - \dfrac{c}{\sqrt{c^2+1}}\right)$

17. $\dfrac{7\pi}{12}$

19. $\dfrac{ha^3}{12};\quad \dfrac{\pi a^2 h^2}{48}$

21. $\lambda < \dfrac{3}{2},\ \mu + \lambda > \dfrac{3}{2}$

Section 4.6 (page 208)

1. $4\pi A\left[a - \sqrt{B}\tan^{-1}\left(\dfrac{a}{\sqrt{B}}\right)\right]$ units

3. $2\pi km\rho(h + \sqrt{a^2+(b-h)^2} - \sqrt{a^2+b^2})$

5. $2\pi km\rho\left[a - \dfrac{1}{3b^2}\left((2b^2-a^2)\sqrt{a^2+b^2}\right.\right.$
$\left.\left. -(2b+a)(b-a)^2\right)\right]$

7. $\left(\dfrac{1}{3}, \dfrac{1}{3}, \dfrac{1}{2}\right)$

9. $\left(\dfrac{3a}{8}, \dfrac{3a}{8}, \dfrac{3a}{8}\right)$

11. $\left(0, \dfrac{a}{4}, \dfrac{5a}{8}\right)$

13. The model still involves angular acceleration to spin the ball—it doesn't just fall. Part of the gravitational energy goes to producing this spin even in the limiting case.

15. $I = \pi\rho a^2 h \left(\dfrac{h^2}{3} + \dfrac{a^2}{4}\right)$, $\quad \bar{D} = \left(\dfrac{h^2}{3} + \dfrac{a^2}{4}\right)^{1/2}$

17. $I = \dfrac{\pi\rho a^2 h}{3}\left(\dfrac{2h^2 + 3a^2}{20}\right)$, $\quad \bar{D} = \left(\dfrac{2h^2 + 3a^2}{20}\right)^{1/2}$

19. $I = \dfrac{5a^5\rho}{12}$, $\quad \bar{D} = \sqrt{\dfrac{5}{12}}\,a$

21. $I = \dfrac{8}{3}\rho abc(a^2 + b^2)$, $\quad \bar{D} = \sqrt{\dfrac{a^2 + b^2}{3}}$

23. $m = \dfrac{4\pi}{3}\rho(a^2 - b^2)^{3/2}$, $\quad I = \dfrac{1}{5}m(2a^2 + 3b^2)$

25. $\dfrac{5a^2 g \sin\alpha}{7a^2 + 3b^2}$

29. The moment of inertia about the line $\mathbf{r}(t) = At\mathbf{i} + Bt\mathbf{j} + Ct\mathbf{k}$ is
$$\dfrac{1}{A^2 + B^2 + C^2}\Big((B^2 + C^2)P_{xx} + (A^2 + C^2)P_{yy} + (A^2 + B^2)P_{zz} - 2ABP_{xy} - 2ACP_{xz} - 2BCP_{yz}\Big).$$

CHAPTER 5.   CURVES

Section 5.1   (page 222)

1. $\mathbf{v} = 2t\mathbf{i} - 2t\mathbf{j}$, $v = 2\sqrt{2}t$, $\mathbf{a} = 2\mathbf{i} - 2\mathbf{j}$, path is the straight half-line $x + y = 0$, $z = 1$, $(x \geq 0)$

3. $\mathbf{v} = -a\sin t\mathbf{i} + a\cos t\mathbf{j} + c\mathbf{k}$, $v = \sqrt{a^2 + c^2}$, $\mathbf{a} = -a\cos t\mathbf{i} - a\sin t\mathbf{j}$, path is a circular helix

5. $\mathbf{a} = \mathbf{v} = \mathbf{r}$, $v = \sqrt{a^2 + b^2 + c^2}\,e^t$, path is the straight line $\dfrac{x}{a} = \dfrac{y}{b} = \dfrac{z}{c}$

7. $\mathbf{v} = -(e^{-t}\cos e^t + \sin e^t)\mathbf{i}$
$\quad +(-e^{-t}\sin e^t + \cos e^t)\mathbf{j} - e^t\mathbf{k}$
$v = \sqrt{1 + e^{-2t} + e^{2t}}$
$\mathbf{a} = [(e^{-t} - e^t)\cos e^t + \sin e^t]\mathbf{i}$
$\quad +[(e^{-t} - e^t)\sin e^t - \cos e^t]\mathbf{j} - e^t\mathbf{k}$
The path is a spiral lying on the surface $z = -1/\sqrt{x^2 + y^2}$

9. $\mathbf{r} = \mathbf{r}_o e^{2t}$, $\mathbf{a} = 4\mathbf{r}_o e^{2t}$; the path is a straight line through the origin in the direction of $\mathbf{r}_o$

11. $\mathbf{r} = \cos t\mathbf{i} + \sin t\mathbf{j} + \mathbf{k}$; the curve is a circle of radius 1 in the plane $z = 1$

21. $\dfrac{d}{dt}\left(\mathbf{u} \times (\mathbf{v} \times \mathbf{w})\right) = \dfrac{d\mathbf{u}}{dt} \times (\mathbf{v} \times \mathbf{w})$
$\quad + \mathbf{u} \times \left(\dfrac{d\mathbf{v}}{dt} \times \mathbf{w}\right) + \mathbf{u} \times \left(\mathbf{v} \times \dfrac{d\mathbf{w}}{dt}\right)$

23. $\mathbf{u}''' \bullet (\mathbf{u} \times \mathbf{u}')$

25. $\dfrac{e - 1}{e}$, $\quad \dfrac{e^2 - 1}{e^2}$

27. $\dfrac{\pi^2 R}{72}$ towards the ground, where R is the radius of the earth; $4.76°$ west of south

Section 5.2   (page 229)

1. $x = \sqrt{a^2 - t^2}$, $y = t$, $0 \leq t \leq a$

3. $x = a\sin\theta$, $y = -a\cos\theta$, $\dfrac{\pi}{2} \leq \theta \leq \pi$

5. $\displaystyle\int_1^T \dfrac{\sqrt{4a^2 t^4 + b^2 t^2 + c^2}}{t}\,dt$ units;
$a(T^2 - 1) + c\ln T$ units

7. $\pi\sqrt{2 + 4\pi^2} + \ln(\sqrt{2}\pi + \sqrt{1 + 2\pi^2})$ units

9. $\sqrt{2e^{4\pi} + 1} - \sqrt{3} + \dfrac{1}{2}\ln\dfrac{e^{4\pi} + 1 - \sqrt{2e^{4\pi} + 1}}{e^{4\pi}}$
$\quad - \dfrac{1}{2}\ln(2 - \sqrt{3})$ units

11. $\mathbf{r} = \dfrac{1}{\sqrt{A^2 + B^2 + C^2}}(As\mathbf{i} + Bs\mathbf{j} + Cs\mathbf{k})$

13. $\mathbf{r} = a\left(1 - \dfrac{s}{K}\right)^{3/2}\mathbf{i} + a\left(\dfrac{s}{K}\right)^{3/2}\mathbf{j} + b\left(1 - \dfrac{2s}{K}\right)\mathbf{k}$,
$\quad 0 \leq s \leq K$, $K = (\sqrt{9a^2 + 16b^2})/2$

15. $\hat{\mathbf{T}} = \dfrac{1}{\sqrt{1 + 16t^2 + 81t^4}}(\mathbf{i} - 4t\mathbf{j} + 9t^2\mathbf{k})$

17. $\hat{\mathbf{T}} = \dfrac{1}{\sqrt{1 + \sin^2 t}}(\cos 2t\mathbf{i} + \sin 2t\mathbf{j} - \sin t\mathbf{k})$

Section 5.3   (page 241)

1. $\hat{\mathbf{T}} = \dfrac{1}{\sqrt{1 + t^2 + t^4}}(\mathbf{i} + t\mathbf{j} + t^2\mathbf{k})$,
$\hat{\mathbf{B}} = \dfrac{1}{\sqrt{t^4 + 4t^2 + 1}}(t^2\mathbf{i} - 2t\mathbf{j} + \mathbf{k})$,
$\hat{\mathbf{N}} = \dfrac{-(t + 2t^3)\mathbf{i} + (1 - t^4)\mathbf{j} + (t^3 + 2t)\mathbf{k}}{\sqrt{t^4 + 4t^2 + 1}\sqrt{1 + t^2 + t^4}}$,
$\kappa = \dfrac{\sqrt{t^4 + 4t^2 + 1}}{(t^4 + t^2 + 1)^{3/2}}$, $\quad \tau = \dfrac{2}{t^4 + 4t^2 + 1}$

3. $\hat{\mathbf{T}} = \dfrac{(\cos t - t\sin t)\mathbf{i} + (\sin t + t\cos t)\mathbf{j} + \mathbf{k}}{\sqrt{2 + t^2}}$,
$\hat{\mathbf{N}} = -\Big(\dfrac{(4 + t^2)\sin t + (3t + t^3)\cos t)\mathbf{i}}{\sqrt{2 + t^2}\sqrt{8 + 5t^2 + t^4}}$
$\quad + \dfrac{((4 + t^2)\cos t - (3t + t^3)\sin t)\mathbf{j} - t\mathbf{k}}{\sqrt{2 + t^2}\sqrt{8 + 5t^2 + t^4}}$,
$\hat{\mathbf{B}} = \dfrac{-(2\cos t - t\sin t)\mathbf{i} - (2\sin t + t\cos t)\mathbf{j} + (2 + t^2)\mathbf{k}}{\sqrt{8 + 5t^2 + t^4}}$,
$\kappa = \dfrac{\sqrt{8 + 5t^2 + t^4}}{(2 + t^2)^{3/2}}$, $\quad \tau = \dfrac{6 + t^2}{8 + 5t^2 + t^4}$

5. i) $\hat{\mathbf{T}} = \mathbf{i}$, $\hat{\mathbf{N}} = \dfrac{2\mathbf{j} - \mathbf{k}}{\sqrt{5}}$,

   $\hat{\mathbf{B}} = \dfrac{\mathbf{j} + 2\mathbf{k}}{\sqrt{5}}$, $\kappa = \sqrt{5}$, $\tau = 0$

   ii) $\hat{\mathbf{T}} = \sqrt{\tfrac{2}{3}}(\mathbf{j} - \tfrac{1}{\sqrt{2}}\mathbf{k})$, $\hat{\mathbf{B}} = \tfrac{1}{\sqrt{13}}(-\mathbf{i} + 2\mathbf{j} + 2\sqrt{2}\mathbf{k})$,

   $\hat{\mathbf{N}} = -\tfrac{1}{\sqrt{39}}(6\mathbf{i} + \mathbf{j} + \sqrt{2}\mathbf{k})$, $\kappa = \tfrac{2\sqrt{39}}{9}$, $\tau = -\tfrac{6\sqrt{2}}{13}$

7. max a/b^2, min b/a^2

9. $\kappa = \dfrac{e^x}{(1 + e^{2x})^{3/2}}$,

   $\mathbf{r} = (x - 1 - e^{2x})\mathbf{i} + (2e^x + e^{-x})\mathbf{j}$

11. $\dfrac{3}{2\sqrt{2ar}}$ **19.** $\mathbf{r} = -4x^3\mathbf{i} + (3x^2 + \tfrac{1}{2})\mathbf{j}$

21. $f(x) = \dfrac{1}{8}(15x - 10x^3 + 3x^5)$

Section 5.4   (page 251)

3. velocity: $1/\sqrt{2}$, $1/\sqrt{2}$;
   acceleration: $-e^{-\theta}/2$, $e^{-\theta}/2$.

7. 40,800 km: the equatorial plane

9. $\dfrac{T}{4\sqrt{2}}$ **13.** $\dfrac{3}{4}$

17. $r = A \sec\omega(\theta - \theta_0)$, $\omega^2 = 1 - (k/h^2)$ if $k < h^2$,
   $r = 1/(A + B\theta)$ if $k = h^2$,
   $r = A e^{\omega\theta} + B e^{-\omega\theta}$, $\omega^2 = (k/h^2) - 1$,   if $k > h^2$;
   there are no bounded orbits which do not approach the
   origin except in the case $k = h^2$ if $B = 0$ when there are
   circular orbits. (Now aren't you glad gravitation is an
   inverse square rather than an inverse cube attraction?)

19. centre $\left(\dfrac{\ell\epsilon}{\epsilon^2 - 1}, 0\right)$;

   asymptotes in directions $\theta = \pm\cos^{-1}\left(-\dfrac{1}{\epsilon}\right)$;

   semi-transverse axis $a = \dfrac{\ell}{\epsilon^2 - 1}$;

   semi-conjugate axis $b = \dfrac{\ell}{\sqrt{\epsilon^2 - 1}}$;

   semi-focal separation $c = \dfrac{\ell\epsilon}{\epsilon^2 - 1}$.

CHAPTER 6.   VECTOR FIELDS

Section 6.1   (page 258)

1. field lines: $y = x + C$

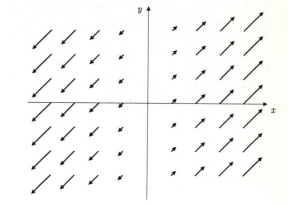

3. field lines: $y^2 = x^2 + C$

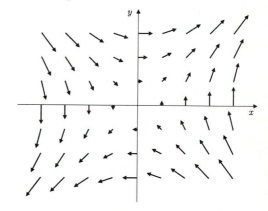

5. field lines: $y = -\tfrac{1}{2}e^{-2x} + C$

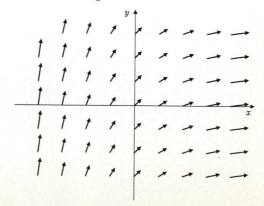

7. field lines: $y = Cx$

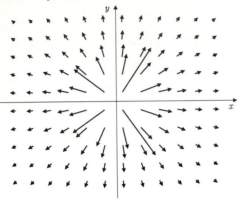

9. streamlines are lines parallel to $\mathbf{i} - \mathbf{j} - \mathbf{k}$

11. streamlines: $x^2 + y^2 = a^2$, $x = a\sin(z - b)$ (spirals)

Section 6.2   (page 267)

1. conservative; $\dfrac{x^2}{2} - y^2 + \dfrac{3z^2}{2}$

3. not conservative

5. conservative; $x^2 y + y^2 z - z^2 x$

7. $-2\dfrac{\mathbf{r} - \mathbf{r}_0}{|\mathbf{r} - \mathbf{r}_0|^4}$

9. $(x^2 + y^2)/z$; equipotential surfaces are paraboloids $z = C(x^2 + y^2)$; field lines are ellipses $x^2 + y^2 + 2z^2 = A$, $y = Bx$ in vertical planes through the origin

11. $\mathbf{v} = \dfrac{m(x\mathbf{i} + y\mathbf{j} + (z - \ell)\mathbf{k})}{[x^2 + y^2 + (z - \ell)^2]^{3/2}}, \dfrac{m(x\mathbf{i} + y\mathbf{j} + (z + \ell)\mathbf{k})}{[x^2 + y^2 + (z + \ell)^2]^{3/2}},$

     $\mathbf{v} = \mathbf{0}$ only at the origin; $\mathbf{v}(x, y, 0) = \dfrac{2m(x\mathbf{i} + y\mathbf{j})}{(x^2 + y^2 + \ell^2)^{3/2}}$;

     speed maximum on the circle $x^2 + y^2 = \ell^2/2$, $z = 0$

15. $\phi = -\dfrac{\mu y}{r^2}$,

     $\mathbf{F} = \dfrac{\mu(2xy\mathbf{i} + (y^2 - x^2)\mathbf{j})}{r^4}, \quad (r^2 = x^2 + y^2)$

Section 6.3   (page 271)

1. $\dfrac{a^2}{2}\left(\sqrt{2} + \ln(1 + \sqrt{2})\right)$ **3.** $\dfrac{e}{6}\left((2e^{4\pi} + 1)^{3/2} - 3^{3/2}\right)$

5. $3\sqrt{14}$ **7.** $\left(\sqrt{2} + \ln(\sqrt{2} + 1)\right)a^2/2$

9. $\pi/\sqrt{2}$

11. $4\sqrt{b^2 + c^2}\, E\left(\sqrt{\dfrac{b^2 - a^2}{b^2 + c^2}}\right);$

     $\sqrt{b^2 + c^2}\, E\left(\sqrt{\dfrac{b^2 - a^2}{b^2 + c^2}}, T\right)$

Section 6.4   (page 279)

1. $-1/4$ **3.** $1/2$

5. 0 **7.** $19/2$

9. $e^{1 + (\pi/4)}$

11. a) πa^2, b) $-\pi a^2$ **13.** a) $\dfrac{\pi a^2}{2}$, b) $-\dfrac{\pi a^2}{2}$

15. a) $ab/2$, b) $-ab/2$

19. The plane with origin removed is not simply connected.

Section 6.5   (page 292)

1. $dS = ds\, dz = \sqrt{(g(\theta))^2 + (g'(\theta))^2}\, d\theta\, dz$

3. $\dfrac{\pi ab\sqrt{A^2 + B^2 + C^2}}{|C|}$ sq. units $(C \neq 0)$

5. $\dfrac{\pi}{8}$ **7.** $16a^2$ sq. units

11. spiral ramp, radius a, height $2\pi b$;

     $\pi a\sqrt{a^2 + b^2} + \pi b^2 \ln\dfrac{a + \sqrt{a^2 + b^2}}{b}$ sq. un.

13. $2\pi\sqrt{A^2 + B^2 + C^2}/|D|$

15. one-third of the way from the base to the vertex on the axis

17. $2\pi k\sigma ma\left(\dfrac{1}{\sqrt{a^2 + (b - h)^2}} - \dfrac{1}{\sqrt{a^2 + b^2}}\right)$

19. $I = \dfrac{8}{3}\pi\sigma a^4$; $\bar{D} = \sqrt{\dfrac{2}{3}}\, a$

21. $\dfrac{3}{5}g\sin\alpha$

Section 6.6   (page 298)

1. 6 **3.** $3abc$

5. $4\pi m$ **7.** a) $2\pi a^2$, b) 8

11. $\mathbf{n} = \left(2\cos 2u(2 + v\cos u)\sin u - v\sin 2u\right)\mathbf{i}$

     $+ \left(2\sin 2u(2 + v\cos u)\sin u + v\cos 2u\right)\mathbf{j}$

     $- 2\cos u(2 + v\cos u)\mathbf{k}$;

     Note that $\mathbf{n} \neq \mathbf{0}$ at any point of S, which is a Möebius band covered twice with the normal $\mathbf{n}$ on opposite sides. (Thus the flux of any smooth vector field across S is zero.)

CHAPTER 7.   VECTOR CALCULUS

Section 7.1   (page 307)

1. div $\mathbf{F} = 2$, curl $\mathbf{F} = \mathbf{0}$

3. div $\mathbf{F} = 0$, curl $\mathbf{F} = -\mathbf{i} - \mathbf{j} - \mathbf{k}$

5. div $\mathbf{F} = 1$, curl $\mathbf{F} = -\mathbf{j}$

7. div $\mathbf{F} = f'(x) + g'(y) + h'(z)$, 　**curl** $\mathbf{F} = 0$

9. div $\mathbf{F} = \cos\theta\left(1 + \dfrac{1}{r}\cos\theta\right)$;

　curl $\mathbf{F} = -\sin\theta\left(1 + \dfrac{1}{r}\cos\theta\right)\mathbf{k}$

11. div $\mathbf{F} = 0$; 　**curl** $\mathbf{F} = (1/r)\mathbf{k}$

Section 7.2　(page 312)

7. div $\mathbf{F}$ can have any value,
　curl $\mathbf{F}$ must be normal to $\mathbf{F}$

9. $f(r) = Cr^{-3}$

15. If $\mathbf{F} = \nabla\phi$ and $\mathbf{G} = \nabla\psi$ then $\nabla \times (\phi\nabla\psi) = \mathbf{F} \times \mathbf{G}$.

17. $\mathbf{G} = ye^{2z}\mathbf{i} + xye^{2z}\mathbf{k}$ is one possible vector potential.

Section 7.3　(page 319)

11. $\dfrac{2}{3}\pi a^2 b + \dfrac{3}{10}\pi a^4 b + \pi a^2$

13. a) $12\sqrt{3}\pi a^3$,　b) $-4\sqrt{3}\pi a^3$,　c) $16\sqrt{3}\pi a^3$

15. $(6 + 2\bar{x} + 4\bar{y} - 2\bar{z})V$

Section 7.4　(page 326)

1. $\pi a^2 - 4a^3$ 　　　　　　**3.** 9

5. 0

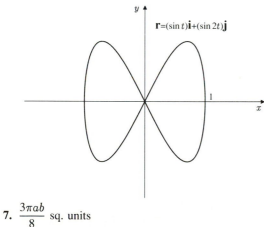

$\mathbf{r} = (\sin t)\mathbf{i} + (\sin 2t)\mathbf{j}$

7. $\dfrac{3\pi ab}{8}$ sq. units

9. $-3\pi a^2$ 　　　　　**11.** 1/2

13. yes, $\phi\nabla\psi$ (See also Exercise 18.2.13.)

Section 18.6　(page 348)

1. $\nabla f(r, \theta, z) = \theta z \hat{\mathbf{r}} + z\hat{\boldsymbol{\theta}} + r\theta\mathbf{k}$

3. div $\mathbf{F}(r, \theta, z) = 2$, 　　**curl** $\mathbf{F}(r, \theta, z) = 0$

5. div $\mathbf{F}(R, \phi, \theta) = \dfrac{2\sin\phi}{R}$, 　**curl** $\mathbf{F}(R, \phi, \theta) = -\dfrac{\cos\phi}{R}\hat{\boldsymbol{\theta}}$

7. div $\mathbf{F}(R, \phi, \theta) = 0$, 　　**curl** $\mathbf{F}(R, \phi, \theta) = \cot\phi\hat{\mathbf{R}} - 2\hat{\boldsymbol{\phi}}$

9. scale factors: $h_u = \left|\dfrac{\partial \mathbf{r}}{\partial u}\right|$, 　$h_v = \left|\dfrac{\partial \mathbf{r}}{\partial v}\right|$.

local basis: $\hat{\mathbf{u}} = \dfrac{1}{h_u}\dfrac{\partial \mathbf{r}}{\partial u}$, 　$\hat{\mathbf{v}} = \dfrac{1}{h_v}\dfrac{\partial \mathbf{r}}{\partial v}$.
area element: $dA = h_u h_v\, du\, dv$.

$$\nabla f(r, \theta) = \frac{\partial f}{\partial r}\hat{\mathbf{r}} + \frac{1}{r}\frac{\partial f}{\partial \theta}\hat{\boldsymbol{\theta}}$$

11. 　**div** $\mathbf{F}(r, \theta) = \dfrac{\partial F_r}{\partial r} + \dfrac{1}{r}F_r + \dfrac{1}{r}\dfrac{\partial F_\theta}{\partial \theta}$

　curl $\mathbf{F}(r, \theta) = \left(\dfrac{\partial F_\theta}{\partial r} + \dfrac{F_\theta}{r} - \dfrac{1}{r}\dfrac{\partial F_r}{\partial \theta}\right)\mathbf{k}$.

13. u-surfaces: vertical elliptic cylinders with focal axes at $x = \pm a$, $y = 0$.
v-surfaces: vertical hyperbolic cylinders with focal axes at $x = \pm a$, $y = 0$.
z-surfaces: horizontal planes.
u-curves: horizontal hyperbolas with foci at $x = \pm a$, $y = 0$.
v-curves: horizontal ellipses with foci at $x = \pm a$, $y = 0$.
z-curves: vertical straight lines.

15.
$$\Delta f = \frac{\partial^2 f}{\partial R^2} + \frac{2}{R}\frac{\partial f}{\partial R} + \frac{1}{R^2}\frac{\partial^2 f}{\partial \phi^2}$$
$$+ \frac{\cot\phi}{R^2}\frac{\partial f}{\partial \phi} + \frac{1}{R^2\sin^2\phi}\frac{\partial^2 f}{\partial \theta^2}.$$

APPENDIX I. VELOCITY, ACCELERATION AND PLANE VECTORS　(page 360)

1. (a) $3\mathbf{i} - 2\mathbf{j}$, (b) $-3\mathbf{i} + 2\mathbf{j}$,
(c) $2\mathbf{i} - 5\mathbf{j}$, (d) $-2\mathbf{i} + 4\mathbf{j}$, (e) $-\mathbf{i} - 2\mathbf{j}$, (f) $4\mathbf{i} + \mathbf{j}$, (g) $-7\mathbf{i} + 20\mathbf{j}$, (h) $2\mathbf{i} - (5/3)\mathbf{j}$

3. $\mathbf{u} + \mathbf{v} = 2\mathbf{i}$, $\mathbf{u} - \mathbf{v} = 2\mathbf{j}$, $|\mathbf{u}| = |\mathbf{v}| = \sqrt{2}$, $\mathbf{u} \bullet \mathbf{v} = 0$, angle $= 90°$

5. $\mathbf{u} + \mathbf{v} = \mathbf{j}$, $\mathbf{u} - \mathbf{v} = 2\mathbf{i} - 5\mathbf{j}$, $|\mathbf{u}| = \sqrt{5}$, $|\mathbf{v}| = \sqrt{10}$, $\mathbf{u} \bullet \mathbf{v} = -7$, angle $= \cos^{-1}(-7/\sqrt{50}) \approx 171.9°$

7. $\mathbf{u}+\mathbf{v}=3\mathbf{i}+\mathbf{j}$, $\mathbf{u}-\mathbf{v}=-\mathbf{i}+3\mathbf{j}$, $|\mathbf{u}|=|\mathbf{v}|=\sqrt{5}$,
$\mathbf{u}\bullet\mathbf{v}=0$, angle $=90°$

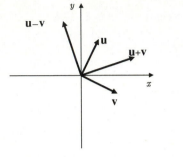

9. $\mathbf{v}(1)=\mathbf{i}-\mathbf{j}$, $\mathbf{a}(1)=-\mathbf{j}$, **11.** $\mathbf{v}(1)=\mathbf{i}+\mathbf{j}$, $\mathbf{a}(1)=-6\mathbf{j}$,
$\mathbf{v}(2)=\mathbf{i}-2\mathbf{j}$, $\mathbf{a}(2)=-\mathbf{j}$ $\mathbf{v}(2)=\mathbf{i}-8\mathbf{j}$, $\mathbf{a}(2)=-12\mathbf{j}$

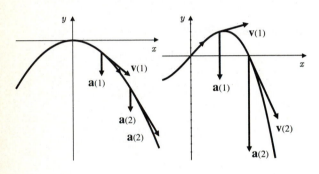

13. path is a straight line through (x_0,y_0) parallel to $\mathbf{u}$; parametric equations $x=x_0+at$, $y=y_0+bt$, where $\mathbf{r}_0=x_0\mathbf{i}+y_0\mathbf{j}$ and $\mathbf{u}=a\mathbf{i}+b\mathbf{j}$

15. $\mathbf{r}=\left(\dfrac{t^3}{6}-\dfrac{t}{2}-\dfrac{2}{3}\right)\mathbf{i}+\mathbf{j}$

17. $\mathbf{r}=(2t-\sin t)\mathbf{i}+(t+e^{-t}-1)\mathbf{j}$

19. if $\mathbf{r}_0=x_0\mathbf{i}+y_0\mathbf{j}$ and $\mathbf{v}_0=ka\mathbf{i}+kb\mathbf{j}$ then the solution simplifies to
$(y_0x-x_0y)^2+(bx-ay)^2=(ay_0-bx_0)^2$,
which is a bounded quadratic curve, so is an ellipse or circle; it is a circle if $x_0y_0+ab=0$ and $x_0^2+a^2=y_0^2+b^2$.

21. $\mathbf{v}=\dfrac{k}{\sqrt{1+e^{2x}}}(\mathbf{i}+e^x\mathbf{j})$,
$\mathbf{a}=\dfrac{k^2}{(1+e^{2x})^2}\left(-e^{2x}\mathbf{i}+e^x\mathbf{j}\right)$

APPENDIX II.   CONICS   (page 374)

1. single point $(-1,0)$ **3.** ellipse, centre $(0,2)$

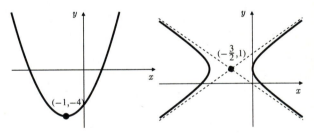

5. parabola, vertex $(-1,-4)$ **7.** hyperbola, centre $\left(-\frac{3}{2},1\right)$ asymptotes $2x+3=\pm 2^{3/2}(y-1)$

9. ellipse, centre $(1,-1)$ **11.** rectangular hyperbola, centre $(1,-1)$, semiaxes $a=b=\sqrt{2}$, eccentricity $\sqrt{2}$, foci $(\sqrt{2}+1,\sqrt{2}-1)$, $(-\sqrt{2}+1,-\sqrt{2}-1)$, asymptotes $x=1$, $y=-1$

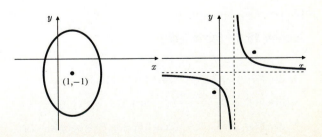

13. hyperbola, centre $(0,0)$, semiaxes
$a = 1/\sqrt{2 + \sqrt{2}}$,
$b = 1/\sqrt{2 - \sqrt{2}}$,
foci
$\pm\left(\cos(\pi/8), \sin(\pi/8)\right)$,
asymptotes $x = 0$, $y = -x$

15. ellipse, centre $(0,0)$, semi-axes $a = 2$, $b = 1$,
foci $\pm\left(2\sqrt{\frac{3}{5}}, -\sqrt{\frac{3}{5}}\right)$

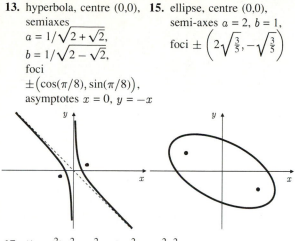

17. $(1 - \epsilon^2)x^2 + y^2 - 2p\epsilon^2 x = \epsilon^2 p^2$

APPENDIX III.   FIRST ORDER DIFFERENTIAL EQUATIONS   (page 385)

1. $y^2 = Cx$

3. $x^3 - y^3 = C$

5. $Y = Ce^{t^2/2}$

7. $y = \dfrac{Ce^{2x} - 1}{Ce^{2x} + 1}$

9. $y = -\ln\left(Ce^{-2t} - \frac{1}{2}\right)$

11. $y = x^3 + Cx^2$

13. $y = \frac{3}{2} + Ce^{-2x}$

15. $y = x - 1 + Ce^{-x}$

17. $2\tan^{-1}(y/x) = \ln(x^2 + y^2) + C$

19. $\tan^{-1}(y/x) = \ln|x| + C$

21. $2xy + x^2y^2 = C$

23. $\ln|x| - \dfrac{y}{x^2} = C$

25. $y^3 + 3y - 3x^2 = 24$

27. $4\tan^{-1}\dfrac{y - 1}{x - 2} = \ln\left((y - 1)^2 + (x - 2)^2\right) + C$

29. $\dfrac{1}{\mu}\dfrac{d\mu}{dx} = \dfrac{\frac{\partial N}{\partial x} - \frac{\partial M}{\partial y}}{xM - yN}$ must depend only on xy; $\dfrac{\sin x}{y} - \dfrac{y}{x} = C$

33. If $a = b$ the given solution is indeterminate $0/0$; in this case the solution is $x = a^2kt/(1 + akt)$.

35. $v = \sqrt{\dfrac{mg}{k}}\dfrac{e^{2\sqrt{kg/mt}} - 1}{e^{2\sqrt{kg/mt}} + 1}$, $v \to \sqrt{\dfrac{mg}{k}}$

37. the hyperbolas $x^2 - y^2 = C$

APPENDIX IV.   DIFFERENTIAL EQUATIONS OF SECOND ORDER   (page 401)

1. $y = \ln|x + C_1| + C_2$

3. $y = C_1(x + 1)^2 + C_2$

5. $y = \dfrac{1}{C_1}\ln(C_1 x + C_2)$

7. $y = Ae^{-5t} + Be^{-2t}$

9. $y = A + Be^{-2t}$

11. $y = (A + Bt)e^{-4t}$

13. $y = (A\cos t + B\sin t)e^{3t}$

15. $y = (A\cos 2t + B\sin 2t)e^{-t}$

19. $y = C_1 x^2 + C_2 x^3$

21. $y = \sqrt{|x|}(C_1 + C_2\ln|x|)$

23. $y = 3\cos\omega x - \dfrac{2}{\omega}\sin\omega x$

25. $y = 1 - 2\ln|x|$, $(-\infty < x < 0)$

29. $y = x^{-1/2}(C_1\cos x + C_2\sin x)$

31. $y = C_1 e^x + C_2 e^{-2x} - \dfrac{1}{4} - \dfrac{x}{2}$

33. $y = C_1 e^x + C_2 e^{-2x} + \dfrac{1}{3}xe^x$

35. $C = 1/2$; no; no; $y = Ae^x$ and $y = Bxe^x$ are both solutions of the homogeneous equation $y'' - 2y' + y = 0$

37. $y_p = -\dfrac{2}{125} - \dfrac{4x}{25} + \dfrac{x^2}{5} + \dfrac{e^x}{8}$

39. $y_p = -\dfrac{1}{4}x\cos(2x)$

41. $y_p = -\dfrac{1}{4}xe^{-x}\cos(2x)$

43. $y = a_0\left(1 + \displaystyle\sum_{k=1}^{\infty}\dfrac{(x - 1)^{4k}}{4(k!)(3)(7)\cdots(4k - 1)}\right)$
$+ a_1\left(x - 1 + \displaystyle\sum_{k=1}^{\infty}\dfrac{(x - 1)^{4k+1}}{4(k!)(5)(9)\cdots(4k + 1)}\right)$

45. $y = 1 - \dfrac{1}{6}x^3 + \dfrac{1}{120}x^5 + \cdots$

47. $y_1 = 1 + \displaystyle\sum_{k=1}^{\infty}\dfrac{(-1)^k x^k}{(k!)(2)(5)(8)\cdots(3k - 1)}$,
$y_2 = x^{1/3}\left(1 + \displaystyle\sum_{k=0}^{\infty}\dfrac{(-1)^k x^k}{(k!)(4)(7)\cdots(3k + 1)}\right)$

INDEX

INTEGRATION RULES

$$\int (Af(x) + Bg(x))\, dx = A \int f(x)\, dx + B \int g(x)\, dx$$

$$\int f'(g(x))\, g'(x)\, dx = f(g(x)) + C$$

$$\int U(x)\, dV(x) = U(x)\, V(x) - \int V(x)\, dU(x)$$

$$\int_a^b f'(x)\, dx = f(b) - f(a)$$

$$\frac{d}{dx} \int_a^x f(t)\, dt = f(x)$$

ELEMENTARY INTEGRALS

$$\int x^r\, dx = \frac{1}{r+1} x^{r+1} + C \text{ if } r \ne -1$$

$$\int \frac{dx}{x} = \ln|x| + C$$

$$\int e^x\, dx = e^x + C$$

$$\int a^x\, dx = \frac{a^x}{\ln a} + C$$

$$\int \sin x\, dx = -\cos x + C$$

$$\int \cos x\, dx = \sin x + C$$

$$\int \sec^2 x\, dx = \tan x + C$$

$$\int \csc^2 x\, dx = -\cot x + C$$

$$\int \sec x \tan x\, dx = \sec x + C$$

$$\int \csc x \cot x\, dx = -\csc x + C$$

$$\int \tan x\, dx = \ln|\sec x| + C$$

$$\int \cot x\, dx = \ln|\sin x| + C$$

$$\int \sec x\, dx = \ln|\sec x + \tan x| + C$$

$$\int \csc x\, dx = \ln|\csc x - \cot x| + C$$

$$\int \frac{dx}{\sqrt{a^2 - x^2}} = \sin^{-1}\frac{x}{a} + C$$

$$\int \frac{dx}{a^2 + x^2} = \frac{1}{a} \tan^{-1}\frac{x}{a} + C$$

$$\int \frac{dx}{a^2 - x^2} = \frac{1}{2a} \ln\left|\frac{x+a}{x-a}\right| + C$$

$$\int \frac{dx}{x\sqrt{x^2 - a^2}} = \frac{1}{a} \sec^{-1}\left|\frac{x}{a}\right| + C$$

TRIGONOMETRIC INTEGRALS

$$\int \sin^2 x\, dx = \frac{x}{2} - \frac{1}{4} \sin 2x + C$$

$$\int \cos^2 x\, dx = \frac{x}{2} + \frac{1}{4} \sin 2x + C$$

$$\int \tan^2 x\, dx = \tan x - x + C$$

$$\int \cot^2 x\, dx = -\cot x - x + C$$

$$\int \sec^3 x\, dx = \frac{1}{2} \sec x \tan x + \frac{1}{2} \ln|\sec x + \tan x| + C$$

$$\int \csc^3 x\, dx = -\frac{1}{2} \csc x \cot x + \frac{1}{2} \ln|\csc x - \cot x| + C$$

$$\int \sin ax \sin bx\, dx = \frac{\sin(a-b)x}{2(a-b)} - \frac{\sin(a+b)x}{2(a+b)} + C \text{ if } a^2 \ne b^2$$

$$\int \cos ax \cos bx\, dx = \frac{\sin(a-b)x}{2(a-b)} + \frac{\sin(a+b)x}{2(a+b)} + C \text{ if } a^2 \ne b^2$$

$$\int \sin ax \cos bx\, dx = -\frac{\cos(a-b)x}{2(a-b)} - \frac{\cos(a+b)x}{2(a+b)} + C \text{ if } a^2 \ne b^2$$

$$\int \sin^n x\, dx = -\frac{1}{n} \sin^{n-1} x \cos x + \frac{n-1}{n} \int \sin^{n-2} x\, dx$$

$$\int \cos^n x\, dx = \frac{1}{n} \cos^{n-1} x \sin x + \frac{n-1}{n} \int \cos^{n-2} x\, dx$$

$$\int \tan^n x\, dx = \frac{1}{n-1} \tan^{n-1} x - \int \tan^{n-2} x\, dx \text{ if } n \ne 1$$

$$\int \cot^n x\, dx = \frac{-1}{n-1} \cot^{n-1} x - \int \cot^{n-2} x\, dx \text{ if } n \ne 1$$

$$\int \sec^n x\, dx = \frac{1}{n-1} \sec^{n-2} x \tan x + \frac{n-2}{n-1} \int \sec^{n-2} x\, dx \text{ if } n \ne 1$$

$$\int \csc^n x\, dx = \frac{-1}{n-1} \csc^{n-2} x \cot x + \frac{n-2}{n-1} \int \csc^{n-2} x\, dx \text{ if } n \ne 1$$

$$\int \sin^n x \cos^m x\, dx = -\frac{\sin^{n-1} x \cos^{m+1} x}{n+m} + \frac{n-1}{n+m} \int \sin^{n-2} x \cos^m x\, dx \text{ if } n \ne -m$$

$$\int \sin^n x \cos^m x\, dx = \frac{\sin^{n+1} x \cos^{m-1} x}{n+m} + \frac{m-1}{n+m} \int \sin^n x \cos^{m-2} x\, dx \text{ if } m \ne -n$$

$$\int x \sin x\, dx = \sin x - x \cos x + C$$

$$\int x \cos x\, dx = \cos x + x \sin x + C$$

$$\int x^n \sin x\, dx = -x^n \cos x + n \int x^{n-1} \cos x\, dx$$

$$\int x^n \cos x\, dx = x^n \sin x - n \int x^{n-1} \sin x\, dx$$

INTEGRALS INVOLVING $\sqrt{x^2 \pm a^2}$

$$\int \sqrt{x^2 \pm a^2}\, dx = \frac{x}{2}\sqrt{x^2 \pm a^2} \pm \frac{a^2}{2}\ln|x + \sqrt{x^2 \pm a^2}| + C$$

$$\int \frac{dx}{\sqrt{x^2 \pm a^2}} = \ln|x + \sqrt{x^2 \pm a^2}| + C$$

$$\int \frac{\sqrt{x^2 + a^2}}{x}\, dx = \sqrt{x^2 + a^2} - a\ln\left(\frac{a + \sqrt{x^2 + a^2}}{x}\right) + C$$

$$\int \frac{\sqrt{x^2 - a^2}}{x}\, dx = \sqrt{x^2 - a^2} - a\sec^{-1}\frac{x}{a} + C$$

$$\int x^2\sqrt{x^2 \pm a^2}\, dx = \frac{x}{8}(2x^2 \pm a^2)\sqrt{x^2 \pm a^2} - \frac{a^4}{8}\ln|x + \sqrt{x^2 \pm a^2}| + C$$

$$\int \frac{x^2}{\sqrt{x^2 \pm a^2}}\, dx = \frac{x}{2}\sqrt{x^2 \pm a^2} \mp \frac{a^2}{2}\ln|x + \sqrt{x^2 \pm a^2}| + C$$

$$\int \frac{\sqrt{x^2 \pm a^2}}{x^2}\, dx = -\frac{\sqrt{x^2 \pm a^2}}{x} + \ln|x + \sqrt{x^2 \pm a^2}| + C$$

$$\int \frac{dx}{x^2\sqrt{x^2 \pm a^2}} = \mp\frac{\sqrt{x^2 \pm a^2}}{a^2 x} + C$$

$$\int \frac{dx}{(x^2 \pm a^2)^{3/2}} = \frac{\pm x}{a^2\sqrt{x^2 \pm a^2}} + C$$

$$\int (x^2 \pm a^2)^{3/2}\, dx = \frac{x}{8}(2x^2 \pm 5a^2)\sqrt{x^2 \pm a^2} + \frac{3a^4}{8}\ln|x + \sqrt{x^2 \pm a^2}| + C$$

INTEGRALS INVOLVING $\sqrt{a^2 - x^2}$

$$\int \sqrt{a^2 - x^2}\, dx = \frac{x}{2}\sqrt{a^2 - x^2} + \frac{a^2}{2}\sin^{-1}\frac{x}{a} + C$$

$$\int \frac{\sqrt{a^2 - x^2}}{x}\, dx = \sqrt{a^2 - x^2} - a\ln\left|\frac{a + \sqrt{a^2 - x^2}}{x}\right| + C$$

$$\int \frac{x^2}{\sqrt{a^2 - x^2}}\, dx = -\frac{x}{2}\sqrt{a^2 - x^2} + \frac{a^2}{2}\sin^{-1}\frac{x}{a} + C$$

$$\int x^2\sqrt{a^2 - x^2}\, dx = \frac{x}{8}(2x^2 - a^2)\sqrt{a^2 - x^2} + \frac{a^4}{8}\sin^{-1}\frac{x}{a} + C$$

$$\int \frac{dx}{x^2\sqrt{a^2 - x^2}} = -\frac{\sqrt{a^2 - x^2}}{a^2 x} + C$$

$$\int \frac{\sqrt{a^2 - x^2}}{x^2}\, dx = -\frac{\sqrt{a^2 - x^2}}{x} - \sin^{-1}\frac{x}{a} + C$$

$$\int \frac{dx}{x\sqrt{a^2 - x^2}} = -\frac{1}{a}\ln\left|\frac{a + \sqrt{a^2 - x^2}}{x}\right| + C$$

$$\int \frac{dx}{(a^2 - x^2)^{3/2}} = \frac{x}{a^2\sqrt{a^2 - x^2}} + C$$

$$\int (a^2 - x^2)^{3/2}\, dx = \frac{x}{8}(5a^2 - 2x^2)\sqrt{a^2 - x^2} + \frac{3a^4}{8}\sin^{-1}\frac{x}{a} + C$$

INTEGRALS OF INVERSE TRIGONOMETRIC FUNCTIONS

$$\int \sin^{-1}x\, dx = x\sin^{-1}x + \sqrt{1 - x^2} + C$$

$$\int \tan^{-1}x\, dx = x\tan^{-1}x - \frac{1}{2}\ln(1 + x^2) + C$$

$$\int \sec^{-1}x\, dx = x\sec^{-1}x - \ln|x + \sqrt{x^2 - 1}| + C$$

$$\int x\sin^{-1}x\, dx = \frac{1}{4}(2x^2 - 1)\sin^{-1}x + \frac{x}{4}\sqrt{1 - x^2} + C$$

$$\int x\tan^{-1}x\, dx = \frac{1}{2}(x^2 + 1)\tan^{-1}x - \frac{x}{2} + C$$

$$\int x\sec^{-1}x\, dx = \frac{x^2}{2}\sec^{-1}x - \frac{1}{2}\sqrt{x^2 - 1} + C$$

$$\int x^n\sin^{-1}x\, dx = \frac{x^{n+1}}{n+1}\sin^{-1}x - \frac{1}{n+1}\int \frac{x^{n+1}}{\sqrt{1 - x^2}}\, dx + C \text{ if } n \neq -1$$

$$\int x^n\tan^{-1}x\, dx = \frac{x^{n+1}}{n+1}\tan^{-1}x - \frac{1}{n+1}\int \frac{x^{n+1}}{1 + x^2}\, dx + C \text{ if } n \neq -1$$

$$\int x^n\sec^{-1}x\, dx = \frac{x^{n+1}}{n+1}\sec^{-1}x - \frac{1}{n+1}\int \frac{x^n}{\sqrt{x^2 - 1}}\, dx + C \text{ if } n \neq -1$$

EXPONENTIAL AND LOGARITHMIC INTEGRALS

$$\int xe^x\, dx = (x - 1)e^x + C$$

$$\int x^n e^x\, dx = x^n e^x - n\int x^{n-1}e^x\, dx$$

$$\int \ln x\, dx = x\ln x - x + C$$

$$\int x^n \ln x\, dx = \frac{x^{n+1}}{n+1}\ln x - \frac{x^{n+1}}{(n+1)^2} + C$$

$$\int x^n(\ln x)^m\, dx = \frac{x^{n+1}}{n+1}(\ln x)^m - \frac{m}{n+1}\int x^n(\ln x)^{m-1}\, dx$$

$$\int e^{ax}\sin bx\, dx = \frac{e^{ax}}{a^2 + b^2}(a\sin bx - b\cos bx) + C$$

$$\int e^{ax}\cos bx\, dx = \frac{e^{ax}}{a^2 + b^2}(a\cos bx + b\sin bx) + C$$

INTEGRALS OF HYPERBOLIC FUNCTIONS

$$\int \sinh x\, dx = \cosh x + C$$

$$\int \cosh x\, dx = \sinh x + C$$

$$\int \tanh x\, dx = \ln(\cosh x) + C$$

$$\int \coth x\, dx = \ln|\sinh x| + C$$

$$\int \text{sech} x\, dx = \tan^{-1}|\sinh x| + C$$

$$\int \text{csch} x\, dx = \ln\left|\tanh\frac{x}{2}\right| + C$$

$$\int \sinh^2 x\, dx = \frac{1}{4}\sinh 2x - \frac{x}{2} + C$$

$$\int \cosh^2 x\, dx = \frac{1}{4}\sinh 2x + \frac{x}{2} + C$$

$$\int \tanh^2 x\, dx = x - \tanh x + C$$

$$\int \coth^2 x\, dx = x - \coth x + C$$

$$\int \text{sech}^2 x\, dx = \tanh x + C$$

$$\int \text{csch}^2 x\, dx = -\coth x + C$$

$$\int \text{sech} x\tanh x\, dx = -\text{sech} x + C$$

$$\int \text{csch} x\coth x\, dx = -\text{csch} x + C$$